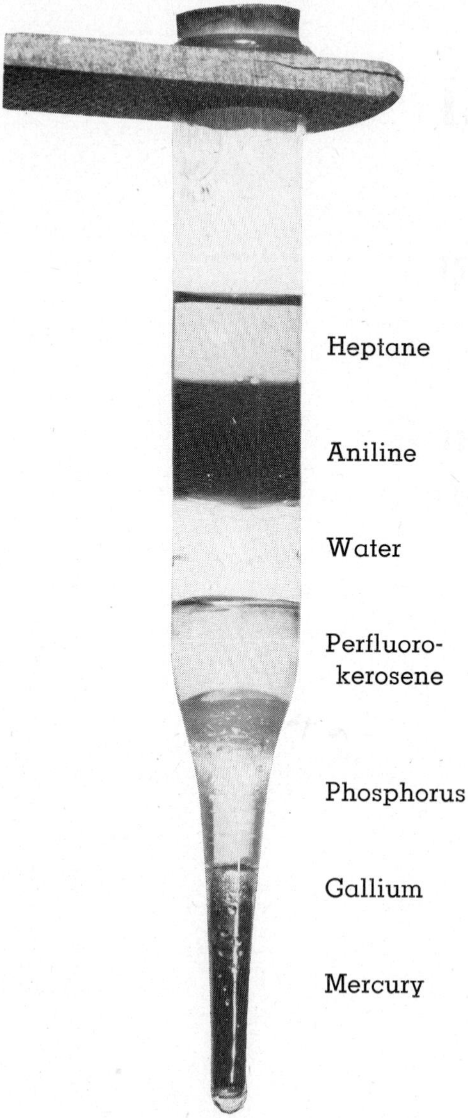

System of Seven Incompletely Miscible Liquids

The SOLUBILITY of NONELECTROLYTES

BY

JOEL H. HILDEBRAND

Professor of Chemistry, University of California

AND

ROBERT L. SCOTT

Assistant Professor of Chemistry, University of California

THIRD EDITION

American Chemical Society
Monograph Series

REINHOLD PUBLISHING CORPORATION

330 West Forty-second Street, New York, USA

Printed in the United States of America by
THE GUINN CO., NEW YORK, N. Y.

GENERAL INTRODUCTION

American Chemical Society's Series of Chemical Monographs

By arrangement with the Interallied Conference of Pure and Applied Chemistry, which met in London and Brussels in July, 1919, the American Chemical Society was to undertake the production and publication of Scientific and Technologic Monographs on chemical subjects. At the same time it was agreed that the National Research Council, in cooperation with the American Chemical Society and the American Physical Society, should undertake the production and publication of Critical Tables of Chemical and Physical Constants. The American Chemical Society and the National Research Council mutually agreed to care for these two fields of chemical progress. The American Chemical Society named as Trustees, to make the necessary arrangements for the publication of the Monographs, Charles L. Parsons, secretary of the Society, Washington, D. C.; the late John E. Teeple, then treasurer of the Society, New York; and the late Professor Gellert Alleman of Swarthmore College. The Trustees arranged for the publication of the ACS Series of (a) Scientific and (b) Technological Monographs by the Chemical Catalog Company, Inc. (Reinhold Publishing Corporation, successor) of New York.

The Council of the American Chemical Society, acting through its Committee on National Policy, appointed editors (the present list of whom appears at the close of this sketch) to select authors of competent authority in their respective fields and to consider critically the manuscripts submitted.

The first Monograph of the Series appeared in 1921. After twenty-three years of experience certain modifications of general policy were indicated. In the beginning there still remained from the preceding five decades a distinct though arbitrary differentiation between so-called "pure science" publications and technologic or applied science literature. By 1944 this differentiation was fast becoming nebulous. Research in private enterprise had grown apace and not a little of it was pursued on the frontiers of knowledge. Furthermore, most workers in the sciences were coming to see the artificiality of the separation. The methods of both groups of workers are the same. They employ the same instrumentalities, and frankly recognize that their objectives are common, namely, the search for new knowledge for the service of man. The officers of the Society therefore combined the two editorial Boards in a single Board of twelve representative members.

Also in the beginning of the Series, it seemed expedient to construe rather broadly the definition of a Monograph. Needs of workers had to be recognized. Consequently among the first hundred Monographs appeared works in the form of treatises covering in some instances rather broad areas. Because such necessary works do not now want for publishers, it is considered advisable to hew more strictly to the line of the Monograph character, which means more complete and critical treatment of relatively restricted areas, and, where a broader field needs coverage, to subdivide it into logical sub-areas. The prodigious expansion of new knowledge makes such a change desirable.

These Monographs are intended to serve two principal purposes: first, to make available to chemists a thorough treatment of a selected area in form usable by persons working in more or less unrelated fields to the end that they may correlate their own work with a larger area of physical science discipline; second, to stimulate further research in the specific field treated. To implement this purpose the authors of Monographs are expected to give extended references to the literature. Where the literature is of such volume that a complete bibliography is impracticable, the authors are expected to append a list of references critically selected on the basis of their relative importance and significance.

Preface

The first edition of this book appeared in 1924. The state of the subject at the time was such that only qualitative relations could be given, and the author could write it pretty much out of his head. The van der Waals equation expressed nearly all that was generally known about the liquid state, and the gas equation for osmotic pressure dominated the usual textbook treatment of the physical chemistry of solutions. This orthodox approach had long stood in the way of progress by ascribing to solvents merely the role of space for quasi-gaseous solutes, neglecting the intermolecular forces between individual solvents and solutes. There existed, it is true, the remarkable treatment by van Laar of the vapor pressure of binary mixtures; but this had made comparatively little impression, doubtless because of its too close dependence upon the van der Waals equation, its neglect of the different types of molecular forces (the present distinctions were then unknown), the weakness of his experimental evidence and, most of all, his studied disrespect for contemporary thermodynamic authorities.

By the time the second edition appeared, in 1936, we had learned from Debye how to express polarity by dipole moments, and from London the nature of the forces between nonpolar molecules. Raoult's law had become rather generally recognized as the most useful norm for studying the thermodynamic properties of solutions, and the fruitful concept of the "regular solution", with a Raoult's law entropy, had become familiar. Zernicke and Prins, Debye and Menke, and others had developed the x-ray method of investigating liquid structure. The radial distribution function thus obtained could be combined with the additive intermolecular potentials of London to yield an expression for the heat of mixing of nonpolar substances, and Scatchard and Hildebrand had both given numerous examples of the degree to which solubilities in regular solutions could be correlated by combining this heat of mixing with the regular solution entropy of mixing. The special effects of hydrogen bonding upon solubility had begun to be appreciated.

Since the appearance of the second edition, interest in the field has grown rapidly, and many able investigators have been contributing valuable experimental data as well as advances in theory. The most striking of these have had to do with the entropy of mixing molecules of different shapes and sizes, stimulated enormously by the study of solutions of high polymers, where these effects are extreme. We are now in a position for the first time to combine both the energy and the entropy to yield the free energy of mixing.

The theory of dipole interaction developed by Onsager and Kirkwood has given a more rational basis for distinction between dipoles of differing geometry.

The book has been almost entirely rewritten, and we have introduced new chapters on Multicomponent Systems, Mixtures of Gases, Solid Solutions, High Polymer Solutions, Surface Phenomena, and Chemical Equilibria and Reaction Rates, and we have greatly extended the treatment of metallic solutions.

The book has become much larger than before and we believe that the additional material will be found useful, whether as information or as suggesting problems calling for solution. We are conscious, nevertheless, of our neglect of much material that might well have been included. Our excuse must be that no book on this subject at this stage could be complete and final; to try to make it so would be never to publish it. We have tried only to give a consistent theory and a report of progress. What it lacks in finality will, we trust, furnish suggestions for research. The complexity of the liquid state and the large differences between our simple models and the actual solutions of molecules of a variety of sizes, shapes and force fields leaves ample room for further study.

We have not included in this book any consideration of rate processes in liquids and solutions, such as diffusion and viscosity, in spite of the influence which the study of such phenomena has had upon current theories of the liquid state, because we had to stop somewhere and we decided not to go beyond the equilibria involved in solubility.

I have insisted upon writing this preface in order to be able to state my great obligation to the junior author. Dr. Scott has been no mere assistant but a full partner; without his collaboration, this edition would have been smaller, later in appearing, and not nearly so good.

Joel H. Hildebrand

Berkeley, California
June 29, 1948

Contents

Acknowledgments

We wish to express our gratitude to the following:

1. The Office of Naval Research, for a grant which has defrayed much of the expense of preparing the manuscript and has contributed to some of the experimental work which has thrown light on important points.

2. To Bell Telephone Laboratories, Inc., for the Frank B. Jewett Fellowship, which the junior author has held for two years while this book has been in preparation.

3. To our colleagues, Professors Leo Brewer, Robert E. Connick, George Jura, Kenneth S. Pitzer, Richard E. Powell and Bruno H. Zimm, and to Dr. Hans A. Benesi for generous and helpful criticisms.

4. To Mrs. Dorothy Thompson for her skillful transcription of the difficult manuscript.

5. To Mr. Wilbur Zelinsky for the illustrations.

Joel H. Hildebrand
Robert L. Scott

CHAPTER I

Introductory

The entire history of chemistry bears witness to the extraordinary importance of the phenomena of solubility. The somewhat mysterious nature of solution and recrystallization invited the speculations of ancient philosophers.[1] The medieval alchemist took an interest in the "Alkahest", or universal solvent, inferior only to his interest in gold and in eternal life Although this faith in the existence of a universal solvent survives only in the mind of the freshman who invokes aqua regia to dissolve all precipitates, the importance of the subject has not diminished with the development of chemistry, and the chemist encounters problems in solubility upon every hand. He takes advantage of differences in solubility in the separation and purification of materials, and his methods of analysis are based almost entirely thereon. He selects materials for his vessels, in the laboratory or in the plant, because they resist the solvent action of their contents; or, again, a given liquid may owe its value in his estimation chiefly to its solvent powers. Most chemical reactions occur in solution and are influenced by the solubilities of the substances involved. Even solid solutions have to be reckoned with, as in the study of alloys, and in the process of recrystallization. The most delicate methods available for separating similar molecular species without destroying them are based upon differences in solubility.

The subject properly has a much wider scope than the term itself. The forces of attraction and repulsion which determine the solubility of one species of molecule in the liquid or solid phase of another control every kind of phase equilibrium between two or more components: lowering of freezing point by a solute, which is equivalent to the solubility of the solid form of the solvent in the solution; rise in boiling point, which expresses the same for the vapor; osmotic pressure; partition between two immiscible solvents; chemical equilibrium between molecular species present in solution; electrode potentials of alloy solutions; adsorption at surfaces. These processes all present problems of scientific interest as well as practical importance. The fundamental question underlying them all is the nature and strength of intermolecular forces. The variety confronting us is strikingly illustrated by the system of seven incompletely miscible liquids shown in the frontispiece[1a].

---

[1] The history of theories of solution is treated in a very entertaining fashion in a book by P. Walden, "Die Lösungstheorien in Ihrer Geschichtlichen Aufeinanderfolgerung", Ahren's "Sammlung Chemisch Technischer Vorträge", Enke, Stuttgart, 1910.

[1a] J. H. Hildebrand, *J. Phys. & Colloid Chem.*, **53**, 944 (1949).

The seven component liquids, beginning at the top, are heptane. aniline, water, "perfluorokerosene" (approximately $C_{12}F_{26}$), phosphorus (P_4), gallium, and mercury. The order of the layers is determined by their densities when mutually saturated. For example, pure aniline has a density a little greater than that of water, but it dissolves enough heptane in this system to raise it above the water layer. The layers are thermodynamically stable against coalescence. The upper temperature limit is the consolute temperature of heptane and wet aniline, the lower limit is the temperature at which either phosphorus or gallium may crystallize. Their melting points are 44° and 38.5°, respectively, but both can be kept in the liquid state indefinitely below room temperatures. If shaken, the seven phases would persist, but the globules would have trouble separating into seven layers, because interfacial tensions would hinder them from resuming their proper gravitational levels. This system illustrates the wide differences existing in the kinds and the strengths of intermolecular forces in liquids and suggests the problems, in all their variety, upon which this book endeavors to throw some light

Until recently the chemist has had to get along with the rough rules concerning solubility that are derived from experience. He quickly learns that water is a good solvent for substances whose molecules are rich in hydroxyl groups such as sugar; that hydrocarbons are likely to be mutually soluble; that carbon disulfide is a particularly good solvent for sulfur, iodine, or active phosphorus but a poor solvent for molecules with "polar" groups. Such experience has been expressed by the maxim, "*similia similibus solvuntur*", which may be freely translated as, "substances are best dissolved by others which are most like them"; but this, however imposing in the Latin, does not get us very far for it leaves unstated the criteria for likeness. Chloroform and beryllium chloride contain almost the same large percentage of chlorine, 89, but the latter is insoluble in the former; stannic iodide is more soluble in benzene than it is in carbon tetrachloride, another tetrahalide; propyl alcohol and propyl iodide are alike in the alkyl group and nearly alike in dipole moment, but solubility of the former in water is unlimited at 20° C while the solubility of the latter is only 0.1 per cent. Such facts as these emphasize the necessity for as careful, detailed, and quantitative an analysis of the various factors evidently involved in "likeness" as is permitted by the present state of our knowledge.

This book has been written with a triple purpose, first to assist in the solution of practical problems involving intermolecular forces; second, to give a coherent treatment of the present state of the theory of solubility; and third, to stimulate further research by inviting attention to the present limitations of our knowledge of the subject.

The first three chapters deal with units and thermodynamic quantities and their application to the types of systems that present themselves for study. Chapters IV—XII present the theories which have been developed to deal with the thermodynamic behavior of liquids and liquid mixtures. Research in this field is very active and we shall not be able to do full justice to all of the progress being made; we try only to lay a foundation for the understanding of the various phenomena of solubility and, by abundant references, to assist such deeper delving into special topics as the reader may feel impelled to make. Chapters XIII—XXII are devoted to the application of the theories to numerous actual systems. There are so many factors involved that such case study is necessary if one is to develop a real measure of skill in understanding particular solutions.

It will be evident throughout the book that there are wide differences in the accuracy possible in the treatment of different systems. Indeed, the sober-minded worker in this field is likely to come to regard as utopian any hope of predicting solubilities from the properties of the pure components to better than, say, ten per cent. If one must know a solubility to one per cent, he should measure it, and that with some care. From a practical standpoint, however, that is not the usual aim. Indeed, temperature is seldom controlled within corresponding limits. One often wishes to select the best of several promising solvents, or to narrow down the list of possible ones to the few worth measuring. This sort of thing we are now in a position to do to an extent undreamed of a generation ago, thanks to the efforts of the considerable number of able investigators who have turned their attention to the interesting problems presented by liquids and solutions. It was inevitable that the gaseous state, where relations are simplest, should have been studied first; the crystal state, where molecules are in ordered array, next; and now, finally, the liquid state, where there is no longrange order.

A first step in clarifying the subject must be to understand the different terms now in use for expressing solubility and to select the one most appropriate for a given purpose or theoretical treatment.

Although the composition of a given solution is independent of the units used in stating it, the choice of units is by no means a matter of indifference when we are comparing solubilities or solvent powers. This is illustrated by the figures in Table 1, which show that, if judged by weight

Table 1. — Solubility of Sulfur (S_8) at 25° C.

Solvent	Weight per cent	Grams per liter	Mole per cent
Benzene	2.07	18.5	0.641
Toluene	2.02	17.8	0.735

per cent, benzene and toluene have nearly equal solvent power for sulfur; if equal volumes of solvent are considered, the former is distinctly the better solvent, while reckoned in mole per cent the toluene is better.

Units used in stating solubility. Solubilities may be stated in terms of weights, moles, volumes, or combinations of them. The symbols we shall use are, denoting the components by subscripts, $_{1}, _{2}$ etc.

m, mass, weight, in grams.
M, molal weight, grams.
$N = m/\text{M}$, number of moles.
V, volume, liters.
$\text{v} = V/N$, molal volume (pure liquid).
$\text{M} = N/V$, concentration, molality, moles per liter.
m_1/m_2, weight ratio.
$w_1 = m_1/(m_1 + m_2)$, weight fraction of component 1.
$100\,w_1$, weight per cent of component 1.
$x_1 = N_1/(N_1 + N_2)$, mole fraction of component 1.
$100\,x_1$, mole percent of component 1.
$\varphi_1 = N_1\text{v}_1/(N_1\text{v}_1 + N_2\text{v}_2)$, volume fraction (neglecting any expansion on mixing).
$c_1 = m_1/V$, concentration in grams per unit volume of solution.

The solubility of a gas depends, of course, upon its partial pressure, so that this must be expressed or at least understood. **Henry's law,** which is obeyed rather well in most cases, states that the amount of the gas which dissolves is proportional to its partial pressure. The amount may be expressed in grams or moles per liter or in mole fraction, *i. e.*, $p_1 = Kc_1$; $p_1 = K'\text{M}_1$; $p_1 = K''x_1$. The numerical value of the constant K or K' or K'', depending upon the formula used, therefore suffices to calculate the solubility at any pressure. Since increasing the pressure of the gas increases the mass dissolved, by Henry's law, and decreases its volume by the same ratio by the gas law, the volume of gas going into a given volume of solution is nearly independent of the pressure; this is expressed by the **Ostwald absorption coefficient,** $\lambda = V_1^g/V^l$. The **Bunsen absorption coefficient** is the volume of gas, reduced to 0° C and 1 atmosphere, which dissolves, at the temperature of the experiment in 1 liter of solvent when the partial pressure of the gas is 1 atmosphere. The **Kuenen absorption coefficient** differs from the Bunsen in that the amount of solvent is given in grams.

The solvent and the solute. It is customary to regard one of the components of a binary solution as the solvent, or dispersing medium, the other as the solute, or substance which goes into solution. It is well to remember, however, that this distinction is somewhat arbitrary. For example, a little alcohol in much water may by regarded as the solute, and *vice versa*, but as the composition changes there is no obvious point at which the solvent and solute exchange roles. Where one pure component of the solution is liquid and the other solid or gaseous, the former is usually designated as the solvent, even though the latter may be present in much larger amount.

Mortimer[2] has defined the solute as that component which first separates on cooling. Accordingly, solid silver nitrate, which is in equilibrium, at -5°, with an aqueous solution containing 49 per cent of silver nitrate, would be designated the solute, whereas ice could be called the solute when in equilibrium with a solution at the same temperature containing 30 per cent of silver nitrate (or 70 per cent of ice). It is just as logical to speak of the solubility of ice as of silver nitrate, strange as it may sound.

We shall have to recognize the rather arbitrary and sometimes contradictory nature of ordinary usage of the terms solvent and solute; this need cause no real difficulty if we are careful only to avoid the concept of the solvent as merely providing space for the solute to display the properties of a gas, a concept that has been historically very useful, but which may be very misleading in the treatment of concentrated solutions.

Thermodynamic quantities. It is assumed that the reader of this book has at least an elementary knowledge of thermodynamics; therefore we do not derive but only summarize the main relationships which are used throughout the book. The following symbols are used for the various thermodynamic quantities (See page IX for summary of all symbols).

A Helmholtz free energy.
C Heat capacity.
F Free energy (Gibbs).
N Number of moles.
P Pressure.
R Gas constant, 1.986 cal./deg. mole; 0.08206 liter atm./deg. mole.
S Entropy.
T Temperature, degrees Kelvin.
V Volume.

Extensive quantities per mole of substance are designated by small caps, *e. g.* $\text{F} = F/N$; $\text{H} = H/N$; etc.

Partial molal (extensive) quantities of a component of a system are denoted by bars above the symbol for molal quantities, with the component designated by a subscript, *e. g.*, $\overline{\text{F}}_1$, $\overline{\text{S}}_2$, etc. These partial molal quantities are defined as the rate of increase in the content of the system in that particular quantity while the component considered is being added to the system; for example, $\overline{\text{H}}_1 = (\partial H/\partial N_1)_{N_2}$ is the partial molal heat content of component 1 of a binary system when ∂N_1 moles of it are added while the amount of component 2 is kept constant.

The partial molal free energy of a component is often called its "chemical potential", and the symbol μ used for it in place of $\overline{\text{F}}$.

We use superscripts to distinguish states and kinds of processes, as follows:

[2] F. S. Mortimer, *J. Am. Chem. Soc.*, **44**, **1416** (1922).

^{g} gas	^{f} free (volume)
^{l} liquid	^{V} vaporization
^{s} solid	^{F} fusion
^{c} critical	^{S} sublimation
^{i} ideal	^{T} transition
^{r} regular (solution)	^{M} mixing, solution

We use Δ to denote increments, *e. g.*, ΔH, increase in heat content in a process, $\Delta \mathrm{H}$, increase in heat content per mole of substance. We could write, accordingly. $\Delta \mathrm{H}^{V} = \mathrm{H}^{g} - \mathrm{H}^{l}$.

We use p for vapor pressure and make it more explicit, where necessary, by p^{l}, p^{s}, etc. Thus, in a saturated solution of component 1, $p_1^l = p_1^s$.

The following are the thermodynamic equations most frequently used.

$$A = E - TS, \text{ and correspondingly,} \tag{1}$$

$$\Delta \mathrm{A} = \Delta \mathrm{E} - T\Delta \mathrm{S}, \quad \mathrm{A} = \mathrm{E} - T\mathrm{S}, \quad \overline{\mathrm{A}}_1 = \overline{\mathrm{E}}_1 - T\overline{\mathrm{S}}_1$$

$$F = H - TS, \text{ etc., as above} \tag{2}$$

$$A = F - PV \tag{3}$$

$$E = H - PV \tag{4}$$

The signs can be remembered conveniently by noting the alphabetical order and the minus sign in all of the above.

The extensive quantities of a solution are additive with respect to the partial molal quantities, *e. g.*,

$$\mathrm{V} = x_1 \overline{\mathrm{V}}_1 + x_2 \overline{\mathrm{V}}_2 \tag{5}$$

$$V = N_1 \overline{\mathrm{V}}_1 + N_2 \overline{\mathrm{V}}_2 \tag{6}$$

and similarly for free energy, heat and entropy.

$$P + \left(\frac{\partial E}{\partial V}\right)_T = T\left(\frac{\partial P}{\partial T}\right)_V \tag{7}$$

This can be called a thermodynamic equation of state. It is instructive to compare it with the van der Waals equation in the form

$$P + \frac{\mathrm{a}}{\mathrm{V}^2} = \frac{RT}{\mathrm{V} - \mathrm{b}} \tag{8}$$

$$\left(\frac{\partial P}{\partial T}\right)_V = \left(\frac{\partial S}{\partial V}\right)_T \tag{9}$$

$$\left(\frac{\partial A}{\partial V}\right)_T = -P \tag{10}$$

$$\left(\frac{\partial A}{\partial T}\right)_V = -S \tag{11}$$

$$\left(\frac{\partial F}{\partial P}\right)_T = V \tag{12}$$

$$\left(\frac{\partial F}{\partial T}\right)_P = -S \tag{13}$$

Several derived quantities are of considerable interest, the heat capacities measured at constant volume and constant pressure, C_v and C_p respectively the coefficient of thermal expansion α and the isothermal compressibility β:

$$C_v = \left(\frac{\partial E}{\partial T}\right)_V \tag{14}$$

$$C_p = \left(\frac{\partial H}{\partial T}\right)_P \tag{15}$$

$$\alpha = \frac{1}{V}\left(\frac{\partial V}{\partial T}\right)_P \tag{16}$$

$$\beta = -\frac{1}{V}\left(\frac{\partial V}{\partial P}\right)_T \tag{17}$$

Care should be taken in using tables of experimental values for α and β. The α's so tabulated are frequently defined as $(1/V_0)\ (\partial V/\partial T)_P$ and to obtain the α as defined by Equation 16 we must multiply by V_0/V. The β's so tabulated are usually obtained by measurements of volume change with pressure increments of as much as 500 atmospheres, and do not represent the differential quantity at atmospheric pressure. This may be avoided by using a thermodynamic equation[3] which relates β to α and $(\partial P/\partial T)_V$:

$$\left(\frac{\partial P}{\partial T}\right)_V = -\left(\frac{\partial V}{\partial T}\right)_P \left(\frac{\partial P}{\partial V}\right)_T = \frac{\alpha}{\beta} \tag{18}$$

A convenient summary of thermodynamic relations is given in Table 2.

We shall have occasion to use the term "fugacity", designated by f, introduced by G. N. Lewis[4] as a measure of "escaping tendency".

The fugacity in two states, A and B, is related to the molal free energy in these states by the equation:

$$\mathrm{F_B} - \mathrm{F_A} = RT \ln (f_\mathrm{B}/f_\mathrm{A}) \tag{19}$$

and therefore, by Equation 12

$$\left(\frac{\partial \ln f}{\partial P}\right)_T = \frac{\mathrm{V}}{RT} \tag{20}$$

---

[3] J. H. Hildebrand, *Phys. Rev.*, **34**, 649 (1929).

[4] G. N. Lewis, *Proc. Am. Acad.*, **37**, 49 (1901); *Z. physik. Chem.*, **38**, 205 (1901); G. N. Lewis and M. Randall, "Thermodynamics and the Free Energy of Chemical Substances". McGraw Hill Book Co., New York, 1923.

Table 2 — A Summary of Relations between Thermodynamic Functions.

$A = F - PV$; $E = H - PV$; $F = H - TS$; $A = E - TS$; (Note alphabetical order and minus signs).

$X =$	F	H	S	E	A
$\left(\frac{\partial X}{\partial T}\right)_V =$	$V\left(\frac{\partial P}{\partial T}\right)_V - S$	$C_v + V\left(\frac{\partial P}{\partial T}\right)_V$	C_v/T	$C_v = C_p - T\left(\frac{\partial V}{\partial T}\right)_P \left(\frac{\partial P}{\partial T}\right)_V$	$-S = \frac{A-E}{T}$
$\left(\frac{\partial X}{\partial T}\right)_P =$	$-S = \frac{F-H}{T}$	$C_p = C_v + T\left(\frac{\partial V}{\partial T}\right)_P \left(\frac{\partial P}{\partial T}\right)_V$	C_p/T	$C_p/T\left(\frac{\partial V}{\partial T}\right)_P$	$-P\left(\frac{\partial V}{\partial T}\right)_P - S$
$\left(\frac{\partial X}{\partial V}\right)_T =$	$V/\left(\frac{\partial V}{\partial P}\right)_T = -1/\beta$	$T\left(\frac{\partial P}{\partial T}\right)_V + V/\left(\frac{\partial V}{\partial P}\right)_T$	$\left(\frac{\partial P}{\partial T}\right)_V$	$T\left(\frac{\partial P}{\partial T}\right)_V - P$	$-P$
$\left(\frac{\partial X}{\partial P}\right)_T =$	V	$V - T\left(\frac{\partial V}{\partial T}\right)_P$	$-\left(\frac{\partial V}{\partial T}\right)_P$	$-T\left(\frac{\partial V}{\partial T}\right)_P - P\left(\frac{\partial V}{\partial P}\right)_T$	$-P\left(\frac{\partial V}{\partial P}\right)_T$
$\left(\frac{\partial X}{\partial P}\right)_V -$	$V - S/\left(\frac{\partial P}{\partial T}\right)_V$	$V + C_v/\left(\frac{\partial P}{\partial T}\right)_V$	$C_v/T\left(\frac{\partial P}{\partial T}\right)_V$	$C_v/\left(\frac{\partial P}{\partial T}\right)_V$	$-S/\left(\frac{\partial P}{\partial T}\right)_V$
$\left(\frac{\partial X}{\partial V}\right)_P =$	$-S/\left(\frac{\partial V}{\partial T}\right)_P$	$C_p/\left(\frac{\partial V}{\partial T}\right)_P$	$C_p/T\left(\frac{\partial V}{\partial T}\right)_P$	$C_p/\left(\frac{\partial V}{\partial T}\right)_P - P$	$\frac{-S}{\left(\frac{\partial V}{\partial T}\right)_P} - P$

It can be replaced by gas pressure whenever the latter obeys the perfect gas laws with the desired accuracy.

Lewis and Randall give several methods for calculating fugacity; we here reproduce only one which suffices for our purpose. Deviations from the ideal gas law may be expressed by α (not the coefficient of thermal expansion discussed earlier) in the equation:

$$\mathrm{V} = \frac{RT}{P} - \alpha \tag{21}$$

The fugacity is then given by

$$RT \ln f = RT \ln P - \int_0^P \alpha dP \tag{22}$$

The integral may be evaluated by plotting α against P and getting the area between the limits.

It has been found that α approaches a constant value at lower pressure, giving

$$\ln \frac{f}{P} = -\frac{\alpha P}{RT} \tag{23}$$

and since $e^{-x} = 1 - x$ when x is small,

$$\frac{f}{P} = 1 - \frac{\alpha P}{RT} = \frac{P\mathrm{V}}{RT} \tag{24}$$

or, if P^i denotes the pressure of the ideal gas, which is RT/V,

$$\frac{f}{P} = \frac{P}{P^i} \tag{25}$$

To illustrate the application of the last formula, let us consider fluorobenzene, which, according to Young,[5] has a saturation pressure of 1.974 atmospheres at $T = 382.0°$ K. The molal volume of the vapor under these conditions is 15,000 cc. The ideal gas pressure of this volume of vapor would be $RT/\mathrm{V} = 82.06 \times 382.0/15{,}000$ or 2.085 atmospheres. Substituting this for P^i in Equation 25 gives

$$\frac{f}{P} = \frac{P}{P^i} = \frac{1.974}{2.085} = 0.947$$

and $f = 1.87$ atmospheres.

Again, taking the weight of 1 liter of chlorine as 3.220 g., at 0° and 1 atmosphere, the molal volume becomes 22,030 cc. The value of RT/P being

[5] S. T. Young, *Phil. Mag.*, **33**, 153 (1892).

22,410 cc., α in Equation 21 becomes 380 cc. To find the fugacity of the saturated vapor at 0°, where the saturation pressure is 3.66 atmospheres, we can use Equation 24 getting

$$\frac{f}{3.66} = 1 - \frac{380}{82.1 \times 273} \times 3.66 = 0.938$$

and $f = 3.43$ atmospheres.

These examples serve to illustrate the magnitude of the error made in similar cases by the common assumption that a saturated vapor obeys the gas laws.

Since we will be interested frequently in the vapor pressures and fugacities of pure liquids, it is instructive to observe the magnitude of the error involved in using the pressure instead of the fugacity for vapor pressures up to one atmosphere. Table 3 gives a series of vapor pressures, P, and molal vapor volumes, V, of normal heptane, according to Young[6] together with the calculated values of the ideal gas pressure, P^i, and the corresponding ratios, f/P.

Table 3. — Ratio of Fugacity to Pressure for *n*-Heptane at Saturation Pressure.

t° C	V (liters)	P(mm.)	P^i(mm.)	$P/P^i = f/P$
80	50.10	426.6	440.4	0.969
100	27.86	785.2	837.0	0.950
120	16.49	1367.0	1489.0	0.918

Other saturated vapors show ratios of the same order of magnitude at similar pressures, thus, the difference between fugacity and vapor pressure at the boiling point is about 5 per cent, and at 0.5 atmosphere it is about 3 per cent.

Where the critical pressure and temperature are known, the molal volume of an imperfect gas can be calculated with considerable accuracy by the aid of the well known equation of state of Berthelot,

$$\mathrm{V}^g = R\left\{\frac{T}{P} - 0.0686\frac{T_c}{P_c}\left[6\left(\frac{T_c}{T}\right)^2 - 1\right]\right\} \tag{26}$$

Using this equation to calculate V^g for heptane at 80° C. and 426.6 mm., with $P_c = 26.8$ atmospheres and $T_c = 540°$ *K.*, gives 50.11 liters, agreeing with the measured value in Table 3 within the limit of error. The ideal gas volume at the same temperature and pressure is 51.63 liters. Since we

[6] S. T. Young, *Phil. Mag.*, **33**, 153 (1892); *J. Chem. Soc.*, **73**, 675 (1898); *Proc. Roy. Dublin Soc.*, **12**, 374 (1910).

can set $P/P^i = V^i/V$, we can obtain $f/P = 50.10/51.63 = 0.970$, practically identical with the value given in Table 3.

The Berthelot equation is particularly useful for calculating the heat of vaporization from accurate vapor pressure data by aid of the rigid thermodynamic equation derivable from Equation 9,

$$\frac{dp}{dT} = \frac{\Delta H^v}{T(V^g - V^l)} \tag{27}$$

instead of the ordinary Clausius-Clapeyron equation,

$$\frac{d\ln p}{dT} = \frac{\Delta H^v}{RT^2} \tag{28}$$

which contains the assumption that vapor obeys the gas laws.

A completely general form for expressing gas imperfections in an Equation of state is the infinite series first suggested by Kammerlingh-Onnes:

$$P = RT\left\{\frac{1}{V} + \frac{B}{V^2} + \frac{C}{V^3} + \frac{D}{V^4} + \ldots\right\} \tag{29}$$

The coefficients B, C, D, etc. are termed respectively, the second, third and fourth virial cœfficients, and are functions only of the temperature. We may obtain the fugacity by transformation of Equation 29 to a power series in the pressure and integration of Equation 20:

$$\ln f = \frac{1}{RT}\int_0^P VdP = \ln P + \frac{BP}{RT} + \frac{(C - B^2)}{2\,(RT)^2}P^2 + \frac{(D - 3\,BC + 2\,B^3)}{3\,(RT)^3} + \ldots \tag{30}$$

or expressed differently

$$\frac{f}{P} = 1 + \frac{BP}{RT} + \frac{CP^2}{2(RT)^2} + \frac{(2\,D - 3\,BC + 2\,B^3)}{6\,(RT)^3}P^3 + \ldots.. \tag{31}$$

The **activity,** a, of a substance in a particular solution, is the ratio of its fugacity in that solution to its fugacity in some arbitrarily chosen standard state, which in this book is always the pure liquid. The relation is, therefore,

$$a_1 = f_1/f_1^\circ \tag{32}$$

The standard state usually chosen for electrolytes is the substance in its infinitely dilute solution in a given solvent. This choice of standard state is particularly appropriate for dilute aqueous electrolytes, in which as a first approximation, the ions obey Henry's law, and, as a next approximation, the Debye-Hückel theory. The standard state is found by extrapolating to zero concentration the ratio of fugacity to composition, where it is arbitrarily set at unity. To choose the pure substance as the standard state would involve, for dilute aqueous electrolytes, the experimental determination of the fugacity of the solute (*e. g.*, by vapor pressure or e. m. f.) throughout the long range from dilute through concentrated solutions, where no known laws are ordinarily obeyed.

Lewis and Randall[7], to make clearer their methods of dealing with dilute electrolytes, used the measurements of Hildebrand and Eastman[8] upon thallium amalgams. In their treatment they selected the pure liquid as the standard state of mercury and the infinitely dilute solution of thallium in mercury as the standard state of thallium. This places mercury and thallium in the respective roles of solvent and solute, corresponding to water and salt. The procedure generally adopted in this book does not follow this convention, but is based upon the selection of the pure liquid as the standard state for both components, even though this involves an extrapolation below the melting point as a supercooled liquid. There are two principal reasons for this choice, first, to maintain the symmetry of the expressions for solvent and solute desirable in dealing with concentrated solutions, second, to facilitate comparisons between solutions in different solvents by using the same standard state for all. This necessity has been overlooked by some investigators, who have simply compared activity coefficients based upon the infinitely dilute solute in two or more different solvents. This important point may be made clearer by reference to Fig. 2, in which the activity of a single solute in three different solvents based upon the pure liquid solute as standard state, is plotted against the mole fraction. Curve B represents a solution which is ideal in the sense of obeying Raoult's law.

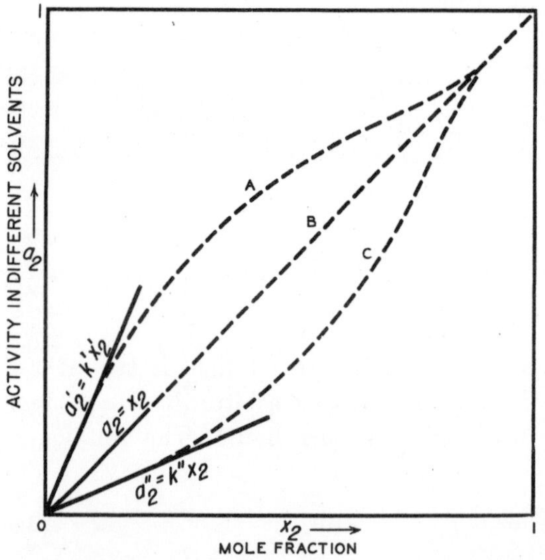

Fig. 2. Relation between activity coefficients based upon different standard states.

A and C represent solvents in which the activity of the solute deviates from Raoult's law. These deviations are indicated in very dilute solution by difference from unity of the Henry's law constants, K' and K'', respectively, which are identical with the corresponding activity cœfficients at infinite dilution.

---

[7] Lewis and Randall, "Thermodynamics", pp. 259 ff.

[8] J. H. Hildebrand and E. D. Eastman, *J. Am. Chem. Soc.*, **37**, 2452 (1915).

When, however, the standard states are no longer identical, but are solute at infinite dilution in the several solvents, all three solutions are regarded as ideal in the range in which they follow the relation $a_2 = Kx_2$ within the limit of error. The deviation from ideality in this sense is merely the deviation of curves B and C from their tangents, not their deviation from A, as was the case when the standard state was the pure solute.

The **activity coefficient** of a component of a solution is the ratio of its activity to its mole fraction, *i. e.*,

$$\gamma_1 = a_1/x_1 \tag{33}$$

From Equations 19 and 32 we may write

$$\Delta \bar{F}_1 = \bar{F}_1 - F_1^{\circ} = RT \ln (f_1/f_1^{\circ}) = RT \ln a_1 \tag{34}$$

In dealing with the solubility of solids, we shall have occasion to calculate the activity of the solid referred to the pure supercooled liquid, $a_1^s = f_2^s/f_1^{\circ}$. The equation

$$\frac{d \ln a_1^s}{dT} = \frac{H_1^l - H_1^s}{RT^2} = \frac{\Delta H_1^F}{RT^2} \tag{35}$$

can be integrated under the assumption that the heat of fusion ΔH^F, is constant, giving

$$\ln a^s = - \Delta H^F \left(\frac{1}{T} - \frac{1}{T_m} \right) \tag{36}$$

where T_m denotes the fusion temperature. When the molal heat capacities of the liquid and solid forms, C_p^l and C_p^s, are known, it is better to consider the variation of ΔH with temperature,

$$\frac{d(H^l - H^s)}{dT} = C_p^l - C_p^s = \Delta C_P^F \tag{37}$$

from which we obtain

$$\Delta H^F = \Delta H_m^F - \Delta C_p (T_m - T) \tag{38}$$

where ΔH_m^F is the heat of fusion at the melting point, T_m. Introducing this into Equation 35 and integrating gives

$$\ln a^s = \frac{-\Delta H_m^F}{R} \left(\frac{T_m - T}{TT_m} \right) + \frac{\Delta C_p}{R} \left(\frac{T_m - T}{T} \right) - \frac{\Delta C_p}{R} \ln \frac{T_m}{T} \tag{39}$$

or, with $R = 1.985$ cals. per degree,

$$\log a^s = \frac{-\Delta H_m^F}{4.575}\left(\frac{T_m - T}{TT_m}\right) + \frac{\Delta C_p}{4.575}\left(\frac{T_m - T}{T}\right) - \frac{\Delta C_p}{1.985}\log\frac{T_m}{T} \quad (40)$$

The variation in heat capacity at ordinary temperatures is often expressed by an equation in the form,

$$C = C_0 + aT + \beta T^2 + \ldots\ldots \quad (41)$$

where C_0 is a fictitious value extrapolated to 0° K. Equations of this type lead to a similar equation for ΔH^F in terms of ΔH_0 at 0° K. The integrated form looks simpler than Equation 39, but is practically less simple and the latter is to be preferred for our purposes because experimental values can be directly substituted therein.

Osmotic pressure. When the free energy of a solvent liquid has been diminished by the addition of a solute, it is possible to compensate for this reduction by applying hydrostatic pressure to the solution so that the partial molal free energy of the solvent will be increased to equal that of the pure solvent, as indicated by no passage of the solvent through a semipermeable membrane. This extra pressure is the osmotic pressure.

Integrating Equation 12 between the limits of the solution and the solvent, neglecting the extremely small change in V for moderate pressures, gives

$$\bar{F}_1 - F_1^\circ = -V_1 \Delta P = -\Pi V_1 \quad (42)$$

Using the symbol Π for the osmotic pressure we may combine this with Equation 34 to give

$$\Pi V_1 = RT \ln (f_1/f_1^\circ) = RT \ln a_1 \quad (43)$$

When we proceed to calculate the change of fugacity or any of the partial molal quantities with the composition of a solution, we go beyond the realm of pure thermodynamics into one less carefully charted but one in which every chemist must travel. The better charting of this region is the purpose of this book.

Partition Functions. For the purposes of statistical mechanics, it is useful to define a partition function Q for a system such that

$$Q = \sum_n e^{-E_n/kT} \quad (44)$$

where the summation is extended over all nondegenerate quantum states n of the system, each with total energy E_n.

For systems composed of independent particles, such as a perfect gas, the assumption is usually made that the various degrees of freedom are separable, and one writes for the partition function of a single molecule

$$q = q_{nu}\, q_{el}\, q_{vib}\, q_{rot}\, q_{tr} \tag{45}$$

where the subscripts refer to the nuclear, electronic, vibrational, rotational and translational parts of the partition function.

Where the system is composed of dependent particles, that is of molecules which show an appreciable amount of interaction, as is the case for all systems considered in this book, the partition function is more complex. In discussing the partition functions for liquids and solutions in subsequent chapters we shall find it necessary to make simplifying assumptions to permit calculations. For the moment, it will suffice to note the relation between the partition function Q and the thermodynamic properties of the system.

$$A = -kT \ln Q \tag{46}$$

$$P = -\left(\frac{\partial A}{\partial V}\right)_T = kT\left(\frac{\partial \ln Q}{\partial V}\right)_T \tag{47}$$

$$S = -\left(\frac{\partial A}{\partial T}\right)_V = k\left[\ln Q + \left(\frac{\partial \ln Q}{\partial \ln T}\right)_V\right] \tag{48}$$

$$E = A + TS = kT^2\left(\frac{\partial \ln Q}{\partial T}\right)_V = kT\left(\frac{\partial \ln Q}{\partial \ln T}\right)_V \tag{49}$$

$$PV = kT\left(\frac{\partial \ln Q}{\partial \ln V}\right)_T \tag{50}$$

$$F = A + PV = kT\left[-\ln Q + \left(\frac{\partial \ln Q}{\partial \ln V}\right)_T\right] \tag{51}$$

$$H = E + PV = kT\left[\left(\frac{\partial \ln Q}{\partial \ln T}\right)_V + \left(\frac{\partial \ln Q}{\partial \ln V}\right)_T\right] \tag{52}$$

$$C_v = \left(\frac{\partial E}{\partial T}\right)_V = k\left[2\left(\frac{\partial \ln Q}{\partial \ln T}\right)_V + T^2\left(\frac{\partial^2 \ln Q}{\partial T^2}\right)_V\right] \tag{53}$$

References.

J. Willard Gibbs, "Collected Works", 1873—1902 (Longmans, Green, **1931**) Vol. I. "Thermodynamics", Vol. II, "Statistical Mechanics, Dynamics, etc".

G. N. Lewis and M. Randall, "Thermodynamics and the Free Energy of Chemical Substances" (Mc Graw-Hill Book Co., 1923).

F. G. Donnan and A. Haas, editors;
"A Commentary on the Scientific Writings of J. Willard Gibbs", (Yale, **1936**), Vol. I, "Thermodynamics", Vol. II. "Theoretical Physics".

E. A. Guggenheim, "Modern Thermodynamics by the Methods of Willard Gibbs", (Methuen **1933**).

F. H. Mac Dougall, "Thermodynamics and Chemistry", 3rd Edition, (John Wiley and Sons, **1939**).

R. H. Fowler and E. A. Guggenheim, "Statistical Thermodynamics", (Cambridge, **1939**).

J. E. Mayer and M. G. Mayer, "Statistical Mechanics", (John Wiley and Sons, **1940**).

CHAPTER II

The Ideal Solution

The concept of the ideal solution offers advantages similar to those furnished by the concept of the ideal gas. Just as the laws of the ideal gas suffice to describe the behavior of actual gases as a first approximation, so the laws of the ideal solution suffice to describe actual solutions within certain limits. In both cases one can decide with fair accuracy the degree of approximation to ideal behavior that is to be expected, and, further, that this should be closer the greater the dilution. Deviations from the ideal gas laws are accounted for in two distinct ways, first, as due to the formation of new molecular species, second, as the effect of the molecular volumes and non-specific intermolecular forces. The former is illustrated by the behavior of iodine at high temperatures, where the molecules I_2 and I are in equilibrium; the latter would ordinarily be used to explain the much smaller deviations of iodine vapor from the gas laws in the neighborhood of its saturation point. The forces between iodine atoms are often designated as "chemical". Those between iodine molecules are regarded as "physical", and are usually called "van der Waals forces", since they furnish the basis for the van der Waals equation.

Very large deviations from ideal gas behavior are ordinarily due to the presence of a chemical equilibrium, for the effect of van der Waals forces is seldom so great. In liquid solutions, however, this is not necessarily the case, since the close crowding of molecules in the liquid state may give rise to very large van der Waals effects. The concentrations which we consider "ordinary" in liquids are much greater than those gases at "standard conditions". For example, the HCl in a 10 per cent aqueous solution would exert a gas pressure of over 70 atmospheres in the same volume if the water were not present, and be far from a perfect gas in behavior. It is a mistake, therefore, to attribute all deviations from ideal solution laws to chemical effects, association, dissociation, and solvation, as has been so often done, to the neglect of the van der Waals effects. There is a published instance in which the calculated water of hydration of the solute far exceeded all of the water present. Other more or less obvious absurdities will be referred to in the course of the book.

These considerations are essential to an appreciation of the meaning and limitations of any statement of ideal behavior and to the derivation of any particular form of ideal solution law.

Raoult's law. There are many pairs of molecular species so nearly alike in their attractive forces that their liquids mix with little or no heat effect. We designate such solutions as **athermal.** An individual molecule of either species, in order to escape from such a solution, requires the same kinetic energy as to escape from its own pure liquid. The number of molecules so escaping depends somewhat upon the configuration of the mixture, which is influenced by the relative sizes and shapes of the two component molecules. This makes it a matter of entropy. This entropy of mixing is analyzed in some detail in Chapter VI, where it will be shown that in the absence of strong dipoles, particularly those known as hydrogen bonds, (see Chapter XI), the moderate differences in molal volume of most of the familiar nonpolar or slightly polar nonelectrolytes have rather small effect upon the entropy of mixing. We shall see, in Chapter VI, that any structure in which the molecules of one species can be interchanged with those of another without altering the structure, whether it be the lattice of a solid solution or the instantaneous structure of a solution composed of molecules of the same size, shape and attractive fields, has an entropy of mixing given by

$$-\frac{\Delta S^M}{R} = N_1 \ln \frac{N_1}{N_1 + N_2} + N_2 \ln \frac{N_2}{N_1 + N_2} \quad (1)$$

where N_1 and N_2 are the respective number of moles of the two components. This leads to a partial molal entropy of

$$\Delta \bar{S}_1 = \bar{S}_1 - S_1^\circ = -R \ln \frac{N_1}{N_1 + N_2} = -R \ln x_1 \quad (2)$$

and similarly, with subscripts interchanged for component 2. Now in an athermal solution such as we are postulating, we can write, by Equation I—2

$$\Delta \bar{F}_1 = \bar{F}_1^i - F_1^\circ = = -T(\bar{S}_1 - S_1^\circ) = RT \ln x_1 \quad (3)$$

and this, with Equation I—34 gives

$$f_1 = f_1^\circ x_1 \text{ and } a_1 = x_1 \quad (4)$$

If vapor pressures are substituted as a close approximation for fugacities, we have

$$p_1 = p_1^\circ x_1 \text{ and } p_2 = p_2^\circ x_2 \quad (5)$$

which is the well known relation known as Raoult's law[1]. It is illustrated graphically in Fig. 1 for the system CCl_4—$SnCl_4$, assuming that Raoult's law is obeyed.

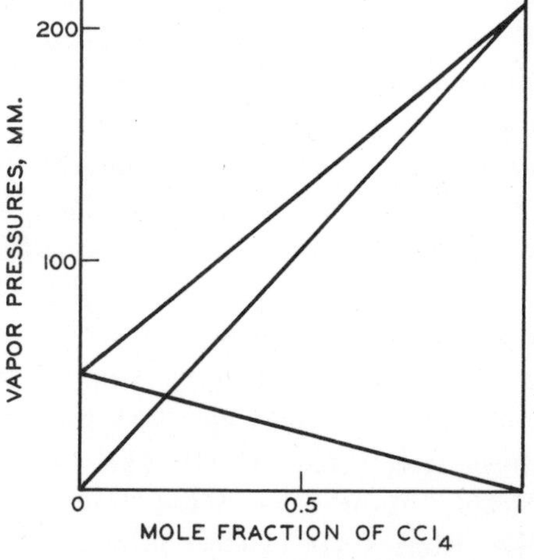

Fig. 1. Raoult's law for solutions of $SnCl_4$ with CCl_4

[1] F. M. Raoult, *Compt. rend.*, **104**, 1430 (1887); *Z. physik. Chem.*, **2**, 353 (1888)

We can see a simple kinetic justification for it in the sort of solution here postulated by noting first, that the escaping tendency of any single molecule of species 1 is not altered by changing a fraction of the surrounding molecules to species 2 and, second, that the number of species 1 escaping per second per unit area of surface is reduced to the same fraction. We can see, also, that the structure of the liquid need not be much affected by moderate differences in molecular volume since the radius ratio is only the cube root of the volume ratio. This is well supported by experiment, as will be seen from numerous examples cited in later chapters where Raoult's law is obeyed within a few per cent throughout a large range, not only for pairs of approximately equal molal volume, such as benzene toluene, benzene-ethylene chloride, and the near paraffin isomers, but also for such unequal components as Cl_2-CCl_4, I_2-SnI_4, chlorobenzene-naphthalene.

Henry's law. In the foregoing approach to an ideal solution law the disturbing influence of changing molecular field has been avoided by assuming the selection of components possessing fields as nearly equal as possible. This difficulty may be avoided in another way, that is, by considering only solutions so dilute that the solute molecules seldom are close enough together to influence each other, hence their environment is nearly constant, although, perhaps, very different from what it would be if they were surrounded by their own species. Their tendency to escape, therefore, is proportional to their concentration. Since this condition can exist, in general, only in very dilute solutions, it makes little difference how the concentration is expressed. The several expressions that may be used,

$$p_2 = K_2 N_2/(N_1 + N_2) = K_2 x_2; \; p_2 = K_2' N_2/N_1; \; \text{and} \; p_2 = K_2'' N_2/V,$$

do not differ significantly for sufficiently dilute solutions. It should be noted, however, that the first form reduces to Raoult's law for the special case that the molecular constraints remain constant over the whole range of composition, for when $N_1 = 0$, p_2 becomes p_2°, which equals K_2. The second form leads to absurdity when $N_1 = 0$, and the third, for the reason stated earlier, should be replaced by the first; therefore, we shall, ordinarily express the general conclusion, known as Henry's law, in terms of mole fraction, as with Raoult's law.

It may be noted further, that when the solution is sufficiently dilute for the solute to obey Henry's law to a given degree of approximation, the solvent must obey Raoult's law with a corresponding degree of approximation, and *vice versa*. This result of the application of the Gibbs equation will be given later (Chapter III). These conditions, accordingly, are the criteria of ideality, through a limited range, as Raoult's law for both components is the criterion for ideality through the entire range of composition.

An ideal solution is formed from its liquid components with zero heat of mixing and no change in total volume. In the foregoing paragraph, we have deduced Raoult's law on the assumptions of zero heat of mixing and an entropy of mixing that is independent of temperature and of peculiarities of molecular sizes and shapes. Let us now reverse the process, and deduce certain characteristics of a solution that obeys Raoult's law, not merely at some particular temperature, but through a range of temperature. When the intermolecular forces in a solution are sufficiently independent of the composition for Raoult's law to hold, as previously explained, it seems reasonable to suppose that a change of temperature would affect all of these forces in very much the same way, so that the escaping tendency of the individual molecules would still remain practically independent of the composition. No one temperature has any special significance in this connection, and we may well expect that if a solution is truly ideal at any temperature, it will be ideal throughout a range of temperature. As a matter of fact this supposition is in accord with the experimental facts, which show that in general the greater the (positive) deviation from the ideal behavior the greater is the effect of temperature upon this deviation.

A similar remark may be made with respect to the effect of pressure. Although we usually find it convenient to work with a liquid system either under one atmosphere or under its own vapor pressure, the properties of the liquid are not unique at these pressures, and a solution that is truly ideal should remain so at all pressures, that is, the escaping tendency of a molecule from the solution should be affected by the application of pressure to the solution to the same extent as when an equal pressure is applied to the pure liquid. In order to measure this fugacity we may use a porous piston to apply the pressure to the liquid while allowing the molecules of vapor to escape.

Ewan[2] many years ago stated that "An ideal solution is distinguished by the facts that no heat is evolved or absorbed and no change of volume occurs when it is diluted. The osmotic pressure of such a solution is proportional to its concentration so long as the temperature remains unchanged".

From Equation I—2 we write:

$$\mathrm{F}_1^i - \mathrm{F}_1^\circ = \overline{\mathrm{H}}_1^i - \mathrm{H}_1^\circ - T(\overline{\mathrm{S}}_1^i - \mathrm{S}_1^\circ) \tag{6}$$

and from Equation I—13,

$$\frac{\partial(\overline{\mathrm{F}}_1^i - \mathrm{F}_1^\circ)}{\partial T} = (\overline{\mathrm{S}}_1^i - \mathrm{S}_1^\circ) \tag{7}$$

Now, when Raoult's law holds over a range of temperature, Equation 3 gives

$$\frac{\partial(\overline{\mathrm{F}}_1^i - \overline{\mathrm{F}}_1^\circ)}{\partial T} = R \ln x_2 \tag{8}$$

Combining Equations 6 — 8 gives $\overline{\mathrm{H}}_1 - \mathrm{H}_1^\circ = 0$, *i.e.*, there is no heat of mixing.

---

[2] T. Ewan, *Z. physik. Chem.*, **31**, 22 (1899).

Similarly, if Raoult's law holds through a range of total pressure, Equations 3 and I—12 give

$$\frac{\partial(\bar{F}_1^i - F_1^\circ)}{\partial P} = RT\frac{\partial \ln x_1}{\partial P} = 0 = \bar{V}_1^i - V_1 \qquad (9)$$

and $\bar{V}_1^i = V_1$, *i. e.*, there is no volume change on mixing.

Other expressions for Raoult's law. It is well to recognize Raoult's law in various other expressions which may easily be derived from the one previously used. Thus we may write

$$\ln f_1 = \ln f_1^\circ + \ln x_1 \qquad (10)$$

and the differentials,

$$\frac{df_1}{dx_1} = f_1^\circ \qquad (11) \qquad\qquad \frac{df_1}{dx_1} = \frac{f_1}{x_1} \qquad (13)$$

$$\frac{d^2 f_1}{dx_1^2} = 0 \qquad (12) \qquad\qquad \frac{d\ln f_1}{d\ln x_1} = 1 \qquad (14)$$

The last three follow also from Henry's law, and are therefore more general than 4, 10, and 11.

The decrease in free energy which takes place when a mole of one component is transferred from the pure liquid state to an infinite amount of solution is equal to the work done in an ideal distillation process, so that we may write

$$\Delta \bar{F}_1 \text{ (liquid to solution)} = \bar{F}_1 - F_1^\circ = RT\ln\frac{f_1}{f_1^\circ} \qquad (15)$$

and since $f_1/f_1^\circ = x_1$, for an ideal solution,

$$\bar{F}_1^i - F_1^\circ = RT\ln x_1 \qquad (16)$$

Equations involving fugacities are, of course, approximately true if partial vapor pressures are used instead.

Variations of activity and partial molal free energy and entropy with mole fraction. Since, by our choice of standard state, (cf. I — p. 11) $a = 1$ when $x = 1$, the plot of activities vs. mole fraction has a very simple, symmetrical form for an ideal solution, shown in Fig. 2.

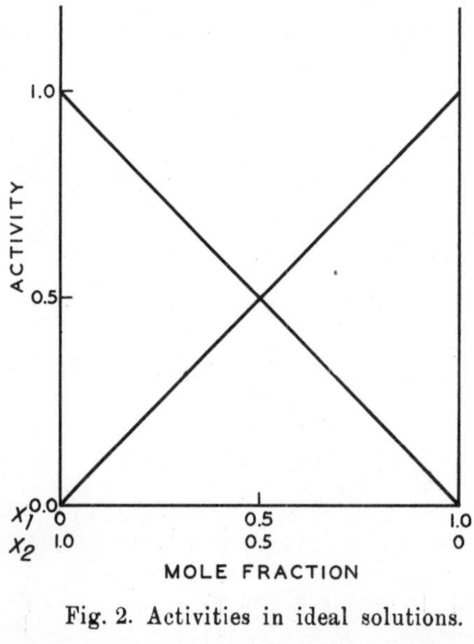

Fig. 2. Activities in ideal solutions.

The partial molal free energies vary from 0, for the pure liquids, to $-\infty$ at infinite dilution, according to Equation 3, and are plotted vs. x for 25° C. in Fig. 3, together with the total molal free energy of mixing,

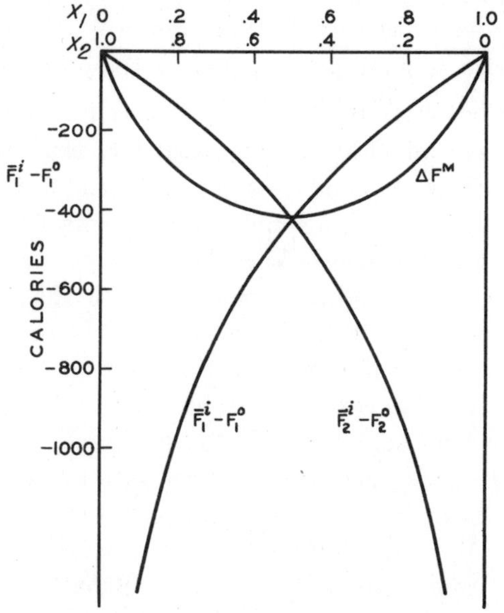

Fig. 3. Partial and total free energies of mixing in ideal solutions.

$$\Delta F^M = (\bar{F}_1^i - F_1^\circ)x_1 + (\bar{F}_2^i - F_2^\circ)x_2 \tag{17}$$

Since ideal solutions are athermal, the partial molal and total entropies of mixing have the same form but positive sign and are equal to the corresponding free energies divided by the absolute temperature. These are shown in Fig. 4.

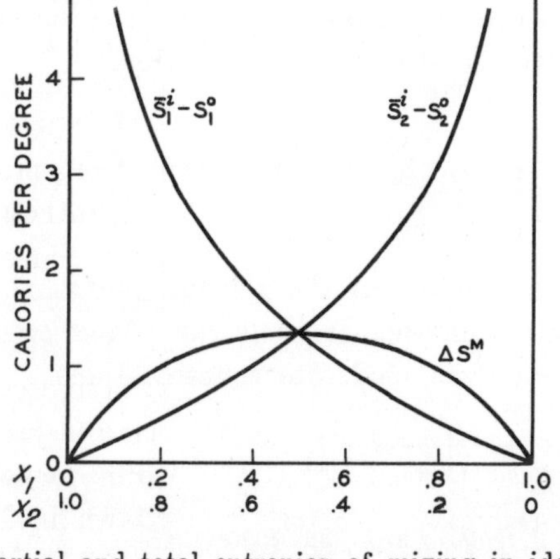

Fig. 4. Partial and total entropies of mixing in ideal solutions.

Van't Hoff's law for osmotic pressure is historically the most important definition of the ideal solutions, and the one most widely used in elementary textbooks on physical chemistry. According to this law the osmotic pressure, Π, of a substance in dilute solution obeys the relation $\Pi V = N_2 RT$, which is formally the same as the ideal gas law, i. e., the osmotic pressure of a dissolved substance is numerically equal to the pressure it would exert if present alone as a gas in the same volume.

The widespread use of this law has been due, first, to the fact that van't Hoff used it to derive a number of important and useful relationships, such as the formulas for calculating molecular weights from the lowering of the freezing point and the rise in the boiling point, and, second, to the formal identity of the osmotic pressure equation with the gas law equation, so that the familiar operations with the latter could be easily repeated with the former. The limitations of the van't Hoff law were clearly stated by van't Hoff himself[3], although later writers have not always borne them in mind. It is a limiting law, applying only to very dilute solutions, and to solutions which obey Henry's law; its theoretical basis is, therefore, no better than that of Henry's law. The relations between the composition of the solution and the various thermodynamic quantities might just as well have been derived directly from Henry's law, or from Raoult's law, which is a special case, without any cognizance of osmotic pressure. It is merely a historical accident that osmotic pressure was first used for this purpose. This is not said to detract in the least from the importance of the service rendered by van't Hoff in applying thermodynamics to solutions, but only to point out that the historical approach is not today the most direct or enlightening, and does not lead to the best description of concentrated solutions[4]. Moreover, the concept of osmotic pressure as an effect primarily of the solute, with the solvent simply furnishing space, has obscured the effects of intermolecular forces and the interchangeability of solute and solvent and retarded progress.

The osmotic pressure of a solution which obeys Raoult's law, if we neglect the compressibility, is given by the equation[5]

$$\Pi = -\frac{RT}{V_1} \ln (1 - x_2) = \frac{RT}{V_1} x_2 \left(1 + \frac{x_2}{2} + \frac{x_2^{\,2}}{3} + \ldots\ldots\right) \qquad (18)$$

where V_1 is the molal volume of the solvent and x_2 the mole fraction of the solute. This differs from the original van't Hoff equation and leads to very different results at even moderate concentrations.

---

[3] J. H. van't Hoff, *Z. physik. Chem.*, **1**, 489 (1887); Vorlesungen, **II**, **23** Vieweg, Braunschweig, **1901**.

[4] Cf. J. H. Hildebrand, *J. phys. Chem.*, **32**, 1086 (1928).

[5] G. N. Lewis, *J. Am. Chem. Soc.*, **30**, 668 (1908).

Osmotic pressure offers an experimental advantage for very dilute solutions in that its magnitude is much larger than the lowering of vapor pressure, and hence easier to measure in cases where a suitable membrane can be found. It is particularly valuable in the study of solutions of high polymers (cf. Chapter XX). To illustrate, let us consider an ideal solution of 0.001 mole of a solute, 2, in 1 mole of a solvent of molal volume 100 cc., whose vapor pressure is 100 mm. at 25 °C. The vapor pressure lowering of the solvent, $p_1^\circ - p_1 = 0.1$ mm., while osmotic pressure Π at 25 °C is 186 mm.

Partial vapor pressures. Raoult's law is a direct expression of the solubility of a vapor in a solution. Where it holds, the mole fraction of a component in the solution is equal to the ratio of its partial vapor pressure above the solution to the saturation pressure of its pure vapor, *i. e.*, $x = p/p^\circ$. Let us consider, for example, a solution of carbon tetrachloride in stannic chloride, assuming Raoult's law which, we have good reason to believe, is followed rather closely. The vapor pressures of pure carbon tetrachloride and stannic chloride at 40° are 211 mm. and 51 mm. respectively. If the partial vapor pressure of carbon tetrachloride vapor in equilibrium with the solution of the two liquids is kept at, say, 45 mm., which is 45/211 of the saturation pressure, the mole fraction of the carbon tetrachloride in the solution will have the same value, 0.213, and the mole fraction of stannic chloride will be 1 — 0.213 or 0.787. We may further calculate the partial vapor pressure of the latter, from the equation, $p/51 = 0.787$, giving $p = 40$ mm. These relations were shown graphically in Fig. 1.

Total vapor pressure. We may proceed further to calculate the total vapor pressure and the composition of the vapor in equilibrium with the solution. The total vapor pressure is, from the above figures, 45 mm. + 40 mm., or 85 mm. The mole fractions of the components in the vapor state in equilibrium with a solution of the above composition are, by Dalton's law of partial pressures, 45/85 = 0.53 and 40/85 = 0.47 (or 1 — 0.53) respectively. If the solution were boiled under these conditions, the carbon tetrachloride would be enriched in the first portions of distillate from mole fraction 0.213 to mole fraction 0.53.

The relation between the partial vapor pressures of the components, the total vapor pressures and the mole fractions in the liquid phase was represented graphically in Fig. 1, where the algebraic relations used above, *i. e.*,

$$p_1 = p_1^\circ x_1, \; p_2 = p_2^\circ x_2$$

and

$$p_1 + p_2 = p_1^\circ x_1 + p_2^\circ x_2 = x_1 (p_1^\circ - p_2^\circ) + p_2^\circ, \tag{19}$$

have an obvious geometric significance.

Boiling point-composition curve. When the vapor pressures of the pure liquids are known throughout a range of temperature, it is possible to calculate the boiling point-composition curve, useful in connection with the problem of fractional distillation. Suppose we have the vapor pressures for CCl_4 and $SnCl_4$ shown in Table 1.

Table 1

		77°	80°	90°	100°	110°	114°
CCl_4	p_1	760	836	1112	1450	1880	....
$SnCl_4$	p_2	....	258	362	497	673	760
Liquid	x_1	1.000	0.868	0.531	0.274	0.072	0.000
Vapor	x_1	1.000	0.955	0.777	0.523	0.178	0.000

At the boiling point, $p_1 + p_2 = 760$ mm., and, by Equation 19

$$x_1^l = (760 - p_2^\circ)/(p_1^\circ - p_2^\circ) \tag{20}$$

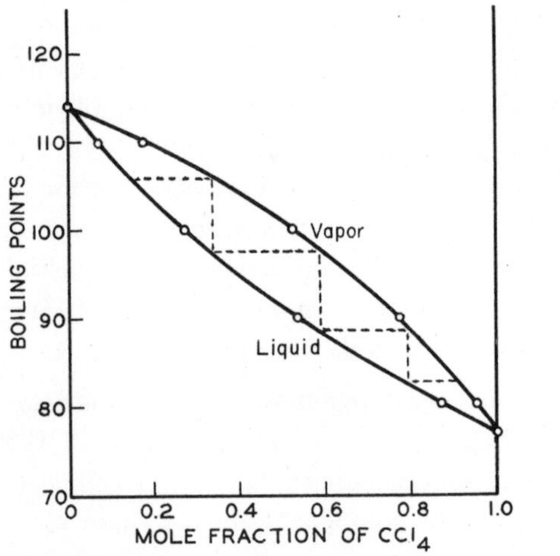

Fig. 5. Boiling point composition-curves for $SnCl_4$—CCl_4 solutions calculated from Raoult's law.

From the known values of p_1° and p_2° at any temperature we can calculate x_1 (and x_2) giving the values in the third row of the table. These can be plotted against the corresponding temperatures to get the boiling point-composition curve shown in Fig. 5. The composition of the vapor, and hence the distillate from liquid of the composition x_1, is readily obtained from the partial pressures. Thus, at $x_1 = 0.531$, at 90°, we calculate

$$p_1 = p_1^\circ x_1 = \\ = 0.531 \times 1112 = 590 \text{mm.},$$

and the mole fraction of CCl_4 in the vapor, or distillate, is $590/760 = 0.777$. Similar calculations yield the other figures given in the last row of the table, and which are plotted in the upper curve of Fig. 2.

Conversely, if the boiling point-composition curve is known, it is possible to determine whether a mixture obeys Raoult's law, since the values of p_1°, p_2° and x_1 should give the pressure under which the mixture boils when substituted in Equation 19.

Other functions may be plotted, *e. g.*, the ration of the compositions of the vapor and liquid against the temperature, or the total pressure.

The important practical problem of the choice of conditions for obtaining the best separation in fractional distillation can be easily solved. Let us designate the less volatile species by the subscript 1, the more volatile by 2. The mole fraction of the former in the liquid is x_1 and in the vapor x'_1. The larger the ratio x_1/x'_1, then the better is the separation. The value of x^1 is given by Dalton's law, $x'_1 = p_1/(p_1 + p_2)$. The values of p_1 and p_2 are given by Raoult's law, *i. e*, $p_1 = p_1^\circ x_1$ and $p_2 = p_2^\circ x_2$, which gives

$$x_1/x'_1 = x_1 + (p_2^\circ/p_1^\circ)\, x_2. \tag{21}$$

From this we see that the ratio, x_1/x'_1, is increased, corresponding to better fractionation, by any factor tending to increase the ratio p_2°/p_1°. For a given pair of liquids this ratio may be altered by altering the temperature, and, hence, the pressure, of distillation.From the familiar Clausius-Clapeyron Equation I—28 we see that

$$\frac{d \ln (p_2^\circ/p_1^\circ)}{dT} = \frac{\Delta H_2^V - \Delta H_1^V}{RT^2} \tag{22}$$

It will usually be the case that the liquid having the higher boiling point (lower vapor pressure) will have the higher heat of vaporization ΔH_1^V, *i. e.*, ΔH_1^V will be greater than ΔH_2^V, and the ratio, p_2°/p_1°, will decrease with increasing temperature. The normal liquids, which are most likely to give ideal solutions, obey the Hildebrand-Trouton rule (cf. Chapter V) and uniformly show this inverse relation of volatility to heat of vaporization. We can, therefore, state as a general rule that the fractional distillation of a given ideal solution is more efficient the lower the temperature at which it is carried out.

The expression, "number of theoretical plates" which is commonly used in fractional distillation, is the minimum number of steps required to obtain a distillate of a certain composition when starting with a liquid of another. Fig. 5 shows that 4 such steps are required to obtain a distillate with 90 mole per cent of CCl_4 from an initial solution in which it is 15 mole per cent. A fractionating column which would accomplish this enrichment would have an efficiency of 4 theoretical plates.

Solubility of gases. The treatment of the solubility of vapors used in the preceding section can be applied to any gas below its critical temperature, as has been shown by Dolezalek[6]. However, the saturation pressure of many gases is high, and the deviations from the ideal gas laws may be considerable. In such a case it is possible, where the necessary data are available, to calculate the fugacity of the gas instead of its vapor pressure by the method previously outlined, but it will not ordinarily be worth while to do so, since the deviations from Raoult's law are usually so large as to outweigh those resulting from the use of pressures instead of fugacities.

---

[6] F. Dolezalek, *Z. physik. Chem.*, **71**, **191** **(1910)**.

Dolezalek has attempted to correct for the departure from the ideal gas laws by using $p + a/v^2$ in place of p. This is not sufficient, however, to give what he called the "reduced pressure" of a perfect gas, for the term a/v^2 does not account for the entire departure.

If the gas is above its critical temperature, p° ceases to have any meaning as a saturation pressure, but by extrapolating the vapor pressure above the critical temperature a fictitious value of p° can be obtained which can be used for an approximate calculation of the solubility of the gas. This procedure will be explained in Chapter XV.

Expressing the solubility of a gas in terms of its mole fraction, if Raoult's law holds:

1. **The solubility of a gas is proportional to its partial pressure (Henry's law),** since p° depends only upon the temperature.

2. **The gas with the higher critical temperature, and boiling point, is more soluble than one with a lower critical temperature,** since p° is smaller for the former. This is approximately true, in most cases, even when Raoult's law is not obeyed, as illustrated in Table 2.

Table 2. Solubilities of Gases at 1 Atmosphere, in Mole Per Cent.

	Crit. Temp.	Solvent				Temp. °C
Gas	°K	C_6H_6	$CHCl_3$	CS_2	C_6H_{14}	
H_2	38	0.026				20
N_2	127	0.041	0.043	0.013		20
CO	132	0.061	0.063	0.020		20
CO_2	304	0.94	1.23	0.23		20
CH_4	177	0.18			0.31	25
C_2H_4	283	1.25			0.59	25
C_2H_6	307				1.71	25

3. **The solubility of a gas diminishes with increasing temperature.**

4. **The solubility of a gas expressed in terms of the volume of solution is greater the less the molal volume of the solvent,** since, at a given pressure, the mole fraction of a gas is the same in all ideal solutions.

Miscibility of liquids. When two liquids are sufficiently alike to obey Raoult's law, it is evident that they must be miscible in all proportions, because only where the internal forces are sufficiently unlike could there be separation into two liquid phases. If two liquids which obeys Raoult's law did form two layers, then when equilibrium is reached the partial vapor pressure of either component must be the same for both phases, otherwise that component would pass from one layer to another until the partial pressures became equal; since the partial vapor pressures are equal, the mole fractions must be equal and the two phases must be identical[7].

Solubility of solids[8]. Raoult's law may be used to calculate the solubility of a solid. In this case, the partial vapor pressure of the solute, p,

[7] Cf. E. Washburn, *Trans. Am. Electrochem. Soc.*, **22**, 330 (1912).

[8] Cf. H. Le Chatelier, *Compt. rend.*, **100**, 50, 441 (1885); I. Schroeder, *Z. physik. Chem.*, **11**, 449 (1893); also E. W. Washburn and J. W. Read, *Proc. Nat. Acad.*, **1**, 191 (1915); *C. A.*, **9**, 1570 (1915).

can be set equal to the vapor pressure of the pure solid, p^s, with which the solution is in equilibrium. (We are assuming that no solid solution is formed). The pressure, p°, is that of the solute in its pure liquid form, which is supercooled. Since the solid is the stable form below the melting point, $p^\circ > p^s$, and we can have equilibrium only because the partial pressure of the solute in the liquid phase is reduced by the presence of the solvent till it is numerically equal to that of the solid.

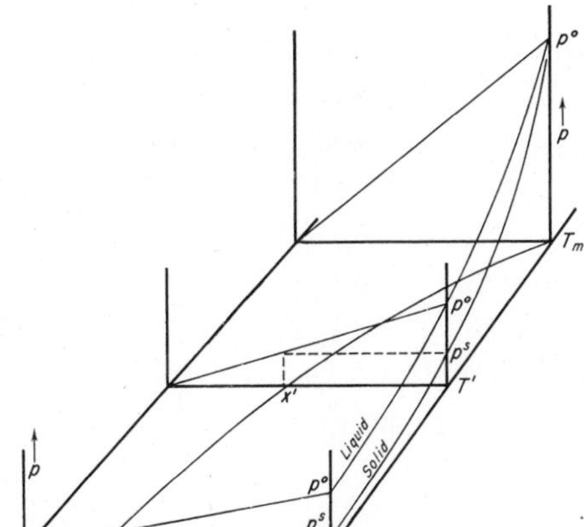

Fig. 6. Effect of temperature upon the ideal solubility of a solid.

These relationships may be made clearer by reference to Figure 6. The vapor pressure curves of the pure liquid and solid forms of the solute are represented along the temperature axis. They intersect, of course, at the melting point, T_m. The pressure-composition relations are shown at three temperatures, T, T', and T_m. At T and T', since the vapor pressure of the solid, p^s, is less than that of the pure liquid, p°, equilibrium requires that p° be reduced to $p = p^s$ by diluting with a solvent to mole fractions x and x', respectively. The variation of solubility with temperature is shown on the basal plane of the figure, having the values x, x' and 1 at the respective temperatures T, T' and T_m.

The solubility of a solid in any solvent in which it forms an ideal solution may be calculated from Equation I—36 by substituting x^i for a^s, which in turn is f^s/f°, or approximately p^s/p°. Since $x < 1$ it is convenient to avoid negative logarithms and write

$$\log \frac{1}{x^i} = \frac{\Delta H^F}{4.575} \left(\frac{T_m - T}{T_m \; T} \right) \tag{23}$$

where ΔH^F is the heat of fusion of the solid and T_m the melting temperature.

For greater accuracy, we may consider the change in the heat of fusion with temperature and use Equation I—39, which yields

$$\log \frac{1}{x^i} = \frac{\Delta H^F_m}{4.575} \left(\frac{T_m - T}{T T_m} \right) - \frac{\Delta C_p}{4.575} \left(\frac{T_m - T}{T} \right) + \frac{\Delta C_p}{1.987} \log \frac{T_m}{T} \tag{24}$$

To illustrate the use of these equations we may calculate the ideal solubility of naphthalene. According to Bogojawlenski[9] the heat of fusion is 4,440 cal. per mole; the molal heat capacity of the liquid near the melting point is 56.6 cal. per degree, that of the solid, extrapolated to the melting point, 80.05°, is 51.8 cal. per degree. Substituting in Equation 23 gives $x = 0.311$ at 25°C, while the more nearly accurate Equation 24 gives the slightly higher value, 0.322. The agreement of the results of such calculations with experimental values will be discussed in Chapter XVII.

Some useful qualitative rules can be deduced from Equation 23.

1. The solubility of a given solid is greater the higher the temperature. This fact is too well known to need illustration. Only occasionally do we find the reverse, and only in cases where the heat of mixing is greater than the heat of fusion. Such situations involve a wide departure from Raoult's law.

2. A solid having a higher melting point is less soluble at a given temperature than one having a lower melting point[10], (provided the heat of fusion of the lower melting substance is not notably greater). Abundant illustration of this might be given, but Table 3 will suffice for the present.

Table 3. Influence of Melting Point Upon Solubility.

Solute	melting point °C	Solubility, mole per cent in Benzene[11]	Solubility, mole per cent in Hexane[12]	temp °C.
Phenanthrene. $C_{14}H_{10}$	100	18.6	4.2	25
Anthracene, $C_{14}H_{10}$	217	0.63	0.18	25
m-Dinitrobenzene $C_6H_4(NO_2)_2$	90	37.6[12]		50
o-Dinitrobenzene $C_6H_4(NO_2)_2$	116	17.5		50
p-Dinitrobenzene $C_6H_4(NO_2)_2$	170	3.1		50

A very satisfactory graphic representation of ideal solubility[13] is to plot $\log x$ against $1/T$. This gives a nearly straight line whose slope is $\Delta H^F/4.575$ and whose upper limit is $\log x = 0$ at the melting point. If the melting point of the solute is known, together with a single point on the solubility curve, a straight line drawn through these two points will give very closely the solubility at other temperatures. If the heat of fusion of the solute is known it may be used to give the slope of the line and hence the solubility curve.

---

[9] A. Bogojawlenski *Chem. Zentr.*, [5] **9II**, 945 (1905).

[10] A. L. Lavoisier, "Traité elementaire de chimie", Tom. II, Partie III, p. **104** (1794). T. Carnelly, *Phil. Mag.*, **5**, 13, 180 (1878).

[11] J. H. Hildebrand, E. T. Ellefson and C. W. Beebe, *J. Am. Chem. Soc.*, **39**, 2301 (1917).

[12] R. Kremann, *Sitz. Akad. Wiss. Wien*, **117**, IIb, 569 (1908).

[13] J. M. Braham, *J. Am. Chem. Soc.*, **41**, 1707 (1919).

CHAPTER III

Nonideal Solutions: General

Measurements of partial vapor pressures of binary solutions show that most of them can be classified into two main types, with positive and negative deviations, respectively, from Raoult's law. The former is illustrated by the system carbon disulfide-acetone, plotted in Fig. 1, and the latter by acetone-chloroform, in Fig. 2, both taken from the pioneering investigation of Zawidzki[1]. We should note that in both cases Raoult's law is approached for the component approaching purity, and that the percentage deviation from Raoult's law increases as the component in question becomes more dilute. We shall see in later chapters that positive deviations are favored by differences in "internal pressure" or molecular attractive force and that negative deviations are favored by a tendency to compound formation between the two components or by a marked difference in size. The vapor pressure of the "solvent" will not, of course, approach the straight line of Raoult's law at the upper end unless the true mole fraction is used. For example, the partial vapor pressure of water over dilute HCl solutions gives the curve *a* shown in Fig. 3, plotted against $N_{H_2O}/(N_{H_2O} + N_{HCl})$, but it gives the curve *b* in Fig. 3, if plotted against $N_{H_2O}/(N_{H_2O} + N_{H^+} + N_{Cl^-})$. This is, of course, a test of ionization.

It is instructive to compare the related functions: activity a, which we will assume to be equal to p/p°; the activity coefficient, $\gamma = a/x$; and its logarithm, log γ, which is proportional, in an isothermal system, to the difference, $\overline{F} - \overline{F}^i$, between the actual partial molal free energy and what it would be in an ideal solution. These functions are shown in Figs. 4—11, for the systems shown in Figs. 1 and 2. When the partial quantities are known, it is possible also to calculate the total free energy of mixing a mole of solution from its pure liquid components by the relation, (cf. Equation I—5).

$$\Delta F^M = x_1(\overline{F}_1 - F_1^\circ) + x_2(\overline{F}_2 - F_2^\circ) = RT(x_1 \ln a_1 + x_2 \ln a_2) \qquad (1)$$

This is likewise shown in Figs. 6 and 7. The total heat of mixing and the total entropy of mixing are similarly related to the partial quantities and any one of these three functions can of course be calculated when the other two are known. Similarly one can define an excess free energy of mixing,

$$\Delta F^E = x_1(\overline{F}_1 - \overline{F}_1^i) + x_2(\overline{F}_2 - \overline{F}_2^i) = RT(x_1 \ln \gamma_1 + x_2 \ln \gamma_2) \qquad (2)$$

This is plotted in Figs. 10 and 11.

---

[1] J. v. Zawidzki, *Z. physik. Chem.*, **35**, 129 (1900).

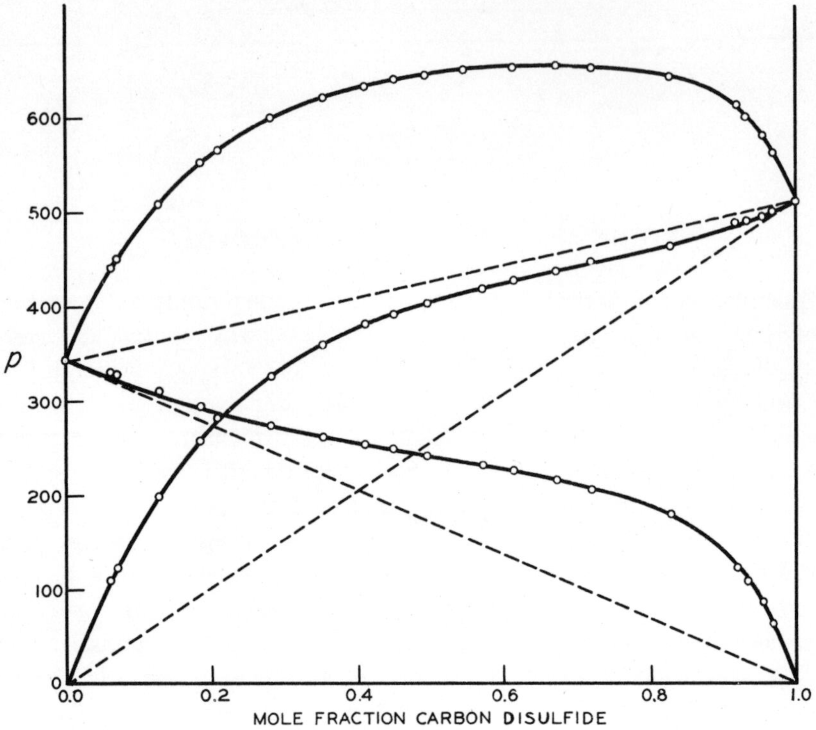

Fig. 1 Partial and total vapor pressures of carbon disulfide-acetone solutions, 35.17 °C.

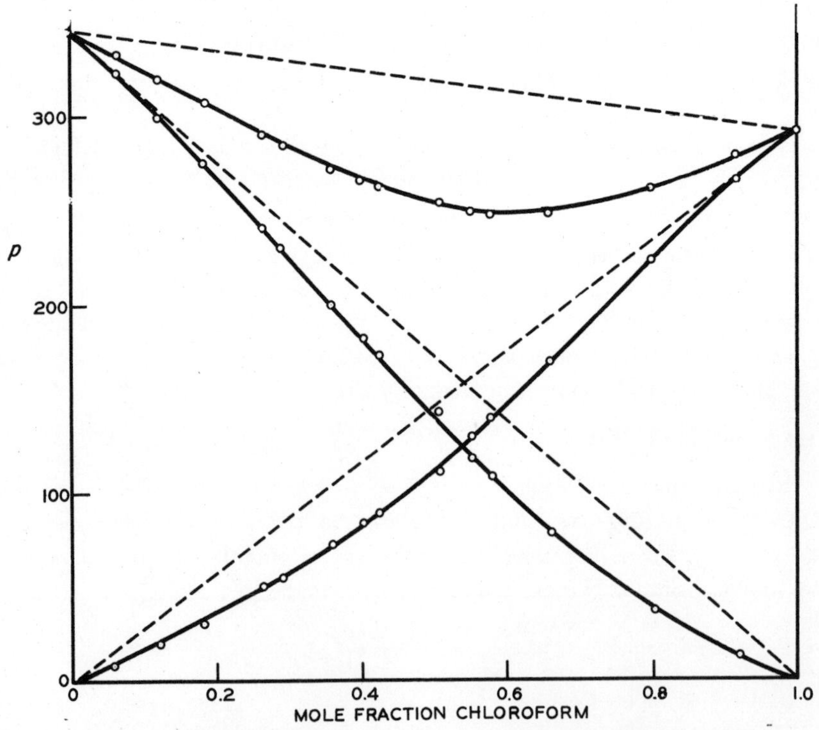

Fig. 2 Partial and total pressures, chloroform-acetone, 35.17 °C.

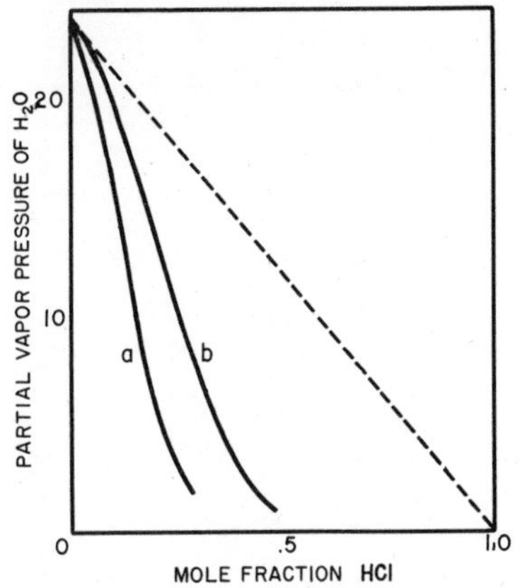

Fig. 3 Partial vapor pressure of H_2O from HCl solutions against mole fraction of HCl; curve *a* disregarding ionization, curve *b* with ionization.

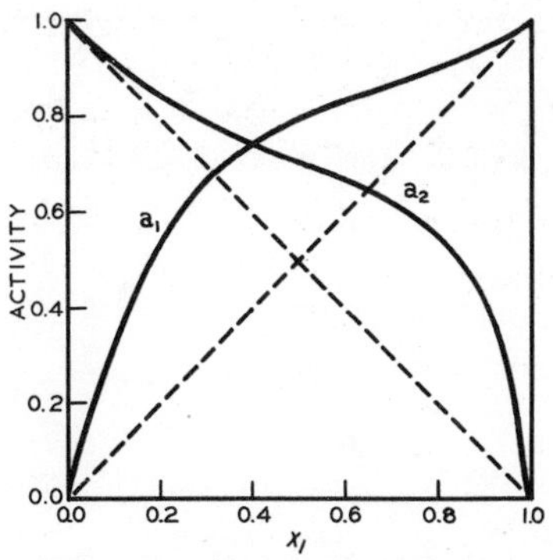

Fig. 4 Activities for carbon disulfide-acetone solutions.

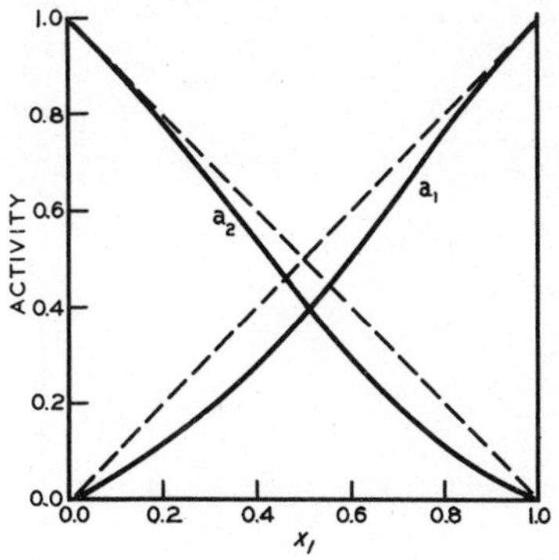

Fig. 5 Activities for chloroform-acetone solutions.

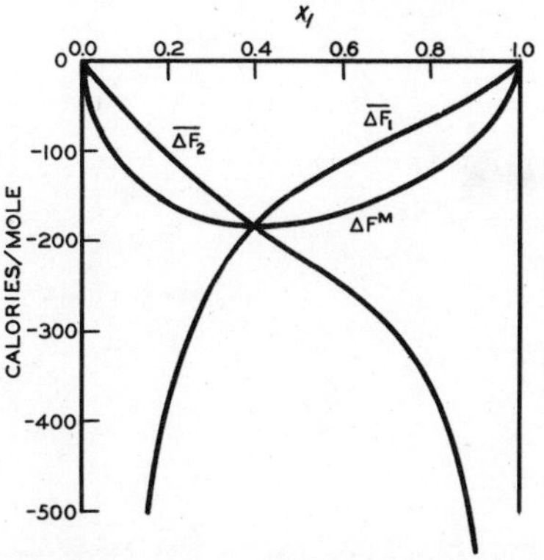

Fig. 6 Free energy relations for carbon disulfide-acetone solutions.

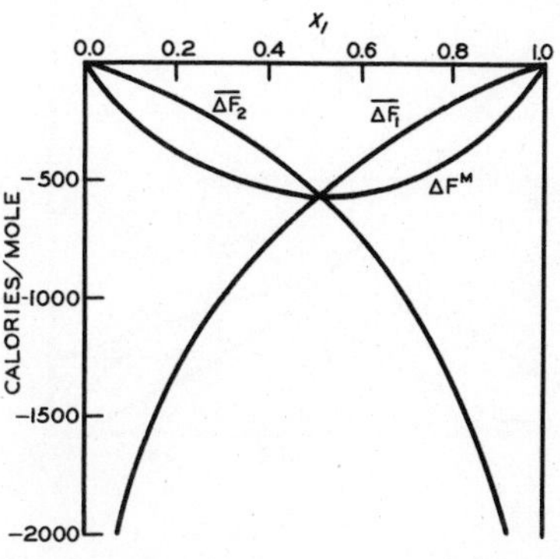

Fig. 7 Free energy relations for chloroform-acetone solution.

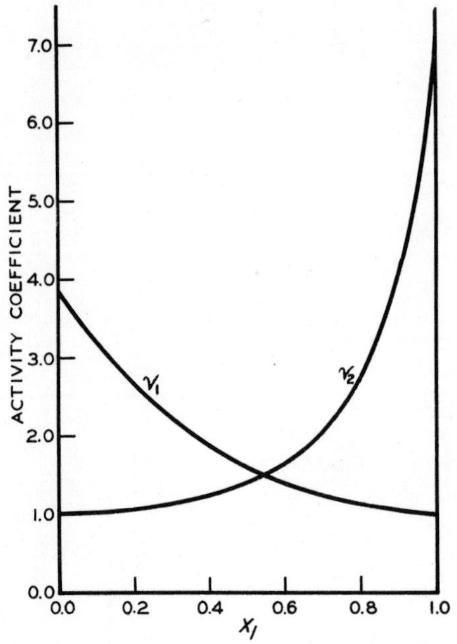

Fig. 8 Activity coefficients for carbon disulfide-acetone solutions.

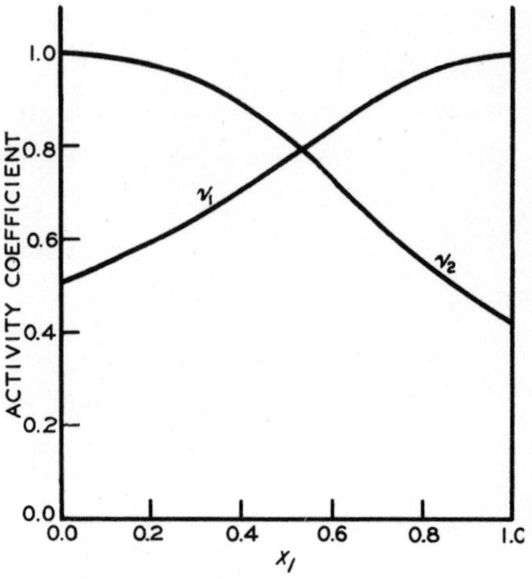

Fig. 9 Activity coefficients for chloroform-acetone solutions.

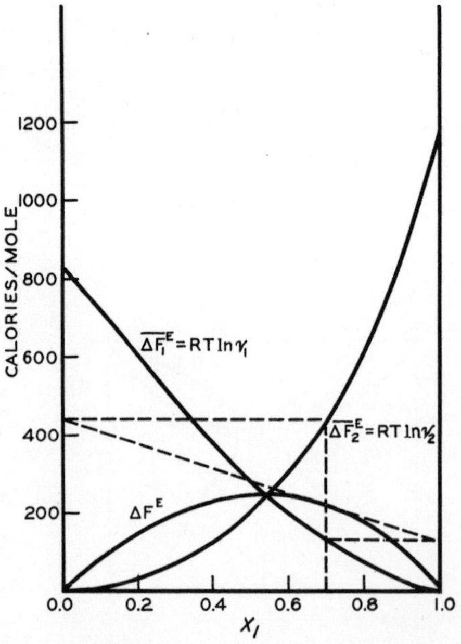

Fig. 10 Partial and total excess free energies for carbon disulfide-acetone solutions.

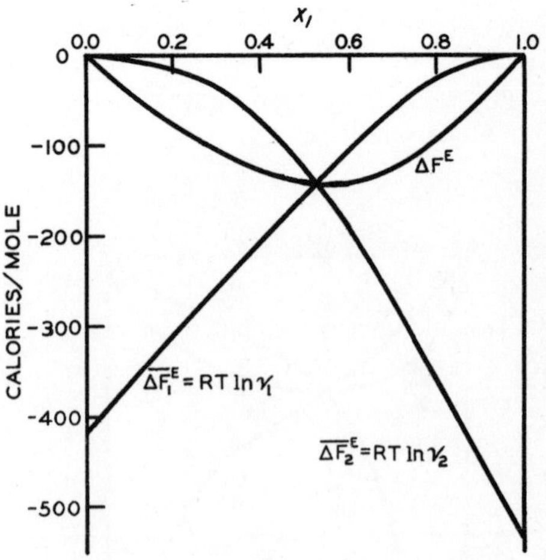

Fig. 11 Total excess free energies for chloroform-acetone solutions.

Relation between the activities of the components of a solution. The Gibbs-Duhem equation.

It is possible to change the composition of a solution in two thermodynamically equivalent ways, and therefore to equate the free energy changes. One process is to add dN_1 moles of component 1 to a solution composed of N_1+N_2 moles of the two components. The increase in the partial molal free energy $\overline{F}_1$, may by written as $dN_1(\partial\overline{F}_1/\partial N_1)_T$. The other process is to add an amount of the same solution containing dN_1 moles of 1 and the proportionate amount dN_2 of 2, and to distill out the dN_2 moles of 2, thus obtaining the same final solution as in the first process. The addition of more solution of the same composition leaves $\overline{F}_1$ unchanged, while the change on distillation is $-dN_2(\partial\overline{F}_1/\partial N_2)_T$. But

$$\left(\frac{\partial \overline{F}_1}{\partial N_2}\right)_T=\left(\frac{\partial^2 F}{\partial N_1\,\partial N_2}\right)_T=\left(\frac{\partial \overline{F}_2}{\partial N_1}\right)_T \tag{3}$$

and $dN_2=(N_2/N_1)\,dN_1$. Making the necessary substitutions, and equating we obtain

$$N_1\left(\frac{\partial \overline{F}_1}{\partial N_1}\right)_T+N_2\left(\frac{\partial \overline{F}_2}{\partial N_1}\right)_T=0 \tag{4}$$

Had we considered the change in $\overline{F}_2$ in the same processes, we would have obtained

$$N_1\left(\frac{\partial \overline{F}_1}{\partial N_2}\right)_T+N_2\left(\frac{\partial \overline{F}_2}{\partial N_2}\right)_T=0 \tag{5}$$

The independent variable may be left out, and the equations written as

$$N_1\,d\overline{F}_1+N_2\,d\overline{F}_2=0 \tag{6}$$

This equation was first derived by Gibbs[2], although usually attributed to Duhem[3] or to Margules[4]. In view of the number of "Gibbs equations", we shall designate this one and its equivalent forms as the "Gibbs-Duhem equation". It can be transformed into

$$x_1\,d\overline{F}_1+x_2\,d\overline{F}_2=0 \tag{7}$$

Again, since $\overline{F}_1-F_1^{\circ}=RT\ln a_1=RT\ln(f_1/f_1^{\circ})$, we can write either

$$x_1\,d\ln a_1+x_2\,d\ln a_2=0 \tag{8}$$

or

[2] J. W. Gibbs, "Collected Works", New York, Longmans, Green & Co., (1931).
[3] P. Duhem, *Compt. rend.*. **102,** 1449 (1886).
[4] M. Margules, *Sitzungsber. Wien. Akad.*, [**2**], **104,** 1243 (1895).

$$x_1\, d\ln f_1 + x_2\, d\ln f_2 = 0 \tag{9}$$

and since $dx_1 = -\,dx_2$,

$$\frac{\partial \ln a_1}{\partial \ln x_1} = \frac{\partial \ln a_2}{\partial \ln x_2} \text{ and } \frac{\partial \ln f_1}{\partial \ln x_1} = \frac{\partial \ln f_2}{\partial \ln x_2} \tag{10}$$

In all these equations, N and x are interchangeable, also f and a, and to the extent that vapor imperfections can be neglected, f and p. If the solutions contain more than two components, corresponding terms are to be added, *e. g.*,

$$x_1\, d\,\overline{F}_1 + x_2\, d\,\overline{F}_2 + x_3\, d\,\overline{F}_3 + \ldots\ldots = 0 \tag{11}$$

Several interesting and important conclusions can be drawn from the relationship embodied in Equations 4 to 11 as follows.

1. **If Raoult's law holds throughout the whole range of composition for one component of a binary solution it holds for the other likewise,** because if $a_1 = x_1$, $\partial \ln a_1/\partial \ln x_1 = 1$ and, by Equation 10, then $\partial \ln a_2/\partial \ln x_2 = 1$. On integrating, $\ln a_2 = \ln x_2 + \ln K_2$, or $a_2 = x_2 K_2$ where K_2 is the constant of integration, which can be evaluated by the condition that when $x_2 = 1$, $a_2 = 1$ by definition of a_2, hence $K_2 = 1$ and $a_2 = x_2$, which is Raoult's law.

2. If a solute is very dilute, its molecules are too far apart to affect one another; therefore the activity of the solute must be at least approximately proportional to their number, *i. e.*, $a_2 \sim x_2$ or $a_2 = K_2 x_2$, which is Henry's law. This, like Raoult's law, gives $\partial \ln a_2/\partial \ln x_2 = 1$, and the Gibbs-Duhem relation can be applied as in the preceding case to show that **if the solute obeys Henry's law in dilute solution the solvent obeys Raoult's law.**

3. Equation 10 shows also that since $x_1 + x_2 = 1$, $d\ln x_1$ and $d\ln x_2$ have opposite signs and therefore **a_1 and a_2 or p_1 and p_2 curve in opposite directions,** as illustrated in Figs. 1, 2, 4, and 6.

4. **When the activity-composition curve is known for one component of a binary solution it can be determined for the other.**

Either an analytic or a graphic method may be used. The former may be illustrated by aid of a pair of empirical equations proposed by Margules[4,5] and suggested, doubtless, by the form of the curves for $RT\ln\gamma$, shown in Figs. 10 and 11. The equations are:

$$\ln\gamma_1 = \ln a_1 - \ln x_1 = A_1 x_2 + B_1 x_2^2 + C_1 x_2^3 + D_1 x_2^4 + \ldots \tag{12a}$$

$$\ln\gamma_2 = \ln a_2 - \ln x_2 = A_2 x_1 + B_2 x_1^2 + C_2 x_1^3 + D_2 x_1^4 + \ldots \tag{12b}$$

[5] The equations were made still more elastic by the addition of exponents to x_1 and x_2 in the left-hand members of Equations 12a, b, but this is probably an unnecessary complication and is here omitted to simplify the later operations.

where A_1, B_1, C_1, D_1 and A_2, B_2, C_2 and D_2 are empirical constants chosen to fit the data. To apply the Gibbs-Duhem relation, we may transpose $\ln x_1$ and $\ln x_2$ to the right-hand members, differentiate both equations with respect to x_1, multiply them by x_1 and x_2, respectively, replace x_2 wherever it occurs by $1-x_1$ add them and equate the sum to zero. The coefficients of each power of x_1 may be equated to zero, giving a set of simultaneous equations whose solution yields the following relations between the two sets of coefficients:

$$A_2 = A_1 = 0 \tag{13a}$$

$$B_2 = B_1 + 3\,C_1/2 + 2\,D_1 + \dots \tag{13b}$$

$$C_2 = -(C_1 + 8\,D_1/3 + \dots) \tag{13c}$$

$$D_2 = D_1 + \dots \tag{13d}$$

The disappearance of the terms, $A_1 x_2$ and $A_2 x_1$ is a particularly striking and important result. Its physical significance can be seen from case 2, above, in which the necessary approach to Henry's law for a very dilute solute necessitates a corresponding approach to Raoult's law for the solvent.

In many systems, the curves for the two components are nearly symmetrical, and in such cases they can often be represented rather well by the simple equations,

$$\ln \gamma_1 = Bx_2^2 \text{ and } \ln\gamma_2 = Bx_1^2, \tag{14}$$

$$\log \gamma_1 = B'x_2^2 \text{ and } \log \gamma_2 = B'x_1^2 \tag{15}$$

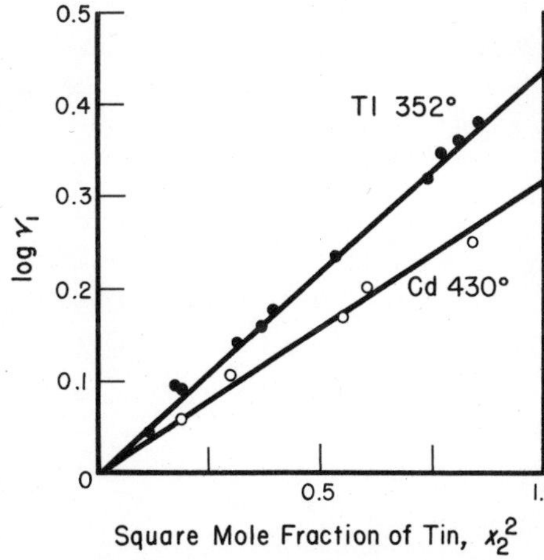

Fig. 12 Activity of coefficients of tin in alloys with thallium and cadmium.

and a plot of $\log \gamma_1$ vs. x_2^2 gives a straight line, serving well to smooth out experimental points. Fig. 12 for alloys of cadmium in tin[6] and thallium in tin[7] illustrates this relation. (The values of γ here used were derived not from vapor pressures but from e. m. f. of alloy concentration cells, by a method described in Chapter XIX).

Another analytical expression that lends itself readily to the correlation of the activities of the two components is one derived by van Laar[8] from

[6] N. W. Taylor, *J. Am. Chem. Soc.*, **45**, 2865 (1923).
[7] J. H. Hildebrand and J. N. Sharma, *Ibid.*, **51**, 462 (1929).
[8] J. J. van Laar, *Z. physik. Chem.*, **72**, 723 (1910); **83**, 599 (1913).

van der Waals theory, to be discussed later, (Chapter VII) but which we may consider for our present purpose simply as an empirical, two-constant equation;

$$\ln \gamma_1 = \frac{A_1 x_2^2}{(x_2 + B_1 x_1)^2} \text{ and } \ln \gamma_2 = \frac{A_2 x_1^2}{(x_1 + B_2 x_2)^2} \quad (16)$$

The constants A and B in these equations of course are different from those in Equations 12—15. These equations become simpler if the mole ratios, $y_1 = x_1/x_2$ and $y_2 = x_2/x_1$, are substituted for mole fractions, giving

$$\ln \gamma_1 = \frac{A_1}{(1 + B_1 y_1)^2} \text{ and } \ln \gamma_2 = \frac{A_2}{(1 + B_2 y_2)^2} \quad (17)$$

Applying the Gibbs-Duhem relation to this pair yields $B_2 = 1/B_1$ and $A_2 = A_1/B_1$, so that

$$\ln \gamma_2 = \frac{A_1 B_1}{(y_2 + B_1)^2} \quad (18)$$

The two curves are symmetrical when $B_1 = B_2 = 1$, giving

$$\ln \gamma_1 = \frac{A_1}{(1 + y_1)^2} \text{ and } \ln \gamma_2 = \frac{A_1}{(1 + y_2)^2} \quad (19)$$

These are identical with Equations 14, 15 if the y's are replaced by x's.

Equations for $\ln \gamma$ or $\ln a$ with a theoretical basis will be found in Chapters VI — VIII. It should hardly be necessary to emphasize the fact that no such pair of equations can be considered valid which does not satisfy the Gibbs-Duhem relation.

To illustrate the application of such an empirical equation to the calculation of the activity of one component when that of the other is known, we may use the data of Hildebrand, Foster and Beebe[9] upon the vapor pressures of mercury in cadmium and tin amalgams at 323°, represented in Figures 13 and 14 respectively. The authors found that these curves were given closely by the following equations:

For cadmium amalgams $\log \gamma_1 = \dfrac{-1.40}{(1 + 1.90 y_1)^2}$

For tin amalgams $\log \gamma_1 = \dfrac{0.22}{(1 + 0.26 y_1)^2}$

These give the values of A and B in Equation 16 as follows;

	$0.434\ A_1$	B_1
Cadmium amalgams	− 1.40	1.90
Tin amalgams	+ 0.22	0.26

Substituting these values in Equation 18 for the other component, we have for cadmium amalgams:

$$\log \gamma_2 = \frac{0.4343\,A_1 B_1}{(y_2 + B_1)^2} = \frac{-1.40 \times 1.90}{(y_2 + 1.90)^2} = \frac{-2.66}{(y_2 + 1.90)^2}$$

and for tin amalgams;

$$\log \gamma_2 = \frac{0.22 \times 0.26}{(y_2 + 0.26)^2} = \frac{0.0572}{(y_2 + 0.26)^2}$$

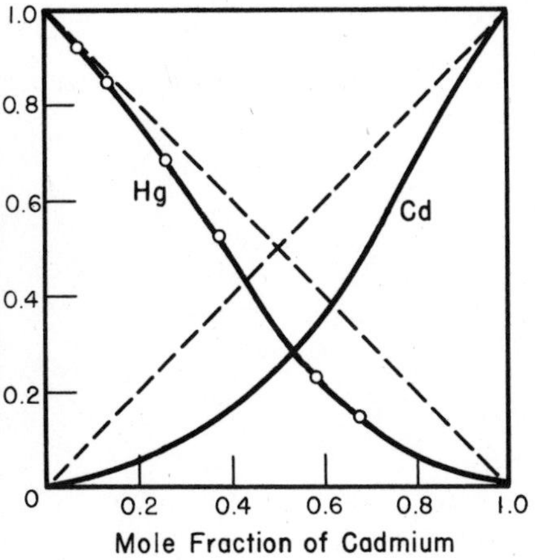

Fig. 13 Activities of cadmium and mercury in their amalgam. 322 °C.

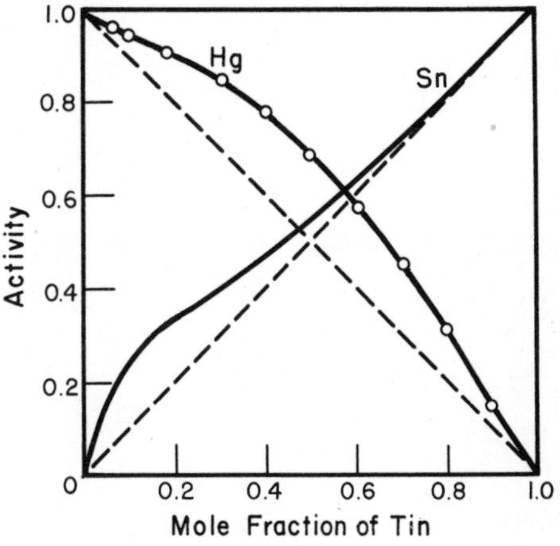

Fig. 14 Activities of tin and mercury in their amalgam. 323 °C.

These last expressions give the activity curves for cadmium and tin shown in the preceding figures.

Equations 12a, b, may of course, be applied in a similar manner and should give identical results in so far as the constants chosen in both processes accurately represent the experimental data.

The graphic application of the Gibbs equation to obtain the activity of one component of a binary mixture when that of the other is known may be made on the basis of Equation 8. Transforming it into

$$d \ln a_1 = -\frac{x_2}{x_1}\, d \ln a_2, \tag{20}$$

integrating, and changing to common logarithms gives

$$\log \frac{a_1}{a'_1} = -\int_{x'_2}^{x_2} \frac{x_2}{x_1}\, d \log a_2. \tag{21}$$

[9] J. H. Hildebrand, A. H. Foster and C. W. Beebe, *J. Am. Chem. Soc.*, **42**, 545 (1920).

This equation is suitable for the determination of the ratio of the activities of component 1 at two concentrations, but not when x_2 approaches 0, since then a_2 approaches 0 and log a_2 approaches $-\infty$. Lewis and Randall[10] have avoided this difficulty by plotting log γ_2, that is, log (a_2/x_2), which becomes a finite positive or negative quantity when x_2 (and hence x_2/x_1) is 0.

Since $x_1 + x_2 = 1$, $dx_1 = -dx_2$, $x_1 d\ln x_1 = -x_2 d\ln x_2$, and

$$d\ln x_1 = -\frac{x_2}{x_1} d\ln x_2 \tag{22}$$

Subtracting Equation 22 from Equation 20 gives

$$d\ln\frac{a_1}{x_1} = -\frac{x_2}{x_1} d\ln\frac{a_2}{x_2} \tag{23}$$

Integrating and substituting common logarithms gives

$$\log\frac{a_1}{x_1} - \log\frac{a'_1}{x'_1} = -\int_{x'_2}^{x_2} \frac{x_2}{x_1} d\log\frac{a_2}{x_2} \tag{24}$$

When $x'_2 = 0$, Raoult's law holds, and $a'_1/x'_1 = 1$ and $\log(a'_1/x'_1) = 0$ therefore

$$\log\frac{a_1}{x_1} = -\int_0^{x_2} \frac{x_2}{x_1} d\log\frac{a_2}{x_2} \tag{25}$$

To make a graphic integration of this equation, log $\frac{a_2}{x_2}$, that is, log γ_2, is plotted against x_2/x_1, as shown in Figure 15, where the data are for the vapor pressures of mercury in bismuth amalgams, according to measurements by Eastman and Hildebrand[11]. The area between the curve and the vertical axis between $x_2/x_1 = 0$ and any finite value of x_2/x_1 gives $-\log(a_1/x_1)$ at that composition. A series of values for a_1 can thus be obtained, as shown in Table 1. These values of a_1, for bismuth, are plotted in Figure 16, together with the experimental data for mercury from which they have been thus calculated.

Table 1. Activities of Bi, a_1, in Amalgams Calculated from Activities of Hg, a_2.

x_1	0.091	0.167	0.333	0.500	0.667	0.833
a_1	0.181	0.252	0.384	0.525	0.675	0.835

[10] G. N. Lewis and M. Randall, *J. Am. Chem. Soc.*, **43**, 233 (1921); also "Thermodynamics", McGraw-Hill, (1923) p. 269.

[11] E. D. Eastman and J. H. Hildebrand, *J. Am. Chem. Soc.*, **36**, 2020 (1914).

The various curve-pairs given in this chapter, as well as others given by Zawidski[1], who checked his measurements by means of the Gibbs-Duhem equation, illustrate the shapes of corresponding curves.

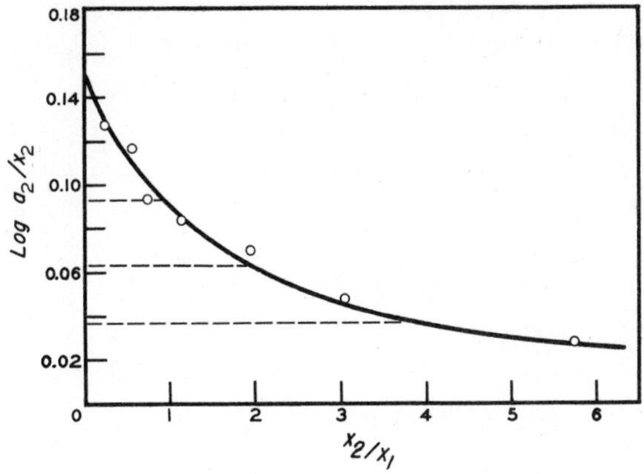

Fig. 15 Graphic integration of Gibbs-Duhem Equation.

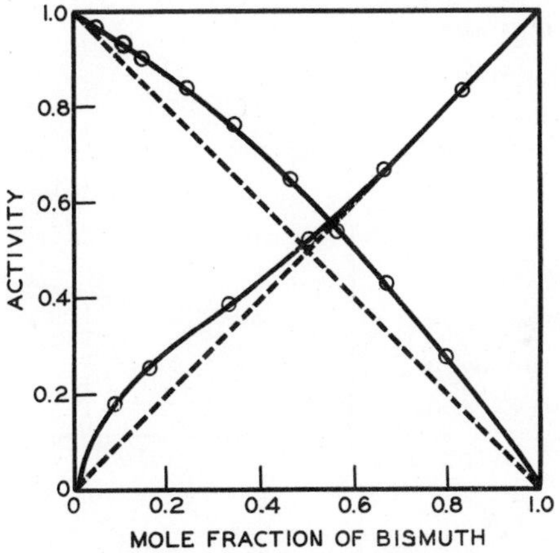

Fig. 16 Bismuth-mercury amalgams.

Graphic relation between partial and total molal quantities. If we differentiate Equation 2 with respect to x_1 we obtain:

$$\frac{\partial(\Delta F^E)}{\partial x_1} = (\overline{F}_1 - F_1^i) - (\overline{F}_2 - F_2^i) + x_1 \frac{\partial(\overline{F}_1 - F_1^i)}{\partial x_1} + x_2 \frac{\partial(\overline{F}_2 - F_2^i)}{\partial x_1} \qquad (26)$$

But the sum of the last two terms on the right is zero, by the Gibbs-Duhem equation, therefore:

$$\frac{\partial(\Delta F^E)}{\partial x_1} = (\overline{F}_1 - F_1^i) - (\overline{F}_2 - F_2^i) \qquad (27)$$

This equation furnishes a basis for a simple graphical relation between excess partial and total molal quantities, as may be seen by reference to Fig. 10. The tangent to the curve of ΔF^E at any volume of x_1, here 0.7, intercepts the $x_1 = 0$ axis at the value of $\bar{F}_2 - F_2^i$ and the $x_1 = 1$ axis at the value of $\bar{F}_1 - F_1^i$. This relation is not very useful in the case of free energies, because it is the partials rather than the total which are yielded by experiment; the total pressure, which is easily determined, does not of itself give ΔF^E. But a corresponding relation holds for partial and total volumes of mixtures, and since it is easy to determine ΔV by experiment, the corresponding treatment of a ΔV vs. x plot offers a simple method of calculating partial molal volumes. Fig. 17 illustrates the relation.

There is a simple form of the equations for ΔF^E and ΔV that may be pointed out in this connection. If the system is symmetrical, as is usually the case, when $V_1 = V_2$ (as we shall see later), Equations 14 enable us to write:

$$\bar{F}_1 - F_1^i = kx_2^2 \text{ and } \bar{F}_2 - F_2^i = kx_1^2 \tag{28}$$

where k is, at this stage at least, an empirical constant. Substituting these in Equation 2 gives:

$$\Delta F^E = kx_1 x_2 \tag{29}$$

A similar relation given by Biron[12] exists for molal volumes, so that, when $V_1 = V_2$,

$$\Delta V = k' x_1 x_2 \tag{30}$$

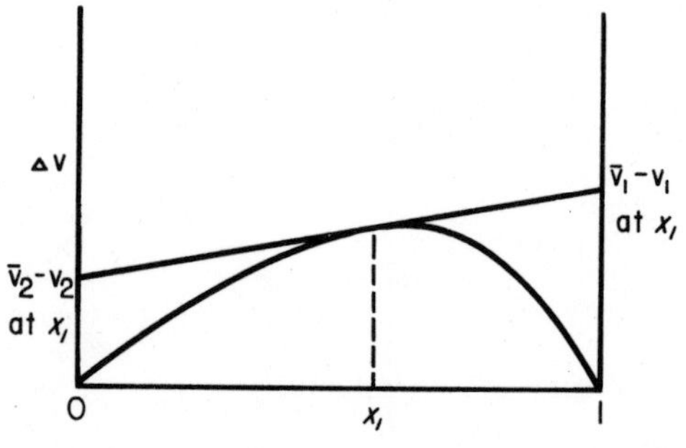

Fig. 17 Graphic method of obtaining partial from total thermodynamic quantities.

Its validity can be illustrated by figures for ΔV for mixtures of carbon and tin tetrachlorides obtained by Hildebrand and Carter[13] as follows:

x_1 (CCl_4)	x_2 ($SnCl_4$)	$\frac{100\Delta V}{V}$	$\frac{100\Delta V}{V x_1 x_2}$
0.636	0.364	0.374	1.615
.445	.555	.403	1.620
.247	.753	.303	1.630

[12] E. V. Biron, *J. Russ. Phys.-Chem. Soc.* **41**, 569 (1909).
[13] J. H. Hildebrand and J. M. Carter, *J. Am. Chem. Soc.*, **54**, 3592 (1932).

The two molal volumes 97.1 and 117.6 do not differ sufficiently to have much effect upon the constancy of k′. We shall see later that where V_1 differs greatly from V_2, it will be preferable to use the product of the volume fractions, $\varphi_1 \varphi_2$, in place of $x_1 x_2$.

Formation of two liquid phases. It is important to understand the effect of increasing the deviation from ideal behavior either by lowering the temperature or by choosing components more unlike in attractive forces. Either of these changes, pursued far enough, can bring about a separation into two liquid phases, as we shall now explain.

By rigorous thermodynamics, we may relate the temperature dependence of the activity coefficient and the heat of mixing. Recalling the definitions of a and γ (Equations I—32 to 34), we may write:

$$\frac{d \ln \gamma_1}{dT} = \frac{d \ln a_1}{dT} = -\frac{1}{RT^2} \frac{d \ln(\Delta \overline{F}_1/T)}{d(1/T)} = -\frac{\Delta \overline{H}_1}{RT^2} \tag{31}$$

Where the entropy of mixing is ideal ($\Delta \overline{S}_1 = - R \ln x_1$), we may integrate Equation 26 or substitute directly in Equation I—33 and obtain:

$$\ln \gamma_1 = \frac{\Delta \overline{H}_1}{RT} \tag{32}$$

Let us assume for the sake of algebraic simplicity that the systems are symmetrical and obey Equations 14, 15. We see from Equation 26 and 27 that for a solution with a positive heat of mixing $\ln \gamma_1$ would increase as the temperature is lowered, corresponding to an increase in the value of B′ in Equation 15.

In Fig. 18 are plotted values of $\log \gamma_1$ against x_1 for three values of B′, 0.50, 0.87 and 1.25. The three curves are all simply parabolic. But the corresponding values of the activity, a_1, shown in Fig. 19 look quite different, the simple curve for B′ = 0.50 changes, for B′ = 0.87, to a curve with zero slope at C and for B′ = 1.25 into a curve with the same value of a_1, at three different values of x_1. The significance of this is like that of the familiar P vs V plot of the van der Waals equation; it means that there are two stable liquid compositions in which the component has the same activity, *i. e.*, there are two liquid phases at any value of B′ > 0.87. The composition of these phases when B′ = 1.25 is given by the points at the extremities of the straight line, DE.

The broken portion of the curve is not realizable except in so far as supersaturation might be attained. If component 1 were added to component 2, its activity would increase along the curve for B′ = 1.25, until the point D is reached, where, instead of the solution becoming more concen-

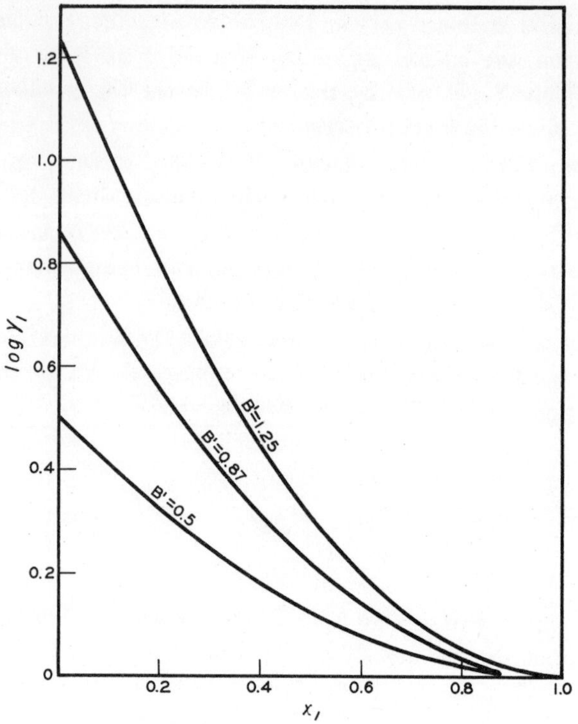

Fig. 18 Plot of function $\log \gamma_1 = B'x_2^2$.

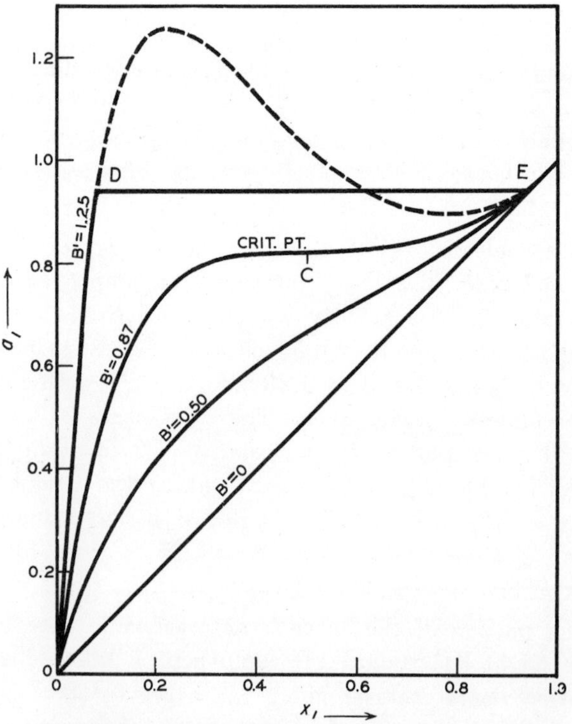

Fig. 19 Activity vs. x from function $\log \gamma_1 = B'x_2^2$.

trated with a still further increase in the activity of 1, a new phase is formed having the composition represented by E, which is much richer in 1, although the activity or fugacity of 1 therein is the same as in the first phase. Further addition of 1 results in an increase in the amount of the second phase and a decrease in the amount of the first until it has disappeared, when the second can vary as shown by the curve to the right of E.

The corresponding curves for the second component are not shown in Fig. 18 and 19, but it is evident that, having used one of a pair of symmetrical equations, they would be symmetrical with those given for 1. If a more general equation were used, similar curves would be obtained, although not symmetrical for the two components. The ends of the line AB would no longer be at the same distances from the vertical axes, although they would necessarily be at identical mole fractions respectively for the two components.

As the value of B′ is decreased, the line DE obviously decreases in length, corresponding to larger mutual solubility for the components, finally becoming a point, represented by C on a curve having a horizontal tangent at that point. This corresponds to the critical solution temperature for the two liquids. In nearly all cases increased deviations from Raoult's law, here illustrated by increased values of B′, are produced by lowering the temperature, resulting, when the deviation becomes sufficient, in the formation of two liquid phases whose mutual solubility decreases with further decrease in temperature. This yields the familiar type of solubility-temperature curve illustrated in Figure 20, for mixtures of aniline and hexane.[14]

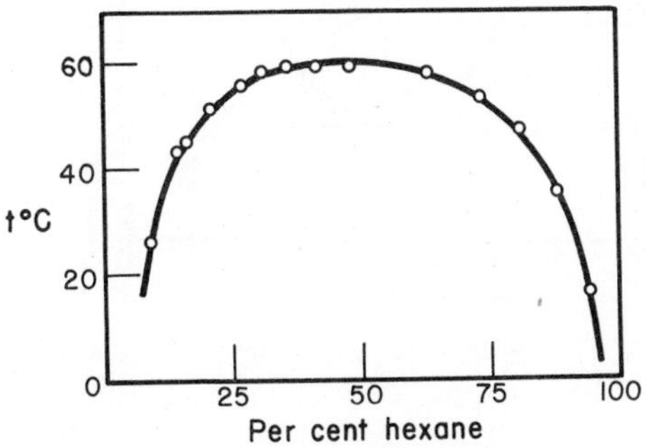

Fig. 20 Solubility of aniline — hexane mixtures.

At the critical solution temperature we have the conditions that $da/dx = 0$ and $d^2a/dx^2 = 0$ for both components. It is more convenient to apply the equivalent conditions $d\ln a/dx = 0$ and $d^2\ln a/dx^2 = 0$. For a system

[14] D. B. Keyes and J. H. Hildebrand. *J. Am. Chem. Soc.*, **39**, **2126** (**1917**).

obeying Equation 14 this yields $x_1 = x_2 = 0.5$, $B = 2$ and for Equation 15, $B' = 2 \times 0.4343$. The more complicated Equations 12 and 16 can, of course, be similarly treated.

Another way of looking at phase separation is to consider the change in the total free energy of mixing ΔF^M (See Equation 1) Fig. 21 shows the function $\Delta F^M/RT$ plotted against composition for the four values of B′ shown in Figs. 18 and 19. The equation is of course:

$$\frac{\Delta F^M}{RT} = x_1 \ln x_1 + x_2 \ln x_2 + B x_1 x_2 = 2.303\,(x_1 \log x_1 + x_2 \log x_2 + B' x_1 x_2) \tag{33}$$

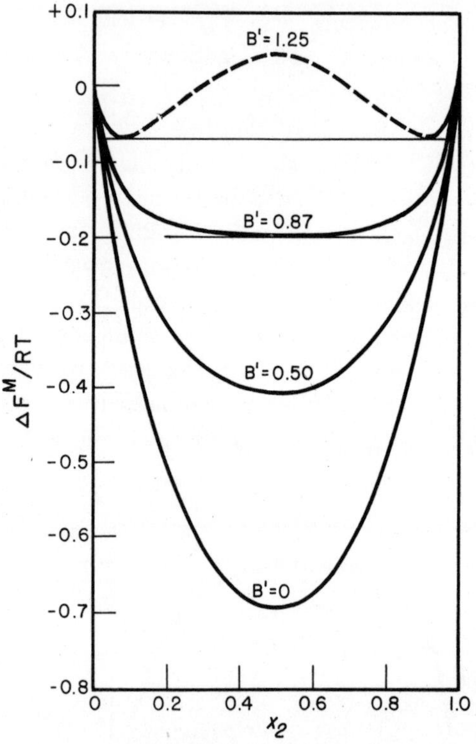

Fig. 21 The free energy of mixing for different values of B′ showing phase separation.

The condition for equilibrium in any system is that the total free energy be minimized. Obviously, if the free energy of the system can be reduced by separation into two phases, they will be formed. The mathematical condition for this is that two phases are formed whenever a straight line can be placed in such a way that it is simultaneously tangent to the free energy curve at two points; any intermediate point on this straight line represents a lower free energy than a point on the unstable one-phase curve.

Such a line for $B' = 1.25$ is shown in Fig. 21, the points of tangency define the composition of the conjugate phases in equilibrium. While for this symmetrical system the tangent line is horizontal and the points of tangency are at minima on the free energy curve this is not in general true. At $B' = 0.87$, the two conjugate phases have just coalesced to one. The conditions for the critical solution temperature require that the *second* and *third* derivatives of the free energy with respect to composition vanish.

$$\frac{d^2 \Delta F^M}{d x^2} = 0 \qquad \frac{d^3 \Delta F^M}{d x^3} = 0 \tag{34}$$

Except for symmetrical curves, as noted above, the first derivative does not vanish. The relation between these equations and those involving the activities should be obvious.

It is in general simpler to use the activity curves in calculating the composition of the conjugate phases; a graphical method has been given by Scatchard[15]. However it is sometimes easier to understand the qualitative aspects of the problem from schematic diagrams of the function ΔF^M; we shall use such curves in discussing the various types of solid solutions in Chapter XVIII.

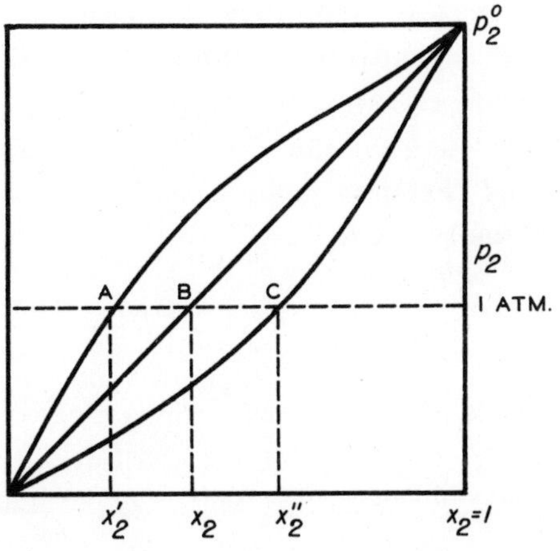

Fig. 22 Relation of type of deviation to gas solubility.

Effect of deviations upon the solubility of gases. Having discussed in Chapter II, the rules governing the solubility of gases in cases where Raoult's law holds, it is appropriate to point out the effect upon the solubility of deviations from Raoult's law. In Figure 22 are represented the three main types of vapor pressure curve plotted against composition. When Raoult's law holds, the solubility of the gas, $x_2 = p_2/p_2^\circ$, where, as in Chapter II, p_2° is the vapor pressure of the gas over its own pure liquid, and p_2 is the

[15] G. Scatchard, *J. Am. Chem. Soc.*, **62**, 2426 (1940).

partial pressure of the gas over the solution. If p_2 is taken as 1 atm., the point B in the figure represents a saturated solution, and x_2 its mole fraction, and we can write $x_2 = 1/p_2^\circ$. If, however, the system, instead of obeying Raoult's law, shows a positive deviation, corresponding to the upper curve in the figure, a partial pressure of 1 atm. will be reached at A, at a smaller mole fraction of gas, x_2', and we can write $x_2' < 1/p_2^\circ$. In like manner, if the deviation is negative, as in the lower curve, the solution will be saturated with the gas at C, at a mole fraction x_2'', and we can write $x_2'' > 1/p_2^\circ$.

The foregoing discussion can be summarized in the statement that **a positive deviation from Raoult's law corresponds to a smaller solubility for a gas and a negative deviation corresponds to a greater solubility than would be estimated by the methods used in Chapter II.**

Effect of deviations upon the solubility of solids. The preceding discussion of the solubility of gases can be applied to solids by substituting for the partial pressure of the gas the vapor pressure of the pure solid solute, p_2^s. In Chapter II it was shown how the solubility of a solid could be calculated when Raoult's law holds, *i. e.*, $x_2 = p_2^s/p_2^\circ$. We may note now that for positive deviations from Raoult's law $x_2 < p_2^s/p_2^\circ$, and for negative deviations $x_2 > p_2^s/p_2^\circ$, or in words, **a positive deviation from Raoult's law corresponds to a smaller solubility for a solid and a negative deviation corresponds to a greater solubility than would be calculated from the melting point and the heat of fusion of the solid.**

Regular solutions.[16] Many nonideal solutions have sufficient thermal energy virtually to overcome the tendency to segregation due to different molecular fields, and therefore possess nearly ideal entropy of mixing due to maximum randomness, *i. e.*,

$$\overline{S}_1^r - S_1^\circ = -R \ln x_1 \tag{35}$$

just as in an ideal solution. In other words, there would be no change in randomness and therefore of entropy in transferring one component from the solution to an ideal solution of the same composition, *i. e.*,

$$\overline{S}^r - \overline{S}^i = 0 \tag{36}$$

Such solutions have been designated as "regular". The name was suggested by the family of solubility curves of a single solute, such as iodine or sulfur, in a variety of solvents, (see Chapter XVII) plotted as $\log x_2$ vs. $1/T$, which exhibit an obvious regularity, the significance of which is that stated above. Where the entropy of solution is as formulated above (see Chapter VI), it remains only to evaluate the heat of mixing in order to calculate free energies and therefore all the solubility relations. We shall see in Chapter VII, how

[16] J. H. Hildebrand, *J. Am. Chem. Soc.*, **51**, 66 (1929); **57**, 866 (1935); *Proc. Nat. Acad. Sci.*, **13**, 267 (1927); J. H. Hildebrand and S. E. Wood, *J. Chem. Phys.*, **1**, 817 (1933).

this assumption of randomness leads to a simple formulation of the heat of mixing of regular solutions.

We saw, in Chapter II, that an ideal solution is formed from its pure liquids with zero heat of mixing. The same reasoning shows that a regular solution with a positive deviation from Raoult's law, as illustrated in Fig. 1, must be formed with absorption of heat. Since $RT\ln a_1 = \overline{H}_1 - H_1^\circ - RT\ln x_1$, if $a_1 > x_1$, $\overline{H}_1 - H_1^\circ$ is positive, and *vice versa*. It is easy to see that compound formation, which causes negative deviations, as in Fig. 2, should be accompanied by evolution of heat, *i. e.*, $\overline{H}_1 - H_1^\circ$ is negative.

We have seen that calculation of the partial molal free energy of a component of a binary solution, and hence of its various solubility relations, involves determining or calculating both the partial molal heat and the partial molal entropy of solution. In Chapter II we have considered the case of the ideal solution, where the heat is zero and the entropy a maximum. In this chapter we have called attention to the existence of regular solutions, where the entropy is the same as in an ideal solution of the same composition but where the heat content increases on mixing. In Chapter VII will be found methods for calculating the magnitude of this contribution from the properties of the pure components. In Chapter VI will be found a discussion of the effects of molecular sizes and shapes upon the entropy of mixing. The extreme cases of this are dealt with in Chapter XX on High Polymer Solutions.

The following tabulation should serve to make clear the manner in which the problem of solubility has been broken down for the purposes of this book.

It should be understood that this represents merely an analysis of the problem and is not intended to imply that solutions fall naturally into distinct types. Many actual solutions involve compromises between opposing factors, such as positive heat of mixing and less than ideal entropy of mixing due to unequal molal volumes, or solvation between two associated solvents. The tabulation is given mainly to emphasize collectively the various factors that may be involved in a particular solubility problem.

Type of solution	$\overline{H}_1 - H_1^\circ$	$\overline{S}_1 - S_1^\circ$	Remarks	Ref. Chapter
Ideal	0	$-R\ln x_1$	$a_1 = x_1$ $V_1 \cong V_2$	II
Regular	+	$-R\ln x_1$	$a_1 > x_1$ $V_1 \cong V_2$	VII
Athermal, nonideal	0	$< -R\ln x_1$	$a_1 < x_1$ $V_2 \gg V_1$	VI, XX
Associated (1 component)	+	$> -R\ln x_1$	$a_1 > x_1$	XI
Solvated	—	$< -R\ln x_1$	$a_1 < x_1$	XI

CHAPTER IV

Intermolecular Forces

It is necessary for our purposes to recognize the following different types of intermolecular force: (1) coulombic force between ions; (2) forces between permanent dipoles; (3) the force between a permanent dipole and an induced dipole; (4) force between nonpolar molecules; (5) metallic forces; (6) forces leading to the formation of electron-pair, covalent bonds; (7) repulsive forces.[1] In this chapter, we shall not discuss metallic forces or covalent bonds.

The coulombic forces are the easiest to understand and to subject to quantitative treatment. They obey the inverse square law and have the longest range of all. They make the largest contribution to the energy of ionic lattices and are chiefly responsible for the comparatively high melting points of such crystals. They are mentioned here for completeness, but are not included within the scope of this book because electrolytic solutions have received a vast amount of attention and been treated extensively in other works.[2] It may properly be remarked in passing, however, that a high degree of success in treating such solutions has been achieved only in the rather dilute range, where the longer range coulombic forces between ions and those between ions and solvent dipoles predominate. The short range, more specific forces, which determine the behavior of nonelectrolytic solutions, become more important as solutions become more concentrated, and the methods used in this book for nonelectrolytic solutions should eventually have a bearing also upon electrolytic solutions. In solid alkali halides, Born, Mayer and Helmholtz,[3,4] computed the noncoulombic component of the lattice energies of the alkali halides and found that it amounts to as much as 5 per cent of the total for the heavy elements.

Orientation effect. (Dipole-dipole interaction) The interaction energy between two permanent dipoles, 1 and 2, depends upon their relative orientation, expressed by the equation:

$$\varepsilon = -\frac{\mu_1 \mu_2}{r^3}\left[2 \cos \theta_1 \cos \theta_2 - \sin \theta_1 \sin \theta_2 \cos (\varphi_1 - \varphi_2)\right] \qquad (1)$$

[1] An excellent summary of the theories of intermolecular force is given in an article by H. Margenau, "Van der Waals Forces", *Rev. Mod. Phys.*, **11**, 1 (1939).

[2] *e. g.*, H. S. Harned and B. B. Owen, "The Physical Chemistry of Electrolytic Solutions", A. C. S. Monograph No. 45. New York, Reinhold, 1943.

[3] M. Born and J. E. Mayer, *Z. Physik*, **75**, 1, (1932).

[4] J. E. Mayer and L. Helmholtz, *Ibid.*, **75**, 19 (1932).

where θ and φ are polar coordinates giving the orientations of the dipoles, with dipole moments μ_1 and μ_2, at a distance, r, from each other, the polar axis being the line between their centers. In the most favorable orientation, parallel to the line joining them, this reduces to

$$\varepsilon = -\frac{\mu_1 \mu_2}{r^3}, \tag{2}$$

but thermal agitation interferes with this orientation, and the attraction would disappear at sufficiently high temperatures. At intermediate temperatures, the attractive orientations are statistically preferred, and Keesom[5], applying Boltzmann statistics, derived the expression for the average potential energy,

$$\bar{\varepsilon} = -\frac{2\mu_1^2 \mu_2^2}{3r^6 kT} \tag{3}$$

It is evident, however, that no more than a part of the attraction between molecules is to be accounted for by dipole interactions because there is attraction between molecules without permanent dipoles, and also because the attraction between polar molecules does not fall off so rapidly with temperature as this formulation would require. In condensed phases, when steric and other factors prevent free molecular rotation, simple Boltzmann statistics are inapplicable and Equation 3 is invalid. The dipole interaction known as "hydrogen bonds" is such a case, and is discussed in Chapters IX and X.

Induction effect. Debye[6] pointed out that one molecule with a permanent dipole can induce a dipole in another molecule because of the polarizability, α, of the latter. The resulting force is always attractive, and the mean potential is given by

$$\bar{\varepsilon} = -\frac{1}{r^6}\,(\alpha_1 \mu_2^2 + \alpha_2 \mu_1^2) \tag{4}$$

But even this does not suffice to account for the interaction between molecules which have no permanent dipoles, so it seemed necessary to assume the existence of quadruple moments. This suffered from the fact that there is no independent method of measuring such moments.

Dispersion effect. We are indebted to London[7] for the foundations of a satisfactory theory of the interaction between nonpolar molecules. The nature of this interaction is best explained in his own words, as follows:

"Though it is of course not possible to describe this interaction mechanism in terms of our customary classical mechanics, we may still illustrate it in a kind of semi-classical language.

[5] W. H. Keesom, *Physik. Z.*, **22**, 126, 643 (1921); **23**, 225 (1922).

[6] P. Debye, *Physik. Z.*, **21**, 178 (1920); **22**, 302 (1921).

[7] R. Eisenschitz and F. London, *Z. Physik.*, **60**, 491 (1930); F. London. *Ibid.*, **63**, 245 (1930); *Z. physik. Chem.*, **B 11**, 222 (1930); *Trans. Faraday Soc.*, **33**, 8 (1937).

"If one were to take an instantaneous photograph of a molecule at any time, one would find various configurations of nuclei and electrons, showing in general dipole moments. In a spherically symmetrical rare gas molecule, as well as in our isotropic oscillators, the average over very many of such snapshots would of course give no preference for any direction. These very quickly varying dipoles, represented by the zero-point motion of a molecule, produce an electric field and act upon the polarisability of the other molecule and produce there induced dipoles, which are in phase and in interaction with the instantaneous dipoles producing them. The zero-point motion is, so to speak, accompanied by a synchronised electric alternating field, but not by a radiation field: The energy of the zero-point motion cannot be dissipated by radiation."

Applying this concept, London arrived at the formula

$$\varepsilon = -\frac{3\alpha_1\alpha_2}{2r^6}\cdot\frac{h\nu_{0,1}\,.\,h\nu_{0,2}}{h\nu_{0,1}+h\nu_{0,2}} \tag{5}$$

where ν_0 refers to the frequency characteristic of a molecule in its unperturbed state, corresponding to its "zero-point energy". The perturbation of electronic motion by another molecule is related to its perturbation by light of varying energies (frequencies), as expressed by the formula for the dispersions of light, i. e., the variation of refractive index, n, with frequency, ν, which, for gases is

$$n-1=\frac{C}{\nu_0^2-\nu^2} \tag{6}$$

It is this which gives to this type of molecular interaction the name, "dispersion effect".

Values of $h\nu_0$ can be calculated for substances for which the refractive index has been measured over a range of wavelengths. Again, $h\nu_0$ is very nearly equal to the ionization energy, **I**, so that Equation 5 can be written

$$\varepsilon = -\frac{3}{2}\,\frac{\alpha_1\alpha_2}{r^6}\cdot\frac{\mathbf{I}_1\mathbf{I}_2}{\mathbf{I}_1+\mathbf{I}_2} \tag{7}$$

Where the two molecules are of the same species, Equations 5 and 7 become

$$\varepsilon = -\frac{3\alpha^2 h\nu_0}{4r^6} = -\frac{3\alpha^2\mathbf{I}}{4r^6} \tag{8}$$

Notable features of this effect are that it is approximately additive and not temperature dependent. Another is the short range character of the potential, due to the inverse sixth power, as contrasted with the inverse first power of interionic potential. We see why the long range order in a salt crystal is in general less easily destroyed by melting than it is in crystals composed of nonpolar molecules. We should note, further, that these dispersion forces are dependent on the number and "looseness" of the electrons, particularly the valence electrons, as illustrated by the series of halogens F_2 to I_2. It is shown quantitatively by Table 1, taken from London. $h\nu_I$ values were taken from ionization potentials, $h\nu_D$ from optical dispersion.

Table 1. DISPERSION EFFECT BETWEEN SIMPLE MOLECULES.

	$h\nu_I$ [e.Volts]	$h\nu_D$ [e.Volts]	$\alpha \cdot 10^{24}$ cm^3	$^3/_4\, \alpha^2 h\nu_0 \cdot 10^{48}$ e.Volts · cm^6
He	24.5	25.5	0.20	0.77
Ne	21.5	25.7	0.39	2.93
A	15.4	17.5	1.63	34.7
Kr	13.3	14.7	2.46	69
Xe	11.5	12.2	4.00	146
H_2	16.4		0.81	8.3
N_2	17	17.2	1.74	38.6
O_2	13	14.7	1.57	27.2
CO	14.3		1.99	42.4
CH_4	14.5		2.58	73
CO_2		15.45	2.86	94.7
Cl_2	18.2		4.60	288
HCl	13.7		2.63	71
HBr	13.3		3.58	128
HI	12.7		5.4	278
Na		2.1	29.7	960

London also called attention to the relative magnitudes for different substances of the three effects, orientation, induction, and dispersion, by the figures in Table 2.

Table 2. THE THREE CONSTITUENTS OF THE VAN DER WAALS FORCES.

	$\mu \cdot 10^{18}$	$\alpha \cdot 10^{24}$	$h\nu_0$ (e.Volts)	Orientation	Induction	Dispersion
				erg · cm^6 · 10^{60}		
CO	0.12	1.99	14.3	0.0034	0.057	67.5
HI	0.38	5.4	12	0.35	1.68	382
HBr	0.78	3.58	13.3	6.2	4.05	176
HCl	1.03	2.63	13.7	18.6	5.4	105
NH_3	1.5	2.21	16	84	10	93
H_2O	1.84	1.48	18	190	10	47

It should be noted that the induction effect is practically negligible and that the dispersion effect contributes far more than the orientation effect except with NH_3 and H_2O, which have few electrons but large dipole moments, especially effective because of the fourth power.

Slater and Kirkwood[9] have derived a similar expression,

$$\varepsilon_a = -1.36\, \varepsilon_0 a_0^{3/2} \alpha^{3/2} n^{1/2}/r^6 \tag{9}$$

where ε_0 and a_0 are, respectively, the energy and the Bohr radius of the hydrogen atom in its normal state, and n is the number of electrons in the outer shell. Equations 8 and 9 can be used to calculate the van der Waals a, since

$$\mathrm{a} = 2\pi \boldsymbol{N}^2 \int_{\mathrm{d}_0}^{\infty} -\varepsilon_a r^2\, dr \tag{10}$$

where $\boldsymbol{N}$ is the Avogadro number and d_0 the minimum distance of approach, related to the van der Waals b by the equation

$$\mathrm{d}_0^3 = \frac{3\mathrm{b}}{2\pi \boldsymbol{N}} \tag{11}$$

If a is in atmospheres $\times$ (cc. per mole)^2, b is in cc. per mole and **I** is in volts, Equations 9 and 10 become, respectively,

$$\mathrm{a} = 1.13 \cdot 10^{54} \alpha^2 \mathbf{I}/\mathrm{b} \tag{12}$$

and

$$\mathrm{a} = 1.084 \cdot 10^{43} \alpha^{3/2} n^{1/2}/\mathrm{b} \tag{13}$$

Wohl[10] has compared these formulas with experiment, getting results here reproduced in simplified form in Table 3. It will be seen that both approximate the experimental values, which are subject, themselves, to considerable uncertainty. The agreement is doubtless all that could be expected in view of the various simplifying assumptions made.

Table 3 — VALUES OF VAN DER WAALS a

	n	$\alpha \cdot 10^{24}$	b	I	Eq. 12	Eq. 13	Expt.
He	2	0.20	22.8	24.5	4.95	6.0	3.5
Ne	8	0.39	21.6	21.5	17.4	34.6	20.7
A	8	1.64	41.2	15.4	116	156	127
Kr	8	2.48	53.0	13.3	178	226	206
H_2	2	0.82	21.0	15.4	57	55	20
N_2	10	1.74	51.7	15.7	104	152	145
O_2	12	1.58	44.4	14.1	92	168	149
Cl_2	14	4.60	73.0	18.2	610	548	632
CO_2	16	2.86	57.1	14.3	236	366	361
CH_4	8	2.58	56.5	14.5	197	224	228
CO	10	1.99	51.5	14.3	111	197	134
HBr	8	3.85	58.9	13.3	385	393	442
HCl	8	2.71	53.5	13.7	217	256	366

[9] J. C. Slater and J. G Kirkwood, *Phys. Rev.*, **37**, 682 (1931).
[10] K. Wohl, *Z. physik. Chem.*, (Bodenstein Festband), p. 807 (1931).

It is worth noting that the zero-point energies as indicated by ionization potentials of different molecules do not ordinarily differ nearly as much as their polarizabilities, so that the latter, with their quadratic effect, according to Equation 8, are usually more significant in determining intermolecular potentials.

Repulsive force. The discussion, thus far, has considered only the attractive potential. Actually, at small distances, a repulsive potential sets in rather suddenly. This has been computed for atomic hydrogen by Heitler and London[11] and for helium by Slater[12]. It appears possible to represent it approximately by the formula:

$$\varepsilon_r = \mathrm{j}e^{-cr} \tag{14}$$

where j and c are constants. A formula for larger atoms, obtained by Unsöld[13], is discouragingly complicated. It has been more customary to represent the repulsive potential by a high inverse power law, first suggested by Mie[14]:

$$\varepsilon_r = \mathrm{j}/r^n, \tag{15}$$

usually with $n = 12$. This has the advantage, at least, of mathematical convenience since its form is the same as that for attraction. Lennard-Jones[15] has reproduced the experimental behaviors of gases by combining Equations 8 and 15 to give:

$$\varepsilon = \mathrm{j}/r^n - \mathrm{k}/r^6 \tag{16}$$

with $n = 12$. His plot of ε against r for five gases is reproduced in Fig. 1. The dotted curve for helium is one calculated by Slater. The repulsion rises so steeply for the heavier molecules that an approximate test of methods for calculating k can be made by considering the molecules as rigid and using their radii as determined from viscosity or from the van der Waals b. This has been done by London and also by Slater.

It is frequently useful to transform Equation 8 into what may be called a reduced form. The potential energy ε of a molecular pair passes through a minimum at which $(d\varepsilon/dr) = 0$. This condition may be used to define a distance d_0 and a minimum (negative) energy ε_0. If we differentiate ε with espect to r, we find:

$$\frac{d\varepsilon}{dr} = -\frac{n\mathrm{j}}{r^{n+1}} + \frac{6\mathrm{k}}{r^7} \tag{17}$$

---

[11] W. Heitler and F. London, *Z. Physik.*, **44**, 455 (1927); Y. Suguira, *Ibid.*, **45**, 484 (1927)
[12] J. C. Slater, *Phys. Rev.*, **32**, 349 (1928).
[13] A. Unsöld, *Z. Physik.*, **43**, 563 (1927).
[14] G. Mie *Ann. Physik.*, [4] **II**, 657 (1903).
[15] J. E. Lennard-Jones, *Proc. Roy. Soc. (London)*, **A 112**, 214 (1926).

If we set the derivative equal to zero, the resulting equations for d_0 and ε_0 are:

$$d_0^{\,n-6} = \frac{nj}{6k} \tag{18}$$

$$\varepsilon_0 = \frac{j}{d_0^n} - \frac{k}{d_0^6} = -(n-6)\left(\frac{6^6\,k^n}{n^n\,j^6}\right)^{\frac{1}{n-6}} \tag{19}$$

We may now rewrite Equation 16 in the form:

$$\varepsilon(r) = \varepsilon_0\left[\frac{n}{n-6}\left(\frac{d_0}{r}\right)^6 - \frac{6}{n-6}\left(\frac{d_0}{r}\right)^n\right] \tag{20}$$

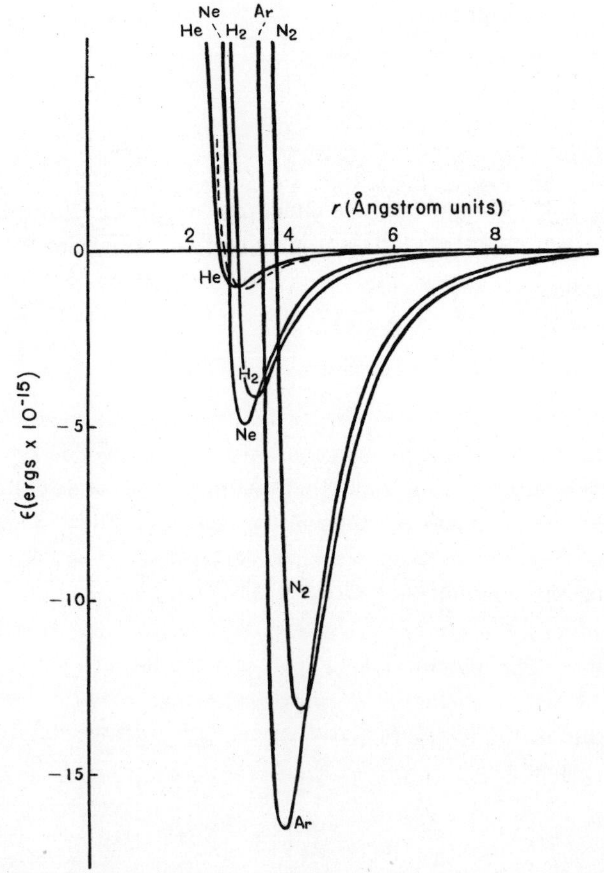

Fig. 1 Intermolecular potential functions for gaseous elements.

If the molecules approach closer than the distance d_0 the potential energy ε increases again and at a distance d^* is equal to zero. This distance d^* may be regarded as an effective collision diameter for slow molecules. If we set 6 (r) in Equation 20 equal to zero we may solve for d^*, obtaining

$$d^* = d_o \left(\frac{6}{n}\right)^{\frac{1}{n-6}} \tag{21}$$

and in turn for $\varepsilon(r)$

$$\varepsilon(r) = \varepsilon^* \left[\frac{6}{n-6}\left(\frac{n}{6}\right)^{\frac{n}{n-6}}\left(\frac{d^*}{r}\right)^n - \frac{n}{n-6}\left(\frac{n}{6}\right)^{\frac{6}{n-6}}\left(\frac{d^*}{r}\right)^6\right] \tag{22}$$

where ε^* is $-\varepsilon_o$ and hence a positive number.

If we set $n = 12$, an enormous simplification is achieved:

$$d_o = \frac{2j}{k} \tag{23}$$

$$\varepsilon_o = \frac{k^2}{4j} \tag{24}$$

$$\varepsilon(r) = \varepsilon_o\left[2\left(\frac{d_o}{r}\right)^6 - \left(\frac{d_o}{r}\right)^{12}\right] \tag{25}$$

$$d^* = \sqrt[6]{1/2}\, d_o = 0.8909 d_o. \tag{26}$$

$$\varepsilon(r) = 4\,\varepsilon^* \left[\left(\frac{d^*}{r}\right)^{12} - \left(\frac{d^*}{r}\right)^6\right] \tag{27}$$

Fig. 2 shows the relations between ε_o, ε^*, d_o and d^* schematically for $n = 12$. In Equations 20, 22, 25, and 27 the ε_o and d_o or ε^* and d^* are separable, a fact which we will see in later chapters is extremely important for certain calculations.

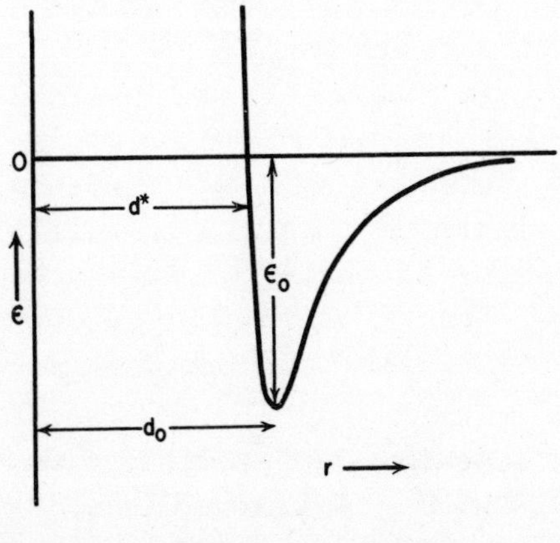

Fig. 2 Schematic intermolecular potential diagram, showing ε_o, d_o and d^*

Additivity of intermolecular energies. In the preceding pages we have discussed the potential energy of an isolated pair of molecules. We shall want to use these potential functions to discuss the energy of liquids and solutions, so it is important to know whether the total energy is the sum of all the pair interactions. It is easy to show by means of classical theory that the coulombic interactions and dipole-dipole interactions are additive, and as a first approximation, the dispersion forces have been assumed to be additive also. Recently, Axilrod and Teller[16] have carried out a third order perturbation calculation for dispersion or "van der Waals" forces, and find the additivity rule to be only approximate. For a set of three molecules, we may represent the potential energy in the form:

$$\varepsilon_{123} = \varepsilon_{12} + \varepsilon_{13} + \varepsilon_{23} + \Delta \tag{28}$$

where ε_{12}, ε_{13} and ε_{23} are pair potentials of the form of Equations 5, 7, and 8. If the energy were truly additive, the difference function Δ would be identically zero. Actually Axilrod and Teller found that for a triangle of three like atoms:

$$\Delta = C\,\frac{3\cos\theta_1\,\cos\theta_2\,\cos\theta_3 + 1}{r_{12}{}^3\;r_{13}{}^3\;r_{23}{}^3} \tag{29}$$

where θ_1, θ_2, and θ_3 are the angles of the triangle at atoms 1, 2 and 3 while r_{12}, r_{13} and r_{23} are the interatomic distances. C is a positive quantity of the order of $\mathbf{I}\alpha^3$.

The sign and magnitude of Δ depend upon the particular configuration of the atoms. For an equilateral triangle, the term in brackets $(3\cos\theta_1\cos\theta_2\cos\theta_3 + 1)$ is equal to 1.375; for a right triangle it is $+1$, while for a linear arrangement it is -2. Thus for the first two cases, the correction factor is a repulsion, while for the third, it is an attraction. Under optimum conditions Δ is of the order of magnitude of $\mathbf{I}\alpha^3/r^9$ while the pair energies are $\mathbf{I}\alpha^2/r^6$. Thus the ratio Δ/ε_{12} is of the order of magnitude of α/r^3 or, transforming to molal units, of the order of $\mathrm{P_E}/\mathrm{V}$ where $\mathrm{P_E}$ is the molal electronic polarization (see Chapter IX) and V is the molal volume. This dimensionless ratio is of the order of $0.2 - 0.4$, hence the contribution of the nonadditivity could be considerable. Fortunately the difference in sign for different configurations leads to a cancellation of terms which, one suspects, largely eliminates this factor for a large number of atoms as closely packed as in a liquid. Thus, to a good approximation, even the dispersion forces are additive, and we shall so assume throughout the remainder of this book.

Intermolecular potentials and energies of vaporization. It will be shown in Chapter V, that the "distribution function" for liquids, $\varrho(r)$, de-

[16] B. M. Axilrod and E. Teller, *J. Chem. Phys.*, **11**, 299 (1943)

rived by aid of x-ray diffraction and which describes the average distribution of molecules in the liquid, may be used to relate the potential ε between molecular pairs to the potential energy of the whole liquid which, reversing the sign, is the molal energy of vaporization, ΔE^V.

Polyatomic molecules. In the foregoing discussion it has been assumed that the London forces are sphericaly symmetrical, a condition that we can expect to apply strictly only to monatomic molecules. The problem presented by polyatomic molecules is one of baffling complexity and we shall have to be content, for the purposes of this book, to gain a general idea of the errors involved in extending relations based upon the monatomic model to various types of polyatomic molecules. London[17] has discussed these matters in an important paper "On Centers of van der Waals Attraction". He refers to earlier attempts to distribute centers of attraction within molecules and remarks upon two points, "(1) The elementary units of the dipole-dipole interactions are, in general, not at all spherically symmetrical central forces. They have rather to be built up by highly *anisotropic force centers*. (2) In certain large molecules we encounter characteristic, long, extended electronic oscillators. In these molecules the *special extension* of the oscillators has to be accounted for, ... and it is suggested in these cases that the molecular forces be built up by certain smaller units, which forces however, are *no longer additive*." Since dispersion forces result from the same oscillators which determine polarizability, several authors have followed up the suggestion by Meyer and Otterbein[18] that the polarization of a compound be referred to the bonds rather than to additive atomic polarizabilities, with corrections for bond types. Denbigh[19] gives the polarizabilities of a number of bonds parallel and perpendicular to the bond directions, here reproduced in Table 4. These values can be contemplated profitably by anyone concerned with the practical problems of relative solubilities. They emphasize, for example, the large differences to be expected between saturated and unsaturated aliphatic hydrocarbons; between those containing C=O and those containing C=S.

London shows how it is possible to set up expressions for the interaction between two polarization ellipsoids in terms of the vector sum of dond frequencies and polarizations, parallel and perpendicular. These reduce to Equation 5 for spherical symmetry. Our interest in this is limited to the theoretical by our ignorance of the bond frequencies.

Molecules with conjugated double bonds behave as virtual oscillators of great length and low frequency like miniature pieces of metal, and this contributes greatly to the strength and range of intermolecular attraction.

---

[17] F. London, *J. Phys. Chem.*, **46**, 305 (1942).

[18] E. H. L. Meyer and G. Otterbein, *Physik. Z.*, **32**, 290 (1931); **35**, 249 (1934). C. Sachse. *Ibid.*, **36**, 357 (1935); C. H. D. Clark, *Nature*, **138**, 1261 (1936); S. N. Wang *J. Chem. Phys.*, **7**, 1012 (1939).

[19] K. G. Denbigh, *Trans. Faraday Soc.*, **36**, 936 (1940).

Table 4. Bond Polarizabilities

	Parallel $\alpha \cdot 10^{25}$ cc.	Perpendicular $\alpha \cdot 10^{25}$ cc.
C—C	18.8	0.2
C—C, aromatic	22.5	4.8
C=C	28.6	10.6
C≡C	35.4	12.7
C—Cl	36.7	20.8
C—Br	50.4	28.8
C=O	19.9	7.5
C=S	75.7	27.7
C≡N	31	14
C—H	7.9	5.8
N—H	5.8	8.4
S—H	23.0	17.2
O_2	24.3	11.9
N_2	24.3	14.3
CO	26.0	16.2
Cl_2	60.0	36.2
HCl	31.3	23.9
HBr	42.3	33.2
HI	65.8	48.9
SO_2	29.0	14.7

Using rubber for illustration, London gives the picture of bending of bonds in unvulcanized rubber possible by reason of the attachment of molecules at relatively few centers of attraction, and plasticity due to displacement of these centers. The cross linking introduced by vulcanization provides strong, fixed points of attachment without destroying the possibility of bond bending. Stretching pulls the saturated segments into close parallel position, where short range forces come into play and can cause crystallization.

We will see in the following Chapter V that the assumption of radial intermolecular forces when coupled with certain other conditions leads to a theory of corresponding states for liquids. For polyatomic molecules, the forces may be far from radial, and it is not surprising that the theory fails to apply to many of these. No adequate treatment of non-radial intermolecular forces exists, but we shall discuss in Chapter V a number of useful semi-empirical treatments, such as the "Hildebrand rule" for entropies of vaporization.

Tetrahalide molecules have invited investigation as offering the best practical approximation to spherical symmetry. They are far more available than the rare gas elements of Group 0 and can be studied in more convenient and overlapping temperature ranges; they present widely different London forces and moderately different bond types; one can examine independently the effects of changing either the central atom or the halogen atoms. The senior author[20] has made a comprehensive study of the available data pertinent to the intermolecular forces of these substances with results which we summarize as follows.

1. The molecules of the tetrahalides of the elements in both branches of Group 4 are regular tetrahedra; those of Group 6 are not, and were therefore excluded from the study.

2. CCl_4 and CBr_4 molecules are sufficientlo compact to rotate, not only in the liquid but even in the solid state, as well. Unlike the others they have transition points well below their melting points and their entropies of fusion are very low, less than their entropies of transition and much less than the entropies of fusion of other tetrahalides. The figures are given in Table 5.

Table 5. Entropies of Transition and Fusion

Substance	T_t	ΔS^T	T_m	ΔS^F	$\Delta S^T + \Delta S^F$
CBr_4	320.0	4.44	363.2	2.61	7.05
CCl_4	225.44	4.79	250.23	2.31	7.10
$TiCl_4$			250.0	9.00	9.00
$TeCl_4$			497.2	9.07	9.07
$SiCl_4$			205.5	9.08	9.08
$SnCl_4$			239.9	9.11	9.11
SnI_4			417.6	11.01	11.01

It is now well known[21] that many solid substances with very symmetrical molecules can acquire sufficient entropy through the rotation or libration beginning at a transition point that melting is postponed to a higher temperature and the entropy of fusion and the normal liquid range are much diminished. The magnitude of the entropy of fusion of a "rotating" solid has received considerable attention;[22] Hirschfelder, Stevenson and Eyring[23] have derived the value, 2 e. u., not far from the experimental values in Table 6 for CCl_4 and CBr_4. We shall return to this problem in Chapter V.

Particularly striking confirmation of such rotation in solids has been obtained by Smyth and co-workers. Baker and Smyth[24] clearly proved by the temperature dependence of the dielectric constants of solid tertiary butyl

---

[20] J. H. Hildebrand, *J. Chem. Phys.*, **15**, 727 (1947).

[21] C. P. Smyth, *Chem. Rev.*, **19**, 329 (1936).

[22] K. F. Herzfeld and M. G. Mayer. *Phys. Rev.*, **46**, 995 (1934); J. Frenkel, O. M. Todes and S. Ismailow, *Acta Physicochim. URSS.* **1**, 97 (1934); J. Frenkel, *Ibid.*, **4**, 341 (1936).

[23] J. Hirschfelder, D. Stevenson and H. Eyring, *J. Chem. Phys.*, **5**, 896 (1937).

[24] W. O. Baker, and C. P. Smyth, *J. Am. Chem. Soc.*, **61**, 1695, 2798 (1939).

chloride and bromide that their molecules are rotating between their transition points and their melting points, and Turkevich and Smyth[25] and Conner and Smyth[26] showed that they form solid solutions with CCl_4.

Such rotation is consistent with the atomic dimensions in CCl_4. The C-Cl distance, from electron diffraction[27], is 1.76 Å, the intermolecular Cl-Cl distance in solid[28] Cl_2 is 2.77 Å, so that the intermolecular C-C distance in CCl_4 would have to be at least 6.29 Å to permit free rotation. Bray and Gingrich[29] found 6.4 Å by x-ray diffraction of liquid CCl_4, which is sufficient. The molal volume of the liquid, likewise, is large enough to harbor rotating spheres of radius (1.76 + 1.39) Å. On substituting central atoms of increasing size, however, the observed liquid molal volumes are such as to indicate gradually increasing hindrance to free rotation.

3. In spite of the restriction of rotation in the tetrahalides of higher molecular weights, their solubility relations can be calculated by aid of the equations based upon the assumption of spherical symmetry, as will be shown in later chapters, with errors no greater than those introduced by other necessary assumptions.

4. Attraction between molecules of different species is not appreciably influenced by the kind of bonding orbitals of the central atom, because $TiCl_4$ falls in line with $GeCl_4$ and $SnCl_4$ while $HfCl_4$ and $ZrCl_4$ do not. But attraction is strongly influenced by the degree of ionic character of the bonds, which increases with the size and electropositive character of the central atom. For example, ZrI_4 is colorless and melts at 772° K while SnI_4 is orange and melts at 418° K, close to the melting points of GeI_4, 419° K and TiI_4 423° K. Pitzer and Hildebrand[30] called attention to the color of SnI_4 as indication of covalent bond character.

5. The intermolecular forces in liquid $SiCl_4$ are considerably lower than those in CCl_4, $TiCl_4$ and $SnCl_4$, as shown by its low boiling point and solvent power for solutes with high force fields, but this is mainly the effect of the comparatively large increment in molal volume between CCl_4 and $SiCl_4$ and not to any unique character on the part of the latter. The forces of attraction in the latter at the equilibrium distance are less but the constant of attraction is greater, and increases uniformly from CCl_4 to $SnCl_4$ as shown by the values of $V\Delta E^V$ in Table 6 and the approximately equivalent values of $V^2(\partial E/\partial V)_T$ (See Chapter V). The polarizability likewise shows no minimum with $SiCl_4$ but increases uniformly through the series.

---

[25] A. Turkevich and C. P. Smyth, *Ibid.*, **62**, 2468 (1940.)
[26] W. P. Conner and C. P. Smyth, *Ibid.*, **63**, 3424 (1941).
[27] L. O. Brockway, *Rev. Mod. Phys.*, **8**, 231 (1936).
[28] W. H. Keesom and K. W. Taconis, *Proc. Acad. Sci. Amsterdam.*, **39**, 314 (1936).
[29] E. E. Bray and N. S. Gingrich, *J. Chem. Phys.*, **61**, 351 (1943).
[30] K. S. Pitzer and J. H. Hildebrand, *J. Am. Chem. Soc.*, **63**, 2472 (1941).

Table 6.

	T_b	V, 25° C	$V\Delta E^V$ kcal . liters	$V^2\left(\frac{\partial E}{\partial V}\right)_T$	$\alpha \cdot 10^{24}$
CCl_4	350	97.1	7.04	7.56	10.23
$SiCl_4$	330	115.4	7.62	8.23	11.10
$GeCl_4$	357	114.5	8.60		12.12
$SnCl_4$	386	117.6	10.55	10.95	13.45

Again, the isotropic Raman frequencies for both bond bending and stretching, which are independent of the mass of the central atom, when plotted against the distance between the central atom and the halide atom, fall off quite regularly for both the chlorides and the bromides of C, Si, Ge, Sn, Pb. There appears to be no need, therefore, to ascribe to $SiCl_4$ any exceptional nature such as the double-bond resonance that has been invoked to explain its unexpectedly short bond distances.

CHAPTER V

The Liquid State

Gases, liquids and crystalline solids. Of the three usual states of aggregation of matter, gases, liquids and crystalline solids, the liquid state was the last to be studied quantitatively, and is still the most imperfectly understood. The reasons for this are easily found in any qualitative description of the three states.

At most temperatures and pressures, gases are in a highly expanded condition in which the volume actually occupied by the molecules is small compared with the total volume of the container and only occasionally is a molecule close enough to another for inter-molecular forces to be significant. By assuming that the volume in which the molecules may move freely (which we will call an effective "free volume") is identical with the total volume, and neglecting all interactions between molecules, one may derive the laws of perfect gases. These are good approximations for gases in nearly all cases, and by introducing small correction factors for the effect of the actual molecular volume and intermolecular potentials, one may obtain virtually quantitative agreement with experimental data. (c. f. Chapter XIV.)

The ideal crystalline solid[1] on the other hand, consists of a regular arrangement of molecules in some kind of a crystal lattice. The molecules cannot easily move throughout the solid, but are constrained to vibrate like harmonic oscillators around their equilibrium positions in the lattice. Although in any real crystal there are lattice imperfections, anharmonic vibrations and a small amount of self-diffusion, the success of the Einstein[2] and Debye[3] treatment of perfect crystals shows how useful the harmonic oscillator model can be.

But a liquid lies far from either a perfect lattice of harmonic oscillators or a perfect gas. The actual volume of the molecules is a major fraction of the total volume and inter-molecular forces are not occasionally, but always, large in magnitude. Although only slightly less densely packed than in the solid phase, the molecules of a liquid are free to move throughout the medium; all trace of long range order is lost; and the motion of the

---

[1] We shall regard the solid state as always being crystalline. The so-called amorphous solids, such as glasses and some high polymeric substances may usually be treated thermodynamically as liquids with very high viscosity.

[2] A. Einstein, *Ann. Physik*, [4] **22**, 180 (1907).

[3] P. Debye, *Ann. Physik*, [4] **39**, 789 (1912).

molecules is far from that of a mere harmonic vibration. Confronted with this intermediate situation, we can construct no simple idealized model which we might expect to be a limiting case similar to that of a "perfect gas" or a "perfect crystal." We shall use the term "perfect liquid" in a later section, but its meaning will not be entirely analogous.

Structure of liquids. The ability of molecules in a liquid to move easily throughout the medium precludes any regular ordered structure such as we find in crystals. Nevertheless, the distribution of molecules is far from uniform; a large degree of short-range order must exist. Some authors regard this as a crystal-like lattice in which the rapid thermal motion of the molecules has blurred and distorted the regularity, although there is considerable objection to this particular picture.

In any event, a convenient method of describing the structure of liquids is provided by studies on x-ray scattering, such as were first introduced by Menke[4] in Debye's laboratory. The structure of a liquid is expressed by a "probability" or "distribution" function $\varrho(r)$ (designated W_r by Menke, and variously by other writers), defined as follows. The probability that an element of volume dV of a liquid of volume V will contain the center of a given molecule (e. g., the nucleus of a central atom) is dV/V. The probability that a given pair of molecules will occupy two such elements is $(dV/V)^2$, provided that they are sufficiently far apart that the potential between them is negligible and all long range order is lost. When, however, the two elements of volume are small, and their distance apart r is of the same order of magnitude as the molecular radius r_0, the volume of the molecules themselves and the forces between them will help determine their positions, and the probability of a given position is expressed by a function $\varrho(r)\left(\frac{dV}{V}\right)^2$.

If the position of one molecule is fixed (or taken as the center of a coordinate system) the number of molecules in a spherical shell of thickness dr and distance r from this center is therefore $\frac{1}{v}4\pi r^2 \varrho(r)\, dr$, where v is the volume per molecule (i. e. V/N) and $\varrho(r)$ is known as the radial distribution function. These two functions for mercury[5] are shown in Fig. 1. The parabolic curve in Fig. 1a represents a reference curve for $\varrho(r) = 1$ which the actual curve must approach at large values of r. The corresponding plots for crystals are normally represented (as in Fig. 1a) by discrete lines representing the number of atoms at distances corresponding to positions of minimum potential energy in the classical picture of a harmonic oscillator. Actually a real crystal, *even at 0° K*, is vibrating in such a way as to make

[4] H. Menke, *Phys. Z.*, **33**, 593 (1932).

[5] P. Debye and H. Menke, *Physik. Z.*, **31**, 797 (1930); *Ergeb. d. Techn. Röntgenkunde* II (1931).

$\varrho(r)$ a continuous function, although with sharper peaks than those for the corresponding liquid. The successive peaks, unlike the peaks for a liquid, retain much of the sharpness of the first[6] because of the long range order.

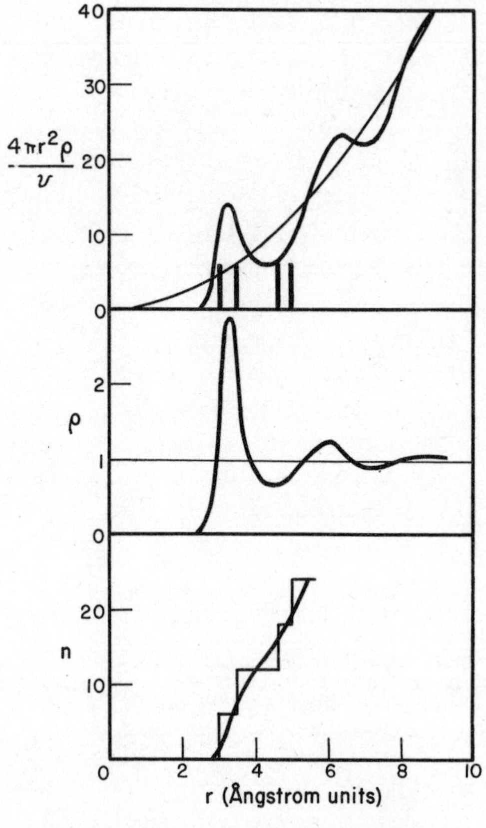

Fig. 1. Structure of liquid and solid mercury.
a. Number of atoms in a spherical shell.
b. Distribution function $\varrho(r)$.
c. Number of atoms surrounding a central atom within a sphere of radius *r*. (See text).

We may integrate the distribution function $\varrho(r)$ to calculate the number of molecules n surrounding a central one within a sphere of radius *r*:

$$\mathrm{n} = \frac{4\pi}{v}\int_0^r r^2 \varrho(r)\, dr \tag{1}$$

[6] The variation in position of atoms in successive shells around a central atom increases because their position depends upon the cumulative effect of all atoms between them and the central one. For a harmonic oscillator solid, the half width of a peak increases as the square root of the distance *r* from the central atom. This broadening, however, is nothing compared with the complete loss of order at large distance which we find in liquids.

For a large sphere this of course reduces to $4\pi r^3/3v$ or V/v. Figure 1c shows n as a function of r for liquid mercury and the corresponding idealized step-like plot for solid mercury.

Similarly one may write the number of molecules Δn in a shell of thickness d_o (one molecular diameter) as:

$$\Delta n = \frac{4\pi}{v}\int_{r}^{r+d_o} r^2 \varrho(r)\, dr \qquad (2)$$

To obtain the number of molecules Δn_1 in the first shell, one integrates Equation 2 from $\frac{1}{2}d_o$ to $\frac{3}{2}d_o$. For all practical purposes, d_o is the same as d_m, the distance to the first maximum. Distribution curves for liquid elements studied prior to 1943 are given in an excellent review by Gingrich[7].

Since the order in liquids is only short range and is determined essentially by the geometry, one might compare it with that obtained by vigorously shaking tennis balls in a box a little bigger than the space required for close packing.

Morrell and Hildebrand[8] constructed such a model of a liquid by placing a lot of gelatine spheres including a few colored ones in a vessel containing a boiled gelatine solution of the same density and refractive index. The vessel was shaken and by means of spark photography, the positions of the colored balls were determined. From a series of such measurements, a distribution curve was constructed, in good agreement with actual ones. The height of the first maximum was found to decrease progressively as higher temperatures were simulated by greater dilutions.

We may compare molecules of different size by plotting $\varrho(r)$ against r/d_m where d_m is the position of the first maximum. Hildebrand[9] has shown that the curves for the metals mercury, gallium, sodium and potassium, when plotted in this way, all superimpose nicely except for height (Fig. 2), and that the curves of xenon and argon[10] at nearly corresponding states fit each other very well.

Eisenstein and Gingrich[11] have determined $\varrho(r)$ for argon at a number of temperatures and pressures. Fig. 3 shows three of their curves at saturation pressures. As the temperature increases and the density decreases (the densities are 1.40 at 84.4 °K, 1.37 at 91.8 °K and 1.11 at 126.7 °K), the heights of the peaks decrease and the curves flatten out, as would be expected.

---

[7] N. S. Gingrich, *Rev. Mod. Phys.*, **15**, 90 (1943). A difference between his symbolism and ours should be noted. The function $\varrho(r)$ as we use it approaches unity as the distance r becomes large; as used by Gingrich, it approaches $1/r$.

[8] W. E. Morrell and J. H. Hildebrand, *J. Chem. Phys.*, **4**, 224 (1936).

[9] J. H. Hildebrand, *Science*, **90**, 1 (1939); *Proc. Phys. Soc.*, **56**, 221 (1944).

[10] J. A. Campbell and J. H. Hildebrand, *J. Chem. Phys.*, **4**, 224 (1936).

[11] A. Eisenstein and N. S. Gingrich, *Phys. Rev.*, **62**, 261 (1942).

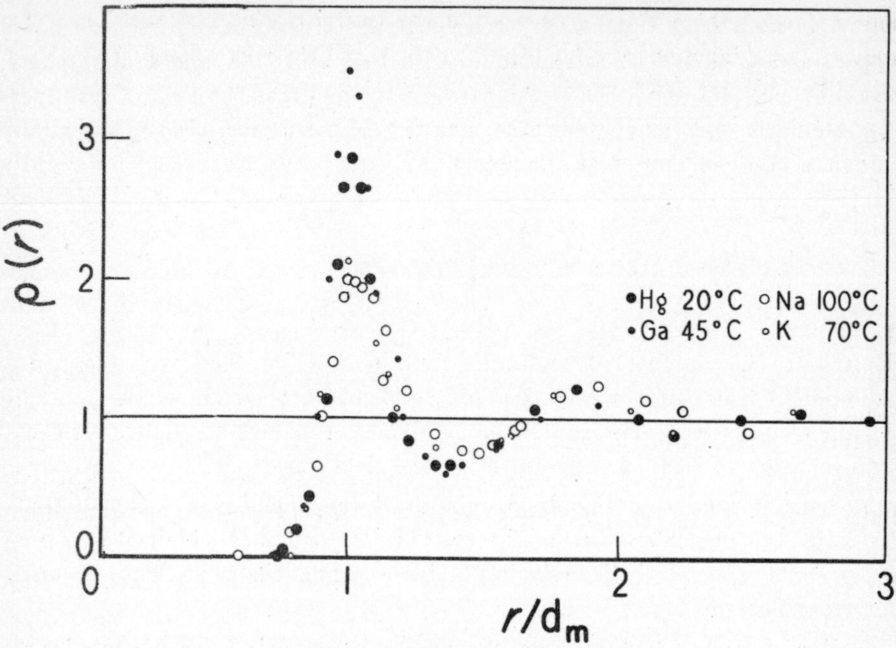

Fig. 2. Distribution curves $\varrho\,(r)$ for liquid mercury, gallium, sodium and potassium.

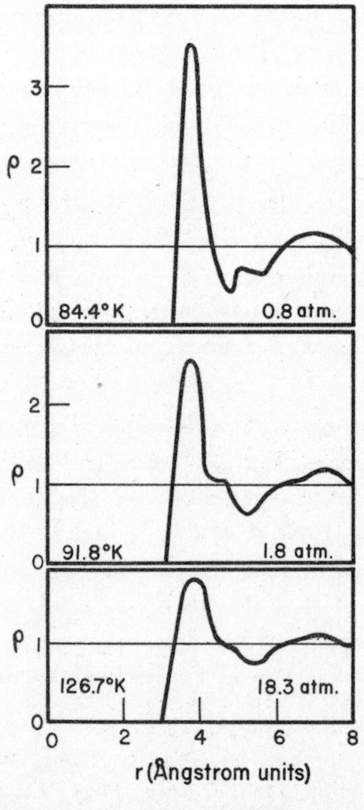

Fig. 3. Distribution functions $\varrho\,(r)$ for argon at different temperatures and saturation pressures (Eisenstein and Gingrich.)

Campbell and Hildebrand[10] compared the distribution function of liquid xenon at 183°K and 130 atmospheres with that at 163°K and 1 atmosphere, chosen to obtain the same density. From the fact that the two curves superimpose with only minor deviations, they concluded that $\varrho(r)$ is essentially a function of volume only, as one might expect it to be, except for slightly smaller minimum distances at higher temperatures due to greater kinetic energies.

Partition function of a normal liquid. In order to calculate the thermodynamic properties of a system by statistical mechanical methods, we must be able to evaluate a partition function for the system. The success of any theoretical treatment of the liquid state will depend upon the validity of the simplifying assumptions made. In the following pages, no attempt will be made to reproduce the detailed mathematics of the various approaches to the problem. Only a few of the more general methods of attack will be mentioned with special attention being given to the usefulness and limitations of the assumptions involved.

The first two assumptions are fairly general and common to most theories of liquids.

I. The translational degrees of freedom of the molecules are essentially classical. This condition is satisfied whenever the spacing of the translational quantum levels is small compared with kT or in other words whenever

$$T \gg \frac{h^2}{mkv^{2/3}}$$

where T is the absolute temperature; h, Planck's constant; k, Boltzmann's constant; m, the mass per molecule, and v, the volume per molecule. This condition excludes liquid hydrogen and liquid helium, and to a lesser degree, liquid neon, but should hold fairly accurately for all other liquids.

II. The internal degrees of freedom are the same in the liquid as in the gas. This means that we assume the rapid free rotation of the molecules to be unaffected by the presence of neighbor molecules in the liquid and the *intra*molecular vibrations to be similarly unchanged. Such a condition is, of course, obeyed by monatomic molecules (which have no internal degrees of freedom,) and we shall see that for a number of other substances the amount of restricted rotation and altered vibration is not great. By making these two assumptions, we permit the factoring out of the internal degrees of freedom from the partition function, and integration of the external (translational) part of the partition function

$$Q = \frac{(q_{\text{int}})^n}{n!} \int\int \cdots \int e^{-\frac{E_{\text{ext}}}{kT}} dq_1 \ldots dq_{3n}\, dp_1 \ldots dp_{3n} \qquad (4)$$

where the bold face **q**'s and **p**'s represent generalized position and momentum coordinates.

The *inter*molecular energy E_{ext} can be written as the sum of kinetic and potential terms

$$E_{ext} = \sum_{i=1}^{3n} \frac{\mathbf{p}_i^2}{2m} + U \tag{5}$$

where $\mathbf{p}_i$ is the momentum in the ith degree of freedom, U is the potential energy. Substituting and integrating over the momenta **p** we obtain

$$Q = \frac{(q_{int})^n \left(\frac{2\pi mkT}{h^2}\right)^{\frac{3n}{2}}}{n!} \int\int \cdots \int e^{-\frac{U}{kT}} \, (d\tau)^n \tag{6}$$

where $(d\tau)^n = dx_1 \, dy_1 \, dz_1 \, \ldots\ldots \, dx_n \, dy_n \, dz_n$

We shall define a configuration integral Q_τ such that

$$Q_\tau = \frac{1}{n!} \int\int \cdots \int e^{-\frac{U}{kT}} \, (d\tau)^n \tag{7}$$

Q_τ is essentially a measure of the number of possible arrangements of the n molecules in space, the factorial n being included to eliminate multiple counting of physically indistinguishable configurations.

Substituting (7) in (6), we obtain

$$Q = (q_{int})^n \left(\frac{2\pi mkT}{h^2}\right)^{\frac{3n}{2}} Q_\tau \tag{8}$$

From Assumption II, the internal partition function q_{int} is a function of temperature only. Remembering this, we may use Equations I 46 - 49 to obtain the thermodynamic functions:

$$A = -nkT \left\{ \ln \left(\frac{2\pi mkT}{h^2}\right)^{\frac{3}{2}} + \ln q_{int} \right\} + kT \ln Q_\tau \tag{9}$$

$$P = kT \left(\frac{\partial \ln Q_\tau}{\partial V}\right)_{T,\,n} \tag{10}$$

$$S = nkT \left\{ \ln \left(\frac{2\pi mkT}{h^2}\right)^{\frac{3}{2}} + \frac{3}{2} + \ln q_{int} + \left(\frac{\partial \ln q_{int}}{\partial \ln T}\right)_V \right\} + kT \left\{ \ln Q_\tau + \left(\frac{\partial \ln Q_\tau}{\partial \ln T}\right)_V \right\} \tag{11}$$

$$E = \mathrm{n}kT\left\{\frac{3}{2} + \left(\frac{\partial \ln q_{int}}{\partial \ln T}\right)_V\right\} + kT\left(\frac{\partial \ln Q_\tau}{\partial \ln T}\right)_V \tag{12}$$

P, V, F, H, and C_V can be obtained from Equations I 50 - 53 when desired. In the future we shall write E_{int} for the expression $\mathrm{n}kT\,(\partial \ln q_{int}/\partial \ln T)_V$ and S_{int} for the expression $\mathrm{n}k\{\ln q_{int} + T(\partial \ln q_{int}/\partial \ln T)_V\}$ in Equations 9 and 10.

The cell method of calculation. In a liquid, the average molecule is pretty well surrounded by its neighbors and is therefore confined to a space one-n^{th} of the total volume of the system or $v = V/\mathrm{n}$.

We may arbitrarily define a function q_τ, a sort of configuration integral per molecule, such that

$$Q_\tau = (q_\tau)^{\mathrm{n}} \tag{13}$$

We may attempt to write for q_τ:

$$q_\tau = \iiint e^{\frac{-u(x,y,z)}{kT}}\,dx\,dy\,dz \tag{14}$$

where the integration is carried out over the volume v of one cell.

Equation 14 is only approximate because of the arbitrary choice of the limits of integration, but Mayer has derived a rigorous cell equation, as we shall see at the end of this chapter.

Equation 14 is not entirely equivalent to the exact Equation 7 even in the simplest case of a perfect gas. For a perfect gas, the actual volume occupied by the molecule is negligible compared with the total volume and there are no intermolecular forces, so we may set $U = 0$ in Equation 7, and obtain for the configuration integral[12]

$$Q_\tau = \frac{V^{\mathrm{n}}}{\mathrm{n}!} = \left(\frac{e}{\mathrm{n}}\right)^{\mathrm{n}} V^{\mathrm{n}} = (ev)^{\mathrm{n}} \tag{15}$$

On the other hand, in the cell model, setting $u = 0$, we obtain $q_\tau = v$ and hence

$$Q_\tau = (q_\tau)^{\mathrm{n}} = v^{\mathrm{n}} \tag{16}$$

---

[12] We use here and elsewhere the familiar approximation of Stirling's formula for the factorial: $\ln \mathrm{n}! = \mathrm{n}\ln \mathrm{n} - \mathrm{n} + \frac{1}{2}\ln 2\pi\mathrm{n} + \ldots$ For sufficiently large values of n, no significant error is introduced if we take $\ln \mathrm{n}! = \mathrm{n}\ln\mathrm{n} - \mathrm{n}$ or $\mathrm{n}! = (\mathrm{n}/e)^{\mathrm{n}}$.

Substitution of Equation 15 in Equations 9—12 will yield the familiar equations for a perfect gas. Equation 16 leads to a corresponding equation for the entropy of the gas, differing by a value of $kn\ln e$ or R per mole. Mathematically, one may attribute this discrepancy to the failure to include in the approximate Equation 14 those configurations in which two or more molecules occupy one cell, leaving other cells empty. Eyring[13,14] has called this term the "communal entropy" and has identified it with the ability of molecules to move throughout the whole system, exchanging places, so to speak. He assumes this to be present in gases and liquids, but not in solids, leading to a term R in the entropy of fusion. This assumption has been the object of considerable criticism and we defer further consideration to a later section where the process of melting is considered in more detail.

Where the communal entropy R is assumed to be available, we may use Equation 14 and write

$$Q_\tau = (eq_\tau)^n \tag{17}$$

The liquid as a compressed gas. A consideration of the properties of a liquid in terms of those of a gas may be illuminating. For the model of a gas of rigid noninteracting spheres, in which the potential function U is either zero or minus infinity, we obtain from Equation 7

$$Q_\tau = (ev^f)^n \tag{18}$$

where v^f is the average volume accessible to a single molecule or the "free volume" per molecule.

To make such a model of any use for the case of liquids, we must introduce some assumption concerning the interaction potential. A crude approximation, first introduced by Guggenheim[15], is obtained by making an additional assumption.

IIIa[16]. The intermolecular potential U may be replaced by its value averaged over all accessible configurations, which shall be denoted by $-n\chi$. Each molecule may then be regarded as moving freely in a uniform potential $-\chi$, which is a function of v only.

Since the value of χ will be determined by the number of nearest neighbor molecules and their distance, the assumption that χ is determined by the density of packing, *i. e.*, the volume per molecule, v, is not unreasonable. The weakness of the model is that no account is taken of the change in interaction energy as the molecule moves around its average position.

---

[13] H. Eyring, *J. Chem. Phys.*, **4**, 283 (1936).

[14] H. Eyring and J. Hirschfelder, *J. Phys. Chem.*, **41**, 249 (1937).

[15] E. A. Guggenheim, *Proc. Roy. Soc.*, **A 135,** 181 (1932).

[16] Assumptions I and II are essential to all the models of liquids discussed in this Chapter. The rest are peculiar to particular treatments and are designated IIIa, IIIb, etc.

Assuming IIIa, we may write

$$Q_\tau = \frac{1}{n!}\int \cdots \int e^{\frac{n\chi}{kT}} (d\tau)^n = \left\{ e v^f e^{\chi/kT} \right\}^n \tag{19}$$

which yields for the Helmholtz free energy per mole:

$$A = -\left\{ N\chi + RT \ln \left(\frac{2\pi mkT}{h^2}\right)^{\frac{3}{2}} + RT \ln v^f + RT + RT \ln q_{int} \right\} \tag{20}$$

If v^f is like χ a function of v only and not of T, then

$$P = \left(\frac{\partial \chi}{\partial v}\right)_T + kT\left(\frac{\partial \ln v^f}{\partial v}\right)_T \tag{21}$$

$$E = -N\chi + \frac{3}{2} RT + E_{int} \tag{22}$$

$$S = R \ln \left(\frac{2\pi mkT}{h^2}\right)^{\frac{3}{2}} + R \ln v^f + \frac{5}{2} R + S_{int} \tag{23}$$

This picture may be made formally correct by replacing χ by χ_0, the potential of the molecules in their equilibrium positions, and permitting v^f to be determined empirically (i. e., to absorb into itself all the correction terms). In this case v^f will be a function of both v and T; Equations 20 and 21 remain valid (with this new interpretation of v^f) and Equations 22 and 23 are replaced by

$$E = -N\chi_0 + \frac{3}{2} RT + RT^2 \left(\frac{\partial \ln v^f}{\partial T}\right)_v + E_{int} \tag{22a}$$

$$S = R \ln \left(\frac{2\pi mkT}{h^2}\right)^{\frac{3}{2}} + R \ln v^f + \frac{5}{2} R + RT\left(\frac{\partial \ln v^f}{\partial T}\right)_v + S_{int} \tag{23a}$$

We may expect the free volume v^f to increase somewhat with temperature even at constant volume because the greater kinetic energy permits more interpenetration of the molecules, as we have noted earlier.

Vaporization to the gas phase. The relation of a liquid to a gas may be seen clearly on consideration of the smoothed potential model developed in the preceding section. As the volume increases, the average distance between molecules increases, causing a decrease in the attractive forces between molecules (*i. e.*, a decrease in χ) and a corresponding increase in the free volume v^f. In the limit as $v \to \infty$, $v^f \to v$ and $\chi \to 0$, and we obtain the equations for a perfect gas.

The choice of any reasonable form for the functions χ and v^f will yield the familiar liquid-gas isotherms of the van der Waals type, which show, at sufficiently low temperatures, a maximum and minimum, indicating a two phase system. For example, from an oversimplified model in which $\chi = \mathrm{a}/v$, $v^f = v - \mathrm{b}$, (a and b constants, here per molecule rather than in the usual form per mole), we may derive the familiar van der Waals equation

$$P = -\frac{\mathrm{a}}{v^2} + \frac{kT}{v - \mathrm{b}} \tag{24}$$

Better agreement may be obtained by a better choice of functions for χ and v^f.

According to the free volume model, we may write for the molal energy and entropy of vaporization, expressing the free volumes in molal rather than molecular units:

$$\Delta \mathrm{E}^{\mathrm{V}} = \boldsymbol{N}\{\chi^l - \chi^g\} + RT^2 y \tag{25}$$

$$\Delta \mathrm{S}^{\mathrm{V}} = R \ln \frac{(\mathrm{V}^f)^g}{(\mathrm{V}^f)^l} + RTy \tag{26}$$

$$\text{where } y = \left[\frac{\partial \ln \frac{(\mathrm{V}^f)^g}{(\mathrm{V}^f)^l}}{\partial T}\right]_{\mathrm{V}^g,\, \mathrm{V}^l}$$

Treating the vapor as a perfect gas, and neglecting y, we may simplify Equations 25 and 26:

$$\Delta \mathrm{E}^{\mathrm{V}} \simeq \boldsymbol{N}\chi^l \tag{27}$$

$$\Delta \mathrm{S}^{\mathrm{V}} \simeq R \ln \frac{\mathrm{V}^g}{\mathrm{V}^f} \tag{28}$$

$$\Delta \mathrm{H}^{\mathrm{V}} = \Delta \mathrm{E}^{\mathrm{V}} + p\Delta \mathrm{V} \simeq \boldsymbol{N}\chi^l + RT \tag{29}$$

At equilibrium

$$\Delta \mathrm{F}^{\mathrm{V}} = \Delta \mathrm{H}^{\mathrm{V}} - T\Delta \mathrm{S}^{\mathrm{V}} = 0 \tag{30}$$

Since for a perfect gas, $\mathrm{V}^g = RT/p$, the equilibrium vapor pressure is

$$p = \frac{RT}{\mathrm{V}^f} e^{-\frac{\Delta \mathrm{H}^{\mathrm{V}}}{RT}} = \frac{RT}{\mathrm{V}^f} e^{-\frac{\Delta \mathrm{S}^{\mathrm{V}}}{R}} \tag{31}$$

Estimation of the free volume. For our purposes, it is desirable to have a definition of the free volume which is independent of the smoothed potential model. The simplest definition is that in terms of the entropy of vaporization, using Equation 28. Where the temperature dependence of v^f is not negligible (*i. e.*, $y \neq 0$), Equation 19 is not consistent with this new definition and Equations 22a, 23a and 25 must be altered accordingly.

If the gas is dilute enough to make the perfect gas law a good approximation, we obtain by reversing Equations 28 and 31.

$$\mathrm{V}^f = \mathrm{V}^g e^{-\frac{\Delta \mathrm{S}^{\mathrm{V}}}{R}} \cong \frac{RT}{p} e^{-\frac{\Delta \mathrm{H}^{\mathrm{V}}}{RT}} \tag{32}$$

where p is the equilibrium vapor pressure, and $\Delta \mathrm{S}^{\mathrm{V}}$ the entropy of vaporization.

From the Clausius-Clapeyron equation,

$$\frac{d \ln p}{dT} = \frac{\Delta \mathrm{H}^{\mathrm{V}}}{RT^2} \tag{33}$$

and on integrating (assuming $\Delta \mathrm{H}^{\mathrm{V}}$ constant)

$$\frac{p}{p_b} = e^{\frac{\Delta \mathrm{H}_b^{\mathrm{V}}}{R}\left(\frac{1}{T_b} - \frac{1}{T}\right)} \tag{34}$$

where the subscript represents the normal boiling point ($p_b = 760$ mm. Hg). Substituting in Equation 32

$$\mathrm{V}^f = \frac{RT}{p_b} e^{-\frac{\Delta \mathrm{H}_b^{\mathrm{V}}}{RT_b}} = \frac{RT}{p_b} e^{-\frac{\Delta \mathrm{S}_b^{\mathrm{V}}}{R}} \tag{35}$$

According to this approximate formula, the free volume increases linearly with the absolute temperature, the proportionality constant being determined by the entropy of vaporization at the boiling point. If the crude Trouton rule were valid $\Delta \mathrm{S}_b^{\mathrm{V}}$ would be a universal constant (about 20 e. u.) and all liquids would have equal free volumes at the same temperature (about 1.1 cc. at 25°C.). Actually, as is well known, Trouton's rule is very inaccurate. If the heat of vaporization at the boiling point is known (and hence the entropy), Equation 35 will give a reasonable value if the extrapolation is not over too great a range of temperature. Where the necessary data are known, Equation 32 is certainly better.

Any other estimation of the free volume requires a suitable choice of functional form for V^f. From thermodynamics, we may take the relation

$$\left(\frac{\partial S}{\partial V}\right)_T = \left(\frac{\partial P}{\partial T}\right)_V = \frac{\alpha}{\beta} \tag{36}$$

where α is the volume coefficient of thermal expansion and β the coefficient of compressibility, constants which have been determined for many liquids. Hildebrand and his co-workers[17] have shown that $\left(\frac{\partial P}{\partial T}\right)_V$ itself, which they have called the "thermal pressure coefficient", may be measured directly. Where available, this quantity should be used, since the compressibility β is usually determined using large increments of pressure, and the values so obtained are markedly different from the differential value at one atmosphere.

From Equation 23

$$\left(\frac{\partial S}{\partial V}\right)_T = \left(\frac{\partial P}{\partial T}\right)_V = R\left(\frac{\partial \ln v^f}{\partial V}\right)_T = \frac{R}{V^f}\left(\frac{\partial V^f}{\partial V}\right)_T \tag{37}$$

The simplest possible assumption concerning V^f is that of van der Waals

$$V^f = V - V_0 \tag{38}$$

where the co-volume V_0 is not necessarily the same constant as that for a dilute gas[18]. Substituting Equation 38 into Equation 37, one obtains

$$\left(\frac{\partial S}{\partial V}\right)_T = \frac{R}{V^f}$$

or

$$V^f = R\Big/\left(\frac{\partial P}{\partial T}\right)_V = \frac{R\beta}{\alpha} \tag{39}$$

Since for normal liquids at 20°, $\left(\frac{\partial P}{\partial T}\right)_V$ varies from 8—16 atmospheres per degree, one obtains values of V^f in the range 5 to 10 cc. per mole.

A better assumption for liquids is that used first by Eyring and Hirschfelder[14] and subsequently by Lennard-Jones and Devonshire.[19]

They assume that the center of each molecule moves in a spherical cage (Fig. 4) whose radius r is the difference between the average distance a between centers of nearest neighbor molecules, and the diameter d of a molecule regarded as a rigid sphere.

---

[17] W. Westwater, H. W. Frantz, and J. H. Hildebrand, *Phys. Rev.*, **31**, 135 (1928).
J. H. Hildebrand, *Phys. Rev.*, **34**, 649, 984 (1929).
J. H. Hildebrand and J. M. Carter, *J. Am. Chem. Soc.*, **54**, 3592 (1932).

[18] For a dilute gas, the free volume is $V - V_0$ where the co-volume V_0 is four times the actual volume occupied by the molecules, or

$$(V^f)^g = V^g - 4N\frac{4}{3}\pi r^3$$

[19] J. E. Lennard-Jones and A. F. Devonshire, *Proc. Royal Soc.* **A 163**, 59 (1937).

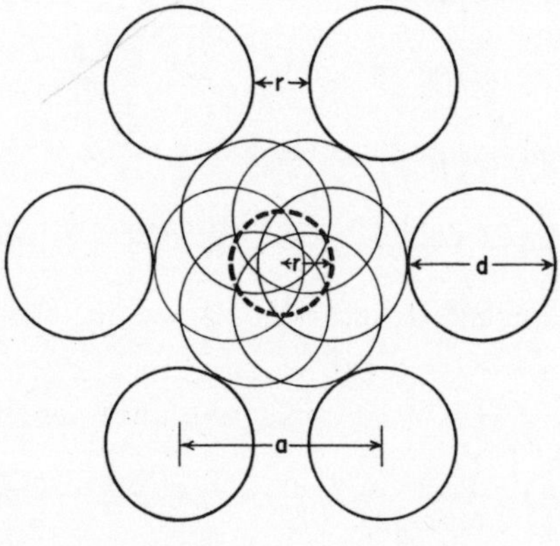

Fig. 4. Spherical cage model for free volume.

$$V^f = \frac{4}{3}\pi(a-d)^3 \tag{40}$$

The molal volume is related to a^3 by the equation

$$Na^3 = \gamma V \tag{41}$$

where γ is a constant depending on the geometry of the packing. We define a constant V_0 (not the same V_0 as in Equation 38), the volume of the unexpanded liquid (i. e., the hypothetical liquid at 0° *K.*).

$$Nd^3 = \gamma V_0 \tag{42}$$

Hence

$$V^f = \frac{4}{3}\pi\gamma\,(V^{\frac{1}{3}} - V_0^{\frac{1}{3}})^3 \tag{43}$$

and substituting into Equation 37,

$$\left(\frac{\partial S}{\partial V}\right)_T = \frac{R}{V^{\frac{2}{3}}\,(V^{\frac{1}{3}} - V_0^{\frac{1}{3}})}$$

or

$$V^f = \frac{4}{3}\pi\gamma\,R^3/V^2\left(\frac{\partial P}{\partial T}\right)_V^3 = \frac{4\pi\gamma}{3V^2}\left(\frac{R\beta}{\alpha}\right)^3 \tag{44}$$

The constant γ depends on the average number of nearest neighbors surrounding a given molecule, which for solids is identical with the lattice coordination number z. For solid lattices, one may calculate γ, given z

$$
\begin{array}{lll}
z = 12 \text{ (face centered cubic)} & \gamma = \sqrt{2} & = 1.414 \\
z = 8 \text{ (body-centered cubic)} & \gamma = \frac{3}{4}\sqrt{3} & = 1.299 \\
z = 6 \text{ (simple cubic)} & \gamma = 1 & = 1.000 \\
z = 4 \text{ (diamond structure)} & \gamma = \frac{3}{8}\sqrt{3} & = 0.650
\end{array}
$$

For most liquids $z = 8 - 10$, so a not unreasonable choice of γ is 1.3 or $\frac{4\pi\gamma}{3}$ about 5.5. This leads to values of V^f around 0.2 to 0.5 cc. per mole.

Table 1 shows values of V^f for several liquids calculated from Equations 32, 39, and 44.

Table 1. Free volumes of liquids at 25° C calculated in various ways.

Substance	V	$\Delta S^V/R$	p mm.	$(\partial P/\partial T)_V$ atm/deg	Free Volume V^f (cm³) Eqn.32	Eqn.39	Eqn.44
Mercury	14.8	24.5	0.00184	4.4	0.23	(19)	(175)
Methanol	40.6	15.1	126	9.8	0.04	8.4	2.0
Carbon disulfide	61	11.3	350	12.3	0.65	6.7	0.45
Acetone	74	13.3	229	11.0	0.13	7.5	0.42
Chloroform	81	12.9	199	12.2	0.23	6.7	0.25
Benzene	89	13.7	96	12.2	0.21	6.7	0.21
Carbon tetrachloride	97	13.2	115	11.1	0.29	7.4	0.24
Ethyl ether	105	10.8	537	8.4	0.70	9.8	0.47
Stannic chloride	118	16.1	24	10.9	0.08	7.5	0.17
Heptane	147	14.8	45	8.4	0.15	9.8	0.24

We see that the figures calculated from the three methods are discordant; for most substances, however, Equation 44 seems to give more reasonable values, indicating that it is derived from a more nearly adequate model. Frank[19a] has considered the problem of a model for the free volume in great detail and by introducing a number of refinements, has been able to correlate the entropy of vaporization with the cage model (Fig. 4) and to explain, at least in part, the discrepancies between Equations 32 and 44.

[19a] H. S. Frank, *J. Chem. Phys.*, **13**, 478, 493 (1945). H. S. Frank and M. W. Evans, *ibid.*, **13**, 507 (1945).

Entropies of vaporization and the Hildebrand rule. According to the crude Trouton rule, the entropy of vaporization at the normal boiling point is the same for a great many normal liquids. An obvious generalization of this is that the entropy of vaporization is a function of the saturation pressure only. A better rule is that first proposed by Hildebrand[20] in 1915, which states that the entropy of vaporization per mole is the same for all normal liquids if measured, not at their boiling points as in Trouton's rule, but at temperatures at which their vapors have equal molal volumes.

The significance of the rule is shown graphically in Fig. 5, where two vapor pressure curves are plotted, p against T. The entropy of vaporization ΔS^V is, of course:

$$\Delta S^V = \frac{\Delta H^V}{T} = \Delta V^V \frac{dp}{dT} \tag{45}$$

where ΔH^V is the heat of vaporization, ΔV^V, the volume change on vaporization, $V^g - V^l$, and dp/dT is the temperature derivative of the vapor pressure. For pressures which are not too high ΔV^V may be replaced by the

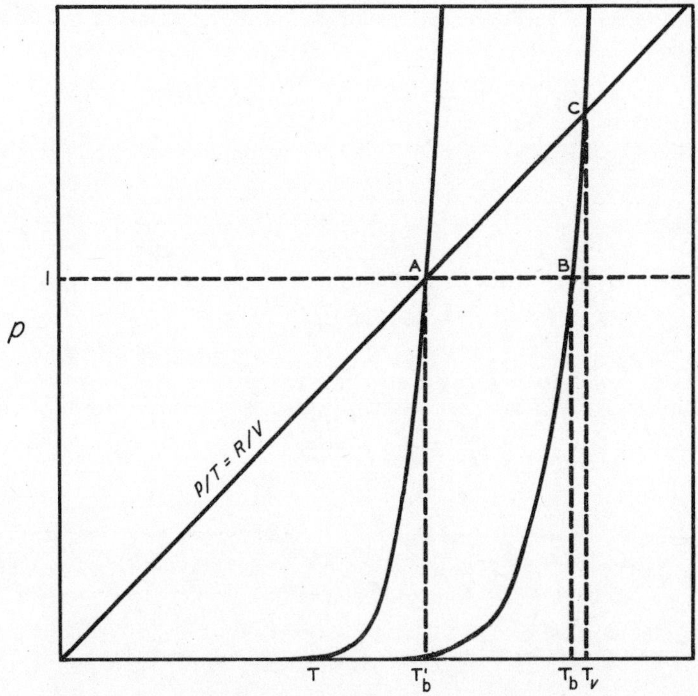

Fig. 5 Vapor pressures and the Trouton and Hildebrand rules.

[20] J. H. Hildebrand. *J. Am. Chem. Soc.*, **37**, 970 (1915); **40**, 45 (1918).

molal volume of the saturated vapor, $V^g = RT/p$. The Hildebrand rule, then, indicates that at points on the vapor pressure curves at which $V_1^g = V_2^g$, the curves for two liquids 1 and 2 have equal slope. Any straight line out from the origin[21] is a line of equal volume; hence every point on one curve corresponds to a point on the other, for which $p_1/T_1 = p_2/T_2$ and $dp_1/dT_1 = dp_2/dT_2$. The important feature is that the p—T curves form a family which never intersect; in fact, to the approximation that the saturated vapor is ideal, they are all identical in shape, differing only in scale. Thus, to the approximation of the Hildebrand rule, the vapor pressures of two substances, if equal at one temperature, are equal at all temperatures.

Let us compare the slopes of the vapor pressure curves of 1 and 2, at their normal boiling points. The horizontal dashed line in Fig. 5 represents an isobar for $p = 1$ atmosphere. The boiling points A and B lie on different constant volume lines; hence they do not have equal entropies of vaporization as predicted by Trouton's rule. It follows, however, that the entropy of vaporization at the boiling point is a function only of the boiling temperature T_b:

$$\Delta S_b^V = f(T_b) \tag{46}$$

The distinction between the Hildebrand and Trouton rules is shown perhaps more clearly in Fig. 6 where $\log p$ is plotted against $\log T$ for liquids

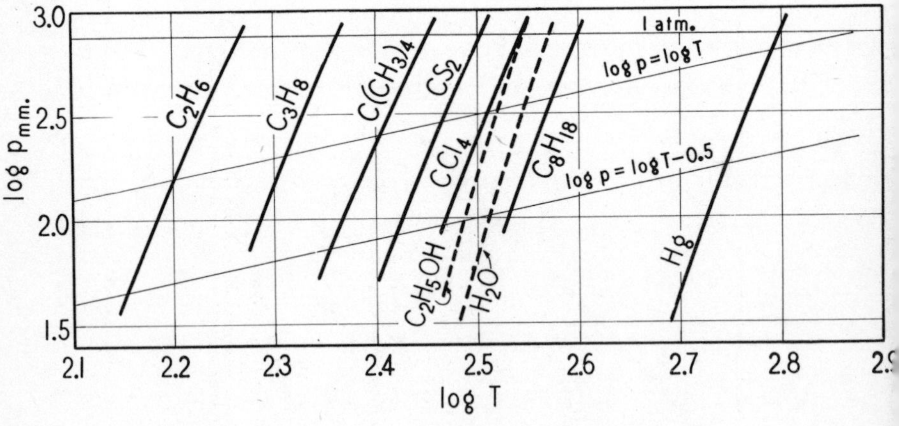

Fig. 6 Vapor Pressures and the Hildebrand Rule.

---

21 At higher pressures, when departures from ideality are of significance, $V < RT/p$ and the curves of constant volume lie below the straight line. This in no way affects the argument about the entropy and heat of vaporization.

covering a wide range of boiling points.[22] The advantage of the logarithmic plot is that it does not compress the low vapor pressure region into insignificance. If we substitute RT/p for ΔV^V into Equation 45, we obtain:

$$\Delta S^V = R \frac{d \ln p}{d \ln T} = R \frac{d \log p}{d \log T} \tag{47}$$

Thus the tangent to a $\log p - \log T$ curve at any point, multiplied by R, gives the entropy of vaporization at that temperature, except for deviations from the gas laws. It will be seen that the curves have the same slope, not at equal pressures (horizontal lines) but at points cut by a line of unit slope, where the vapor volumes are equal. Of the liquids shown in Fig. 6, only water and ethanol deviate significantly, and highly polar liquids, especially those possessing hydrogen bonds (Cf. Chapters IX and X) could hardly be expected to obey the rule.

By plotting in this way fairly accurately known vapor pressures, Hildebrand[23] obtained values for their entropies of vaporization at $\log RV = 0.1$ ($V = 49.5$ liters/mole), shown in Table 2.

Table 2. Entropies of Vaporization at Equal Vapor Volumes

($V^g = 49.5$ liters/mole)

	ΔS^V	$\Delta S^V - 20.1$		ΔS^V	$\Delta S^V - 20.1$
Hg	20.1	0.0	$(C_2H_5)_2O$	21.8	1.7
$C(CH_3)_4$	20.1	0.0	$(CH_3)_2CO$	22.5	2.4
i-C_5H_{12}	20.2	0.1	C_2H_5OH	27.0	6.9
n-C_5H_{12}	20.7	0.6	CH_3OH	26.5	6.4
$(CH_3)_2CH.CH(CH_3)_2$	20.3	0.2	$SnCl_4$	21.8	1.7
$CHCl_3$	21.7	1.6	$C(NO_2)_4$	22.6	2.5

If we take 20.1 as the normal value for ΔS^V at this volume, $\Delta S^V - 20.1$ may be taken as indicating a degree of order; it is to be noted that there is a regular increase in the series neopentane, isopentane, normal pentane again with diisopropyl and normal hexane; and with carbon tetrachloride, stannic chloride, and tetra-nitromethane. Halford[24] has interpreted this shift in terms of restricted molecular rotation in liquids.

[22] Cf. J. H. Hildebrand, *Science*, **90**, 1, (1939); *Proc. Phys. Soc.*, **41**, 221 (1944).

[23] J. H. Hildebrand, *J. Chem. Phys.*, **7**, 233 (1939).

[24] R. S. Halford, *J. Chem. Phys.*, **8**, 496 (1940).

We shall have occasion to return to the Hildebrand rule in a later section after a discussion of perfect and imperfect liquids.

The liquid as a disordered solid. An alternative model for liquids is analogous to that of a solid. An idealized solid consists of molecules arranged in a regular lattice vibrating around their equilibrium positions as harmonic oscillators. Applying this to a quasi-lattice structure for liquids we assume.

IIIb. **The quasi-lattice for n molecules consists of n positions of minimum potential energy $-\chi_\circ(v)$ and each molecule moves around such an equilibrium position in a field corresponding to an isotropic three-dimensional harmonic oscillator of frequency $\nu(v)$.**

In this simplified model, χ and ν are regarded as determined by the magnitude of the intermolecular force constants and the dimensions of the lattice, and are therefore functions of the volume only.

A molecule at a distance r from a minimum position will have a potential energy $-\chi_\circ + \frac{1}{2}m(2\pi\nu)^2r^2$. This leads to

$$Q_\tau = \frac{1}{\mathrm{n}!}\int\cdots\int e^{\frac{\mathrm{n}[\chi_\circ - \frac{1}{2}m(2\pi\nu)^2r^2]}{kT}}(d\tau)^{\mathrm{n}} =$$

$$e^{\frac{\mathrm{n}(\chi_\circ + kT)}{kT}}\left[\int_0^\infty e^{-\frac{1}{2}m(2\pi\nu)^2r^2}\,4\pi r^2\,dr\right]^{\mathrm{n}} = \left[e^{\frac{(\chi_\circ + kT)}{kT}}\left(\frac{RT}{2\pi m\nu^2}\right)^{\frac{3}{2}}\right]^{\mathrm{n}} \tag{48}$$

Substituting into Equation 9:

$$\mathrm{A} = -\left(N\chi_\circ + 3RT\ln\frac{kT}{h\nu} + RT + RT\ln q_{int}\right) \tag{49}$$

and for the other thermodynamic functions we obtain

$$P = \left(\frac{\partial\chi_\circ}{\partial v}\right)_T - 3kT\left(\frac{\partial\ln\nu}{\partial v}\right)_T = N\left(\frac{\partial\chi_\circ}{\partial \mathrm{V}}\right)_T - 3RT\left(\frac{\partial\ln\nu}{\partial \mathrm{V}}\right)_T \tag{50}$$

$$\mathrm{E} = -N\chi_\circ + 3RT + \mathrm{E}_{int} \tag{51}$$

$$\mathrm{S} = 3R\ln\frac{kT}{h\nu} + 4R + \mathrm{S}_{int} \tag{52}$$

As in the case of the free volume treatment these equations may be made empirically correct by regarding ν as an empirical function of V and T, in which case, Equations 51 and 52 are replaced by

$$\mathrm{E} = -N\chi_0 + 3RT + 3RT^2\left(\frac{\partial \ln \nu}{\partial T}\right)_V + \mathrm{E}_{int} \tag{51a}$$

$$\mathrm{S} = 3R \ln \frac{kT}{h\nu} + 4R + 3RT\left(\frac{\partial \ln \nu}{\partial T}\right)_V + \mathrm{S}_{int} \tag{52a}$$

The free volume smoothed potential model and the harmonic oscillator model can be made to agree by equating Equations 20 and 49

$$v^f = \left\{\frac{kT}{2\pi m \nu^2}\right\}^{\frac{3}{2}} \tag{53}$$

$$\nu = \left(\frac{kT}{2\pi m}\right)^{\frac{1}{2}} (v^f)^{\frac{1}{3}} \tag{54}$$

In this case ν is the frequency with which a molecule would travel back and forth between opposite faces of a cube of volume v^f if its kinetic energy in that direction were $\frac{kT}{\pi}$. The free volume v^f and the frequency ν were both defined as functions only of V, but it is evident from the temperature dependence of Equations 53 and 54 that it is obviously impossible for both to be independent of T.

The harmonic oscillator partition function for liquids has recently been discussed by Matsen and coworkers[25], who deduce a functional form for ν from the Morse function for diatomic molecules. The most extensive work in this direction has been that of Frenkel,[26] who approaches an understanding of the liquid state from a study of kinetic processes in crystals.

The process of melting. If we wish to compare the liquid with a solid, we must choose equivalent models. For a perfect crystal, assuming the Einstein approximation that all normal modes have the same frequency ν and that $kT \gg h\nu$ (permitting use of the limiting classical statistics)

$$\mathrm{A}_{\text{solid}} = -N\left\{\chi_0 + 3kT \ln \frac{kT}{h\nu} + kT \ln q_{int}\right\} \tag{55}$$

Assuming that q_{int} goes continuously from solid to liquid phase, one obtains for the fusion process

$$\Delta \mathrm{E}^{\mathrm{F}} = N(\chi_0^s - \chi_0^l) \tag{56}$$

$$\Delta \mathrm{H}^{\mathrm{F}} = \Delta \mathrm{E}^{\mathrm{F}} + p(\mathrm{V}^l - \mathrm{V}^s) \sim \Delta \mathrm{E}^{\mathrm{F}} \tag{57}$$

---

[25] F. A. Matsen and G. M. Watson, *J. Chem. Phys.*, **11**, 343 (1943).
F. A. Matsen and J. E. Walkey, *J. Chem. Phys.*, 13, 135 (1945).

[26] This is summarized in his book: J. Frenkel "The Kinetic Theory of Liquids" (Oxford, 1946).

$$\Delta S^F = 3R \ln \frac{\nu^s}{\nu^l} + R \tag{58}$$

In general $\chi^s > \chi^l$ and $\nu^s > \nu^l$, but the interesting feature is the extra term R in ΔS^F. This term is the "communal entropy" discussed in the earlier section. It appears here simply because the Einstein and Debye treatments of solids use a cell model, while implicit in the derivation of Equation 48 was the assumption that the whole volume of the system (except that excluded by the presence of other molecules) is available to any molecule. The introduction of this term is purely arbitrary unless the choice of two different zeros of entropy (that is, the choice of two different statistical formulations) can be justified by a real difference between solids and liquids.

The initial success of the concept of communal entropy can be attributed to the observation that the entropy of fusion of many substances is approximately two calories per mole, or about R. Eyring[14] used this fact to justify his assumption that the molecules of a solid are rigidly compartmentalized, while those of a liquid share the entire volume. While it is evident that in passing from a crystal at very low temperatures to a gas at elevated temperatures, a term R must accrue, the notion that all the communal entropy is gained in the fusion process has been severely criticized[27] and with some justification. Frank[27] has observed that "whether in a liquid, or a crystal, or a gas, the occasion for considering communal entropy arises only because of the occurrence of fluctuations in density", and therefore proposes the alternative term "fluctuation entropy". Rice[27] has shown that a considerable amount of such a fluctuation entropy must be present in a real crystal at elevated temperatures, while the short range order present in liquids precludes its having the full amount of such entropy available to a gas. While the concept of "communal entropy" is still used, the relation between it and the entropy of fusion is surely not as simple as Equation 58 indicates.

As we shall see later, the more recent formulations of liquid partition functions are in terms of molecular distribution functions which automatically include the effect of density fluctuations; hence any recourse to the concept of communal entropy becomes superfluous, if the solid is treated in an analogous fashion.

---

[27] R. W. Gurney and E. F. Mott, *J. Chem. Phys.*, **6**, 222 (1938); *Trans. Faraday Soc.*, **35**, 364 (1939).
O. K. Rice, *J. Chem. Phys.*, **5**, 492 (1937); **6**, 476 (1938); **7**, 883 (1939); **12**, 1 (1944).
J. G. Kirkwood, *J. Chem. Phys.*, **7**, 908 (1939).
J. Frenkel, "The Kinetic Theory of Liquids", Oxford (1946), p. 171.
H. S. Frank, *J. Chem. Phys.*, **13**, 478 (1945).

The "hole" theory of liquids. Eyring and his coworkers[28] have attempted to combine the divergent concepts of the two preceding treatments by considering liquids as mixtures or "solutions" of molecules and "holes". Eyring was led to this picture from a consideration of viscosity and diffusion in liquids[29], which he explains by a "hole" mechanism, virtually identical to that advanced much earlier by Frenkel.[30] The simplest picture, while never seriously advanced by anyone, would regard holes as the same size as molecules; such an argument would run something like this:

We know that a liquid is expanded over the close-packed lattice of a solid at low temperatures. Let us consider this expansion initially as due to the creation of vacant sites or holes within the lattice. There is no loss in generality if we consider the vacant site or hole as being occupied by a "molecule" of the same size and shape as the liquid molecule, but with no attractive forces. We may thus regard a liquid as a "solution" of holes in a solid lattice, and the conjugate gas phase as a solution of molecules in holes.

Anticipating the results of succeeding chapters we may write the partial molal free energy of the substance (subscript $_1$) and of the holes (subscript $_o$) as

$$\overline{\Delta F_1} = RT \ln x_1 + (\Delta E_1^\circ)\, x_o^2 \tag{59a}$$

$$\overline{\Delta F_o} = RT \ln x_o + (\Delta E_1^\circ)\, x_1^2 \tag{59b}$$

where the x's represent "mole fractions", or really volume fractions of holes and substance respectively and ΔE_1° is the energy of vaporization or sublimation (lattice energy) of the substance in the hole-less state, *i. e.*, at absolute zero.

If we apply the thermodynamics of binary systems to such a system, we obtain several interesting results.

(1) The phase diagram is necessarily symmetrical, which means that the concentration of holes in the liquid phase is the same as the concentration of molecules in the gas phase. The sum of the densities of coexistent liquid and gas must be a constant, the same at all temperatures. This is the law of rectilinear diameters in a more stringent form than is actually observed. (See Eqn. 71).

---

[28] R. F. Newton and H. Eyring, *Trans. Faraday Soc.*, **33**, 73 (1937). J. O. Hirschfelder and H. Eyring, *J. Chem. Phys.*, **41**, 249 (1937); J. F. Kincaid and H. Eyring, *J. Chem. Phys.*, **5**, 587 (1937); *ibid.*, **6**, 620 (1938); *J. Phys. Chem.*, **43**, 37 (1939); J. O. Hirschfelder, D. Stevenson, and H. Eyring, *ibid.*, **5**, 896 (1937); J. Walter and H. Eyring, *J. Chem. Phys.*, **9**, 393 (1941).

[29] H. Eyring, *J. Chem. Phys.*, **4**, 283 (1936). For a detailed discussion see S. Glasstone, K. J. Laidler, and H. Eyring, "The Theory of Rate Processes" (New York, McGraw-Hill, 1941).

[30] J. Frenkel, *Z. Physik*, **35**, 652 (1926).

(2) At the critical temperature, the critical phase is half molecules and half holes; hence the critical volume is twice that of the solid at absolute zero (the observed V_c is about 3.5 V_o).

(3) The critical temperature, above which only one phase exists, is obtained by setting

$$\frac{\Delta E_1^\circ}{RT_c} = 2 \tag{60}$$

For normal liquids, ΔE_1° is of the order of 10 kcal, which yields $T_c = 2500°$ K., a result which is obviously absurd.

We see that this oversimplified picture gives the qualitative aspects of equilibria between liquid and gas and critical phenomena, but the quantitative agreement is very poor. This may be attributed to two related factors:

(1) There is no necessity for the holes in a liquid (as distinguished from those in a solid lattice), to be the size of a molecule; in fact, judging from X-ray studies on the liquids, a liquid contains many small holes, rather than a few large ones.

(2) No account has been taken in the above treatment of the fluctuation in the size of a hole, or equivalently, the fluctuation in position of the liquid molecule.

These difficulties were immediately recognized and numerous attempts to resolve them have been made, mostly of a semi-empirical nature. For example, Walter and Eyring[28] have achieved notable success by taking the liquid partition function as a combination of those for the solid and gas. They assume that the liquid has n^s equilibrium positions of the type present in the solid and n^h new equilibrium positions of volume v^s/n, where v^s is the volume per molecule in the solid and n is the ratio of the volumes of a molecule and an average hole (v^s/n is thus the volume per hole). The number of holes n^h is thus:

$$n^h = \frac{n\, n^s (v^l - v^s)}{v^s} \tag{61}$$

For a molecule in a solid type position, they use the partition function for a Debye solid (merely a refinement of that for the classical harmonic oscillator given in the preceding sections).

$$q^s = \left(\frac{e^{-3\theta_D/8T}}{1 - e^{-3\theta_D/4T}} \right)^3 e^{E^s/RT} \tag{62}$$

where θ_D is the Debye temperature and E^s is the molal energy of the solid (essentially the same as $N\chi_0^s$ of the preceding section or the energy of sublimation of the solid ΔE^S). For the molecules in gas-like positions, they take the partition function for molecules in a free volume v^s/n:

$$q^g = \frac{(2\pi mkT)^{\frac{3}{2}}}{h^3} \frac{v^s}{n} e^{-\delta E^s/RT} \tag{63}$$

where δ is a function of volume to be evaluated empirically.

Equation 63 is the same as Equation 19 except that Walter and Eyring write it in the cell form, per molecule, and include therein the term arising from kinetic energy as well as q_τ.

If the n^s molecules are distributed randomly among the $n^s + n^h$ positions, there will be in addition to the partition functions of the solid-like and liquid-like molecules, a term $(n^s + n^h)!/n^s!\,n^h!$ corresponding to an ideal entropy of mixing of molecules and holes. If, following Walter and Eyring, we assume further that the molecules are distributed among the two kinds according to the ratio of the volumes, *i. e.*, a fraction v^s/v^l in the solid type and a fraction $(v^l - v^s)/v^l$ in the gaseous type, the partition function becomes:

$$q = (q^s)^{v^s/v^l} \cdot (q^g)^{\frac{v^l - v^s}{v^l}} \frac{(n^s + n^h)!}{n^s!\,n^h!} \tag{64}$$

Walter and Eyring introduce a parameter γ, defined as:

$$\gamma = \frac{n^h}{n^s} = \frac{n\,(v^l - v^s)}{v^s} \tag{65}$$

Expressing v^s, v^l n^h, n^s in terms of γ and n, we obtain a simple form for the Helmholtz free energy:

$$A = -RT\left\{\frac{n}{n+\gamma}\ln q^s + \frac{\gamma}{n+\gamma}\ln q^g + \ln(1+\gamma) + \gamma \ln\frac{(1+\gamma)}{\gamma}\right\} \tag{66}$$

For $\gamma = 0$, this equation reduces to that for the Debye solid; for $\gamma \to \infty$, it becomes the equation for a perfect gas provided that $\delta \to 0$ as $\gamma \to \infty$. All the thermodynamic functions may be calculated explicitly from Equation 66 when n has been given a numerical value and a suitable form has been chosen for δ. Walter and Eyring calculated n to be 8.35 from the observed entropy and volume change on melting, and the simplest form of δ which gave fair agreement with experimental data was:

$$\delta = \left(\frac{V^s}{V^l}\right)^2 \Big/ \left(2\gamma + \frac{1}{n-1}\right) \tag{67}$$

With these equations, satisfactory agreement with the experimental data on argon, nitrogen, and benzene was obtained.

Perfect liquids: The theory of corresponding states. Pitzer[31] has suggested an alternative approach which avoids the necessity of choosing an artificial model for a liquid.

In addition to assumptions I (translational partition function is classical) and II (internal degrees of freedom same as in the gas phase), which are features of almost all theories of liquids, two more quite general assumptions must be added.

IIIc. **The inter-molecular potential energy is a function of the various intermolecular distances only.** This assumption excludes specific valence forces and so rules out highly polar liquids, metals (where specific electronic forces exist) and hydrogen bonded molecules, but is consistent with liquids where the only attractive forces are of the London dispersion force type ("van der Waals forces"). In the smoothed-potential and harmonic oscillator treatments, assumption IIIc is implicit, but is tied to much more restrictive assumptions.

IVc. **The potential function for a pair of molecules can be written** $A\Phi(r/d_0)$, where r is the intermolecular distance, A and d_0 characteristic constants and Φ a universal function.

In terms of the potential function $\varepsilon(r)$ discussed in the preceding chapter:

$$\varepsilon(r) = -\frac{k}{r^6} + \frac{j}{r^n} \tag{68}$$

assumption IVc reduces to the assumption that n is a universal constant for all liquids, since we have seen (Chapter IV), that Equation 68 may be rewritten:

$$\varepsilon(r) = -\varepsilon_0 \left[\frac{6}{n-6}\left(\frac{d_0}{r}\right)^n - \frac{n}{n-6}\left(\frac{d_0}{r}\right)^6\right] \tag{69}$$

In this equation, ε_0 is the minimum value of $\varepsilon(r)$ and occurs at d_0, the equilibrium distance.

Assumption IVc is probably never exactly true, just as Equation 68 is only an approximation. However the macroscopic properties of liquids should be fairly insensitive to minor variations in the form of the repulsive force. Actually, no assumption even of the form of Equation 68 is necessary, merely the universality of the function Φ.

[31] K. S. Pitzer, *J. Chem. Phys.*, **7**, 583 (1939).

One may now write for Q_τ

$$Q_\tau = \frac{1}{n!} \int_0^{x_0} \cdots \int_0^{z_0} e^{\frac{-\frac{1}{2} A \sum\limits_{i=1}^{n} \sum\limits_{j=1}^{n} \Phi\left(\frac{\Delta r_{ij}}{d_0}\right)}{kT}} dx_1 \ldots dz_n \tag{70}$$

or transforming

$$Q_\tau = \frac{d_0^{3n}}{n!} \int_0^{\frac{x_0}{d_0}} \cdots \int_0^{\frac{z_0}{d_0}} e^{-\left(\frac{A}{2kT}\right) \sum\sum \Phi(\Delta r_{ij}/d_0)} d\left(\frac{x_1}{d_0}\right) \ldots d\left(\frac{z_n}{d_0}\right) \tag{71}$$

No attempt is made to evaluate the integral, but one may write it as

$$Q_\tau = \left[v \cdot \Psi\left(\frac{kT}{\varepsilon_0}, \frac{v}{d_0^3}\right)\right]^n \tag{72}$$

where Ψ is a universal function.

It can be shown that at the critical point $\frac{kT^c}{\varepsilon_0}$ and $\frac{v_c}{d_0^3}$ must be universal constants; hence one may write using molal quantities:

$$Q_\tau = \left[v \cdot \Psi'\left(\frac{T}{T_c}, \frac{V}{V_c}\right)\right]^n \tag{73}$$

Substituting into Equations 9 and 10, one obtains for the thermodynamic functions

$$A = -RT\left[\ln\left(\frac{2\pi mkT}{h^2}\right)^{\frac{3}{2}} + 1 + \ln v + \ln q_{int} + \ln \Psi'\left(\frac{T}{T_c}, \frac{V}{V_c}\right)\right] \tag{74}$$

$$P = \left(\frac{\partial A}{\partial V}\right)_T = \frac{RT}{V} + RT\left(\frac{\partial \ln \Psi'(T/T_c, V/V_c)}{\partial V}\right)_T \tag{75}$$

Substituting $\pi = \frac{P}{P_c}$, $\theta = \frac{T}{T_c}$, $\varphi = \frac{V}{V_c}$

$$\pi = \frac{RT_c}{P_c V_c}\left\{\frac{\theta}{\varphi} + \left(\frac{\partial \ln \Psi'(\theta, \varphi)}{\partial \varphi}\right)_\theta\right\} \tag{76}$$

Since $\frac{RT_c}{P_c V_c}$ is a universal constant, we may write

$$\pi = f_1 (\theta,\varphi) \tag{77}$$

This is the most general way of expressing the theory of corresponding states. Many empirical equations of state (all those with three arbitrary constants) can be transformed into such a reduced equation of state, but the exact form of f_1 has not been calculated.

Pitzer has called liquids which conform to these assumptions "perfect liquids." Hydrogen, helium and to a lesser extent, neon, fail to follow perfect behavior because of quantum mechanical effects which violate Assumption I. Argon, krypton, xenon and methane are essentially "perfect". Pitzer[31] and Guggenheim[32] have shown that nitrogen, oxygen and carbon monoxide follow the principle fairly closely.

From the principle of corresponding states, they draw the following conclusions:

1. **Vapor pressure.** The equilibrium reduced vapor pressure should be expressible as a function of θ only. Pitzer[31] derives from the data of Meihuizen and Crommelin[33] for krypton the expression

$$\log \pi = -\frac{4.29810}{\theta} - 12.55400 \log \theta + 0.63158 + 3.66652\,\theta \tag{78}$$

2. **Entropy of vaporization.** The entropy of vaporization for perfect liquids should be the same at corresponding states. A corresponding state is uniquely fixed by fixing any one of the four quantities, π, θ, φ^g or φ^l, in as much as they are all interrelated.

Hence

$$\Delta S^V = f(\theta) = g(\varphi^g) = h(\pi) \tag{79}$$

If all substances had the same critical pressure, then $\Delta S^V = h'(p)$, and Trouton's rule ("all substances have the same entropy of vaporization at their boiling points") would be valid. Similarly, if the critical volume were a universal constant, $\Delta S^V = g'(V^g)$ and the Hildebrand rule ("equal entropies of vaporization at equal vapor volumes") would be correct. Since the critical volume is more nearly constant for a wide range of nonpolar substances than is the critical pressure, the Hildebrand rule should be a decided improvement over the Trouton rule, as it usually is. Table 3 shows the entropies of vaporization of the rare gases and other approximately perfect liquids, compared under different conditions. The data are taken primarily from the papers of Pitzer and Guggenheim, with a few extensions and revisions.

---

[32] E. A. Guggenheim, *J. Chem. Phys.*, **13**, 253 (1945).

[33] J. J. Meihuizen and C. A. Crommelin, *Physica*, **4**, 1 (1937).

TABLE 3 Entropies of vaporization for perfect liquids

Substance	ΔS^V at conditions indicated			
	$V^g/V^l = 335$ (Pitzer)	$\pi = 0.02$ (Guggenheim)	$p = 1$ atm. (Trouton)	$V^g = 10$ liters (Hildebrand)
Neon	(17.95)	17.0	15.4	(19.3)
Argon	18.67	17.95	17.85	19.0
Krypton	18.60	17.70	17.99	18.5
Xenon	18.66	17.99	18.29	18.0
Radon			18.60	
Nitrogen	19.1	17.99	17.23	18.7
Oxygen	18.8	18.09	18.07	19.0
Carbon monoxide	19.4	18.31	17.70	19.2
Methane	18.4	17.80	17.51	17.8

We see that the entropies of vaporization of perfect liquids are better represented by the theory of corresponding states than by the Hildebrand rule. In the following section we will find that this is not necessarily the case for imperfect liquids.

3. **Heat capacity**. For perfect liquids, the vibrations and rotations, if any, are the same as for the gas; hence only the translational degrees of freedom concern us. For the translational part of C_p, Pitzer found 10.7 in the normal liquid range. Since the corresponding value for the gas is 5, $\Delta C_p = 5.7$.

4. **Entropy of fusion.** Only monatomic substances which have no internal degrees of freedom can reasonably be expected to obey the theory of corresponding states in the solid phase, because restriction of rotation in the solid phase violates Assumption II. For monatomic substances, one should obtain equal entropies of fusion, equal reduced melting temperatures or triple points, and equal reduced volume ratios. Pitzer and Guggenheim found for the triple point $\theta_t = 0.555$, $\Delta S^F = 3.35$ e. u., $V^l/V^s = 1.15$.

5. **Boyle point.** The Boyle point of the gas, *i. e.*, the temperature at which the second virial coefficient equals zero, $B = \left(\frac{\partial PV}{\partial P}\right)_{T,\, P=0} = 0$, was found by Guggenheim to be at $\theta_B = 2.7$.

6. **Ratio of critical constants.** In any theory of corresponding states, the product of the critical pressure and the critical volume divided by the critical temperature should be a constant. For perfect liquids $P_c V_c / RT_c = 0.292$.

7. **Densities of coexistent vapor and liquid**. Guggenheim finds as approximate formulas for the densities of vapor and liquid in equilibrium

$$\frac{\varrho^l}{\varrho_c} = \frac{1}{\varphi^l} = 1 + \frac{3}{4}(1 - \theta) + \frac{7}{4}(1 - \theta)^{\frac{1}{3}} \tag{80}$$

$$\frac{\varrho^g}{\varrho_c} = \frac{1}{\varphi^g} = 1 + \frac{3}{4}(1-\theta) - \frac{7}{4}(1-\theta)^{\frac{1}{3}} \tag{81}$$

The percentage inaccuracy in ϱ^g becomes serious below $\theta = 0.65$. In fact, ϱ^g goes to zero at $\theta = 0.565$, which however is near the triple point. Combining these yields the familiar law of the rectalinear diameter:

$$\frac{\varrho^l + \varrho^g}{2\varrho_c} = 1 + \frac{3}{4}(1-\theta) \tag{82}$$

From Equation 80, one may calculate the reduced volume of the liquid at absolute zero. $\varphi_o^l = 0.286$.

8. **Surface Tension.** By applying assumption IV to the surface region, Guggenheim derives that

$$\frac{\gamma V_c^{\frac{2}{3}}}{T} = f(\theta) \tag{83}$$

where γ is the surface tension, and f another universal function. By combining Equation 83, the empirical Equations 80 and 81, and the empirical relation of Katayama, he derives for the surface tension

$$\gamma = \gamma_o (1-\theta)^{11/9} \tag{84}$$

It follows that $\frac{\gamma_o V_c^{\frac{2}{3}}}{T_c}$ should have a universal value; this is found empirically to be about 4.4.

Table 4 shows some of these thermodynamic quantities as a function of θ. The table is an extension and modification of that given by Pitzer.

Imperfect liquids. Only argon, krypton and xenon may be regarded as perfect liquids, although methane, oxygen, nitrogen, and a few other substances show only small deviations from perfect behavior. Pitzer[31] has shown that these deviations may reasonably be ascribed to failure to satisfy the assumptions which lead to the theory of corresponding states. These we shall consider separately.

(a) **Quantum mechanical effects.** Assumption I required the translational degrees of freedom to be essentially classical, or that

$$T \gg \frac{2\pi mk}{h^2} v^{\frac{2}{3}}$$

TABLE 4

θ	π	ΔS^V	φ^l	φ^g	V^g/V^l	γ/γ_0
.555	(~.0136)					
.56	.0148	18.68	.376	126	335	.367
.57	.0176	18.20	.379	110	290	.357
.58	.0208	17.72	.382	96	250	.347
.59	.0244	17.25	.385	83	215	.336
.60	.0284	16.82	.387	72.4	187	.326
.62	.0379	15.95	.392	55.6	142	.306
.64	.0496	15.18	.398	43.8	110	.287
.66	.0638	14.42	.404	34.0	84	.267
.68	.0807	13.73	.410	37.5	67	.248
.70	.1062	13.11	.417	22.1	53	.229
.75	.1657	(11.4)	.437	13.6	31	.184
.80	.2563	(9.95)	.461	8.8	19	.140
.85	.3781	(8.4)	490	5.9	12	.098
.90	.5374	(6.55)	.531	3.9	7.3	.059
.95	.7416	(4.6)	.596	2.5	4.2	.026
1.00	1.000	0.0	1.000	1.000	1.0	.000

We may therefore, use as a measure of quantum deviations, the parameter $M^{\frac{1}{2}} T_c^{\frac{1}{2}} V_c^{\frac{1}{3}}$. Table 5 (taken from Pitzer[31]) lists this quantity for a number of substances.

TABLE 5

Substance	$M^{\frac{1}{2}} T_c^{\frac{1}{2}} V_c^{\frac{1}{3}}$	Substance	$M^{\frac{1}{2}} T_c^{\frac{1}{2}} V_c^{\frac{1}{3}}$
Helium	17.6	Oxygen	295
Hydrogen	32.6	Argon	328
Neon	104	Ethane	491
Methane	256	Krypton	600
Nitrogen	266	Mercury	2000

The quantum effects are obviously so large for helium and hydrogen that we can immediately exclude them from consideration. By comparison with a Debye solid, Pitzer concludes that quantum deviations result in larger values for the entropy and heat content than those for perfect liquids. Consequently the heat capacity of the liquid and the entropy of vaporization are smaller than the corresponding quantities for perfect liquids. Similarly, quantum mechanical effects produce a larger liquid volume and hence too small a coefficient of thermal expansion. The deviations of neon from perfect behavior at the triple point (C_p 1.8 cal/deg too low; ΔS^V 0.7 e. u. too low, V 3% too large) may be ascribed to this cause. For all other substances but H_2 He, and Ne, quantum mechanical deviations are almost negligible.

(b) **Restriction of rotation.** With all but monatomic molecules, one may expect to find a considerable restriction of rotation as compared with the gas phase. This may arise in two ways, either from steric hindrance due to the non spherical shape of the molecules or from the orienting effect of interacting dipoles. Pitzer concluded from rough theoretical considerations that restriction of rotation leads to a decrease in liquid entropy, yielding a corresponding increase in the entropy of vaporization. O_2, N_2, HCl, HI, HBr, CS_2, CO, Cl_2, and Br_2 fit a theoretical curve for two degrees of restricted rotation fairly well, and PH_3, H_2S, C_2H_6, C_2H_4 and neopentane fit the curve for three degrees of restricted rotation satisfactorily.

(c) **Changes in intramolecular vibrations.** In deriving the theory of corresponding states, we assumed that the intramolecular vibrations were unaffected by the presence of adjacent molecules. While intermolecular forces have little effect on the principal valence bond vibrations, they may seriously change the torsional motion around bonds and the bending of long chains. Pitzer concludes that, on the whole, the frequencies should be lowered in the liquid, a situation which leads to a higher liquid entropy and a higher heat content, together with corresponding higher heat capacity and a smaller entropy of vaporization. Since the contribution of vibrational degrees of freedom to the partition function (and hence the thermodynamic functions) is small except for low frequencies, this effect will be distinctly secondary to that of restricted rotation except for molecules with very low vibration frequencies. In this latter group are molecules which have degrees of freedom corresponding to hindered rotation around single bonds (as in chain hydrocarbons, etc.). These substances do show marked deviations in the directions indicated. A striking contrast was found between normal pentane and neopentane (tetramethyl methane).

Table 6 summarizes the direction of deviations from perfect behavior arising from these three considerations.

Of these functions, $\frac{V^l}{V_c}$ (φ^l), $\frac{p}{P_c}$ (π), ΔS^V, and $-\Delta C_p$ are uniquely determined by T/T_c (θ) for perfect liquids. Hence, plotting φ^l, π, ΔS^V and $-\Delta C_p$ as functions of θ should be illuminating.

We have seen that the entropy of vaporization of a perfect liquid may be expressed in terms of the ratio of the molal volumes of the liquid and

TABLE 6

	F^l	H^l	S^l	V^l	p	C_p^l	$\Delta S^V = S^g - S^l$	$-\Delta C_p = C_p^l - C_p^g$
Quantum Deviations	+	+	+	+	+	−	−	−
Restricted Rotation		−	−			+	+	+
Vibration ν decreased[34]		+	+			+	−	+

its saturated vapor. If the free volume of a liquid V^f is defined in terms of the entropy of vaporization ΔS^V such that $\Delta S^V = R\ln(V^g/V^f)$ (Equation 28) we see that the theory of corresponding states requires that the free volume, of a liquid be proportional to its molal volume, $V^f \sim V^l$. This would not necessarily be true for polyatomic molecules, and it is conceivable that if the intermolecular molecular forces are not radial but center in the various peripheral parts of the molecules, two liquids with molecules of very different size might have approximately equal free volumes.

This possibility was investigated by Hildebrand and Gilman[35] who compared two liquids with very different molal volumes but which are otherwise as nearly alike as possible. One such pair is Cl_2 and CCl_4, another is C_2H_6, ethane and C_6H_{14}, 2,3 dimethyl butane (di-isopropyl); the results are shown in Table 7.

TABLE 7. Entropy of vaporization

Reference Liquid	T	ΔS^V	ΔS^V at Same V^g	V^g/V^l	T/T_c	For
Cl_2	205	25.3	24.7	27.2	29.7	CCl_4
Cl_2	223	22.6	21.7	24.2	26.3	CCl_4
C_2H_6	148	25.8	25.5	28.3	31.8	C_6H_{14}
C_2H_6	160	23.2	22.7	25.5	28.3	C_6H_{14}

It can be seen that the entropy of vaporization of CCl_4 agrees best with that for Cl_2 when the comparison is made at equal vapor volumes; less well at equal ratios of vapor to liquid, and more poorly still at equal corresponding temperatures. The agreement with the Hildebrand rule is seen to

[34] If the contribution of intermolecular forces were to increase ν, on the average, al the signs in this row would be reversed.

[35] J. H. Hildebrand and T. S. Gilman, *J. Chem. Phys.*, **15**, 229 (1947).

be even better with the pair C_2H_6 and C_6H_{14}. This seems to indicate that the significant separations are those between peripheral atoms or bonds and not between the geometrical centers of the molecules.

The energy of a liquid and its internal pressure. In the early part of this chapter we defined a radial distribution function $\varrho(r)$ which is a measure of the probability of finding, at a given distance r from the center of a given molecule, the center of another molecule. Hildebrand and Wood[36] have shown that if the potential between molecules is $\varepsilon(r)$ a function only of their distances apart (Assumption IIIc discussed earlier), one may evaluate the potential energy of the whole liquid as follows: The number of molecules in a spherical shell of radius r and thickness dr is, as we have seen, $\frac{1}{v}\,4\pi r^2\varrho(r)\,dr$. The number of pairs at a distance r apart in one mole of liquid is therefore $\frac{\boldsymbol{N}}{2}\,\frac{4\pi r^2}{v}\,\varrho(r)\,dr$. (Division by two corrects for counting all pairs twice.). By multiplying by $\varepsilon(r)$, assuming additivity of pair energies (see Chapter IV), we obtain for the potential energy of all such pairs, $(2\pi\boldsymbol{N}/v)\,\varepsilon(r)\,\varrho(r)r^2dr$. Integration over all values of r yields the potential energy per mole:

$$E = 2\pi\,\frac{\boldsymbol{N}^2}{V}\int\varepsilon(r)\,\varrho(r)\,r^2dr \qquad (85)$$

If we introduce the Lennard-Jones equation for the intermolecular potential (Equation 68), we obtain for E:

$$E = \frac{2\pi\boldsymbol{N}^2}{V}\left[\,j\int\frac{\varrho(r)}{r^{n-2}}\,dr - k\int\frac{\varrho(r)}{r^4}\,dr\right] \qquad (86)$$

If $\varrho(r)$ is determined experimentally from x-ray data and $\varepsilon(r)$ is known (the constants k, j, and n can be evaluated in several ways), one may calculate E, and compare it with the experimentally determined energy of vaporization ΔE^V, which should equal $-E$. Hildebrand, Wakeham and Boyd[37] used their data[38] for $\varrho(r)$ at seven different temperatures combined with the experimental data on ΔE^V to determine k, j, and n. Their potential function was found to be (ε in ergs, r in Angstroms).

$$\text{Hg:}\qquad \varepsilon(r) = \frac{54.9\cdot 10^{-10}}{r^9} - \frac{3.52\cdot 10^{-10}}{r^6} \qquad (87)$$

---

[36] J. H. Hildebrand and S. E. Wood, *J. Chem. Phys.*, **1**, 817 (1933).
[37] J. H. Hildebrand, H. R. R Wakeham and R. N. Boyd, *J. Chem. Phys.*, **7**, 1094 (1939).
[38] R. N. Boyd and H. R. R. Wakeham, *J. Chem. Phys.* **7** 959 (1939).,

Fig. 7 shows the function $\varepsilon(r)\,\varrho(r)\,r^2$ for mercury[39] split into its component attractive and repulsive terms, $-\mathrm{k}\,\varrho(r)/r^4$ and $\mathrm{j}\,\varrho(r)/r^7$. We see how similar in form the two terms and their difference are, and how small is the contribution to the energy of vaporization of all molecules beyond the first shell.

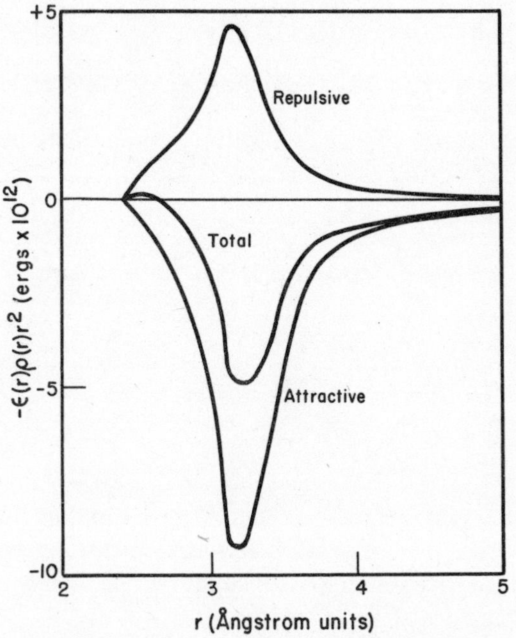

Fig. 7 Contribution of atoms at various distances to the potential energy of liquid mercury.

Recently, Jura[40] has calculated the potential functions of neon, argon, and krypton from data on the energy of sublimation of the solid and the second virial coefficient of the gas:

$$\text{Ne:}\quad \varepsilon(r) = \frac{2.12 \cdot 10^{-10}}{r^8} - \frac{0.243 \cdot 10^{-10}}{r^6} \tag{88}$$

$$\text{A:}\quad \varepsilon(r) = \frac{194.0 \cdot 10^{-10}}{r^{10}} - \frac{1.31 \cdot 10^{-10}}{r^6} \tag{89}$$

$$\text{Kr:}\quad \varepsilon(r) = \frac{14.100 \cdot 10^{-10}}{r^{13}} - \frac{1.77 \cdot 10^{-10}}{r^6} \tag{90}$$

---

[39] Fig. 7 was actually calculated by combining Equation 3 with the Debye and Menke[6] distribution function (Fig. 1). More recently a new set of data on the structure of liquid mercury has been obtained by J. A. Campbell and J. H. Hildebrand, *J. Chem. Phys.*, **11**, 330 (1943); they intended to recalculate the potential function, but the pressure of the war made it impossible, and it has not yet been done.

[40] G. Jura, *private communication*.

By combining Equation 89 with the distribution function for liquid argon, Jura[40] has calculated E for argon. Table 8 compares this value and those of Hildebrand, Wakeham and Boyd for mercury with the experimental ones for ΔE^V.

TABLE 8. Potential Energy of Liquid Elements (kcal.)

	t (°C)	—E (calc.)	ΔE^V (obs.)
A	—186	1.40	1.38
Hg	— 35	14.24	14.21
	30	13.85	14.00
	125	13.77	13.68
	250	13.16	13.28

If $\varrho(r)$ did not vary with temperature, we would have:

$$E = -\frac{a}{V} \tag{91}$$

where a is the constant of the van der Waals equation or something very similar. Were this so, the temperature variation of the energy of vaporization ΔE^V, which is essentially equal to —E, would depend only upon the coefficient of thermal expansion α.

Measurement of the function $(\partial E/\partial V)_T$ throws considerable light upon this problem. Pure thermodynamics yields the equation:

$$P = -\left(\frac{\partial A}{\partial V}\right)_T = -\left(\frac{\partial E}{\partial V}\right)_T + T\left(\frac{\partial S}{\partial V}\right)_T \tag{92}$$

Since $(\partial S/\partial V)_T = (\partial P/\partial T)_V$, we may transform Equation 92 into what has been called the "thermodynamic equation of state":

$$\left(\frac{\partial E}{\partial V}\right)_T = T\left(\frac{\partial P}{\partial T}\right)_V - P \tag{93}$$

For normal liquids below their boiling points, P is entirely negligible in comparison with $T(\partial P/\partial T)_V$, which is 2000—8000 atmospheres, so we may set $(\partial E/\partial V)_T$ equal to $T(\partial P/\partial T)_V$. Determination of the increase in pressure with temperature at constant volume is not difficult, or it may be calculated from the coefficient of thermal expansion α and the compressibility β (cf. Equation 36). Because of the unsatisfactory nature of most compressibility data which we have noted earlier, direct determination of $(\partial P/\partial T)_V$ is preferable.

Hildebrand, together with Westwater, Frantz and Carter[41,42,43], has measured $(\partial P/\partial T)_V$ for a number of liquids and has shown that over a limited range of temperatures:

$$\left(\frac{\partial E}{\partial V}\right)_T \simeq T\left(\frac{\partial P}{\partial T}\right)_V = \frac{a}{V^2} \tag{94}$$

The agreement is not perfect however since the "constant" a is not quite identical with that calculated from the energy of vaporization by using Equation 91. For a more general relation between E/V and $(\partial E/\partial V)_T$, we take advantage of the fact that over a small range of volumes we may always represent them in the functional forms.[44]

$$E = -\frac{a}{V^n} \tag{95}$$

$$\left(\frac{\partial E}{\partial V}\right)_T = \left(\frac{\partial E}{\partial V}\right)_T = \frac{na}{V^{n+1}} = -n\frac{E}{V} = n\frac{\Delta E^V}{V} \tag{96}$$

Thus the ratio of $\Delta E^V/V$ and $(\partial E/\partial V)_T$ is a measure of the exponent n. For a van der Waals liquid $n = 1$, and Equations 95 and 96 reduce to Equations 91 and 94. Although the van der Waals equation is certainly a poor approximation for liquids, the work of Hildebrand and coworkers cited above shows that n is, in fact, not far from unity. Table 9 shows the relevant data.

Table 9

Liquid	$V^2(\partial E/\partial V)_T$ Kcal · liters	$V\Delta E^V$ Kcal · liters	n
n-Heptane	13.14	12.01	1.09
Silicon tetrabromide	12.90	12.40	1.04
Stannic chloride	10.95	10.55	1.04
Titanium tetrachloride	10.15	9.98	1.02
Silicon tetrachloride	8.23	7.56	1.09
Carbon tetrachloride	7.56	7.04	1.07
Benzene	7.07	6.70	1.05
Ethyl ether	6.58	6.49	1.01
Chloroform	5.76	5.67	1.02
Acetone	4.33	4.86	0.89
Carbon disulfide	3.27	3.67	0.89
Methanol	1.16	3.46	0.34
Mercury	0.69	2.11	0.33

[41] W. Westwater, H. W. Frantz and J. H. Hildebrand, *Phys. Rev.*, **31**, 135 (1928).
[42] J. H. Hildebrand, *Phys. Rev.*, **34**, 649, 984 (1929).
[43] J. H. Hildebrand and J. M. Carter, *J. Am. Chem. Soc.*, **54**, 3592 (1932).
[44] Cf. H. S. Frank, *J. Chem. Phys.*, **13**, p 495 (1945).

It might be expected that in a polar liquid, like methyl alcohol, the orientations would greatly alter the normal form of the probability function $\varrho(r)$, and that it would be strongly affected by changes in volume and temperature. Furthermore a liquid which is not greatly expanded over its close-packed structure, such as mercury is at room temperature, is in a region where repulsive forces play an important role in balancing the attractive forces, as we have seen in Fig. 7.

If we differentiate Equation 86 with respect to V, we obtain:

$$\left(\frac{\partial E}{\partial V}\right)_T = -\frac{2\pi N^2}{V^2}\left[j\int\frac{\varrho(r)dr}{r^{n-2}} - k\int\frac{\varrho(r)dr}{r^4}\right]$$

$$+\frac{2\pi N^2}{V}\left[j\int\left(\frac{\partial\varrho(r)}{\partial V}\right)_T\frac{dr}{r^{n-2}} - k\int\left(\frac{\partial\varrho(r)}{\partial V}\right)_T\frac{dr}{r^4}\right] \tag{97}$$

Hildebrand[42] suggested a provisional expression for the right hand side of Equation 97.

$$\left(\frac{\partial E}{\partial V}\right)_T = -\frac{a}{V^2} + \frac{c}{V^{10}} = T\left(\frac{\partial P}{\partial T}\right)_V - P \tag{98}$$

Internal Pressure	Attractive Pressure	Repulsive Pressure	Thermal Pressure	External Pressure

Frank and Foo-Song Lei[45] have obtained somewhat better agreement by altering the values of the exponents. The terms may be given the labels long customary for such "equations of state". The geometrical form of this type of equation is shown in Fig. 8; the corresponding curve for E is shown in the lower plot.

Many nonpolar organic liquids are sufficiently expanded at ordinary temperatures to have the repulsive term of small influence and obey Equations 91 and 94. Mercury, however, is on the steep lefthand descending portion hence the disagreement in Table 9. Fig. 9 shows the actual data calculated from measurements by Bridgman[46] and by Hildebrand and Carter[43]. The hyperbolic curves are for the a/V^2 relationship, followed at sufficiently large

[45] H. S. Frank and Foo-Song Lei, *Phys. Rev.*, **42**, 893 (1932).
[46] P. W. Bridgman, *Proc. Am. Acad. Arts. Sci.*, **47**, 345 (1911).

volumes. Only in this region, of course, is $n = 1$, and $\Delta E^V/V$ equal to $(\partial E/\partial V)_T$. Both these quantities have been called[47] the "internal pressure", but where they are markedly different, they may be distinguished by calling $\Delta E^V/V$ the cohesive energy density, reserving[48] the name "internal pressure"

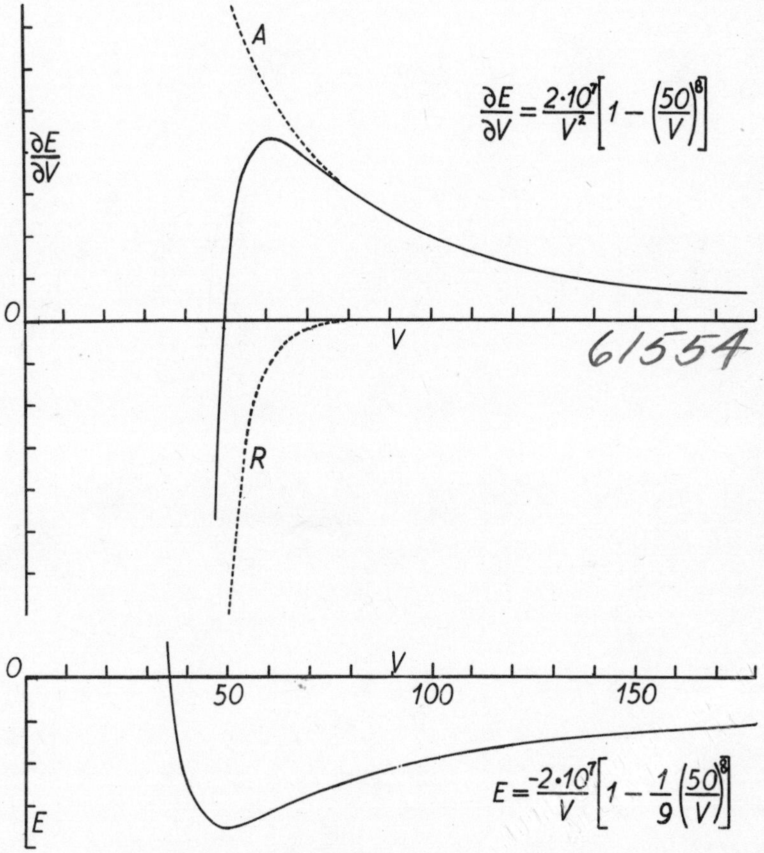

Fig. 8. Variation of internal pressure and potential energy with volume.

for $(\partial E/\partial V)_T$ or the virtually equivalent quantity $T(\partial P/\partial T)_V$. The relation between $\Delta E^V/V$ and $T(\partial P/\partial T)_V$ has been discussed recently by Parshad[49] and Scott[50].

---

[47] Cf. the review by W. C. Mc C. Lewis, *Trans. Faraday Soc.*, **7**, 94 (1911).
[48] Cf. A. Dupré, *Ann. chim. et phys.*, **[4] 2**, 201 (1864),
[49] R. Parshad, *J. Chem. Phys.*, **15**, 761 (1947).
[50] R. L. Scott, *J. Chem. Phys.*, **16**, 256 (1948).

The change of the energy of vaporization ΔE^V with temperature has recently been studied by Benson[51]. Using a smoothed potential model like that discussed earlier in this chapter, he concludes that:

$$E = -\frac{k}{V^2} \tag{99}$$

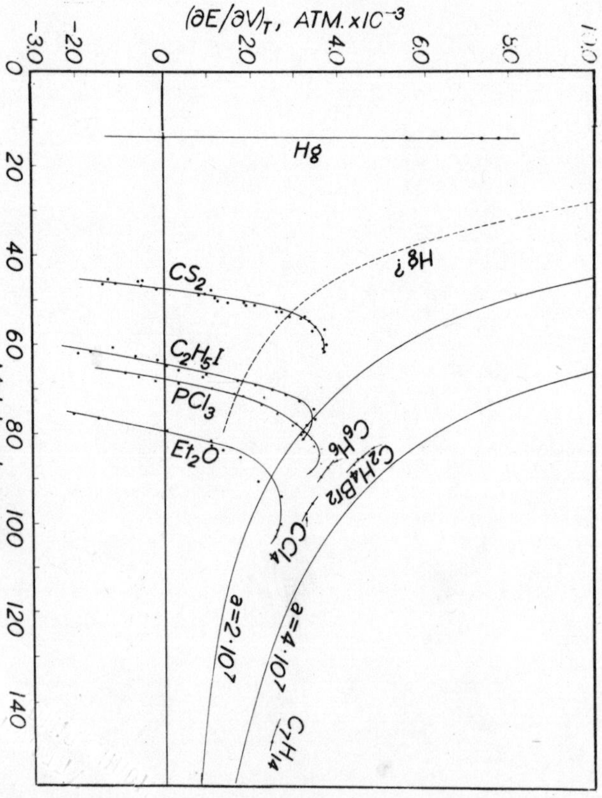

Fig. 9. Relation between internal pressure and molal volume for various liquids.

where k is a constant dependent upon the nature of the particular liquid. Except near the critical temperature the energy of the gas is negligible and ΔE^V should be proportional to $1/V^2$. Since the model corresponds to a uniform expansion of the liquid such that the distribution function $\varrho(r)$ remains unchanged except for a change in the scale, an assumption not in accord with the evidence (cf. Fig. 3), it is not surprising that the agreement with

[51] S. W. Benson, *J. Chem. Phys.*, **15**, 367 (1947).

experiment is only fair. Benson found better agreement by substitution of 5/3 for the exponent 2 in Equation 99. An examination of the data on perfect liquids and aliphatic hydrocarbons[52] indicates that in the normal liquid range the exponent is about 1.5, leading to the equation:

$$\frac{dE}{dV} = \frac{k}{V^{2.5}} \tag{100}$$

Equation 100 expresses the change in E as the volume and temperature are increased in such a way that the liquid is always in equilibrium with its saturated vapor; it is not necessarily in conflict with Equation 94 for the change of E with volume in the entirely different *isothermal* process. We shall return to this problem in Chapter XXIII.

We have seen that for substances whose molecules are spherically symmetrical, we can use the radial distribution function $\varrho(r)$ and a simple potential function $\varepsilon(r)$ to calculate the total potential energy of the liquid. For imperfect liquids the intermolecular potential ε may be a function of orientation and may even involve changes in internal degrees of freedom. In such a case, we must replace the radial distribution function $\varrho(r)$ by a general distribution function $F_2(1,2)$ where (1,2) represents all the coordinates necessary to specify the orientation of a molecule (2) with respect to molecule (1). Expressing ε in terms of the same coordinates:

$$E = \frac{N^2}{2V}\int \varepsilon(1,2)\,F_2(1,2)\,d(1,2) \tag{101}$$

While the energy can be expressed as an integral over all pairs, the free energy and the entropy involve more complex functions, as we shall see.

An equation of state for liquids. The thermodynamic behavior of a substance is completely determined if we have, in addition to its specific heat, an equation of state relating the pressure P, the volume V and the temperature T. We have seen the general development of a reduced equation of state for perfect liquids, but it was not obtained in explicit form. For spherical molecules, Mayer[53] has shown that P, V, and T may be related to

[52] R. L. Scott, unpublished work.

[53] J. E. Mayer, quoted by J. G. Kirkwood, *Am. Scientist,* **30**, 191 (1942).

the distribution function $\varrho(r)$ and the potential function $\varepsilon(r)$ by the equation:

$$P\mathrm{V} = RT - 2\pi \frac{N^2}{\mathrm{V}} \int \frac{d\varepsilon(r)}{dr} \varrho(r)\, r^3\, dr \tag{102}$$

The free energy F may be obtained by integrating the function $\mathrm{V}dP$, but to carry out such a procedure requires a knowledge of $\varrho(r)$ at all values of V between the liquid and the ideal gas. Such a detailed specification of $\varrho(r)$ is very difficult experimentally and virtually impossible theoretically. Fortunately an alternative approach is available, as we shall see in the following section.

The modern theory of molecular distribution functions. A more general treatment of the liquid state than those based upon the artificial models discussed earlier is afforded by the use of molecular distribution functions and most of the more recent theoretical work has been along these lines. Since much of this research is still in progress, any detailed discussion is likely to become obsolete rapidly. It suffices here to trace a little of the underlying background.

We have seen that while the energy of a liquid at given conditions of temperature and pressure may be expressed as the integral (over all pairs) of the potential function and the radial distribution function $\varrho(r)$ for the given state, an analogous expression for the free energy (and hence the entropy) involves a knowledge of $\varrho(r)$ for all intermediate states between the liquid and the infinitely dilute gas. The recent work of Kirkwood[54], Mayer[55], and Born[56] and their coworkers has offered an alternative formulation in terms of higher order distribution functions. Instead of requiring knowledge of the pair distribution function $\varrho(r)$ or more generally $F_2(1,2)$ (cf. Equation 101) for all states, this involves a probability function for three molecules occupying three fixed sites and similar functions for four, five, six, etc. but for the *one* state only. If by the symbol $\{n\}$ we mean[57] all coordinates (internal and external) necessary to describe the positions and internal configurations of n molecules in a system, we may then define a distribution

[54] J. G. Kirkwood, *J. Chem. Phys.*, **3**, 300 (1935), **7**, 908, 919 (1939); J. G. Kirkwood and E. Monroe Boggs, *J. Chem. Phys.*, **8**, 845 (1940); **10**, 307, 394 (1942); J. G. Kirkwood, *Am. Scientist*, **30**, 191 (1942).

[55] J.E.Mayer and coworkers, (P.G.Ackermann, S.F.Harrison, S.F.Streeter, and E.W.Montroll), *J. Chem. Phys.*, **5**, 67, 74 (1937); **6**, 87, 101 (1938); **7**, 1025 (1939); **9**, 2 (1941); **10**, 629 (1942); **15**, 187 (1947).

[56] M. Born and H. S. Green, *Proc. Roy. Soc.*, **A 188**, 10 (1946); **A 189**, 103; **A 190**, 455; **A 191**, 168 (1947).

[57] The symbolism in this section is essentially Mayer's[55], but may be transformed into the analogous forms used by other workers.

function $F_n\{n\}$ such that

$$\frac{1}{V^n} F_n\{n\}\, d\{n\}$$

is the probability that n specified molecules have the coordinates $\{n\}$ within the infinitesimal range $d\{n\}$, where V is the total volume of the system.

The functions are so normalized that when integrated over the complete range of all the coordinates, the probability is unity:

$$\lim_{V \to \infty} \frac{1}{V} \int \cdots \int F_n\{n\}\, d\{n\} = 1 \tag{103}$$

For fluid systems, there is no long range order or structure, so that a single molecule is as likely to be found in one place as in another, so that F_1 depends only upon the internal coordinates. In order to satisfy Equation 61, the integral of F_1 over all the internal coordinates must be unity:

$$\int F_1(j)\, d(j)_{\text{internal}} = 1 \tag{104}$$

If there are no internal coordinates, or rather if the internal degrees of freedom are the same as in the perfect gas (Assumption II), Equation 79 amounts to setting $F_1 = 1$ and making the higher F's functions only of the external coordinates. In this case, we may speak of having integrated the internal coordinates out of the distribution function at zero density. Thermodynamically, this amounts to subtracting out the free energy of the internal degrees of freedom.

For molecules with spherical force fields; i. e., where the intermolecular potential ε is a function only of the intermolecular distance and not of orientation, the angular and internal coordinates factor out and F_2 may be reduced to the radial distribution function $\varrho(r)$.

Mayer[58] has shown that in terms of such a set of functions, one may obtain at least formally, the thermodynamic quantities. Denoting by F°_{int} the free energy of the internal degrees of freedom, he writes for the free energy of the liquid:

$$F = F^\circ_{int} + RT \ln z \tag{105}$$

[58] J. E. Mayer, *J. Chem. Phys.*, **15**, 187 (1947).

where

$$\frac{1}{vz} = 1 + \sum_{n \geq 1} \frac{1}{v^n \, n!} \int\!\!\int \cdots \int F_n \{n\} \cdot \prod_{j=1}^{j=n} f_{ij} \, d\{n\} \tag{106}$$

$$f_{ij} = e^{\frac{-\varepsilon_{ij}}{kT}} - 1 \tag{107}$$

Since f_{ij} becomes zero at large values of r_{ij}, the product of the f_{ij}'s is zero unless *all* of the n molecules are within interacting distance of the molecules i. We see therefore that as the system is expanded to a dilute gas, z approaches $1/v$ and $F - F°_{int}$ approaches $- RT\ln r$. As defined, z, which Mayer calls the "fugacity", is a reciprocal volume; $1/z$ bears the same relation to the free energy that the free volume v^f bears to the entropy.

An equation of this type may be called a "cell equation" since one computes the free energy by considering only the interactions of one molecule with those others which can approach it at one time.

Equations 105—107 are quite rigorous provided that:

(a) There are no internal coordinates, or they are the same as for the gas at zero density (*i. e.*, the free energy of the internal degrees of freedom for the gas at infinite dilution can be subtracted out).

(b) There is no long range order, so that $F_1 = 1$.

(c) It is legitimate to express the potential energy U of the system as a sum of pair terms ε_{ij}.

(d) ε_{ij} is proportional to inverse powers of the intermolecular distance r higher than the third.[59]

A relation must exist between the potential function ε and the functions F_n, such that:

$$F_n = f(\varepsilon, V, T) \tag{108a}$$

$$\text{or} \quad F_n = f(\varepsilon, p, T) \tag{108b}$$

$$\text{or} \quad F_n = f(\varepsilon, p, V) \tag{108c}$$

depending, of course, on the choice of independent variables. Such a relation properly developed would yield not only the thermodynamic properties of a liquid under any specified conditions of temperature, and pressure (or volume), but since the treatment is equally applicable to the gaseous state, would also completely describe the equilibrium between the liquid and its saturated vapor and all the related critical phenomena.

---

[59] This excludes all long range potentials of the coulomb type where $\varepsilon \sim r^{-1}$.

A simplification used extensively in this approach is the superposition approximation first suggested by Kirkwood. This consists essentially in replacing the higher distribution functions F_n by a product of pair functions. For example:

$$F_3(1,2,3) = \frac{F_2(1,2)\,F_2(1,3)\,F_2(2,3)}{F_1(1)\,F_1(2)\,F_1(3)} \tag{109}$$

Kirkwood[54] and Born and Green[56] have used this superposition assumption with considerable success but a clarification of the approximations involved is greatly to be desired.

CHAPTER VI

The Entropy of Athermal Mixing

We have seen in Chapter III that two or more substances can form an ideal solution only if the mixing process takes place at constant temperature and pressure without change in energy or volume. These conditions have long been known as necessary and were once regarded as sufficient to define an ideal solution. In 1933, Guggenheim[1] pointed out that solutions formed with no heat of mixing or change in volume do not necessarily have an ideal entropy of mixing. For such solutions, he proposed the name "semi-ideal". We shall apply the more meaningful term "athermal" to all solutions for which the heat of mixing is zero.

$$\Delta H^{\mathrm{M}} = 0 \tag{1}$$

$$\Delta F^{\mathrm{M}} = -T\Delta S^{\mathrm{M}} \tag{2}$$

Moreover it appears, as we shall see in Chapter VIII, that for athermal solutions, the volume change ΔV^{M} is also zero.

We see from Equation 1 that for such athermal solutions, the calculation of the entropy and free energy become equivalent. In this chapter, we shall show several general methods for calculating these functions, and try to indicate the conditions under which we may expect to find ideal solutions.

Partition function for a mixture. We shall assume throughout this chapter that the internal degrees of freedom of the molecules (rotation, vibration, etc.) are the same in the mixture and in the pure liquids as in the dilute gas. (Assumption II, Chapter V). We suspect that the following treatment could be carried through to much the same conclusions with the assumption that the internal degrees of freedom remain unchanged in the mixing process. Following Equations 4-12 of Chapter V, we may write partition functions for the mixture (m) and the pure liquids (1 and 2):

$$Q_m = (q_1)^{n_1}\ (q_2)^{n_2}\ Q_{\tau,m} \tag{3}$$

$$Q_1 = (q_1)^{n_1}\ Q_{\tau,1} \tag{4a}$$

$$Q_2 = (q_2)^{n_2}\ Q_{\tau,2} \tag{4b}$$

[1] E. A. Guggenheim, "*Modern Thermodynamics*" (Methuen, 1933), p. 103.

where q_1 and q_2 represent the functions

$$q_i = \left(\frac{2\pi m_i kT}{h^2}\right)^{3/2} q_{i,\,int} \tag{5}$$

Thus we may write the Helmholtz free energy:

$$A_m = -kT \ln Q_m = kT\{n_1 \ln q_1 + n_2 \ln q_2 + \ln Q_{\tau,m}\} \tag{6}$$

$$\text{where } Q_{\tau,m} = \frac{1}{n_1!\,n_2!} \iint e^{-U/RT} (d\tau_1)^{n_1} (d\tau_2)^{n_2} \tag{7}$$

$$\Delta A^M = A_m - A_1 - A_2 = -kT(\ln Q_{\tau,m} - \ln Q_{\tau,1} - \ln Q_{\tau,2}) \tag{8}$$

$$\Delta A^M = -kT \ln \frac{Q_{\tau,m}}{Q_{\tau,1}\,Q_{\tau,2}} \tag{9}$$

If the volume change on mixing is zero, then ΔF^M and ΔA^M are, of course identical. The problem reduces, therefore, to a calculation of the configuration integrals for the mixture and the pure liquids. This may be attempted in several ways which correspond roughly to the different models of liquids, discussed in Chapter V.

The free volume method. If we extend the smoothed potential model to mixtures, we may write an expression analogous to Equation V—19

$$Q_{\tau,m} = \frac{e^{\frac{n_1\chi_1 + n_2\chi_2}{kT}}}{n_1!\,n_2!} \int \cdots \int e^{\frac{\Delta\chi^M}{kT}} (d\tau_1)^{n_1} (d\tau_2)^{n_2} \tag{10}$$

where χ_m, the smoothed potential for the mixture, is given by

$$\chi_m = n_1\chi_1 + n_2\chi_2 + \Delta\chi^M \tag{11}$$

For athermal solutions, $\Delta\chi^M$ is obviously zero, and Equation 10 reduces to

$$Q_{\tau,m} = \frac{e^{\frac{n_1\chi_1 + n_2\chi_2}{kT}}}{n_1!\,n_2!} (n_1 v_1^f + n_2 v_2^f)^{n_1+n_2} \tag{12}$$

This step involves the assumption that the same free volume is accessible to both species, and that this is equal to the sum of the free volumes of each component.

Substituting from Equation 12 into Equation 9, one obtains[2]

$$\Delta A^{M} = -kT\ln\left[\frac{e^{\frac{n_1\chi_1+n_2\chi_2}{kT}}}{n_1!\,n_2!}\,(n_1 v_1^f + n_2 v_2^f)^{n_1+n_2}\cdot\right.$$
$$\left.\cdot\frac{n_1!}{e^{\frac{n_1\chi_1}{kT}}(n_1 v_1^f)^{n_1}}\cdot\frac{n_2!}{e^{\frac{n_2\chi_2}{kT}}(n v_2^f)^{n_2}}\right] \tag{13}$$

$$\Delta A^{M} = kT\left[n_1\ln\frac{n_1 v_1^f}{n_1 v_1^f + n_2 v_2^f} + n_2\ln\frac{n_2 v_2^f}{n_1 v_1^f + n_2 v_2^f}\right] \tag{14}$$

A less formal derivation of Equation 14 by Hildebrand[3] may be more enlightening. It may be recalled that the change in entropy in expanding a gas is a function of the change in free volume:

$$\Delta S = S_2 - S_1 = R\ln\frac{V_2^f}{V_1^f} \tag{15}$$

Reasoning by analogy, one may regard the mixing process as equivalent to the sum of two expansions, one for each component. The free volume available to component 1, for example, is initially only its own free volume $N_1 V_1^f$, but after mixing, the free volume of component 2, $N_2 V_2^f$ is also available. Hence

$$\Delta S^{M} = -R\left[N_1\ln\frac{N_1 V_1^f}{N_1 V_1^f + N_2 V_2^f} + N_2\ln\frac{N_2 V_2^f}{N_1 V_1^f + N_2 V_2^f}\right] \tag{16}$$

For an athermal solution[4], Equation 16 is exactly equivalent to Equation 14.

A similar free volume equation has been given by Frank and Evans[5].

It should be emphasized that the equations here derived may be expected to be of more general validity than those obtained for pure liquids from the free volume theory (Equations V—19 to 44). Nowhere in the foregoing derivation is it assumed that the free volumes are functions of volume alone. They can be, and doubtless are, somewhat temperature dependent. However, since we are concerned only with the isothermal entropy of mixing, such an effect need not be considered.

---

[2] Equation 12 is given in Fowler and Guggenheim, *Statistical Thermodynamics* Eqn. 815,1 p. 353, but Equation 14 is not explicitly derived.

[3] J. H. Hildebrand, *J. Chem. Phys.*, **15**, 225 (1947).

[4] For non-athermal solutions, which may be accompanied by volume changes, the free volume in solution is no longer the same as in the pure liquid. Then Equation 16 may be written as

$$\Delta S^{M} = -R\left[N_1\ln\frac{N_1 V_1^f}{N_1 \overline{V}_1^f + N_2 \overline{V}_2^f} + N_2\ln\frac{N_2 V_2^f}{N_1 \overline{V}_1^f + N_2 \overline{V}_2^f}\right] \tag{16a}$$

[5] H. S. Frank and M. W. Evans, *J. Chem. Phys.*, **13**, 507 (1945).

Differentiation of Equation 16 leads to the partial molal entropies of mixing:

$$\Delta\bar{S}_1 = \left(\frac{\partial \Delta S^M}{\partial N_1}\right) = R\left[\ln \frac{N_1 V_1^f}{N_1 V_1^f + N_2 V_2^f} + \frac{N_2 (V_2^f - V_1^f)}{N_1 V_1^f + N_2 V_2^f}\right] \quad (17a)$$

$$\Delta\bar{S}_2 = \left(\frac{\partial \Delta S^M}{\partial N_2}\right) = R\left[\ln \frac{N_2 V_2^f}{N_1 V_1^f + N_2 V_2^f} + \frac{N_1 (V_1^f - V_2^f)}{N_1 V_1^f + N_2 V_2^f}\right] \quad (17b)$$

Where the free volumes of the two components have been determined (from entropies of vaporization, for example) one may substitute the actual values in Equations 17 and compare with the experimental results. Otherwise, further assumptions about the free volume must be made.

Two limiting cases may be distinguished:

1. If we assume the free volumes to be proportional to the molar volumes, $V_1^f/V_2^f = V_1/V_2$,

$$\Delta\bar{S}_1 = -R\left[\ln \varphi_1 + \varphi_2 \left(1 - \frac{V_1}{V_2}\right)\right] \quad (18a)$$

$$\Delta\bar{S}_2 = -R\left[\ln \varphi_2 + \varphi_1 \left(1 - \frac{V_2}{V_1}\right)\right] \quad (18b)$$

where the φ's represent volume fractions.

2. If we assume the free volumes of the two components to be the same, we obtain the familiar expressions for ideal solutions:

$$\Delta\bar{S}_1 = -R \ln x_1 \quad (19a)$$

$$\Delta\bar{S}_2 = -R \ln x_2 \quad (19b)$$

where the x's are mole fractions.

Intuitively, it seems as though these two cases represent the limits of variation for athermal solutions. We shall see this fact more clearly in terms of other formulations.

The quasi-lattice method. Another formulation of the entropy of mixing may be said to depend upon the solid-like model of liquids. In this picture the molecules are regarded as occupying lattice points in a regular arrangement much like a crystal. Of course, no such regular arrangement exists in liquids and their solutions, but it is assumed that the correction for the disorder caused by thermal agitation (i. e., the "fluctuation" or "communal" entropy) is the same for the pure liquids and the solution and hence cancels out of the entropy of mixing. Under such conditions we calculate the entropy by counting the number of possible arrangements of the two kinds of molecules on the available lattice sites. The number of such distinguishable configurations is denoted as Ω, and for athermal solutions is the same as, or at least proportional to, Q_r, the configuration integral. Several simple examples of such a computation may be given.

1. Suppose there are n_1 molecules of the first component and n_2 molecules of the second, each occupying one lattice site[6]. The total number of sites is therefore $n_1 + n_2$. Suppose we wish to place the first molecule in the lattice. There are $n_1 + n_2$ sites available. Similarly there are $n_1 + n_2 - 1$ sites available for the second molecule, and so on until there is only one site available for the last. Thus, there are $(n_1 + n_2) \cdot (n_1 + n_2 - 1) \ldots 1 = (n_1 + n_2)!$ ways of arranging the molecules. Since, however, we cannot differentiate one molecule from another of the same kind, we must divide by $n_1!$ and $n_2!$ to eliminate counting indistinguishable configurations. Then

$$\Omega_m = \frac{(n_1 + n_2)!}{n_1!\, n_2!}; \quad \Omega_1 = \frac{n_1!}{n_1!}; \quad \Omega_2 = \frac{n_2!}{n_2!}. \tag{20}$$

$$\Delta S^M = k \left[\ln \Omega_m - \ln \Omega_1 - \ln \Omega_2 \right] = k \ln \frac{(n_1 + n_2)!}{n_1!\, n_2!} \tag{21}$$

Applying Stirling's approximation for factorials

$$\Delta S^M = -k \left[n_1 \ln \frac{n_1}{n_1 + n_2} + n_2 \ln \frac{n_2}{n_1 + n_2} \right] \tag{22}$$

and differentiating

$$\Delta \overline{S}_1 = -R \ln x_1 \tag{23a}$$

$$\Delta \overline{S}_2 = -R \ln x_2 \tag{23b}$$

and we have again obtained the equations for ideal solutions.

2. The next simplest case for a lattice calculation is that where molecules of one component occupy single sites, and molecules of the second component occupy two sites adjacent to one another. A first attack on this problem was made by Fowler and Rushbrooke[7]; a more general solution was obtained by Chang[8]. These equations may be written as:

$$\Delta S^M = -k \left\{ n_1 \ln \frac{n_1}{n_1 + 2n_2} + n_2 \ln \frac{2n_2}{n_1 + 2n_2} - \frac{z}{2} n_1 \ln \frac{n_1 + \frac{2(z-1)}{z} n_2}{n_1 + 2n_2} \right.$$
$$\left. - (z-1) n_2 \ln \frac{\frac{z}{z-1} n_1 + 2n_2}{n_1 + 2n_2} \right\} \tag{24}$$

$$\Delta \overline{S}_1 = -R \left[\ln \varphi_1 - \frac{z}{2} \ln \left(1 - \frac{1}{z} \varphi_2 \right) \right] \tag{25 a}$$

$$\Delta \overline{S}_2 = -R \left[\ln \varphi_2 - (z-1) \ln \left(1 + \frac{1}{z-1} \varphi_1 \right) \right] \tag{25 b}$$

---

[6] The first analysis of this kind was applied to solid solutions by O. Stern. *Ann. Physik* **[4]**, **49**, 823 (1916); **51**, 237 (1916).

[7] R. H. Fowler and G. S. Rushbrooke, *Trans. Faraday Soc.*, **33**, 1272 (1937).

[8] T. S. Chang, *Proc. Roy. Soc.*, **A169**, 512 (1939); *Proc. Camb. Phil. Soc.*, **35**, 265 (1939).

In the above formulas z, as in Chapter V, represents the coordination number of the lattice or the number of nearest neighbor sites around a given site. For liquids it may be replaced by the average number of nearest neighbors without serious error.

3. Hildebrand[9] has shown for the special case of a linear arrangement of long and short molecules that the number of arrangements is merely

$$\Omega_m = \frac{(n_1 + n_2)!}{n_1!\, n_2!} \tag{26}$$

just the same as for molecules of equal length. Equation 27 is identical with Equation 20 and leads to ideal solutions and Raoult's law.

One might expect almost linear arrangements from mixtures of paraffin hydrocarbons at temperature not far above the melting point of the longer chain. Hildebrand and Sweny[10] find in the virtually ideal behavior of the mixture *n*-hexane — *n*-hexadecane, evidence for such an arrangement. More recently, measurements by Brønsted and Koefoed[11] show a small but unmistakable negative deviation from Raoult's law for mixtures of the normal paraffins: hexane-hexadecane, heptane-hexadecane, hexane-dodecane. Since the measurements were made at only one temperature, it was impossible to evaluate the separate contributions of heat and entropy to the deviation.

4. The first attempts to obtain the entropy of mixing of single molecules with long chains occupying multiple sites were made simultaneously by Huggins[12] and by Flory[13]. Different methods have been used subsequently by Miller[14] and Guggenheim[15], which lead to essentially identical results. The formulas given below are in the more general form given by Guggenheim.

Around any molecule occupying m sites, there will be qz nearest neighbor sites. For a long chain, q, which is a kind of "surface-volume ratio", will be

$$q = \frac{m(z-2)+2}{z}$$

For the somewhat lengthy derivation, we refer the reader to the original paper. For the entropy of mixing of two kinds of molecules of length m_1 and m_2 Guggenheim finds:

$$\Delta S^M = -k\left[n_1 \ln \frac{n_1 m_1}{n_1 m_1 + n_2 m_2}\left(\frac{n_1 m_1 + n_2 m_2}{n_1 q_1 + n_2 q_2}\cdot\frac{q_1}{m_1}\right)^{\frac{1}{2}zq_1} + n_2 \ln \frac{n_2 m_2}{n_1 m_1 + n_2 m_2}\left(\frac{n_1 m_1 + n_2 m_2}{n_1 q_1 + n_2 q_2}\cdot\frac{q_2}{m_2}\right)^{\frac{1}{2}zq_2}\right] \tag{27}$$

[9] J H. Hildebrand, *J. Am. Chem. Soc.*, **59**, 794 (1937).

[10] J. H. Hildebrand and J.W. Sweny, *J. Phys. Chem.*, **43**, 109, 297 (1939).

[11] J. N. Brønsted and J. Koefoed, *Kgl. Dansk. Vid. Selsk.*, **22,** No. 17 (1946).

[12] M. L. Huggins, *J. Chem. Phys.*, **9,** 440 (1941); *Ann. N. Y. Acad. Sci.*, **43,** 1 (1942).

[13] P. J. Flory, *J. Chem. Phys.*, **9,** 660 (1941); **10,** 51 (1942).

[14] A.R. Miller, *Proc. Camb. Phil. Soc.*, **38,** 109 (1942); **39,** 154 (1943).

[15] E. A. Guggenheim, *Proc. Roy. Soc.*, **A 183,** 203 (1944).

$$\Delta \bar{S}_1 = -R\left[\ln \varphi_1 - \frac{zq_1}{2}\ln\left(1 - \frac{2}{zq_2}\frac{(m_2-m_1)}{m_2}\varphi_2\right)\right] \tag{28 a}$$

$$\Delta \bar{S}_2 = -R\left[\ln \varphi_2 - \frac{zq_2}{2}\ln\left(1 - \frac{2}{zq_2}\frac{(m_1-m_2)}{m_1}\varphi_1\right)\right] \tag{28 b}$$

For $m_1 = 1$, $m_2 = 2$, Equations 27-28 reduce to Equations 25-26 of Chang. For $z = \infty$, Equations 27 a, b, reduce to Equations 18 a, b, obtained from the free volume theory by setting $v^f \sim v$. For $z = 2$ the equations reduce to those for ideal behavior in agreement with the earlier derivation of Hildebrand (Equation 26).

We find therefore from the quasi-lattice treatment the same limiting equations as were deduced intuitively from the free volume theory.

It should be noted here that Equations 27-28 are most nearly correct for rigid rods, a situation recognized by Guggenheim in his derivation. Where the coiling of the chains is significant[16], a correction factor, sometimes serious, must be introduced. In every case, however, the correction is in the direction of lessening the deviation from Raoult's law, so that the limits still apply.

The method of excluded volume. A somewhat more general treatment than either of the foregoing is one which is formally independent of any special model (lattice, free volume, etc.). In the form presented here, it was first suggested by Huggins[17], although actually it is a special case of the general theory of multicomponent systems of McMillan and Mayer[18] which will be discussed more thoroughly in Chapter VIII.

Let us calculate the number of configurations (or a number proportional to it) by evaluating the number of ways in which we can place one solute molecule, then a second, third, etc., just as is done in a lattice calculation. The number of places available to the first molecule is proportional to the total volume of the system V. We may write this as

$$\nu_1 = V \tag{29}$$

The center of the second molecule can be located anywhere throughout the system except where its volume overlaps that of the first molecule. Hence

$$\nu_2 = V - \alpha v \tag{30}$$

where α represents the ratio of the excluded volume to the volume of one molecule. (For example, the center of a second-sphere cannot be placed closer

---

[16] This will be discussed in greater detail in Chapter XX, High Polymer Solutions.

[17] M. L. Huggins, *J. Phys. Chem.*, **52**, 248 (1948).

[18] W. G. McMillan and J. E. Mayer, *J. Chem. Phys.*, **13**, 276 (1945).

to the center of the first than a distance equal to 2r. The excluded volume is thus eight times the volume of one sphere; hence $\alpha = 8$). For the third molecule, the volume excluded by the first two molecules will be $2\alpha v$, unless these two are close enough that their regions of excluded volume overlap, in which case, we have measured the same volume twice. A term $\beta \frac{v^2}{V}$ corrects for this possibility, and we obtain for ν_3:

$$\nu_3 = V - 2\alpha v + \beta \frac{v^2}{V} \tag{31}$$

For the $(n+1)^{th}$ solute molecule

$$\nu_{n+1} = V(1 - n\alpha \frac{v}{V} + \frac{n(n-1)}{2!}\beta\left(\frac{v}{V}\right)^2 - \frac{n(n-1)(n-2)}{3!}\gamma\left(\frac{v}{V}\right)^3 + \dots \tag{32}$$

After all the solute molecules are located the remaining space is filled with solvent. The number of ways in which this can be done is independent of the "shape of the container", i. e., the arrangement of solute molecules, and is simply $n_1!$. We may write for Ω_m

$$\Omega_m = \frac{\left(\prod_{n=1}^{n=n_2} \nu_n\right) \cdot n_1!}{n_1!\, n_2!} \tag{33}$$

Substituting in the equation for the entropy

$$S = k \ln \Omega \tag{34}$$

and differentiating with respect to N_1, we obtain for the partial molal entropy of the solvent

$$\Delta\overline{S}_1 = \frac{R}{m}\left\{\varphi_2 + \frac{\alpha}{2}\varphi_2^2 + \frac{(\alpha^2 - \beta)}{3}\varphi_2^3 + \frac{(2\alpha^3 - 3\alpha\beta + \gamma)}{8}\varphi_2^4 + \dots\right\} \tag{35}$$

where m as before is the ratio v_2/v_1 or V_2/V_1.

Where the solute molecules are much larger than the solvent molecules in every dimension[19], the constants $\alpha, \beta, \gamma \dots$ are determined by the geometry of the solute molecules only.

---

[19] For example, in the case of a long rod, not only must the length be many times the length of a solvent molecule, but the diameter of the rod must be much greater than any diameter of the solvent molecule.

For large spherical molecules, α, β, and γ have been calculated[17, 20, 21]

$$\alpha = 8, \qquad \beta = 34, \qquad \gamma = 835$$

$$\Delta \bar{S}_1 = R\left\{\frac{\varphi_2}{m} + \frac{4\varphi_2^2}{m} + \frac{10\varphi_2^3}{m} + \frac{18.36\varphi_2^4}{m} + \ldots.\right\} \quad m \gg 1 \tag{36}$$

For comparison, we may expand the equation for an ideal solution,

$$\Delta \bar{S}_1^i = R\left\{\frac{\varphi_2}{m} + \frac{\varphi_2^2}{m}\left(1 - \frac{1}{2m}\right) + \frac{\varphi_2^3}{m}\left(1 - \frac{1}{m} + \frac{1}{3m^2}\right) + \ldots\right\} \tag{37}$$

For $m \gg 1$, a necessary condition for Equation 36, Equation 37 reduces to

$$\Delta \bar{S}_1^i = R\left\{\frac{\varphi_2}{m} + \frac{\varphi_2^2}{m} + \frac{\varphi_2^3}{m} + \frac{\varphi_2^4}{m} + \ldots..\right\} \quad m \gg 1 \tag{37a}$$

We see that the square and higher terms have different coefficients in Equations 36 and 37, but are of the same small order of magnitude. However for cylindrical rods of length l much greater than diameter d, in an effectively continuous solvent, Zimm[20] and Huggins[17] find

$$\text{Rods } l_2 \gg d_2, \; d_2 \gg d_1 \qquad \alpha = \frac{2l}{d} \tag{38}$$

Where the solute is not large compared with the solvent (with respect to one or more dimensions), the size and shape of the solvent must be considered. To explain this, let us return to the argument at the beginning of this section. We have just placed the first molecule in position. We may place the second molecule anywhere as long as it does not overlap the first. However, all such positions are not equally probable. Placing the second touching the first is more satisfactory than leaving a sizeable gap too small to be filled by a solvent molecule. Solution of this problem requires a knowledge of distribution functions in solution and we defer further consideration to Chapter VIII.

We may, however, consider the limiting case of a lattice. In this case, α, β, and γ may be re-defined in terms of excluded arrangements on the lattice. A simple calculation for rods occupying a linear chain in a lattice, (solvent molecules occupying one lattice site apiece), yields an α-value in agreement with that derived from Equation 28a.

---

[20] B. H. Zimm, *J. Chem. Phys.*, **14**, 164 (1946).

[21] Since for large spheres, the nature of the solvent becomes irrelevant, the problem is equivalent (see Chap. VIII) to the calculation of the imperfect gas virial coefficients for nonattracting rigid spheres. The first three of these were calculated by Happel, Jäger, van der Waals jr., and Boltzmann. See Happel, *Ann. der Physik.*, **21**, 342 (1906).

$$\text{Rods} \quad \alpha = m - \frac{2(m-1)^2}{mz} \tag{39}$$

If one expands Equation 18a in a volume fraction series, one obtains:

$$\Delta \bar{S}_1 = R\left[\frac{\varphi_2}{m} + \frac{1}{2}\varphi_2^2 + \frac{1}{3}\varphi_2^3 + \frac{1}{4}\varphi_2^4 + \ldots\right] \tag{40}$$

corresponding to values $\alpha = m$; $\beta = m(m-1)$; $\gamma = m(m-1)(m-2)$, etc.

Recalling that the expansion of the ideal entropy $R \ln x_1$ may be written

$$\Delta \bar{S}_1 = R\left[x_2 + \frac{1}{2}x_2^2 + \frac{1}{3}x_2^3 + \frac{1}{4}x_2^4 + \ldots\right] \tag{41}$$

we see that, except for the first term, which must follow the van't Hoff Law, Equation 40 is identical with Equation 41 if we substitute the mole fraction for the volume fraction. We may interpret this physically as meaning that the entropy in such a case (excepting the first term) is the same as that which would be found if the solute were split up into independent units of the same size as the solvent. Equation 40 will be approached most closely by those molecules whose various parts or segments are most nearly independent of each other, i. e, long chain polymers. We have seen that for the physically impossible coordination number $z = \infty$, long chains would indeed[22] obey Equation 40.

Values of α less than unity for athermal solution are obviously absurd since they correspond to an excluded volume less than the actual volume of one molecule. One is led to the suspicion that values of α greater than m do not occur. These represent essentially[23] the same limits as previously obtained from other treatments.

Recently Wood[24] has discussed qualitatively the contributions of different effects to the entropy of mixing. He separates the excess entropy of mixing (that is, the excess over the ideal or Raoult's law entropy) into three terms due to (1) differences in the molal volumes of the two substances, (2) lack of randomness in the spatial distribution of the molecules and (3) lack f randomness in the orientational distribution of the molecules. The first effect is essentially that which we have discussed extensively in the preceding pages. The second, the lack of randomness in the positions

---

[22] We may invent a fictitious molecule which would obey Equation 40 or its equivalent Equation 18a: A molecule composed of units or segments of the size of solvent molecules and *not* nearest neighbors but joined by long tenuous threads. For such molecules, the free volume of each segment is the same as that of a solvent, and hence $V_2^f/V_1^f = V_2/V_1 = m$.

[23] To be exact, the lower limit which gives Equation 37 is $\alpha = \frac{2m-1}{m}$, which is the value obtained for rods in a linear array $(z = 2)$.

[24] S. E. Wood, *J. Chem. Phys.*, **15**, 358 (1947).

of the centers of molecules, depends upon the energy of mixing, and results in negative deviations, always small, from the ideal entropy. For athermal solutions it is zero, and does not concern us here; we shall discuss it further in Chapter VIII. The third effect, the lack of randomness in the orientation of molecules in solution, is by far the most difficult to assess, and to it Wood devotes most of his attention. The partial molal excess entropy of the solute at infinite dilution may be regarded as the sum of two terms; (1) a lack of randomness in the orientational distribution of the pure solute which becomes complete at infinite dilution, and (2) the perturbation in the orientational distribution of the solvent caused by the introduction of one solute molecule. It is clear that these effects depend strongly upon the individual characteristics of the solute and solvent molecules; Wood has shown that the behavior of the solutions is consistent with the properties of the pure components.

Recapitulation. In the foregoing pages we have seen that different mathematical formulations of the entropy of mixing of athermal solutions lead to essentially similar conclusions, that the entropy of athermal mixing lies between two limiting values, one being the ideal solution which obeys Raoult's law over all ranges of concentration (Equations 19 a, b) and a higher maximum value (Equations 18 a, b).

$$-(n_1 \ln x_1 + n_2 \ln x_2) \leqq \frac{\Delta S^M}{R} \leqq -(n_1 \ln \varphi_1 + n_2 \ln \varphi_2) \tag{42}$$

$$-\ln x_1 \leqq \frac{\Delta S_1}{R} \leqq -\left(\ln \varphi_1 + \left(1 - \frac{1}{m}\right) \varphi_2\right) \tag{43}$$

These limits may be expressed in terms of activities or activity coefficients for athermal solutions:

$$x_1 \geqq a_1 \geqq \varphi_1 \, e^{\left(1 - \frac{1}{m}\right) \varphi_2} \tag{44}$$

$$1 \geqq \gamma_1 \geqq \left\{1 - \left(1 - \frac{1}{m}\right) \varphi_2\right\} e^{\left(1 - \frac{1}{m}\right) \varphi_2} \tag{45}$$

We see from these equations that deviations from Raoult's law due to the size and shape of the molecules are always negative.

Let us now consider the magnitude of these deviations for solute molecules twice the size of solvent molecules. Table 1 shows the values of the activity coefficients γ_1 and γ_2 calculated from Equations 18 a, b and Equations 25 a, b, for $z = 12$, the largest value of z with physical meaning (close-packed spheres).

TABLE 1. Deviations from Raoult's law with double molecules.

x_1	γ_1		γ_2	
	Eqn. 18a	Eqn. 25a z = 12	Eqn. 18b	Eqn. 25b z = 12
1.0	1.000	1.000	0.736	0.768
0.9	0.995	0.996	0.803	0.824
0.8	0.984	0.986	0.855	0.871
0.7	0.969	0.973	0.895	0.908
0.6	0.951	0.957	0.932	0.938
0.5	0.930	0.940	0.955	0.962
0.4	0.909	0.920	0.974	0.975
0.3	0.887	0.901	0.985	0.986
0.2	0.966	0.881	0.994	0.995
0.1	0.845	0.862	0.998	0.998
0.0	0.824	0.843	1.000	1.000

Fig. 1. shows the activities of the components of a binary athermal solution according to Equations 18ab when $V_2 = 2\,V_1$ and when $V_2 = 5\,V_1$.

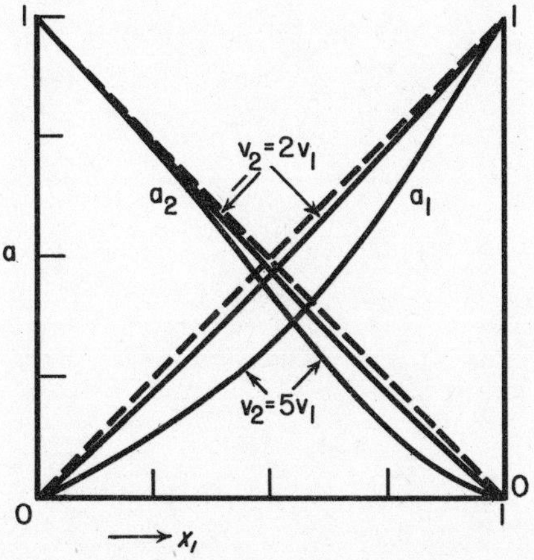

Fig. 1 Effect of disparity in molal volumes according to Equation 18 when (1) $v_2 = 2v_1$ and (2) $v_2 = 5v_1$.

As we can see, the maximum deviation for a molecular volume ratio of two is not large. Most normal substances have molal volumes lying between 60 and 150 cc., so we shall not expect the molecular size effect to be significant in most mixtures. Important exceptions are high polymer solutions, where molecular volume ratios as high as 100,000 are known. Here, as would be expected, and will be discussed in detail in Chapter XX, the negative deviations from Raoult's law are enormous.

As we shall see in the next chapter, differences in intermolecular forces can cause large heats of mixing and correspondingly large deviations from ideality which usually overshadow any small entropy corrections. In view of these effects, we shall find that for substances of not too great difference in molal volume, we may, as a good approximation, regard the *entropy* of mixing as ideal (Equations 19a, b).

CHAPTER VII

Heat of Mixing

In 1906 van Laar[1a] gave a treatment of the vapor pressures of binary liquid mixtures based upon the van der Waals equation for the mixture and the pure components. The relation between the van der Waals a for the mixture and a_1 and a_2 for the pure components had been expressed by van der Waals[2] by the equation

$$a = N_1^2 a_1 + 2 N_1 N_2 a_{12} + N_2^2 a_2 \tag{1}$$

(van Laar used n_1 and n_2 for number of moles)
where a_{12} represents the interaction between the unlike molecular species. The van der Waals b was expressed by the equation:

$$b = N_1 b_1 + N_2 b_2 \tag{2}$$

The heat of mixing, according to van der Waals' theory, is, for unexpanded liquids, *i. e.*, V = b

$$\Delta H^M = N_1 \frac{a_1}{b_1} + N_2 \frac{a_2}{b_2} - \frac{a}{b} \tag{3}$$

If the interaction constant obeys the Berthelot relation[3],

$$a_{12} = \sqrt{a_1 a_2} \tag{4}$$

the above equations can be combined to yield the equation

$$\Delta H^M = \frac{N_1 N_2 b_1 b_2}{N_1 b_1 + N_2 b_2} \left(\frac{a_1^{\frac{1}{2}}}{b_1} - \frac{a_2^{\frac{1}{2}}}{b_2} \right)^2 \tag{5}$$

The heat of mixing can be zero only if $a_1^{\frac{1}{2}}/b_1 = a_2^{\frac{1}{2}}/b_2$, which will be the case, according to van Laar, if the two components have approximately equal critical pressures, since $P_c = 8a/27b^2$.

---

[1] J. J. van Laar (a) "Sechs Vorträge über das thermodynamische Potential" (Braunschweig, 1906.) (b) *Z. physik. Chem.*, **72**, 723 (1910).

[2] J. D. van der Waals, *Z. physik. Chem.*, **5**, 133 (1890).

[3] D. Berthelot, *Compt. rend.*, **126**, 1703, 1857 (1898).

The corresponding partial molal heat of mixing is

$$\Delta \overline{H}_1 = \left(\frac{\partial (\Delta H^M)}{\partial N_1}\right)_{N_2} = \frac{N_2^2 b_1 b_2^2}{(N_1 b_1 + N_2 b_2)^2}\left(\frac{a_1^{\frac{1}{2}}}{b_1} - \frac{a_2^{\frac{1}{2}}}{b_2}\right)^2 \tag{6}$$

He used an equivalent of this equation to obtain equations for the partial vapor pressures

$$RT \ln \frac{p_1}{p_1^\circ x_1} = \frac{N_2^2 b_2^2 b_1}{(N_1 b_1 + N_2 b_2)^2}\left(\frac{a_1^{\frac{1}{2}}}{b_1} - \frac{a_2^{\frac{1}{2}}}{b_2}\right)^2 \tag{7}$$

and, with subscripts interchanged, the equation for component 2.

Van Laar expressed the relations not with the above variables but in terms of $r = (b_2 - b_1)/b_1$ and $\beta = \alpha/RT = (b_2 a_1^{\frac{1}{2}} - b_1 a_2^{\frac{1}{2}})^2/RTb_1^3$, writing

$$\begin{aligned} p_1 &= p_1^\circ x_1 e^{\frac{\beta x_2^2}{(1+r x_2)^2}} \\ p_2 &= p_2^\circ x_2 e^{\frac{\beta x_1^2}{(1+r)(1+r x_2)^2}} \end{aligned} \tag{8}$$

These equations mask the physical significance that we shall be able to attach to the equations in the form 7. It was these equations that were used in Chapter III as empirical equations for applying the Gibbs-Duhem relation.

Dolezalek[4], in 1908, published a paper in which he attempted to account for nonideal solutions by assuming chemical equilibria, association and solvation, with all molecular species obeying Raoult's law. Van Laar[1b] violently attacked this hypothesis and further developed the point of view that difference in van der Waals forces suffices to explain nonideal behavior. Solvation may, of course, be described as equivalent to $a_{12} > \sqrt{a_1 a_2}$. Van Laar was unquestionably right in this controversy, but his findings made little impression, partly because he mixed good thermodynamics inextricably with the inexact van der Waals equation. The use of critical pressures as the criterion for ideal behavior puts too great a strain upon that equation. Dolezalek pointed out that critical pressures do not lead to the correct results. We may here cite Cl_2 and CCl_4, whose critical pressures are 76 and 45 atmospheres, respectively, but which give ideal solutions (cf. Chapter XIII); CS_2 and CH_3OH, 76 and 79 atmospheres, which are so unlike as to yield two liquid phases (cf. Chapter XVI). Van Laar did not recognize the role of polarity till much later. Again, he was content to give illustrations showing merely qualitative correspondence with his equations. Finally, van Laar's views would doubtless

[4] F. Dolezalek, *Z. physik. Chem.*, **64**, 727, (1908).

have won wider acceptance but for a polemic style better calculated to make enemies than friends. Reference 1b affords entertaining reading.

A paper by van Laar and Lorenz[5] in 1925 improved the equations by substituting volumes, V_1 and V_2, for the "constants" b_1 and b_2, Equation 5 thus becoming

$$\Delta H^M = \frac{N_1 N_2 V_1 V_2}{N_1 V_1 + N_2 V_2} \left(\frac{a_1^{\frac{1}{2}}}{V_1} - \frac{a_2^{\frac{1}{2}}}{V_2} \right)^2 \qquad (9)$$

or

$$\Delta H^M = \frac{x_1 x_2 V_1 V_2}{x_1 V_1 + x_2 V_2} \left(\frac{a_1^{\frac{1}{2}}}{V_1} - \frac{a_2^{\frac{1}{2}}}{V_2} \right)^2 \qquad (10)$$

This paper also deals with the question of the entropy of mixing, but attempts to allow formally for the variations in the a's and b's introduce so much algebra that a reader is likely to be completely baffled in trying to follow its physical significance.

In 1916, Hildebrand[6a] published the first of a series of papers on solubility in which he discussed the contentions of van Laar, Dolezalek, and others. He pointed out that Dolezalek had assumed association in liquids which according to all other evidence are quite normal; that no reasonable type of association could account for the formation of two liquid phases; that polarity can play a major role, and that the order of solubility of a given solute in a series of solvents is determined by relative internal pressures except for disturbances due to polarity. In 1919[6b] he gave various methods for obtaining the relative internal pressures, including the energy of vaporization per cc, $\Delta E^V/V$, which has become the quantity most generally useful for calculating deviations from ideal behavior. In 1920[6c] he noted the family of curves obtained when the solubility of iodine in several violet solutions is plotted as log x_2 vs. $1/T$, and in 1927[6d] designated such solutions as "regular" and showed that for them the relation

$$RT \ln \gamma_2 = Bx_1^2 \qquad (11)$$

where B is a constant for an isothermal solution, suffices to account for such diverse thermodynamic properties as the e. m. f. of alloy concentration cells, heats of mixing, and consolute temperatures.

---

[5] J. J. van Laar and R. Lorenz, *Z. anorg. allgem. Chem.*, **146**, 42 (1925).

[6] J. H. Hildebrand, (a) *J. Am. Chem. Soc.*, **38**, 1452 (1916).
(b) *Ibid.*, **41**, 1067 (1919).
(c) *Ibid.*, **42**, 2180 (1920); cf. also sulfur.
(d) *Proc. Nat. Acad. Sci.*, **13**, 267 (1927).
[6] (e) *J. Am. Chem. Soc.*, **51**, 66 (1929).

Heitler[7] in 1926, had derived this equation by assuming a lattice structure for the solution and examining the probability of the various arrangements of the molecular species therein. He tested the formula by showing that the isotherms for the vapor pressure of five mixtures can be calculated with fairly good agreement by getting the heat of mixing from the curve itself, although the agreement with the experimental heat of mixing was not at all good. He further applied the formula to the calculation of the liquid-liquid solubility curve, and tested it with existing data for eight systems, finding that the experimental curves are in all cases somewhat flatter.

Most of the systems cited by Heitler involve one more or less polar constituent and one involves solvation. It is important in this connection to distinguish the systems here designated as regular from those involving solvation or association, in order to gain a correct prediction of the temperature effect, and the change in volume on mixing should be taken into consideration.

In the following years, Hildebrand[6e] interpreted the behavior of regular solutions in terms of entropy as follows: "Now suppose that the component X_2 is transferred from an ideal solution to any regular solution in which it has the same mole fraction. From our picture of a regular solution as one in which orienting and chemical effects are absent, and in which the distribution and orientations are random, just as in the ideal solution, we may conclude that the probability of X_2 is the same in the two solutions and, therefore, that the difference in entropy is zero. We cannot expect this conclusion to hold unless the random distribution of the molecules persists. We may expect, further, that a small correction should be applied to take care of the change in entropy accompanying changes in volume, given by

$$\left(\frac{\partial S}{\partial V}\right)_T = \left(\frac{\partial P}{\partial T}\right)_V \tag{12}$$

or we may state our principle in the following form. A regular solution is one involving no entropy change when a small amount of one of its components is transferred to it from an ideal solution of the same composition, the total volume remaining unchanged."

It was shown that a number of solubilities can be correlated by Equation 11 and its appropriate variants. Although we now know that the volume fraction of the solvent, φ_1, is theoretically preferable to mole fraction, x_1, both are so near unity for dilute solutions of component 2, even where $v_1 \neq v_2$, as to permit B to remain substantially constant over a wide range of temperature and composition. The figures in Table 1 are illustrative.

[7] W. Heitler, *Ann. Physik.* [4], **80**, 630 (1926).

TABLE 1. Solutions of Rhombic Sulfur, S_8

	Mole per cent, S_8		$B/2.3026\,R$ cal.	
t°C.	in CCl_4	in toluene	in CCl_4	in toluene
0	0.203	0.324	529	474
25	0.500	0.734	529	479
54	1.212	1.797	528	480

In 1931, Scatchard[8] published an important paper which, in his own words, "may be regarded also as a quantitative development of the treatment of Hildebrand, although it disagrees with his ideas in some important details, or as a method of freeing the van Laar treatment from the inadequacies of the van der Waals equation". His basic assumptions[9] were: (1) The mutual energy of two molecules depends only upon the distance between them and their relative orientation, and not at all on the nature of the other molecules between or around them or on the temperature. (2) The distribution of the molecules in position and in orientation is random, *i. e.*, independent of the temperature and of the nature of the other molecules present. (3) The change of volume on mixing at constant pressure is zero.

Scatchard's first assumption is essentially that of the additivity of the energies of molecular pairs, which we have discussed in Chapters IV and V. While certainly not exactly true for dispersion forces, it has proved very successful as the basis for nearly all theories of liquids and solutions. The second assumption, that of a random distribution, is the characteristic feature of the theory of regular solutions discussed earlier in this chapter. It is, at best, only a good approximation, since it ignores the ordering effect of molecular shapes and differences in intermolecular potentials; we accept this assumption and the third (no volume change) for the remainder of this chapter, but return for a further discussion of them in Chapter VIII.

These assumptions permit writing the "cohesive energy" of a mole of liquid mixture (essentially its potential energy E, but taken with the opposite sign) as

$$-E_m = \frac{c_{11}V_1^2x_1^2 + 2c_{12}V_1V_2x_1x_2 + c_{22}V_2^2x_2^2}{V_1x_1 + V_2x_2} \tag{13}$$

[8] G. Scatchard, *Chem. Rev.*, **8**, 321 (1931).

[9] G. Scatchard, *Kemisk Maanedsblad*, (*Copenhagen*), **13**, 77 (1932); *J. Am. Chem. Soc.*, **56**, 995 (1934); *Trans. Faraday Soc.*, **33**, 160 (1937).

For the pure components $-E = c_{11} V_1$ etc., and therefore a_{11} is $-E_1/V_1$ or the "cohesive energy density"[10].

Transforming to volume fractions φ_1 and φ_2, we obtain

$$-E_m = (x_1 V_1 + x_2 V_2)(c_{11}\varphi_1^2 + 2c_{12}\varphi_1\varphi_2 + c_{22}\varphi_2^2) \tag{14}$$

From this Scatchard obtained for the energy of mixing

$$\Delta E^M = E_m - E_1 x_1 - E_2 x_2 = (x_1 V_1 + x_2 V_2)(c_{11} + c_{22} - 2c_{12})\varphi_1\varphi_2$$

$$= (x_1 V_1 + x_2 V_2) A_{12}\varphi_1\varphi_2 \tag{15}$$

where $A_{12} = (c_{11} + c_{22} - 2c_{12})$. If we further assume that $c_{12} = (c_{11}c_{22})^{\frac{1}{2}}$, Scatchard's fourth assumption, A_{12} may be written

$$A_{12} = \left(c_{11}^{\frac{1}{2}} - c_{22}^{\frac{1}{2}}\right)^2 \tag{16}$$

For liquids at ordinary temperatures, the vapor is nearly ideal, so we can identify $-E$ with ΔE^V, the energy of vaporization. In our notation, we may write Scatchard's Equation 15 as

$$\Delta E^M = (x_1 V_1 + x_2 V_2)\left[\left(\frac{\Delta E_1^V}{V_1}\right)^{\frac{1}{2}} - \left(\frac{\Delta E_2^V}{V_2}\right)^{\frac{1}{2}}\right]^2 \varphi_1\varphi_2 \tag{17}$$

This is identical with Equation 10 of van Laar and Lorenz if the van der Waals a in the latter equation is defined as $V\Delta E^V$.

This equation was derived by Hildebrand and Wood[11] in 1933 by integrating the intermolecular potentials between pairs throughout the liquid by aid of the continuous distribution function described in Chapter V. This is analogous to the summation used to connect intermolecular potential and lattice energy for crystals, where the distribution function is discontinuous.

As explained in Chapter V, a spherical shell of liquid of thickness dr and radius r would contain $(N/V)4\pi r^2 dr$ molecular centers if the molecules are spherical and r is large, but if r is small, and measured from an arbitrarily selected "central" molecule, the number of molecular centers falling within the shell is expressed by $(N/V)4\pi\varrho r^2 dr$, where ϱ is the "distribution function", expressing the fluctuations in the density of molecular centers about the central molecule. If the potential between the central molecule and each surrounding molecule is designated by ε, we have seen that the energy of a liquid may be written as

[10] In his original derivation, Scatchard used a_{11}, a_{12}, and a_{22} for the cohesive energy densities. We have used c_{11}, c_{12}, and c_{22} to avoid confusion with the van der Waals' a's in Equations 1—10.

[11] J. H. Hildebrand and S. E. Wood, *J. Chem. Phys.*, 1, 817 (1933).

$$E_1 = \frac{2\pi n_1}{v_1} \int \varepsilon_1 \varrho_1 r^2 dr = N_1 \frac{2\pi \mathbf{N}^2}{V_1} \int \varepsilon_1 \varrho_1 r^2 dr \tag{18}$$

where the distribution function ϱ represents the probability of finding the center of a molecule at a distance r from a central one.

In a solution, around a molecule of component 1, molecules of both 1 and 2 may be found, and to the probability of finding a type 1 molecule, we assign a distribution function ϱ_{11} and for type 2 molecules ϱ_{12}. Similarly, around a central molecule of 2, there will be functions ϱ_{22} and ϱ_{21}. We may therefore write for the mixture (assuming $\overline{V}_1 = V_1$, $\overline{V}_2 = V_2$, *i. e.*, no change in volume on mixing).

$$E_m = 2\pi \mathbf{N}^2 \left[\frac{N_1}{V_1} \int \varepsilon_{11} \varrho_{11} r^2 dr + \frac{N_1}{V_2} \int \varepsilon_{12} \varrho_{12} r^2 dr \right.$$

$$\left. + \frac{N_2}{V_1} \int \varepsilon_{21} \varrho_{21} r^2 dr + \frac{N_2}{V_2} \int \varepsilon_{22} \varrho_{22} r^2 dr \right] \tag{19}$$

Now as defined, these functions ϱ are necessarily concentration dependent, inasmuch as the probability of finding a molecule of 1 around a central molecule of 1 is obviously a function of the relative proportions of 1 and 2 in the solution. We may try to eliminate this by changing the normalizing factor. As defined, the limiting value for both ϱ_{11} and ϱ_{21} at large distance is merely the overall probability of finding a molecule of 1, that is the volume fraction φ_1. Similarly ϱ_{12} and ϱ_{22} approach the limit φ_2. We define new variables ϱ^*, such that their limiting values are always 1, as are the distribution functions for pure liquids

$$\varrho_{11}^* = \frac{\varrho_{11}}{\varphi_1} \quad \varrho_{12}^* = \frac{\varrho_{12}}{\varphi_2} \quad \varrho_{21}^* = \frac{\varrho_{21}}{\varphi_1} \quad \varrho_{22}^* = \frac{\varrho_{22}}{\varphi_2}$$

Furthermore as defined $\varrho_{12}^* = \varrho_{21}^*$, and of course $\varepsilon_{12} = \varepsilon_{21}$.

We may then transform Equation 19:

$$E_m = (N_1 V_1 + N_2 V_2)\, 2\pi \mathbf{N}^2 \left[\frac{\varphi_1^2}{V_1^2} \int \varepsilon_{11} \varrho_{11}^* r^2 dr \right.$$

$$\left. + \frac{2\varphi_1 \varphi_2}{V_1 V_2} \cdot \int \varepsilon_{12} \varrho_{12}^* r^2 dr + \frac{\varphi_2^2}{V_2^2} \int \varepsilon_{22} \varrho_{22}^* r^2 dr \right] \tag{20}$$

The energy of the pure components we may obtain by combining Equation 18 with a similar one for component 2 and rewriting:

$$E_1 + E_2 = 2\pi \boldsymbol{N}^2 \left[\frac{N_1}{\mathrm{V}_1}\int \varepsilon_{11}\,\varrho_{11}\,r^2\,dr + \frac{N_2}{\mathrm{V}_2}\int \varepsilon_{12}\,\varrho_{12}\,r^2\,dr\right]$$

$$= 2\pi \boldsymbol{N}^2 (N_1\,\mathrm{V}_1 + N_2\,\mathrm{V}_2)\left[\frac{\varphi_1}{\mathrm{V}^1}\int \varepsilon_{11}\,\varrho_{11}\,r^2\,dr + \frac{\varphi_2}{\mathrm{V}_2^2}\int \varepsilon_{12}\,\varrho_{12}\,r^2\,dr\right] \quad (21)$$

The energy of mixing is therefore

$$\Delta E^{\mathrm{M}} = E_m - E_1 - E_2 = 2\pi \boldsymbol{N}^2 (N_1\,\mathrm{V}_1 + N_2\,\mathrm{V}_2)\ \left[\frac{\varphi_1^2}{\mathrm{V}_1^2}\int \varepsilon_{11}\,(\varrho_{11}{}^* - \varrho_1)\,r^2\,dr\right.$$

$$+ \frac{\varphi_2^2}{\mathrm{V}_2^2}\int \varepsilon_{22}\,(\varrho_{22}{}^* - \varrho_2)\,r^2\,dr + \varphi_1\,\varphi_2\left(\frac{-1}{\mathrm{V}_1^2}\int \varepsilon_{11}\,\varrho_1\,r^2\,dr\right.$$

$$\left.\left. - \frac{1}{\mathrm{V}_2^2}\int \varepsilon_{22}\,\varrho_2\,r^2\,dr + \frac{2}{\mathrm{V}_1\,\mathrm{V}_2}\int \varepsilon_{12}\,\varrho_{12}{}^*\,r^2\,dr\right)\right] \quad (22)$$

As written, this equation is exact, save for the negligible error introduced by neglecting the small volume change. Further simplification will involve additional considerations.

For solutions of molecules of the same inherent size and the same degree of expansion, we may set $\mathrm{V}_1 = \mathrm{V}_2$ and $\varrho_1 = \varrho_2$. If the distribution of molecules throughout the solution is truly random then $\varrho_1 = \varrho_2 = \varrho_{11}{}^* = \varrho_{22}{}^* = \varrho_{12}{}^*$. As we shall see in the following chapter, this requires that the different magnitudes of the forces between like and unlike molecules has no ordering effect on their arrangement, and is never exactly true, but introduces a small and usually negligible correction.

Introducing these assumptions into Equation 22, we obtain for the energy of mixing per mole

$$\Delta \mathrm{E}^{\mathrm{M}} = \frac{2\pi \boldsymbol{N}^2}{\mathrm{V}}\,x_1\,x_2\int (2\,\varepsilon_{12} - \varepsilon_{11} - \varepsilon_{22})\,\varrho\,r^2\,dr \quad (23)$$

Rather than simplifying Equation 23 further, let us consider molecules of different size, for which the problem is more complex. Campbell and Hildebrand[12] showed that the function for liquid xenon has the same form at equal volumes despite differences in temperature and pressure, and, further, that the functions for xenon and argon can be superimposed at equal degrees of expansion by plotting against r/d_m where d_m is the distance to the first maximum. Morrell and Hildebrand[13] had previously drawn this conclusion from an artifical three dimensional model and Hildebrand[14] had approximately superimposed the curves for different metals by plotting vs. r/d_m (See Chapter V).

[12] J. A. Campbell and J. H. Hildebrand, *J. Chem. Phys.*, **11**, 334 (1943).
[13] W. E. Morrell and J. H. Hildebrand, *J. Chem. Phys.*, **4**, 3 (1936).
[14] J. H. Hildebrand, *Science,* **90**, p. 1, July 7, (1939).

We first simplify Equation 22 by setting $\varrho_{11}^* = \varrho_1$ and $\varrho_{22}^* = \varrho_2$, obtaining:

$$\Delta E^{M} = 2\pi N^2 (N_1 V_1 + N_2 V_2)\, \varphi_1 \varphi_2 \left[\frac{2}{V_1 V_2}\int \varepsilon_{12}\, \varrho_{12}^*\, r^2 dr \right.$$

$$\left. - \frac{1}{V_1^2}\int \varepsilon_{11}\, \varrho_1\, r^2 dr - \frac{1}{V_2^2}\int \varepsilon_{22}\, \varrho_2\, r^2 dr \right] \tag{24}$$

The term in brackets is essentially the $(2c_{12} - c_{11} - c_{22})$ of Scatchard or the similar term of van Laar's equation.

Now our purpose being to express the energy of mixing in terms of the properties of the pure components, we must endeavor to evaluate the integral $\int(12)$ in terms of the integrals $\int(11)$ and $\int(22)$.

If ε is expressed by Equation IV—16, we may in general write for any of the integrals:

$$\int \varepsilon\, \varrho(r)\, r^2 dr = -\mathrm{k} \int \frac{\varrho(r)\, dr}{r^4} + \mathrm{j} \int \frac{\varrho(r)\, dr}{r^{n-2}} \tag{25}$$

We have seen in Chapter IV that the minimum energy ε_0 for a molecular pair and its equilibrium separation d_0 are defined in terms of k and j. Reversing this, we may express j, the repulsive coefficient, in terms of k and d_0:

$$\mathrm{j} = \frac{6}{n} (d_0)^{n-6}\, \mathrm{k} \tag{26}$$

Substituting Equation 26 in Equation 25, we obtain:

$$\int \varepsilon\, \varrho(r)\, r^2 dr = -\mathrm{k} \left[\int \frac{\varrho(r)\, dr}{r^4} + \frac{6}{n} (d_0)^{n-6} \int \frac{\varrho(r)\, dr}{r^{n-2}}\right] \tag{27}$$

If we now use the results about the similarity of the distribution functions and assume that we may express all ϱ's as the same function $\varrho(y)$ where $y = \frac{r}{d_m}$ and d_m is the position of the first maximum, we obtain:

$$\int \varepsilon\, \varrho(r)\, r^2 dr = \mathrm{k} \left[\frac{-1}{d_m^3} \int \frac{\varrho(y)\, dy}{y^4} + \frac{6\,(d_0)^{n-6}}{n\,(d_m)^{n-3}} \int \frac{\varrho(y)\, dy}{y^{n-2}}\right] \tag{28}$$

The assumption that the repulsive integral in Equation 28 is a universal function is a somewhat poorer assumption than that concerning the attractive integral, but since it represents the smaller contribution, this error is not too serious.

Finally we expect the position of the first maximum, d_m, to be proportional to the equilibrium distance between isolated molecular pairs d_o. For simplicity we set $d_o = d_m$ and let d be the sum of two molecular radii ($d_{11} = 2r_1$, $d_{12} = r_1 + r_2$, $d_{22} = 2r_2$), although a constant proportionality factor between these quantities is all that is required. Making the indicated substitutions, Equation 28 becomes:

$$\int \varepsilon \varrho(r) r^2 dr = \frac{k}{d^3}\left[-\int \frac{\varrho(y)\,dy}{y^4} + \frac{6}{n}\int \frac{\varrho(y)\,dy}{y^{n-2}}\right] \tag{29}$$

Substituting into Equation 24, we obtain:

$$\Delta E^M = 2\pi N^2 (N_1 V_1 + N_2 V_2\ \varphi_1 \varphi_2 \left[\frac{2k_{12}}{V_1 V_2 (r_1 + r_2)^3} - \frac{k_1}{V_1^2 (2r_1)^3}\right.$$
$$\left. - \frac{k_2}{V_2^2 (2r_2)^2}\right] \cdot \left[-\int \frac{\varrho(y)\,dy}{y^4} + \frac{6}{n}\int \frac{\varrho(y)\,dy}{y^{n-2}}\right] \tag{30}$$

For the relation of k_{12} to k_1 and k_2 we may turn to the London equation, IV—7,8, which yields:

$$k_{12} = \frac{2\,I_1^{\frac{1}{2}} I_2^{\frac{1}{2}}}{I_1 + I_2} \cdot k_1^{\frac{1}{2}} k_2^{\frac{1}{2}} \tag{31}$$

Equation 30 can then be written:

$$\Delta E^M = 2\pi N^2 (N_1 V_1 + N_2 V_2)\, \varphi_1 \varphi_2 \left[\frac{1}{V_1^2} \cdot \frac{k_1}{(2r_1)^3} - \frac{4\, I_1^{\frac{1}{2}} I_2^{\frac{1}{2}} k_1^{\frac{1}{2}} k_2^{\frac{1}{2}}}{V_1 V_2 (I_1 + I_2)(r_1 + r_2)^3}\right.$$
$$\left. + \frac{1}{V_2^2} \cdot \frac{k_2}{(2r_2)^3}\right] \cdot \int \left(\frac{1}{y^4} - \frac{6}{n y^{n-2}}\right) \varrho(y)\,dy \tag{32}$$

The bracketed quantity would be a perfect square if the second term therein were $k_1^{\frac{1}{2}} k_2^{\frac{1}{2}} / 4 (r_1 r_2)^{\frac{3}{2}}$. The error involved in making the substitution depends upon the ratio of the geometric mean to the arithmetic mean for the molecular radii, and the ratio of the geometric mean to the harmonic mean for the ionisation potentials. This error is no more serious than the other approximations that must be made in order to secure a workable formula. We write, accordingly:

$$\Delta E^M = 2\pi N^2 (N_1 V_1 + N_2 V_2)\, \varphi_1 \varphi_2 \left[\frac{1}{V_1}\left(\frac{k_1}{8r_1^3}\right)^{\frac{1}{2}} - \frac{1}{V_2}\left(\frac{k_2}{8r_2^3}\right)^{\frac{1}{2}}\right]^2$$
$$\cdot \int \left(\frac{1}{y^4} - \frac{6}{n y^{n-2}}\right) \varrho(y)\,dy \tag{33}$$

Since $\Delta E_1^V = \frac{2\pi N^2 k_1}{8 V_1 r_1^3} \int \left(\frac{1}{y^4} - \frac{6}{ny^{n-2}}\right) \varrho(y)\,dy$ and similarly for ΔE_2^V, we can simplify Equation 33 to:

$$\Delta E^M = (N_1 V_1 + N_2 V_2) \left[\left(\frac{\Delta E_1^V}{V_1}\right)^{\frac{1}{2}} - \left(\frac{\Delta E_2^V}{V_2}\right)^{\frac{1}{2}}\right]^2 \varphi_1 \varphi_2 \qquad (34)$$

The partial molal energy of mixing for component 1 is then:

$$\Delta \overline{E}_1^M = \varphi_2^2 V_1 \left[\left(\frac{\Delta E_1^V}{V_1}\right)^{\frac{1}{2}} - \left(\frac{\Delta E_2^V}{V_2}\right)^{\frac{1}{2}}\right]^2 \qquad (35)$$

where φ_2 is the volume fraction of 2. If the two components have equal molal volumes, this simplifies to:

$$\Delta \overline{E}_1^M = x_2^2 \left[(\Delta E_1^V)^{\frac{1}{2}} - (\Delta E_2^V)^{\frac{1}{2}}\right]^2 \qquad (36)$$

The quantity, $\Delta E^V/V$ in Equations 34—36, the energy of vaporization per cc., which can be taken as a measure of "internal pressure" as explained in Chapter V, thus assumes an important role in the theory of solutions and values of $(\Delta E^V/V)^{\frac{1}{2}}$ will be so often referred to in later chapters that we propose to call them "solubility parameters" and designate them by a special symbol, δ. Also, we have seen in Chapter V that we can rearrange Equation 16 to read;

$$V \Delta E^V = 2\pi N^2 \int \varepsilon \varrho(r) r^2 dr = a \qquad (37)$$

where a should be nearly constant. Accordingly,

$$\left(\frac{\Delta E^V}{V}\right)^{\frac{1}{2}} = \delta = \frac{a^{\frac{1}{2}}}{V} \qquad (38)$$

But before proceeding let us examine certain direct, experimental evidence in favor of the validity of turning the bracketed term of Equation 29 into a perfect square. Westwater, Frantz and Hildebrand[15], and Hildebrand and Carter[16] made careful measurements of $(\partial P/\partial T)_V$ for a number of liquids

---

[15] W. Westwater, H. W. Frantz and J. H. Hildebrand, *Phys. Rev.*, **31**, 135 (1928).
[16] J. H. Hildebrand and J. M. Carter, *J. Am. Chem. Soc.*, **54**, 3592 (1932).

and their solutions from which they calculated values of $(\partial E/\partial V)_T$ by the thermodynamic relation of Equation I—7 and found that $V^2(\partial E/\partial V)_T$ was rigidly constant over the range studied. Hildebrand[16] had previously shown this to be approximately true for a number of nonpolar liquids and, further, that $\mathrm{V}^2(\partial E/\partial V)_T$ is only slightly different from $\mathrm{V}\Delta\mathrm{E}^{\mathrm{V}}$ for the same liquid, showing that the constancy holds remarkably well throughout the whole process of vaporization over the van der Waals path. (cf. Chapter V, Table 9). We may therefore write with good approximation to experiment,

$$\mathrm{a}_{11} = \mathrm{V}_1^2(\partial E_1/\partial V_1)_T = \mathrm{V}_1\Delta\mathrm{E}_1^{\mathrm{V}} \text{ and } \mathrm{a}_{22} = \mathrm{V}_2^2(\partial E_2/\partial V_2)_T = \mathrm{V}_2\Delta\mathrm{E}_2^{\mathrm{V}} \quad (39)$$

and, by Equation 18 (or Equation V—85)

$$\mathrm{a}_{11} = 2\pi \boldsymbol{N}^2 \int_{11} \text{ and } \mathrm{a}_{22} = 2\pi \boldsymbol{N}^2 \int_{22} \quad (40\,\text{a,b})$$

where $\int_{11}$ and $\int_{22}$ stand for the integrals,

$$\int \varepsilon_1\, \varrho_1\, r^2\, dr \text{ and } \int \varepsilon_2\, \varrho_2\, r^2\, dr \quad (41)$$

Since an equation in the form of Equation 39 holds also for a mixture, we may write

$$\mathrm{a} = \mathrm{V}^2(\partial E/\partial V)_T = -\mathrm{V}_m\mathrm{E}_m \quad (42)$$

where E_m, as in Equation 20, is the potential energy of the solution of $x_1 + x_2$ moles.

Hildebrand and Carter found, further, that all but one out of eight tetrahalide solutions gave values of a agreeing within 1 per cent with the relation

$$\mathrm{a} = (x_1\,\mathrm{a}_{11}^{\frac{1}{2}} + x_2\,\mathrm{a}_{22}^{\frac{1}{2}})^2 \quad (43)$$

in spite of considerable spread in the a's and v's for the components, as illustrated in Table 3. Substituting Equation 40 a, b in 43 and the resulting equation in 42 gives

$$-\mathrm{V}_m\mathrm{E}_m = \mathrm{a} = 2\pi \boldsymbol{N}^2 \left[x_1^2 \int_{11} + x_2^2 \int_{22} + 2x_1 x_2 \int_{11}^{\frac{1}{2}} \int_{22}^{\frac{1}{2}} \right] \quad (44)$$

and combining this with Equation 20 gives,

$$\int_{12} = \int_{11}^{\frac{1}{2}} \int_{22}^{\frac{1}{2}} \tag{45}$$

which corresponds to the Berthelot relation, $a_{12} = a_{11}^{\frac{1}{2}} a_{22}^{\frac{1}{2}}$ mentioned at the beginning of this chapter.

Table 2. Relation of values of a for components and their solutions.

		Pure components	Solutions, $x = 0.5$	
	V	a(obs)	a(obs)	a(calc)
CCl_4	97.09	31.21		
			46.86	46.46
$SnBr_4$	130.62	64.79		
			48.69	48.17
$SiCl_4$	115.36	34.00		
			43.28	43.14
$SiBr_4$	126.52	53.56		

Since any expansion on mixing has been neglected, i. e., $\Delta V^M = 0$, we may identify the energy of mixing with the heat of mixing, $\Delta \overline{H}_1 = \Delta \overline{E}_1 + P\Delta V = \Delta \overline{E}_1$. In so far as the solution is "regular", in the sense stated earlier in this Chapter and in Chapter III, the partial molal entropy of mixing (component 1) is $-R\ln x_1$ and we may combine the heat and entropy terms to give the free energy of mixing,

$$\Delta \overline{F}_1^M = RT\ln a_1 = RT\ln x_1 + V_1\, \varphi_2^2 (\delta_1 - \delta_2)^2 \tag{46}$$

By fixing the activity, *e. g.*, at a_1^s for a solid phase, we can calculate x_1 from values of V and δ for the two pure components.

If the molal volumes of the two components are significantly unequal but thermal agitation is still sufficient to give the maximum entropy of mixing, it may be worth while to substitute for $-R\ln x_1$ the expression derived in Chapter VI, Equation 18, which gives,

$$\ln a_1 = \ln \varphi_1 + \varphi_2 \left(1 - \frac{V_1}{V_2}\right) + V_1\, \varphi_2^2 (\delta_1 - \delta_2)^2/RT \tag{47}$$

Equations 35 and 46 are surprisingly good, considering the approximations involved in their derivation. Although we have simplified the repulsive terms, and neglected the difference between arithmetic and geometric means, and have assumed spherical, monatomic, nonpolar molecules, we find that they are far from inapplicable to polyatomic and even moderately polar molecules. A careful study by Vold[17] of the heats of mixing of binary solutions

[17] R. D. Vold, *J. Am. Chem. Soc.*, **59**, 1515 (1937).

of $SiCl_4$, CCl_4, C_6H_6 and n-C_7H_{16} gave the following results. Solutions of CCl_4 with $SiCl_4$, the pair that most closely resemble the spherical model, show a striking correspondence (Table 3) between observed heats of mixing per mole and those calculated from $\Delta E^V/V$ by aid of Equation 35.

Table 3. Test of Equation 25 for $SiCl_4$—CCl_4 solutions.

x_1 ($SiCl_4$)	0.1840	0.2680	0.5647	0.6594	0.8613
ΔH^M obs. cal.	19.1	24.9	32.3	32.2	15.8
ΔH^M calc. cal.	18 3	23.5	28.0	25.2	13.0

The agreement with solutions of CCl_4 with C_6H_6 and with n-C_7H_{16} is much poorer, as might be expected from the shapes of the molecules of the latter two, but the values of $\Delta\delta$ obtained from the heats of mixing themselves are consistent with the relation as shown in Table 4.

Table 4. Test of Relation $|\delta_2-\delta_3| = |\delta_1-\delta_2| \pm |\delta_1-\delta_3|$

CCl_4 — C_6H_6	CCl_4 — n-C_7H_{16}	C_6H_6 — n-C_7H_{16}
$\|\delta_1-\delta_2\| = 0.949$	$\|\delta_1-\delta_3\| = 1.544$	$\|\delta_2-\delta_3\| = 2.493$ obs.
		2.493 calc.

The identity of the observed and the calculated value in this case is doubtless somewhat fortuitous, but we shall see later further evidence that values of $\Delta\delta$ derived from heats of mixing or from solubility data often give satisfactory results when values calculated from $\Delta E^V/V$ show considerable departure.

It should be appreciated that the activity coefficient, γ, is very sensitive to variations in the figures for ΔE^V, so that even to apply Equation 46 or its equivalents accurately requires accurate values for ΔE_1^V and ΔE_2^V at the temperature in question. The usual uncertainties in the data, added to the only approximate character of the assumptions made in deriving the equations, mean that if we want to know a solubility to say 1 per cent we must measure it carefully. Our theory will, however, indicate which solvents or solutes are most likely to fulfill our specifications, as well as the form of equations with the fewest adjustable empirical constants to use for calculating the effects of changes in temperature and composition. One particularly important result has been to establish the theoretical validity of the volume fraction instead of the mole fraction. Experimental evidence abundantly confirms this, as we shall see in later chapters, (e. g., benzene — carbon disulfide, Chapter XIII, cadmium — lead, Chapter XIX).

Use of "effective volume" fractions. In certain cases, where the shapes of the two component molecules are radically different, a somewhat better quantitative agreement between theory and experiment is obtained by replacing the volumes V_1 and V_2 in Equation 34 (or the equivalent Equation 17) by empirical parameters q_1 and q_2, which may be called generalized or "effective volumes". Then, we may write for the energy of mixing:

$$\Delta E^M = (N_1 q_1 + N_2 q_2) \left[\left(\frac{\Delta E_1^V}{q_1} \right)^{\frac{1}{2}} - \left(\frac{\Delta E_2^V}{q_2} \right)^{\frac{1}{2}} \right]^2 \frac{(x_1 q_1)(x_2 q_2)}{(x_1 q_1 + x_2 q_2)^2} \qquad (48)$$

and for the partial molal energies:

$$\Delta \overline{E}_1 = q_1 \left[\left(\frac{\Delta E_1^V}{q_1} \right)^{\frac{1}{2}} - \left(\frac{\Delta E_2^V}{q_2} \right)^{\frac{1}{2}} \right]^2 \left(\frac{x_2 q_2}{x_1 q_1 + x_2 q_2} \right)^2 \qquad (49a)$$

$$\Delta \overline{E}_2 = q_2 \left[\left(\frac{\Delta E_1^V}{q_1} \right)^{\frac{1}{2}} - \left(\frac{\Delta E_2^V}{q_2} \right)^{\frac{1}{2}} \right]^2 \left(\frac{x_1 q_1}{x_1 q_1 + x_2 q_2} \right)^2 \qquad (49b)$$

We see that in this case the volume fractions are replaced by q-fractions or "effective volume" fractions. Van Laar in his equations (Equations 5, 6, 7, 8) identified the q's with the van der Waals b's as we have seen but in the extensive empirical use of the van Laar equation, especially by chemical engineers this theoretical significance has been abandoned in favor of a freely adjustable set of parameters b or q. (See, for example, Equations III-16-19, which are entirely equivalent to Equations 48 and 49ab of this chapter). In certain cases, the q's can be related to the "effective surfaces" of molecules of different shape. Thus, for example, in the system isooctane-toluene, Drickamer, Brown, and White[18] have found a ratio q_1/q_2 of 1.0, while the volume ratio is $V_1/V_2 = 1.5$; this extreme case is doubtless related to the large difference in shape between the flat toluene molecule and the semi-spherical one of iso-octane, resulting in about equal effective surfaces. We shall see in Chapter IX how Langmuir used surface energies and "surface fractions" to explain the heat of mixing in solutions of polar molecules.

We shall not, however, have occasion to use these "effective volume" fractions since, for the purposes of this book, the more easily justified volume fraction equations are more than adequate.

---

[18] H. G. Drickamer, G. G. Brown and R. R. White, *Trans. Am. Inst. Chem. Engrs.* **41**, 555 (1945).

CHAPTER VIII

The Free Energy of Mixing—Refinements

We have seen in Chapter VI and VII, that we may represent the entropy and energy of mixing by expressions:

$$\Delta S^M = -R\left[x_1 \ln x_1 + x_2 \ln x_2\right] \tag{1}$$

$$\Delta E^M = V_m (\delta_1 - \delta_2)^2 \varphi_1\varphi_2 \tag{2}$$

Combining these, we obtain for the Helmholtz free energy of mixing, ΔA^M

$$\Delta A^M = RT\left[x_1 \ln x_1 + x_2 \ln x_2\right] + V_m (\delta_1 - \delta_2)^2 \varphi_1\varphi_2 \tag{3}$$

and for the partial molal quantities:

$$\Delta\bar{A}_1 = RT \ln x_1 + V_1 (\delta_1 - \delta_2)^2 \varphi_2^2 \tag{4a}$$

$$\Delta\bar{A}_2 = RT \ln x_2 + V_2 (\delta_1 - \delta_2)^2 \varphi_1^2 \tag{4b}$$

Quite aside from the approximations specifically considered in the derivations of Equations 1 and 2, there are two additional problems which require further consideration here:

1. Experimental measurements are almost invariably carried out under conditions of constant pressure, and for this reason, the activities a_1 and a_2 and the corresponding activity coefficients, γ_1 and γ_2 are defined in terms of the Gibbs free energy of mixing ΔF^M. Our theory, however, has been derived with the implied assumption of constant volume. If there is no change in volume on mixing at constant pressure the two free energies ΔA^M and ΔF^M are identical, and we may replace A by F and E by H in Equations 2—5. Since, however, the volume change on mixing, although usually small, is rarely zero, we need to consider the effect of volume change on our treatment.

2. In deriving Equations 1 and 2, we have assumed a random distribution of the two species of molecules throughout the solution. We have seen that a non-zero energy of mixing must be attributed to differences in the interaction potential of 1—1 pairs, 2—2 pairs, and 1— 2 pairs. It is evident

however, that such a difference in the interaction energy must lead to a degree of preferential formation of either unlike pairs (1—2) or like pairs (1—1 and 2—2). To the extent that such a preferential order exists, our calculations of the entropy and the energy of mixing both of which assumed no such ordering, are in error. This, too, will require further consideration.

We see therefore, that in at least two respects, the model of a solution which we have used in Chapters VI and VII may be in error, even when the two components have equal molal volumes.

Errors due to over-simplified models. Before proceeding to a detailed consideration of the effect of volume changes and preferential ordering in solutions, let us consider in a general way the nature of the error introduced in the thermodynamic functions by the use of an oversimplified and insufficient model.

In statistical thermodynamics, we frequently find that the free energy calculated from a simple theory agrees well with experimental results, while the agreement between theory and experiment for the entropy or the heat, taken separately, is not nearly so good. Similarly, if we improve a theory by choosing a better model, the modifications in the expressions for entropy and heat are much greater in magnitude than that involved in the free energy. We shall see in the following discussion that this situation is not accidental but is to be expected.

In order to calculate the thermodynamic properties of a particular system, we assume, as a first approximation, an over-simplified model. Thermodynamic functions calculated from such a model, we denote by $F_\circ$, $H_\circ$, $S_\circ$, etc.

We know, however, that in a particular respect, our system does not correspond to the assumed model. With respect to a particular property (for example, volume or distribution of like and unlike pairs), designated by a parameter α, the system has the value α' rather than $\alpha_\circ$. We may now express the free energy ot the actual system F′ in the form of a Taylor series expansion around $\alpha_\circ$:

$$F' = F_\circ + \left(\frac{\partial F}{\partial \alpha}\right)_{\alpha=\alpha_\circ}(\alpha' - \alpha_\circ) + \frac{1}{2}\left(\frac{\partial^2 F}{\partial \alpha^2}\right)_{\alpha=\alpha_\circ}(\alpha' - \alpha_\circ)^2 + \dots \qquad (5)$$

We may equally well, however, expand around α':

$$F_\circ = F' + \left(\frac{\partial F}{\partial \alpha}\right)_{\alpha=\alpha'}(\alpha_\circ - \alpha') + \frac{1}{2}\left(\frac{\partial^2 F}{\partial \alpha^2}\right)_{\alpha=\alpha'}(\alpha_\circ - \alpha')^2 + \dots \qquad (6)$$

The system, at equilibrium, must have chosen that value of α which minimizes F. Hence we may set $\left(\frac{\partial F}{\partial \alpha}\right)_{\alpha=\alpha'}$ equal to zero.

Rearranging, we obtain:

$$F' - F_0 = \delta F = \frac{1}{2}\left(\frac{\partial^2 F}{\partial \alpha^2}\right)_{\alpha=\alpha'} (\alpha' - \alpha_0)^2 + \ldots \qquad (7)$$

We see that we have lost the term in $\Delta\alpha$ and that the correction to be applied to the free energy depends only on the square of the quantity representing the deviation of the actual system from the model.

On the contrary, the entropy and the heat are not minimized, and applying the same reasoning to them, we obtain:

$$S' - S_0 = \delta S = \left(\frac{\partial S}{\partial \alpha}\right)_{\alpha=\alpha'} (\alpha' - \alpha_0) - \frac{1}{2}\left(\frac{\partial^2 S}{\partial \alpha^2}\right)_{\alpha=\alpha'} (\alpha' - \alpha_0)^2 + \ldots \qquad (8)$$

$$H' - H_0 = \delta H = \left(\frac{\partial H}{\partial \alpha}\right)_{\alpha=\alpha'} (\alpha' - \alpha_0) - \frac{1}{2}\left(\frac{\partial^2 H}{\partial \alpha^2}\right)_{\alpha=\alpha'} (\alpha' - \alpha_0)^2 + \ldots \qquad (9)$$

We may calculate $\Delta\alpha$ from the condition:

$$\left(\frac{\partial F}{\partial \alpha}\right)_{\alpha=\alpha'} = 0 \qquad (10)$$

or equivalently:

$$T\left(\frac{\partial S}{\partial \alpha}\right)_{\alpha=\alpha'} = \left(\frac{\partial H}{\partial \alpha}\right)_{\alpha=\alpha'} \qquad (11)$$

Provided that our initial choice of model was not completely unreasonable, $\Delta\alpha$ will be small, and the series will rapidly converge: Since δF depends only upon $\Delta\alpha^2$ and higher powers, while the δS and δH series begin with $\Delta\alpha$, we conclude that an oversimplified model introduces far more serious errors in the calculation of the heat and the entropy separately than in that of the free energy. In fact, to a first approximation, we may regard the free energy F_0 as correct and apply correction factors only when we are interested in separating the heat and entropy components of the free energy.

The conclusions obtained above are general and are applicable in fields far beyond the province of this book. In the following pages, as we treat the problems introduced at the beginning of this chapter, we shall find these conclusions confirmed.

Change of volume on mixing. We have noted earlier in this chapter the difficulties which arise when there is a volume change on mixing. These difficulties were recognized and partially formulated by Hildebrand[1], but the first quantitative study was made by Scatchard[2].

[1] J. H. Hildebrand, *J. Am. Chem. Soc.*, **51**, 66 (1929).
J. H. Hildebrand, "Solubility" 2nd edition, Reinhold (1936) pp. 57—65.

[2] G. Scatchard, *Trans. Faraday Soc.*, **33**, 160, (1937).

The Scatchard equations were derived from a two-step process, a mixing of the two components at constant volume, followed by an expansion or contraction of the mixture (as the case may be) to recover the initial pressure.

The development of the generalized equations of the preceding section permit us to obtain the same results more directly. Denoting the functions calculated for constant volume as ΔA_v^M, ΔE_v^M and ΔS_v^M, we obtain for the corresponding functions at constant pressure:

$$\Delta A_p^M = \Delta A_v^M + \left(\frac{\partial A}{\partial V}\right)_{V=V_0+\Delta V^M} \Delta V^M - \frac{1}{2}\left(\frac{\partial^2 A}{\partial V^2}\right)_{V=V_0+\Delta V^M} (\Delta V^M)^2$$

$$= \Delta A_v^M - P\Delta V^M - \frac{1}{2\beta V}(\Delta V^M)^2 \tag{12}$$

$$\Delta E_p^M = \Delta E_v^M + \left\{T\left(\frac{\partial P}{\partial T}\right)_V - P\right\}\Delta V^M + \dots \tag{13}$$

$$\Delta S_p^M = \Delta S_v^M + \left(\frac{\partial P}{\partial T}\right)_V \Delta V^M + \dots \tag{14}$$

We now obtain ΔF_p^M and ΔH_p^M by adding $\Delta P V$, which, since the initial and final pressures are the same, is merely $P\Delta V^M$.

$$\Delta F_p^M = \Delta A_p^M + P\Delta V^M = \Delta A_v^M - \frac{1}{2\beta V}(\Delta V^M)^2 + \dots \tag{15}$$

$$\Delta H_p^M = \Delta E_p^M + P\Delta V^M = \Delta E_v^M + T\left(\frac{\partial P}{\partial T}\right)_V \Delta V^M + \dots \tag{16}$$

It should be noted that we did not calculate ΔF_p^M and ΔH_p^M directly from Equations 7 and 9, since we did not know ΔF_v^M and ΔH_v^M explicitly. We have however proved that the first correction term for ΔF_p^M is proportional to the square of ΔV^M, while those for ΔS_p^M and ΔH_p^M depend on the first power of ΔV^M. In Equations 12—16, V, β and $\left(\frac{\partial P}{\partial T}\right)_V$ refer to the properties of the mixture in the final state at the same pressure as initially before mixing.

We now wish to calculate the change in volume ΔV^M. From thermodynamic relations, we may write:

$$\Delta V^M = \left(\frac{\partial \Delta F_p^M}{\partial P}\right)_{T, P=P_0} \tag{17}$$

Substituting from Equation 16, neglecting the small term in $(\Delta V^M)^2$. we obtain:

$$\Delta V^M = \left(\frac{\partial \Delta A_v^M}{\partial P}\right)_{T, P=P_0} = \left(\frac{\partial \Delta E_v^M}{\partial P}\right)_{T, P=P_0} - T\left(\frac{\partial \Delta S_v^M}{\partial P}\right)_{T, P=P_0} \tag{18}$$

To the extent that the entropy of mixing is a function of random configurations and is assumed independent of heat interactions (an assumption we shall reconsider in the following section), it is surely independent of pressure. (In any case, the ΔS_v^M which appears in Equation 18 is that based on the random model, and it is independent of pressure, whether the actual entropy is or not).

We may therefore write:

$$\Delta V^M = \left(\frac{\partial \Delta E_v^M}{\partial P_0}\right)_T = \left(\frac{\partial \Delta E_v^M}{\partial V_0}\right)_T \left(\frac{\partial V_0}{\partial P_0}\right)_T = -\beta_0 V_0 \left(\frac{\partial \Delta E_v^M}{\partial V_0}\right)_T \tag{19}$$

Where β_0, V_0, etc. refer to the compressibility and the volume of the isolated components. Writing ΔE_v^M as $E - E_0$, where E_0 represents the energy of the isolated components, we obtain:

$$\Delta V^M = -\beta_0 V_0 \left\{\left(\frac{\partial E}{\partial V_0}\right)_T - \left(\frac{\partial E_0}{\partial V_0}\right)_T\right\} \tag{20}$$

We have seen in Chapter V that for a large number of "normal liquids" $\left(\frac{\partial E}{\partial V}\right)_T$ is approximately equal to $-\frac{E}{V}$. If we make the substitution, the change in volume becomes:

$$\Delta V^M = -\beta_0 V_0 \left(-\frac{E}{V_0} + \frac{E_0}{V_0}\right) = \beta_0 \Delta E_v^M \tag{21}$$

We see that an increase in volume always accompanies a positive energy (or heat) of mixing, and conversely a decrease in volume takes place when the energy of mixing is negative. Only when the mixing is athermal is there no volume change. The magnitude of the volume change, however, is usually quite small. We shall see later that the energy of mixing ΔE_v^M cannot exceed $\frac{1}{2} RT$ unless the liquids are only partially miscible. For the case that $\Delta E_v^M = 300$ cal./mole $= 1.2 \cdot 10^{+4}$ cc atm/mole, $\beta_0 = 10^{-4}$, we find ΔV^M is only 1.2 cc/mole. If V_0 is about 100 cc., the maximum volume change is only about one or two percent.

If we substitute Equation 21 into Equations 15—17, the thermodynamic functions at constant pressure become (we now drop the subscript p)

$$\Delta F^M = \Delta A^M_v - \frac{\beta_o^2}{2\beta V_o} (\Delta E^M_v)^2 + \ldots \tag{22}$$

$$\Delta S^M = \Delta S^M_v + \alpha \frac{\beta_o}{\beta} \Delta E^M_v + \ldots \tag{23}$$

$$\Delta H^M = \Delta E^M_v + T\alpha \frac{\beta_o}{\beta} \Delta E^M_v + \ldots \tag{24}$$

Here α denotes the thermal expansivity.

We may attempt to calculate β in terms of β_o as follows:

$$\beta = -\frac{1}{V_o + \Delta V^M}\left(\frac{\partial(V_o + \Delta V^M)}{\partial P_o}\right)_T = \frac{\beta_o V_o}{V_o + \Delta V^M} - \frac{1}{V_o + \Delta V^M}\left(\frac{\partial(\beta_o \Delta E^M_v)}{\partial P_o}\right)_T$$

$$= \frac{\beta_o(V_o - \Delta V^M)}{(V_o + \Delta V^M)} - \frac{\Delta V^M}{V_o + \Delta V^M}\left(\frac{\partial \ln \beta_o}{\partial P_o}\right)_T$$

$$= \beta_o - \frac{\Delta V^M}{V_o}\left\{\left(\frac{\partial \ln \beta_o}{\partial P_o}\right)_T + 2\beta_o\right\} + \ldots \tag{25}$$

In his original derivation Scatchard[2] assumed β and β_o to be independent of pressure, and so obtained $\beta = \beta_o\,(1 - 2\,\frac{\Delta V^M}{V})$. In our derivation above, we have avoided the assumption that the β's were pressure independent, and it is difficult to see that $\left(\frac{\partial \ln \beta_o}{\partial P_o}\right)_T$ is negligible compared with $2\beta_o$. In fact, for normal liquids $\left(\frac{\partial \ln \beta_o}{\partial P_o}\right)_T$ is about -10^{-3} atm^{-1}, while β_o is about 10^{-4} atm^{-1}.

For small $\frac{\Delta V^M}{V}$, we shall neglect the correction term entirely and taking $\beta \sim \beta_o$, we obtain as a first approximation:

$$\Delta F^M = \Delta A^M_v \tag{26}$$

$$\Delta S^M = \Delta S^M_v + \alpha \Delta E^M_v \tag{27}$$

$$\Delta H^M = \Delta E^M_v\,(1 + \alpha T) \tag{28}$$

The most important conclusion from the above reasoning is ΔF^M at constant pressure is virtually the same as ΔA^M at constant volume, a result which permits us to use Equations 3, 4, and 5 under the usual conditions of constant pressure. We may therefore calculate the partial pressure, the activity, the activity coefficient and a variety of other properties from

Equations 3, 4, and 5 in spite of the fact that they were derived for different conditions, namely constant volume.

Only when we are interested in the values of the entropy and heat of mixing separately do we need to consider these corrections. When ΔE^M_v is small, the percentage correction for the entropy is small; however this is not so for the heat of mixing. To the approximation of the derivation, the heat of mixing is a constant factor $(1 + \alpha T)$ times ΔE^M_v. At room temperature ($T \sim 300$), formany liquids $\alpha \cong 1.2 \cdot 10^{-3}$, so $\Delta H^M = 1.4\, \Delta E^M_v$, a sizable percentage discrepancy. One should bear this in mind when comparing calorimetric heats of mixing with values of ΔE^M_v calculated from Equation 2.

The corresponding partial molal quantities may be obtained by differentiation of Equations 26, 27, and 28. Before carrying out this step, we must consider the variation of α_o and β_o with composition. If we designate the values for the pure components as α_1 and α_2, β_1 and β_2, α_o and β_o (for the average of the pure components, not for the mixture) are volume fraction averages:

$$\beta_o = \frac{-1}{N_1 V_1 + N_2 V_2} \left(\frac{\partial (N_1 V_1 + N_2 V_2)}{\partial P} \right)_T = \frac{N_1 V_1 \beta_1 + N_2 V_2 \beta_2}{N_1 V_1 + N_2 V_2}$$

$$= \varphi_1 \beta_1 + \varphi_2 \beta_2 \tag{29}$$

$$\alpha_o = \frac{1}{N_1 V_1 + N_2 V_2} \left(\frac{\partial (N_1 V_1 + N_2 V_2)}{\partial T} \right)_P = \frac{N_1 V_1 \alpha_1 + N_2 V_2 \alpha_2}{N_1 V_1 + N_2 V_2}$$

$$= \varphi_1 \alpha_1 + \varphi_2 \alpha_2 \tag{30}$$

For simplicity we shall assume $\alpha_1 = \alpha_2 = \alpha_o$ and $\beta_1 = \beta_2 = \beta_o$, a fairly good approximation for liquids which are not very different. (Where this approximation is not good enough, we can always substitute Equations 29 and 30 before differentiating). Under these conditions we obtain for the partial molal quantities:

$$\Delta \bar{F}_1 = \Delta \bar{A}_{1_v} \qquad \Delta \bar{F}_2 = \Delta \bar{A}_{2_v} \tag{31 a, b}$$

$$\Delta \bar{S}_1 = \Delta \bar{S}_{1_v} + \alpha_o\, \Delta \bar{E}_{1_v} \tag{32 a}$$

$$\Delta \bar{S}_2 = \Delta \bar{S}_{2_v} + \alpha_o\, \Delta \bar{E}_{2_v} \tag{32 b}$$

$$\Delta \bar{H}_1 = \Delta \bar{E}_{1_v} \cdot (1 + \alpha_o T) \tag{33 a}$$

$$\Delta \bar{H}_2 = \Delta \bar{E}_{2_v} \cdot (1 + \alpha_o T) \tag{33 b}$$

$$\Delta \bar{V}_1 = \beta_\circ \, \Delta \bar{E}_{1_v} \tag{34 a}$$

$$\Delta \bar{V}_2 = \beta_\circ \, \Delta \bar{E}_{2_v} \tag{34 b}$$

With respect to the latter set of equations, we may derive a very interesting result. If we assume ΔS_v^M to be ideal (Equation 1), the energy of mixing ΔE_v^M may be identified with the excess free energy ΔF^E and we may write for the partial molal volume changes:

$$\Delta \bar{V}_1 = \bar{V}_1 - V_1 = \beta_\circ \Delta \bar{F}_1^E = \beta_\circ RT \ln \gamma_1 \tag{35 a}$$

$$\Delta \bar{V}_2 = \bar{V}_2 - V_2 = \beta_\circ \Delta \bar{F}_2^E = \beta_\circ RT \ln \gamma_2 \tag{35 b}$$

We now have related the changes in volume $\Delta \bar{V}_1$ and $\Delta \bar{V}_2$ with experimental quantities, the activity coefficients. An empirical relation between $\Delta \bar{V}$ and $\log \gamma$ was noted earlier by Hildebrand[3]. Even earlier Biron[4] had proposed a simple symmetrical relation for ΔV^M

$$\Delta V^M = k x_1 x_2 \tag{36}$$

which yields Equations 35ab when $\log \gamma$ is given by Equation III—15.

Fig. 1 shows the data of Zawidzki[5] and Hubbard[6] for solutions of carbon

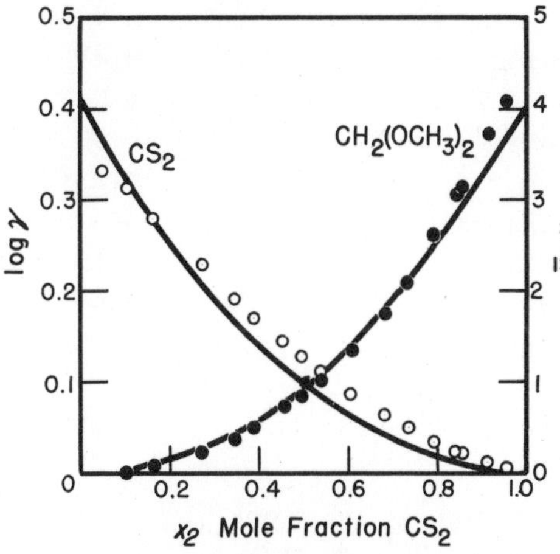

Fig. 1 Partial molal volumes and activity coefficients in carbon disulfide-methylal solutions.

---

[3] J. H. Hildebrand "Solubility", lst Edition (1924) pp. 61—65. See also J. H. Hildebrand and E. D. Eastman, *J. Am. Chem. Soc.*, **37**, 2452 (1915).

[4] E. Biron, *J. Russ. Phys. Chem. Soc.*, **44**, 1264 (1912).

[5] J. v. Zawidzki, *Z. physik. Chem.*, **35**, 129 (1900).

[6] J. C. Hubbard, *Phys. Rev.*, **30**, 740 (1910); *Z. physik. Chem.*, **74**, 207 (1910).

disulfide and methylal. We see that a reasonable fit is obtained for the relation $\log \gamma = 0.10\ \Delta\bar{V}$. The constant derived from Equations 35ab is $1/2.303\ RT\ \beta_0$, which for $\beta = 10^{-4}$ atm^{-1} is 0.18, only fair agreement.

It will be seen in Figure 1 that the volume curves are considerably more symmetrical than those for $\log \gamma$. This discrepancy is doubtless due to the inaccuracy of our assumption of a constant β_0. If we assume the regular solution Equation VII—15 or 34 (Equation 2 of this chapter)

Table 1. Changes on Mixing[14]

Solution	Deviations from Raoult's law Per cent at $t°$ C.		Volume change Per cent at $t°$ C.		Temperature change
Acetone-carbondisulfide	+ 35[5,13]	35°	+ 1.6[6]	35°	− 9.85°[11]
Acetone-chloroform	− 26[5]	35°	− 0.23[6]	35°	+ 12.4°[11]
Benzene-carbontetrachloride	+ 3.5[5]	50°	+ 0.06[6]	50°	− 0.69°[11]
Benzene-chloroform	− 0.6[12]	20°	...	...	− 0°[9]
Benzene-ethylalcohol	+ 60[11]		− 0.01	...	− 3.8°[11]
Benzene-ethylene chloride	+ 0[5,7]	50°	+ 0.34[11]	...	− 0.35°[9,11]
Benzene-hexane	+ 11[11]	70°	+ 0.52[11]	...	− 4.7°[11]
Benzene-stannic chloride	+ 36[7]	30°	+ 2.0[7]	20°	− 31°[9]
Benzene-toluene	+ 9[12]	40°	+ 0.16[11]	...	− 0.45°[9,11]
Bromobenzene-chlorobenzene	0[11]	142°	0[11]	...	0°[11]
Carbondisulfide-methylal	+ 22[5]	35°	+ 1.3[6]	35°	− 6.5°[11]
Carbontetrachloride-ethylacetate	+ 7[5]	50°	+ 0.08[10]	50°	+ 0.55°[11]
Chloroform-ether	− 71[8,13]	33°	− 1.5[8]	20°	+ 16.5°[8]
Ethylacetate-ethyliodide	+ 10[5]	50°	+ 0.7[6]	50°	...
Ethylacetate-methylacetate	− 2[12]	20°	...	...	− 0°[9]

[7] A. Schulze and H. Hock. *Ibid.*, **86**, **445** (1913).

[8] F. Dolezalek and A. Schulze, *Ibid.*, **83**, 45 (1913).

[9] The sign is deduced from the effect of temperature upon vapor pressure.

[10] J. H. Hildebrand, Unpublished measurements.

[11] S. Young, "Fractional Distillation", London, Macmillan Co., 1913, pp 40—42.

[12] G. C. Schmidt, *Z. physik. Chem.*, **99**, 71 (1921). This writer concludes that certain of his mixtures deviate more from Raoult's law at higher temperatures, but this is because he considers the excess vapor pressure rather than the ratio of the actual to the ideal vapor pressure.

[13] P. Kohnstamm and B. M. van Dalfsen. *Proc., Akad. Wet.*, **29**, 156 (1901).

[14] Additional data are given by R. Kremann, R. Meingast and F. Gugl, *Monats.*, **35**, 731 (1914); **37**, 559 (1915).

$$\Delta E_v^M = (x_1 V_1 + x_2 V_2) A_{12} \varphi_1 \varphi_2 \quad (37)$$

where A_{12} is a constant, we find on substituting Equations 37 and 29 into Equation 21:

$$\Delta V^M = A_{12} (x_1 V_1 + x_2 V_2)(\varphi_1 \beta_1 + \varphi_2 \beta_2) \varphi_1 \varphi_2 \quad (38)$$

Differentiating, we obtain for $\Delta \overline{V}_1$ and $\Delta \overline{V}_2$

$$\Delta \overline{V}_1 = A_{12} V_1 \varphi_2^2 [\beta_2 + 2 \varphi_1 (\beta_1 - \beta_2)] \quad (39a)$$

$$\Delta \overline{V}_2 = A_{12} V_2 \varphi_1^2 [\beta_1 + 2 \varphi_2 (\beta_2 - \beta_1)] \quad (39b)$$

Substitution of different values β_1 and β_2 for CS_2 and methylal would doubtless improve the agreement in Fig. 1.

The general relation between volume changes and deviations from Raoult's Law is illustrated in Table 1. Also shown is a third effect, the change in temperature is an adiabatic mixing process which must of course have a sign opposite to that of the heat of mixing; thus for regular solutions, we may expect a decrease in temperature to accompany positive volume changes and positive deviations from Raoult's Law.

Order and disorder in solutions. In the introduction to this chapter, we mentioned briefly the problem of the preferential ordering induced in the solution by differences in the interaction energy. For the case of a quasi-lattice model, the problem has been studied almost exhaustively by Guggenheim[15], Rushbrooke[16], and Kirkwood[17].

One of the reasons for the careful analysis of this problem is that it is a special case of the order-disorder problem for solid solutions (*i. e.* metallic alloys). In this latter case, in addition to the factors considered here, we have in addition the possibility of long-range order in the crystal, which is impossible in liquid mixtures. We shall refer to this again briefly in Chapter XIX. Unfortunately almost all the work has been based upon a very specialized model, that of a quasi-crystalline solution in which the molecules of each component occupy single lattice sites.

We assume that each molecule has z nearest neighbors where z is the so-called "coordination number" of the quasi-lattice, and further that the potential energy is the sum of the energies of all nearest neighbor pairs, all interactions with more distant molecules being neglected. The latter approximation is certainly far from exact since the contribution of the non-

[15] E. A. Guggenheim, *Proc. Roy. Soc.*, **A 148**, 304 (1935). See also R. H. Fowler and E. A. Guggenheim, "Statistical Thermodynamics", (Cambridge, 1939), pp. 350—366.
[16] G. S. Rushbrooke, *Proc. Roy. Soc.*, **A 166**, 296 (1938).
[17] J. G. Kirkwood, *J. Phys. Chem.*, **43**, 97 (1939).

nearest neighbor pairs increases the attractive energy by about 20%[18], but any attempt to include these factors would make the equations prohibitively complicated.

If we make a single exchange of molecules between liquids 1 and 2, we destroy z 1—1 and z 2—2 pairs and form 2 z 1 – 2 pairs. If we define the decrease of potential energy in the process as 2 w, then;

$$w = \frac{z}{2}(2\varepsilon_{12} - \varepsilon_{11} - \varepsilon_{22}) \tag{40}$$

where the ε's are the potential energies of the pairs, all negative of course. If we further define the number of 1 – 2 pairs as zX_{12}, the energy of mixing is clearly:

$$\Delta H^M = \Delta E^M = z \cdot X_{12} \frac{2w}{2z} = X_{12} w \tag{41}$$

Where the interchange energy w is zero, the solution will of course be athermal, and the numbers of 1—1, 2—2 and 1—2 pairs will be those calculated for a random distribution. Where w is positve, there will be a tendency for the formation of a fewer number of 1—2 pairs than the random value, thus producing a smaller energy of mixing than that calculated from the random model. At the same time, however, the entropy of mixing is also decreased, so that the free energy is at least partially compensated. Conversely, if w is negative, the formation of 1 – 2 pairs is favored, and, although the absolute value of ΔE^M is increased over the random value, the increase is in a negative direction, and produces a decrease in the free energy. In this case, the entropy also decreases, causing a similar compensation in the free energy.

The first attempt to calculate X_{12} was made by Guggenheim[15] who assumed without proof what has become known as the "quasi-chemical" condition. If we write the formation of 1—2 pairs from 1—1 and 2—2 pairs symbolically as:

$$(1—1) + (2—2) \rightleftarrows 2(1—2) \tag{42}$$

it seems not unreasonable to try to express the equilibrium condition in a form analogous to the mass-action law for chemical reactions:

$$\frac{(zX_{12})^2}{(zX_{11})(zX_{22})} = 4e^{\frac{-2w}{zkT}} \tag{43}$$

[18] J. E. Lennard-Jones and A. E. Ingham, *Proc. Roy. Soc.*, **A 107,** 636 (1925).

In Equation 39, the molecular partition functions for three species are assumed to be identical except for symmetry numbers of 2 for the like pairs, leading to the entropy contribution of 4. We may express the number of 1—1 and 2—2 pairs in terms of the number of molecules n_1 and n_2 of the two species:

$$z X_{11} = \frac{z n_1 - z X_{12}}{2} \tag{44a}$$

$$z X_{22} = \frac{z n_2 - z X_{12}}{2} \tag{44b}$$

Substituting in Equation 43, we obtain the "quasi-chemical equation" of Guggenheim:

$$\frac{X_{12}^2}{(n_1 - X_{12})(n_2 - X_{12})} = e^{\frac{-2w}{zkT}} \tag{45}$$

If we solve Equation 41 for X_{12}, and rearrange, we have:

$$X_{12} = (n_1 + n_2)\, x_1 x_2 \frac{2}{\xi + 1} \tag{46}$$

where a new function ξ is defined for convenience:

$$\xi = \left\{ 1 + 4 x_1 x_2 \left(e^{\frac{2w}{zkT}} - 1\right) \right\}^{1/2} \tag{47}$$

We thus obtain ΔE^M:

$$\Delta E^M = (n_1 + n_2) \frac{2w}{\xi + 1} x_1 x_2 \tag{48}$$

From this we may obtain the free energy by integration, assuming w independent of temperature. (This is a much better approximation than may be apparent. The integration takes place under conditions of constant volume, and if the interatomic radii remain fixed, the ε's are presumably independent of temperature.)

$$\frac{-\Delta A^M}{T} = \int \frac{\Delta E^M}{T^2}\, dT + C \tag{49}$$

The temperature independent term C is of course the athermal entropy of mixing. The integration is tedious but straight forward and yields:

$$\Delta A^M = (n_1 + n_2)kT\left\{x_1 \ln x_1 + x_2 \ln x_2 + \frac{z}{2} x_1 \ln \frac{\xi - 1 + 2x_1}{x_1(\xi + 1)} + \frac{z}{2} x_2 \ln \frac{\xi - 1 + 2x_2}{x_2(\xi + 1)}\right\} \quad (50)$$

The partial molal quantities may be written:

$$\Delta \bar{A}_1 = RT\left\{\ln x_1 + \frac{z}{2} \ln \frac{\xi - 1 + 2x_1}{x_1(\xi + 1)}\right\} \quad (51a)$$

$$\Delta \bar{A}_2 = RT\left\{\ln x_2 + \frac{z}{2} \ln \frac{\xi - 1 + 2x_2}{x^2(\xi + 1)}\right\} \quad (51b)$$

$$\Delta \bar{E}_1 = (\boldsymbol{N}w)x_2^2 \frac{1}{\xi}\left\{1 + \frac{(\xi - 1)x_1}{(\xi + 1)x_2}\right\} \quad (52a)$$

$$\Delta \bar{E}_2 = (\boldsymbol{N}w)x_1^2 \frac{1}{\xi}\left\{1 + \frac{\xi - 1}{\xi + 1}\frac{x_2}{x_1}\right\} \quad (52b)$$

We may replace $\boldsymbol{N}$w by E* and $\frac{2w}{zkT}$ by $\frac{2E^*}{zRT}$ where E* is the partial molal heat of mixing ot either component at *infinite dilution.* If $\varepsilon_{12} = (\varepsilon_{11}\,\varepsilon_{22})^{1/2}$, then $E^* = V(\delta_1 - \delta_2)^2$ (See Equation 2).

Since ξ is a function of composition, the above equations do not show the nature of the corrections involved. We may expand the various equations as power series in $\frac{2E^*}{zRT}$:

$$\frac{\Delta A^M}{N_1 + N_2} = RT(x_1 \ln x_1 + x_2 \ln x_2) + E^* x_1 x_2 \left\{1 - \frac{1}{2}\left(\frac{2E^*}{zRT}\right) x_1 x_2 - \frac{1}{6}\left(\frac{2E^*}{zRT}\right)^2 x_1 x_2 (x_1 - x_2)^2 + \ldots\right\} \quad (53)$$

$$\frac{\Delta E^M}{N_1 + N_2} = E^* x_1 x_2 \left\{1 - \left(\frac{2E^*}{zRT}\right) x_1 x_2 - \frac{1}{2}\left(\frac{2E^*}{zRT}\right)^2 x_1 x_2 (x_1 - x_2)^2 + \ldots\right\} \quad (54)$$

$$\frac{\Delta S^M}{N_1 + N_2} = -R(x_1 \ln x_1 + x_2 \ln x_2) - \frac{E^* x_1 x_2}{T}\left\{\frac{1}{2}\left(\frac{2E^*}{zRT}\right) x_1 x_2 + \frac{1}{3}\left(\frac{2E^*}{zRT}\right)^2 x_1 x_2 (x_1 - x_2)^2 + \ldots\right\} \quad (55)$$

The corresponding partial molal quantities are:

$$\Delta\bar{A}_1 = RT\ln x_1 + E^* x_2^2 \left\{1 + \frac{1}{2}\left(\frac{2E^*}{zRT}\right) x_1 (1 - 3x_2) + \frac{1}{6}\left(\frac{2E^*}{zRT}\right)^2 x_1 (1 - 11x_2 + 28x_2^2 - 20x_2^3) + \ldots\right\} \quad (56a)$$

$$\Delta\bar{A}_2 = RT\ln x_2 + E^* x_1^2 \left\{1 + \frac{1}{2}\left(\frac{2E^*}{zRT}\right) x_2 (1 - 3x_1) + \frac{1}{6}\left(\frac{2E^*}{zRT}\right)^2 x_2 (1 - 11x_1 + 28x_1^2 - 20x_1^3) + \ldots\right\} \quad (56b)$$

$$\Delta\bar{E}_1 = E^* x_2^2 \left\{1 + \left(\frac{2E^*}{zRT}\right) x_1 (1 - 3x_2) + \frac{1}{2}\left(\frac{2E^*}{zRT}\right)^2 x_1 (1 - 11x_2 + 28x_2^2 - 20x_2^3) + \ldots\right\} \quad (57a)$$

$$\Delta\bar{E}_2 = E^* x_1^2 \left\{1 + \left(\frac{2E^*}{zRT}\right) x_2 (1 - 3x_1) + \frac{1}{2}\left(\frac{2E^*}{zRT}\right)^2 x_2 (1 - 11x_1 + 28x_1^2 - 20x_1^3) + \ldots\right\} \quad (57b)$$

$$\Delta\bar{S}_1 = -R\ln x_1 + \frac{E^*}{T} x_2^2 \left\{\frac{1}{2}\left(\frac{2E^*}{zRT}\right) x_1 (1 - 3x_2) + \frac{1}{3}\left(\frac{2E^*}{zRT}\right)^2 x_1 (1 - 11x_2 + 28x_2^2 - 20x_2^3) + \ldots\right\} \quad (58a)$$

$$\Delta\bar{S}_2 = -R\ln x_2 + \frac{E^*}{T} x_1^2 \left\{\frac{1}{2}\left(\frac{2E^*}{zRT}\right) x_2 (1 - 3x_1) + \frac{1}{3}\left(\frac{2E^*}{zRT}\right)^2 x_2 (1 - 11x_1 + 28x_1^2 - 20x_1^3) + \ldots\right\} \quad (58b)$$

So far we have assumed the quasi-chemical equation without proof. Rushbrooke[16], Guggenheim[19] and Kirkwood[20] have shown that the method is exactly equivalent to the Bethe[21] method of local configurations. Bethe and Kirkwood[22] by applying the exact method of moments to this particular model of a solution, have shown that the series expansion of the quasi-chemical method is correct to terms in the third power of E* (i. e. as

[19] E. A. Guggenheim, *Proc. Roy. Soc.*, **A 169**, 134 (1938); See also R. H. Fowler and E. A. Guggenheim *Ibid*, **A 174**, 189 (1940).

[20] J. G. Kirkwood, *J. Chem. Phys.*, **8**, 623 (1940).

[21] H. A. Bethe, *Proc. Roy. Soc.*, **A 150**, 552 (1935).

[22] H. A. Bethe and J. G. Kirkwood, *J. Chem. Phys.*, **7**, 578 (1939).

far as the expansions are carried in Equations 53-58) but that the terms in $(E^*)^4$ are incorrect. Since, however, even the terms in $(E^*)^2$ introduce only small corrections, we may ignore this minor difference.

Let us now examine the nature of the correction which we have found by allowing for the ordering effect of the energy of mixing. First, we find that if we neglect the higher powers of E^*, we recover the original Equations 1-4 based on random mixing. Equation 7 enables us to predict that there wouldbe no first order correction for ΔA^M, but we could not have anticipated that this was also true for the energy and the entropy. We shall therefore expect the first order corrections in ΔS and ΔH arising from the volume effect to completely swamp the only second order corrections from the non-randomness.

The magnitude of the correction terms might be considered. We shall find in Chapter XVI that at the critical solution temperature (based on Equations 3 and 4) $E^*/RT = 2$. Hence unless two phases exist, the correction term in Equation 53, $\frac{1}{2}\left(\frac{2E^*}{zRT}\right) x_1 x_2$ cannot exceed $\frac{1}{2z}$ or if $z = 10$, 5%.

Let us now combine Equation 53 for the non-randomness effect with Equation 22 for the volume effect. We obtain then for the free energy:

$$\frac{\Delta F^M}{N_1 + N_1} = RT(x_1 \ln x_1 + x_2 \ln x_2) + E^* x_1 x_2 - (E^*)^2 x_1^2 x_2^2 \left(\frac{\beta}{2V} + \frac{1}{zRT}\right) + \dots \quad (59)$$

If we take $\beta = 10^{-4}$ atm^{-1}, $V = 100$ cc., $z = 8$, $RT = 600$ calories, we find $\frac{\beta}{2V} = 2 \times 10^{-5}$ cal^{-1} while $\frac{1}{zRT} = 2 \times 10^{-4}$ cal^{-1}, an order of magnitude greater. It appears therefore that in the case of the free energy, the major correction to be applied is that for the non-random ordering, while in the case of the entropy and heat of mixing, this correction is outweighed by the much greater one due to the volume change.

Unfortunately the quasi-crystalline model is undoubtedly much too simplified. Guggenheim[23] has considered the problem for molecules occupying multiple sites (essentially chain polymers) and has obtained equations entirely analogous to Equations 48—58, but to date no one has successfully removed the restrictions of the lattice model and (which is more serious) the elimination of all interactions between non-adjacent pairs.

Fortunately, the corrections due to the non-randomness are sufficiently small in most cases that for the accuracy desired for the semi-quantitative considerations of this book, they need not be retained. As a matter of fact, there is little or no experimental evidence which permits us to choose between Equation 59 and a simpler one. The main purpose of such a theoret-

[23] E. A. Guggenheim, *Proc. Roy. Soc.*, **A 183**, 213 (1944).

ical study as this was to eliminate the possibility of serious error due to neglect of the non-random ordering; it would have been difficult to predict in advance that the corrections would be of so small a magnitude.

In subsequent chapters we shall assume that the free energy of mixing may be represented as the sum of the athermal entropy of mixing and a heat of mixing calculated without reference to either the volume effect or the ordering effect (*i. e.*, a ΔH^M calculated according to Chapter VII). For most cases this will mean the use of equations identical with Equations 3 and 4 save for the substitution of F for A.

$$\Delta F^M = RT\,(x_1 \ln x_1 + x_2 \ln x_2) + V_m\,(\delta_1 - \delta_2)^2\,\varphi_1\,\varphi_2 \tag{60}$$

$$\Delta \bar{F}_1 = RT \ln x_1 + V_1\,(\delta_1 - \delta_2)^2\,\varphi_2^2 \tag{61}$$

$$\Delta \bar{F}_2 = RT \ln x_2 + V_2\,(\delta_1 - \delta_2)^2\,\varphi_1^2 \tag{62}$$

We shall have occasion to refer to the separate terms of Equations 60-62 as the entropy term and the heat term, although as we have seen, they are not exactly so separable. Only when the heat and entropy are considered separately (i. e. when the temperature dependence of the free energy has been measured, or when the heat has been measured directly by calorimetric methods) shall we need to consider correction factors due to volume change; in such cases, we must use Equations 27 and 28.

The molecular distribution function approach to solutions. We have alluded in previous chapters to a general method of characterizing solutions by means of molecular distribution functions. The method, which is virtually free of any artificiality of model, was developed by McMillan and Mayer[24] along the lines previously applied to gases[25]. The symbolism is entirely analogous to that developed for the treatmend of liquids outlined in Chapter V. A set of distribution functions $F_n\{n\}$ are defined and normalized according to Equations V—102-103 However, when we come to use these functions, we shall need only those for the solute molecules at infinite dilution; the distribution functions of the solvent molecules or those of the solute at finite concentrations are never used. The nature of the solvent will of courseinfluence the solute distribution functions, but the solvent functions never appear explicitly in the equations to follow.

Since there is no long range structure, all the higher distribution functions become equal to the product of the F_1's of the molecules involved when all the intermolecular distances are large. For convenience we define a new set of functions $g_n\{n\}$ which become zero when the molecules are all separated by large distances:

---

[24] W.G. McMillan and J.E. Mayer, *J. Chem. Phys.*, **13**, 276 (1945).

[25] J. E. Mayer and S. F. Harrison, *J. Chem. Phys.*, **5**, 74 (1937). See also J. E. Mayer and M. G. Mayer, "Statistical Mechanics," (John Wiley and Sons, Inc.), **1940**.

$$g_2(i,j) = F_2(i,j) - F_1(i)\,F_1(j) \tag{63}$$

$$g_3(i,j,k) = F_3(i,j,k) - F_2(i,j,)\,F_1(k) - F_2(j,k)\,F_1(i) - F_2(k,i)\,F_1(j) + 2F_1(i)\,F_1(j)\,F_1(k) \tag{64}$$

(For the general definition of $g_n\{n\}$, see reference 24, equation 50). The function g_2 measures the divergence of the pair distribution function $F_2(i,j)$ from a simple product $F_1(i)\,F_1(j)$. For unfavorable configurations of the pair (such as those in which they are so close that there is a large repulsive energy) g_2 is negative; for favorable arrangements (such as those produced by special attractive forces), g_2 is positive; when the two molecules are separated by a sufficiently large distance that interactions are negligible, g_2 is zero. The higher g-functions have similar meanings and are zero whenever it is possible to separate the n molecules of the set into two or more non-interacting sub-sets.

By means of grand partition functions, McMillan and Mayer derived a rigorous series expansion for the osmotic pressure in terms of concentration. In our symbolism we may write this equation as:

$$\Pi = RT\left(\frac{1}{M_2}c + A_2c^2 + A_3c^3 + \ldots\right) \tag{65}$$

where c is the concentration of solute in mass per unit volume of solution. M_2 is the molecular weight of the solute and the A_n are constants at constant temperature. In the absence of long range forces of the coulomb type, this series converges and is valid with constant coefficients at all concentrations.

The coefficients A_n are related to the molecular distribution functions F_n and the corresponding g_n. For the coefficients A_2 and A_3, Mayer and McMillan found:

$$A_2 = \frac{N}{M_2^2}\left[-\frac{1}{2V}\int g_2\{2\}\,d\{2\}\right] \tag{66}$$

$$A_3 = \frac{N^2}{M_2^3}\left[-\frac{1}{3V}\int g_3\{3\}\,d\{3\}\right] + \frac{4N^2}{M_2^3}\left[-\frac{1}{2V}\int g_2\{2\}\,d\{2\}\right]^2$$

$$= \frac{N^2}{M_2^3}\left[-\frac{1}{3V}\int g_3\{3\}\,d\{3\}\right] + 4\,M_2\,A_2^2 \tag{67}$$

The first term in Equation 65 is merely the van't Hoff limiting law, and we see that the coefficient of the second term A_2 depends upon the distribution functions of a pair of solvent molecules; A_3 on the distribution functions of a triplet; and similarly for the higher terms.

Equations 65—67 have an exact correspondence to the virial equation of state of an imperfect gas[25]. If the osmotic pressure Π were replaced by the gas pressure P and the g-functions in Equations 66—67 were defined for the infinitely rarefied gas instead of the infinitely dilute solution, the two would become identical. The first term of the series in each case describes the situation when molecules do not interact, yielding the perfect gas law and van't Hoff's law respectively, while the higher terms correct successively for interactions of pairs, triplets, etc.

For convenience in comparing these equations with others in this book, we wish to convert Equation 65 into the analogous series for the partial molal free energy of the solvent $\Delta \overline{F}_1$ in powers of the volume fraction of solute φ_2:

$$\Delta \overline{F}_1 = - RT \left[\frac{\varphi_2}{m_2} + a_2 \varphi_2^2 + a_3 \varphi_2^3 + \ldots \right] \qquad (68)$$

where m_2 is as before the ratio of molal volumes V_2/V_1 and the a_n form a set of constant coefficients similar to the A_n. The exact transformation from the A_2's in a solution under osmotic pressure, to a_2's in a solution under the same pressure P as the pure substances is tedious since it involves small but not entirely negligible corrections for compressibility, volume changes on mixing, etc. Suffice it to say that the coefficient a_2 and a_3 may be written as:

$$a_2 = \frac{V_1}{V_2^2} \left\{ - \frac{N}{2V} \int g_2 \{2\}\, d\{2\} + \frac{RT}{2} \beta_1 + V_2 - \overline{V}_2{}^* \right\} \qquad (69)$$

$$a_3 = \frac{V_1}{V_2^3} \left\{ - \frac{N^2}{3V} \int g_3 \{3\}\, d\{3\} \right.$$

$$\left. + 4 N^2 \left[- \frac{1}{2V} \int g_2 \{2\}\, d\{2\} \right]^2 + \ldots \right\} \qquad (70)$$

where β_1 is the compressibility of pure solvent and $\overline{V}_2{}^*$ is the partial molal volume of the solute at infinite dilution. For athermal solutions $\overline{V}_2{}^* = V_2$, and the terms involving compressibilities are almost negligible.

We may obtain the volume change $\Delta \overline{V}_1$ from Equation 68 by differentiating with respect to P:

$$\Delta\bar{V}_1 = \left(\frac{\partial \Delta F_1}{\partial P}\right)_T = -RT\left\{\left[\left(\frac{\partial a_2}{\partial P}\right)_T + 2a_2(\beta_1 - \beta_2) - \frac{V_1}{V_2}(\beta_1 - \beta_2)\right]\varphi_2^2 + \right.$$

$$\left.\left[\left(\frac{\partial a_3}{\partial P}\right)_T + 3a_3(\beta_1 - \beta_2) - 2a_2(\beta_1 - \beta_2)\right]\varphi_2^3 + \ldots\right\} \quad (71)$$

For an ideal solution, the a's may be calculated by the series expansion of $RT\ln x_1$ in powers of φ_2 (cf. Equation VI — 37).

$$a_2^i = \frac{(2V_2 - V_1)V_1}{2V_2^2}$$

$$a_3^i = \frac{(3V_2^2 - 3V_1V_2 + V_1^2)V_1}{3V_2^3} \quad (72)$$

Neglecting the correction terms in the compressibility, we conclude from Equations 69 and 70 that for a solution to be ideal, the g-functions must satisfy the conditions

$$-\frac{N}{V}\int g_2\{2\}\,d\{2\} = 2V_2 - V_1 \quad (73)$$

$$-\frac{N^2}{V}\int g_2\{3\}\,d\{3\} = -(9V_2^2 - 9V_1V_2 + 2V_1^2) \quad (74)$$

Actually of course, unless we can determine the g-functions for a given system, the molecular distribution function method, while formally exact, is not very useful. Unless we attempt the almost prohibitively difficult task of evaluating g_2 in terms of the potential functions of solute and solvent molecules, we are reduced to using one of various approximations, mainly two: the continuous solvent or the quasi-lattice. In the former case, we assume that the solute molecules are sufficiently larger (in every dimension) than those of the solvent, that the geometry of packing of the solvent has but a negligible effect on the g-functions. In this case the problem is identicall with that for the imperfect gas except that from the potential function χ of the solute "gas" we subtract a smoothed potential χ_o for the solvent. For the athermal case ($\chi = \chi_o$), g_2 will be zero except for those configurations where the molecules interpenetrate (overlap), where it will be negative. If we assume rigid molecules, $g_2 = -1$ for all overlapping configurations. When the formation of solute pairs is energetically favored, g_2 is positive for such configurations, corresponding to a positive heat of mixing. For those cases in which the intermolecular forces favor solute-solvent interactions (negative heats), g_2 is negative in such regions.

Zimm[26] has used the concept of a continuous and structureless solvent to evaluate A_2 for athermal solutions of large rigid spheres and long rigid cylindrical rods (cf. Chapter VI, Equations 36, and 38).

$$\text{Spheres:}\quad A_2 = \frac{2\boldsymbol{N}\pi r^3}{3M_2^2} = \frac{4}{\varrho_2 M_2} \tag{75}$$

$$\text{Rods:}\quad A_2 = \frac{\boldsymbol{N}\pi d l^2}{4M_2^2} = \frac{4}{\varrho_2^2(\boldsymbol{N}\pi d^3)} \qquad l \gg d \tag{76}$$

where ϱ_2 is the density of the solute, r is the diameter of the sphere; d the diameter of the cylindrical rod, and l its length (very much greater than d), Transforming to a_2 (and neglecting terms in β_1), we find:

$$\text{Spheres:}\quad a_2 = \frac{4V_1}{V_2} = \frac{4}{m} \tag{77}$$

$$\text{Rods:}\quad a_2 = \frac{4V_1}{\boldsymbol{N}\pi d^3} = \frac{V_1}{V_2}\,\frac{l}{d} = \frac{l}{dm} \qquad l \gg d \tag{78}$$

It is interesting to note that A_2 and a_2 are constant for a series of rods of the same diameter but of differing lengths while for spheres A_2 and a_2 decrease regularly with increasing size. Experimentally we find A_2 and a_2 constant for solutions of homologous linear polymers, but not for solutions of the more compact protein molecules. In addition to the case of spheres and rods mentioned above, Zimm[26] has applied molecular distribution methods to solutions of flexible chain polymers, but we defer consideration of this to Chapter XIX.

Similar considerations hold for a quasi-lattice treatment. If we assume that a solute molecule may occupy s sites in a certain way, $g_2 = -1$ for all configurations of two solute molecules in which one or more sites are occupied simultaneously by both molecules, and $g_2 = 0$ for all other configurations. The integrals in Equations 66—67 are replaced by summations over all arrangements of the molecules in the lattice, proper consideration being given to the ways in which solvent molecules may occupy lattice sites. Where interaction energies alter the probabilities of occupying different sites, appropriate changes must be made in g_2.

In the lattice approximation, the molecular distribution method is of course only a different formulation of the quasi-lattice method discussed in Chapter VI, while the continuous solvent approximation is analogous to the excluded volume treatment of Huggins in its simplest form. The treatment developed here has the advantage that the approximations are made at the

[26] B. H. Zimm, *J. Chem. Phys.*, **14**, 164 (1946).

end where it is easier to evaluate the seriousness of the errors introduced; in particular, the molecular distribution approach affords us a general model to which all over-simplified theories can be related and compared. In addition, with respect to the quasi-lattice method, a great deal of tedious algebra in evaluating Ω and transforming it into ΔF^M is avoided. The series method is of course most effective for dilute solutions where the higher terms are unimportant. Evaluation of the higher integrals A_4, A_5, etc. is of such difficulty as to be practically impossible, and for concentrated solutions we have to fall back upon approximate theories which give the free energy in closed forms which are certainly inexact but frequently useful. It should be noted that if we regard the "excluded volume" of Huggins (see Chapter VI) in a general sense, and define the ratios α, β, γ, etc. in terms of the g-functions, his theory becomes formally exact and entirely equivalent to the Mayer and McMillan treatment.

CHAPTER IX

Polarity

The average attractive potential betwen two isolated dipoles, $\bar{\varepsilon}$, according to the theory of Keesom, already stated in Chapter IV, is

$$\bar{\varepsilon} = \frac{-2\mu_1^2 \mu_2^2}{3r^6 kT} \tag{1}$$

where μ_1 and μ_2 are the dipole moments of the two dipoles, r the distance between their centers and k the Boltzmann constant. Favorable orientations occur at low temperatures but rapidly diminish with rising temperature. The effect is very sensitive to the value of μ, being proportional to μ^4 for a single species; it is consequently important to consider the magnitude of any dipole moments involved in the molecular interactions occurring in solutions. We are indebted mainly to Debye[1] for the theory involved in the determination of dipole moments. Since the orientations of molecules in liquids and solids are dependent upon molecular shapes, and they are not free to assume the Boltzmann distribution of dipole orientations implied in Equation 1, the theory is limited, initially, to gases.

The quantity directly measured is, of course, the dielectric constant ε. A consideration of the interaction between the external field and the polarizability, α, of the individual molecules has led to the Clausius-Mosotti[2] relation,

$$\frac{\varepsilon - 1}{\varepsilon + 2} = \tfrac{4}{3}\pi n \alpha \tag{2}$$

where n is the number of molecules per cc. It is preferable to substitute molar quantities

$$\frac{\varepsilon - 1}{\varepsilon + 2} \cdot V = \frac{4}{3}\pi N \alpha = \mathbf{P} \tag{3}$$

where N is the Avogadro number and **P** the molar polarization. Now there are three possible contributions to **P**; the distortion of the electron cloud of the molecule, $\mathbf{P}_E$, the distortion of the molecule itself due to atomic shifts,

---

[1] P. Debye, "Polar Molecules", Chem. Catalog Co., Inc., New York, (1929).

[2] O. F. Mosotti, *Mem. di Math. e di fisico di Modena*, **24**, II, 49 (1850).
R. Clausius, "Die mechanische Wärmetheorie" Vol. II, p. 62, Vieweg (1879).

$\mathbf{P}_A$, usually relatively small, and the orientation of permanent dipoles, $\mathbf{P}_O$. The last is temperature dependent. While Debye originally defined the polarizability as including all three terms, later workers have tended to use it as the sum of only the electronic and atomic contributions, *i.e.*

$$\alpha = \alpha_E + \alpha_A \tag{4}$$

so that

$$\mathbf{P} = \frac{\varepsilon - 1}{\varepsilon + 2} \cdot \mathrm{V} = \frac{4}{3} \pi \boldsymbol{N} (\alpha + \frac{\mu^2}{3kT}) = (\mathbf{P}_E + \mathbf{P}_A) + \mathbf{P}_O \tag{5}$$

The two parts can be separately determined in either of two ways. One is to plot **P** against $1/T$, the slope giving the value of $\mathbf{P}_O$ and the intercept at $1/T = 0$ the value of $\mathbf{P}_E + \mathbf{P}_A$. The other is to determine ε at frequencies so high that the atomic and molecular shifts cannot occur. $\mathbf{P}_O$ cannot respond to frequencies greater than about 10^{10} per second, corresponding to short radio waves; $\mathbf{P}_A$ persists to about 10^{12}, or infra-red frequencies; $\mathbf{P}_E$ persists to over 10^{15}, or far into the ultra-violet. The first two effects are eliminated by using visible light, determining the refractive index, n, substituting n^2 for ε at these frequencies according to the Maxwell relation. This gives the Lorenz-Lorentz[3] formula

$$\frac{n^2 - 1}{n^2 + 2} \cdot \mathrm{V} = \mathbf{P}_E \tag{6}$$

This expression is known also as the "molar refraction". In working with gases where both n and ε are close to unity, it is customary to substitute 3 for $n^2 + 2$ in this equation, as well as for $\varepsilon + 2$ in Equations 2, 3 and 5. This equation affords a means of evaluating α in the equations for the dispersion potential, Chapter IV, Equations 5—8.

A valuable compilation of dipole moments has recently been made by Wesson[4].

The values reported for one substance often vary considerably. Those for chloroform, for example, range from 0.95 to $1.27 \cdot 10^{-18}$ e. s. u. Differences have been due not only to the ordinary errors of measurement, but to the method used to eliminate electron polarization, whether optical or thermal; to the choice of gas or dilute solution for the measurement of dielectric constant and, in the latter case, to the choice of solvent. It is customary

---

[3] H. A. Lorentz, "Theory of Electrons", *Ann. Physik.* **9**, 641 (1880); L. Lorenz, *Ibid.* **11**, 70 (1880).

[4] L. G. Wesson, "Tables of Electric Dipole Moments", Tech. Report No. II, Lab. of Insulation Research, Mass. Inst. Tech., April, 1947. See also, N. V. Sidgwick, *Trans. Faraday Soc.*, **30**, (1934), Appendix. C. P. Smyth, "Dielectric Constant and Molecular Structure", (1931), Reinhold Pub. Corp., New York.

to express dipole moments either in electrostatic units, designated "e. s. u.", or in Debye units; 1 Debye unit $= 10^{-18}$ e. s. u.

It should be remembered that the contribution of dipoles to intermolecular potential according to Equation 1 varies as the fourth power of the dipole moment, therefore a change from 1 to 2 represents a 16-fold increase in the effect.

We shall see in later chapters that solutions of non polar molecules with molecules of dipole moments of the order of 1 or less can often be dealt with to the practical neglect of polarity.

When the Clausius-Mosotti equation is applied to liquids, it is found that the values of dipole moment so obtained do not agree with those derived from measurements of the same substance in the gaseous state, and that the dipole moments for a polar substance in a non-polar solvent depend considerably upon the solvent and upon concentration except in the case of the weaker dipoles. Onsager[5], by regarding the field as homogeneous right up to the surface of the molecule, derived an equation similar to Equation 5, but with $(\varepsilon - 1)/(\varepsilon + 2)$ replaced by $(\varepsilon - 1)(2\varepsilon + 1)/9\varepsilon$. Kirkwood[6] introduced a parameter $\bar{\mu}$, to take into account the hindering effect of a molecule upon its neighbors, writing

$$\frac{(\varepsilon - 1)(2\varepsilon + 1)}{9\varepsilon} \cdot \mathrm{V} = \mathbf{P}_{\mathrm{E}} + \mathbf{P}_{\mathrm{A}} + \frac{4\pi N}{3} \frac{\mu \cdot \bar{\mu}}{3kT} \tag{7}$$

The product $\mu\bar{\mu}$ was set equal to $g\mu^2$, g being expressed as

$$g = 1 + \iint \cos\gamma \; \mathrm{F}_2\{2\}\, d\{2\} \tag{8}$$

where γ is the angle between the dipole moments of a representative pair of molecules, and $\mathrm{F}_2\{2\}$ is the generalized pair distribution function (see Chapter V) specifying the probability of two molecules having a given position and orientation with respect to each other. The integration is to be extended over all relative orientations and positions within the sphere beyond which the local dielectric constant has effectively reached its macroscopic value.

Judging by the success of the nearest-neighbor approximation in other fields (see Chapters V, VII, VIII, and XIX), it seems reasonable to assume a quasi-crystalline model in which each molecule possesses a co-ordination shell of z nearest neighbors beyond which orientational correlation does not extend. For such a model, Kirkwood writes for g

$$g = 1 + \mathrm{z}\,\overline{\cos\gamma} \tag{9}$$

[5] L. Onsager, *J. Am. Chem. Soc.*, **58**, 1486 (1936)

[6] J. G. Kirkwood, *J. Chem. Phys.*, **7**, 911 (1939); *Trans. Faraday Soc.*, **42 A**, 7 (1946).

$$\overline{\cos \gamma} = \int \cos \gamma \exp(-W/kT)\, d\omega \tag{10}$$

where z is the number of nearest neighbors, γ the angle between the dipole moments of a representative pair of molecules and W the potential of average torque hindering their rotation. In the words of Kirkwood, "The departure of g from the value unity is a measure of the degree of hindered relative molecular rotation arising from short-range intermolecular forces. From general statistical mechanical considerations it is evident that the value of g must be qualitatively related to the rotational entropy of the liquid. Examination of the values of g calculated from observed dielectric constants brings out the relationship rather clearly. Those polar substances possessing values of g departing but slightly from unity exhibit the thermodynamic properties of "normal" liquids. Those substances possessing values of g departing significantly from unity exhibit the properties of "abnormal" or "associated" liquids". The values of g in Table 1, taken from a paper by Oster and Kirkwood[7], show how values of g serve to set apart the associated liquids as a class in which rotation is strongly hindered.

Table 1

	t°C	$\mu \cdot 10^{18}$	ε	g
Benzonitrile	25	3.90	25.2	0.8
Pyridine	20	2.20	12.5	0.9
Ethyl bromide	20	1.80	9.4	1.1
Nitrobenzene	20	3.90	36.1	1.1
Acetone	20	2.85	21.5	1.1
Ammonia	15	1.48	17.8	1.3
Ethyl ether	20	1.15	4.4	1.7
Water	25	1.84	78.5	2.7
Hydrogen peroxide	0	2.13	91.	2.8
Ethyl alcohol	20	1.70	24.6	3.0
Hydrogen fluoride	0	1.8	83.6	3.1
Hydrogen cyanide	20	2.80	116.	4.1

Oster[8] has discussed the dielectric properties of liquid mixtures and calculated from experimental data the g-factor for polar molecules in nonpolar solvents. The behavior is easy to interpret in terms of Equation 9. In

[7] G. Oster and J. G. Kirkwood, *J. Chem. Phys.* **11**, 175 (1943).

[8] G. Oster, *J. Am. Chem. Soc.*, **68**, 2036 (1946).

very dilute solutions, the dipoles are surrounded entirely by solvent molecules, there is no hindered rotation and g is unity. At higher concentrations, solute pairs become important (See the discussion of molecular distribution functions in Chapter VIII); since isolated dipole pairs will always orient anti-parallel, ($\cos \gamma = -1$), the g-factor in this range is less than unity. At higher concentrations, larger clusters of dipoles become important, parallel arrangements contribute to g, and after passing through a minimum, g rises continuously to the value for the pure polar solute.

In an application of Onsagers's theory, Wilson[9] has attempted to take into account the actual shapes of molecules.

It is evident that a rigid quantitative treatment of these relations is beset with enormous difficulties, and that any quantitative calculation of the effects of dipoles upon the thermodynamic quantities is still far removed. The subject is under active discussion[10] and it will be interesting to see what the coming years will bring forth.

It is desirable, nevertheless, to be able to appraise, even qualitatively, the effects of dipoles upon the fugacities of the components of solutions. One may well become somewhat familiar with the moments of certain of the frequently occurring dipoles.

Molecules having no permanent dipoles, and which are therefore symmetrical, include the elements; *e. g.* Br_2, P_4, O_2, N_2, S_8, most hydrocarbons, the tetrahalides and other tetrahedral molecules such as $C(NO_2)_4$, and the linear molecules CO_2, CS_2, and p-$C_6H_4Cl_2$. The high moments of such molecules as H_2O, H_2S, SO_2, and $(CH_3)_2O$ are evidence that they are not linear.

Attempts have been made to assign definite values to the moments of a number of bonds. It has become evident, however, that these are modified by the structure of the rest of the molecule. Sutton[11] assigned values for alkyl and aryl derivatives; the substituent groups followed approximately the same order in both series but the same groups could have very different values in the two series; *e. g.* $-NO_2$ gave -3.93 in aryl and -3.05 in alkyl compounds.

It should be understood that the mere magnitudes of dipole moments do not suffice to afford an understanding of their influence upon intermolecular forces. The actual geometry of the molecules must be considered. This was strongly emphasized by Bernal[12] in the following words:

"Finally, I should like to say a few words on the methods now available for treating intermolecular forces in liquids. In my opinion the time is now past when we were restricted to considering a molecule as a sphere of uncertain dimensions possessing only a loose dipole and van der Waals attraction

---

[9] J. N. Wilson, *Chem. Rev.*, **25**, 377 (1939).
[10] See "A general discussion on dielectrics", *Trans. Faraday Soc.*, **42A** (1946); 256 pp.
[11] L. E. Sutton, *Proc. Roy. Soc. London* **A133**, 668 (1931).
[12] J. D. Bernal, *Trans. Faraday Soc.*, **33**, 210 (1937).

and a measurable dipole moment. We know enough both of the shapes of molecules and the nature of the forces between them to go at any rate in many cases far beyond this. The most important characteristic is whether the molecule possesses, not so much a dipole moment, but a highly divergent electrical field, *i. e.*, where its attraction is not spread largely over its surface, but is concentrated at one or two points. Where this is not the case we may enquire whether the shape of the molecule is such that free rotation may be expected to take place in the liquid. This will be so not only for all liquids in which such rotation is known to take place in the crystalline phase but for many others, because in a liquid the irregularity of configuration means effectively that the potential field in respect to rotary movements is much more even than in the case of a crystal and is also, owing to the increase in volume, much weaker. It should be possible in most cases to determine whether such free rotation takes place by the study of Raman spectra in the liquid. All liquids in which free rotation takes place can be reasonably strictly treated as liquids with spherical molecules and the many remarkable uniformities observed in liquids and commented on in the present discussion are probably due to this cause. For liquids whose molecules are so aspherical in shape that the free rotation cannot take place theoretical treatment is obviously more difficult though some help could probably be got from the study of the libration frequencies given by the wings of the Raman spectrum."

A good example of geometrical influence is afforded by the substituted benzenes. The overall dipole moments of the dichlorobenzenes is approximately the vector sum of the C-Cl moments. This is illustrated by the following figures.

	$\mu \cdot 10^{18}$ e. s. u.	
	obs.	calc.
C_6H_5Cl	1.56	(1.56)
o-$C_6H_4Cl_2$	2.24	2.70
m-$C_6H_4Cl_2$	1.48	1.56
p-$C_6H_4Cl_2$	0.	0.

Now if the dipole moment of the whole molecule were considered as the criterion of the polarity, we would expect very different solubilities for ortho, meta, and para di-substituted benzenes. This is not the case, however, for neighboring molecules of the other species are small enough to respond almost identically to the two polar groups of three such isomers. This was demonstrated by Hildebrand and Carter[13] by a study of the solutions of the mono-,

[13] J. H. Hildebrand and J. M. Carter, *Proc. Nat. Acad. Sci.*, **16**, 285 (1930).

di-and tri-substituted nitrobenzenes in benzene. The freezing points of solutions of nitrobenzene in benzene have been obtained by Dahms[14], those of the dinitrobenzenes by Kremann[15], and of symmetrical trinitrobenzene by Desvergnes[16]. The heats of fusion of all but the last have been measured by Andrews, Lynn and Johnston[17]. In the absence of any figure for the trinitrobenzene we have assumed its solubility in ortho-and in meta-dinitrobenzene and in 2-4-6 dinitrotoluene, which are all practically identical[18], to be ideal.

These data enable one to calculate $\bar{F}_2 - \bar{F}_2^{i}$ for each solute, which expresses the deviation from Raoult's law after elimination of the peculiarities

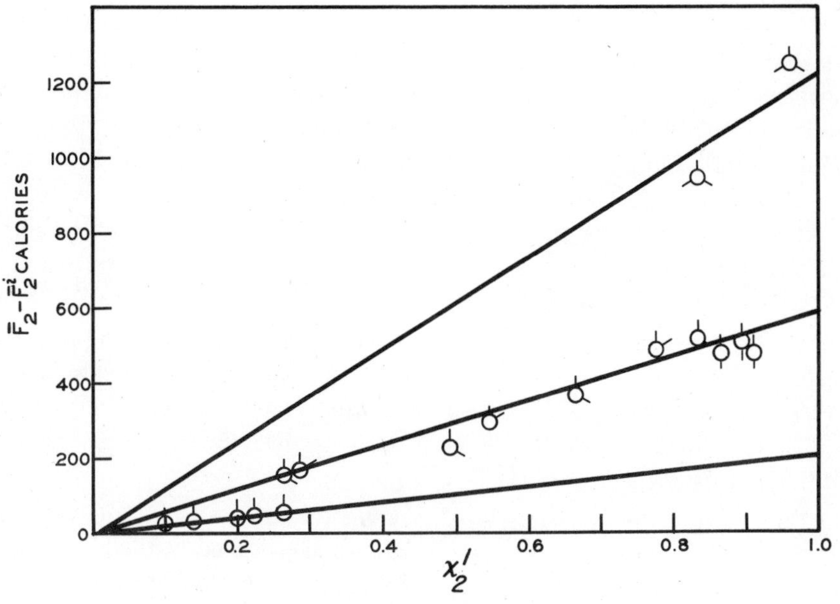

Fig. 1 Relation between number of nitrogroups in nitrobenzenes and deviation from Raoult's law in benzene solutions.

of the solid phase. These solutions obey sufficiently closely the relation $\bar{F}_2 - \bar{F}_2^{i} = Bx_1^2$, so that we may represent them all on the same plot of $\bar{F}_2 - \bar{F}_2^{i}$ against x_1^2, where x_1 is the mole fraction of the solvent, benzene. Figure 1 shows this plot. There is no need to tabulate the data, since the

[14] A. Dahms, *Wied. Ann.* **54**, **496** (1895). More recently L. G. Davy and N. V. Sidgwick have investigated this system, but unfortunately, give concentrations only in moles per liter.

[15] R. Kremann, *Sitz. Akad. Wiss. Wien*, **117**, IIb, **569** (1908).

[16] L. Desvergnes, *Mon. Sci*, **16**, 149 (1925).

[17] D. H. Andrews, G. Lynn and J. Johnston, *J. Am. Chem. Soc.*, **48**, 1274 (1926).

[18] Cf. Int. Crit. Tables, **IV**. 474—475 McGraw Hill Book Co, 1933).

figure illustrates clearly the point to be made. The appendages to the circles representing the experimental points indicate the number and the positions of the nitrogroups in the benzene ring. It will be seen that the different dinitrobenzenes, in spite of their different moments, all show the same deviation from ideal behavior in their solutions in benzene. The mononitrobenzene shows much less deviation and the trinitrobenzene much more. It is evident that it is the number of nitro-groups and not the resultant moment which determines the degree of unlikeness to benzene. The same conclusion can be drawn from the fact the three dinitrobenzenes form ideal solutions with each other.

We may draw the general inference that, for the purpose of evaluating the fields of molecules having more than one polar group, it is necessary to take into account not simply the resultant field but rather what we may call the total polarity of the molecule. This need not, however, be a simple additive matter, for the field of the polar bond may be so thoroughly buried within the molecule as to have little effect upon other molecules. Tetranitromethane, for example, is a typical nonpolar substance, insoluble in water. Again, the bond between tin and chlorine in stannous chloride must be rather strongly ionic in view of its salt-like nature, but in stannic chloride, although the same bonds are doubtless polar, they have little effect upon the external field of the molecule, which is typically nonpolar.

There are several other properties that may serve to distinguish polar substances, but the recent elucidation of the subject from the standpoint of electric moments has made these of less relative value than formerly, hence we will not devote to them the space they seemed to deserve in the first edition of this book[19].

Finally, the dipoles capable of forming "hydrogen bonds" or "bridges", which include —OH, —NH_2, —NH, are so exceptional in their behavior as to require separate consideration, which is given in the following chapter.

THE HEAT OF MIXING OF POLAR MOLECULES

Since the treatment of the heat of mixing discussed in Chapter VII applies primarily to nonpolar molecules where the intermolecular attraction is due to dispersion or London forces, it is important to consider what modifications are necessary in order to treat solutions in which one or both components are polar. Several approaches may be illuminating.

Langmuir's treatment of the energy of mixing in terms of surface energies. Langmuir[20] has analyzed the problem of energy of mixing in a

[19] Cf. W. E. S. Turner, "Molecular Association", Longmans, Green and Co., London, 1915; G. G. Longinescu, *Chem. Rev.*, 6, 381 (1929).

[20] I. Langmuir, Colloid Symposium, Monograph, (1925), p. 48.
The symbols of the following section are those used by Langmuir, except for the mole fraction x; they do not conform with those used elsewhere in this book.

manner particularly suitable for molecules composed of different parts with different field strengths, cases which do not conform to the assumptions made in the preceding pages. He splits the energy of evaporation into three parts, first, that between the two nonpolar portions, second, that between the polar groups, and, third, that between the polar and the nonpolar portions, If S is the surface of a molecule of which the fraction a is non polar and the fraction c is polar, then the a-surface of a molecule is Sa, of which the fraction c is in contact with the c-surface of surrounding molecules, with a corresponding surface energy of $Sac\,\gamma_{ac}$. Similarly, the energy of contact of the c-surface with the surrounding molecules, is also $Sac\,\gamma_{ac}$. The total surface energy of a given molecule is thus $2Sac\gamma_{ac}$. If the molecule is now removed from the liquid, leaving a cavity, there appears the energy $S\,(a\gamma_a + c\gamma_c)$ both on the molecule and in the cavity. When the cavity collapses its energy changes to $Sac\,\gamma_{ac}$.

Langmuir believes that in the vapor phase the larger hydrocarbon molecules tend to become spherical, with partial submergence of the hydroxyl group, so that the surface fractions a and c are different in the vapor phase. This leads to the following expression for the energy of vaporization of a molecule.

$$\lambda = S\left[\, a_c\gamma_a + (a - a_c - ac)\gamma_{ac} + c_c\gamma_c \right] \tag{11}$$

He gives the following values of γ for groups making up the alcohols; 32.7 ergs per cm.^{2} for $—CH_3$, 38.2 for $—CH_2$, 190 for —OH and 34 for —OH against hydrocarbon.

A solution of two different species is treated according to the same methods, considering the five "interfacial" energies involved, yielding for the energy of vaporization of a molecule of component A from the solution,

$$\lambda_{AV} = S_A(a\gamma_a - ac\gamma_{ac} + c\gamma_c - \varphi\beta^2), \tag{12}$$

where

$$\varphi = ab\gamma_{ab} + ad\gamma_{ad} + bc\gamma_{bc} + cd\gamma_{cd} - ac\gamma_{ac} - bd\gamma_{bd} \tag{13}$$

and β is the "surface fraction" of component B,

$$\beta = \frac{S_B N_B}{S_A N_A + S_B N_B} \tag{14a}$$

The surface fraction of A is, similarly,

$$\alpha = \frac{S_A N_A}{S_A N_A + S_B N_B} \tag{14b}$$

By placing $\beta = 0$, in Equation 12, the energy of evaporation of a molecule of A from its own pure liquid is obtained,

$$\lambda'_{AV} = S_A (a\gamma_a - ac\gamma_{ac} + c\gamma_c), \tag{15}$$

and Equation 12 may be written

$$\lambda_{AV} = \lambda'_{AV} - S_A \varphi \beta^2. \tag{16}$$

The Boltzmann equation is next invoked in the form:

$$\frac{p_A}{x_A} = Ke^{\frac{-\lambda_{AV}}{kT}} \tag{17}$$

where K is a general factor, including the difference in units between p and x and assumed to be the same for solution and pure substance. For pure A, the pressure p_A° is obtained by putting $x_A = 1$ in Equation 17, giving

$$p_A^\circ = Ke^{\frac{-\lambda_{AV}}{kT}} \tag{18}$$

which, substituted in 17 gives

$$p_A = p_A^\circ x_A e^{\frac{\varphi \cdot S_A \cdot \beta^2}{kT}} \tag{19a}$$

and for component B, similarly,

$$p_B = p_B^\circ x_B e^{\frac{\varphi \cdot S_B \cdot \alpha^2}{kT}} \tag{19b}$$

These equations may be compared with Equations III—15.

Langmuir gives the values here reproduced in Table 4 for γ for various combinations.

Table 4. Values of Surface Energy γ Calculated from Experimental Data on Vapor Pressures.

	Surfaces	γ, ergs per cm.^{2}
1.	Hydrocarbon-Iodine	13.7
2.	Hydrocarbon-Chlorine	4.1
3.	Hydrocarbon-COO-	33.7
4.	Chlorine-Iodine	4.1
5.	Chlorine-COO-	17.7
6.	Iodine-COO-	16.6
7.	Hydrocarbon-bromine	10.
8.	Hydrocarbon-hydroxyl	33.7
9.	Bromine-hydroxyl	49.6
10.	Hydrocarbon-water	37.4
11.	Hydroxyl-water	12.6

By the aid of these data the following comparisons were made between φ, observed and calculated.

Table 5. Mixture Energies, φ, Observed and Calculated.

	Propyl Bromide $x = 0.5$		Isobutyl Bromide $x = 0.5$		Water		
	Obs.	Calc.	Obs.	Calc.	Obs.	Calc.	α
Methanol	8.90	8.76	7.33	8.52	6.1	6.0	0.46
Ethanol	6.97	5.82	6.61	5.58	11.5	11.7	0.36
Propanol	5.39	4.52	3.24	4.28	15.1	15.0	0.31
Butanol	3.43	3.76	2.89	3.53	..	..	..

Smyth and Engel[21] have made a rather exhaustive test of Langmuir's theory and find it to have only approximate validity. In a series of solutions whose components are hexane, heptane, carbon tetrachloride, ethyl bromide and iodide, and butyl chloride and bromide, they find that the φ calculated from the partial vapor pressures of one component are neither constant nor do they agree with the values calculated from the other component. Furthermore, the interfaces R-Cl and R-Br demand different values for different pairs of components. Their results are summarized in Table 6.

[21] C. P. Smyth and E. W. Engel, *J. Am. Chem. Soc.*, **51**, 2646, 2660 (1929).

Table 6. Values of Surface Energy, γ

Substance	Surface area (A²)	Inter-face	System	φ	γ (ergs. cm²)	γ(ergs./cm²) Lang-muir.
C_7H_{16}	154	R-Cl	C_7H_{16}-CCl_4	0.6	0.6	4.1
C_4H_9Cl	123	R-Cl	C_7H_{16}-C_4H_9Cl	1.14	10.0	
C_2H_5Br	99	R-Br	C_7H_{16}-C_2H_5Br	1.6	6.8	10.0
C_4H_9Br	125	R-Br	C_7H_{16}-C_4H_9Br	1.36	9.2	
C_2H_5I	104	R-I	C_7H_{16}-C_2H_5I (30°)	2.52	7.9	13.7
Cl	41.5	R-I	C_7H_{16}-C_2H_5I (50°)	2.29	7.2	
Br	48.1	Cl-Br	C_4H_9Cl-C_4H_9Br	0+	0+	
I	58 8	Cl-I		. . .	. . .	4.1

Solutions of alcohols with hydrocarbons and alkyl halides show much larger deviations from Raoult's law and also from the Langmuir equations. One system, heptane-ethyl alcohol at 30°, is quoted from their paper in Table 7.

Table 7. Heptane (A) with Ethyl Alcohol (B) at 30°.

x_B	$p_A/p_A^\circ x_A$	$p_B/p_B^\circ x_B$	φ_A	φ_B
0.2	1 192	3.900	34.1	8.71
0.4	1.561	2.062	17.0	6.67
0.6	2.277	1.449	11.0	6.04
0.8	3.952	1.151	7.88	6.99

These authors state their general conclusion as follows:

"It appears that the deviations of liquids from the behavior required by the Langmuir equation may be qualitatively explained in terms of the forces acting between the molecular dipoles. Forces which greatly restrict the freedom of orientation of the dipoles in an externally applied electric field may yet be insufficient to impair seriously the validity of the Langmuir equation. As the effects of the dipoles upon one another depend not only upon their electric moments but also upon their location in the molecules and upon the sizes and shapes of these molecules and probably upon the electronic constraints in them, it appears impossible to formulate any generally valid expression for the exact quantitative representation of the interaction of molecular dipoles. Evidently the assumptions upon which the Langmuir equation is derived are too simple to permit of its general and exact application, but the approximate agreement between the calculated and the observed results for the less polar liquids and the general trend of the surface energies calculated indicate that the theory bears a relation to fact beyond a mere resemblance of the equation to the Duhem thermodynamic equation, and the idea of molecular surface energies may lead to most interesting results in spite of the difficulties in its exact quantitative application."

An alternative treatment: Another approach, first suggested by van Arkel,[22] similar in some respects to Langmuir's, may be helpful for understanding solutions of polar substances. We assume that the heat of mixing is of the form of Equation VII-15.

$$\Delta H^M = (x_1 V_1 + x_2 V_2)(c_{11} + c_{22} - 2c_{12})\varphi_1 \varphi_2 \quad (20)$$

with the usual dependence on volume fractions. The parameters c_{11}, c_{22}, and c_{12} (or the corresponding k's in Equation VII-30) are proportional to the intermolecular attractive forces, but where dipoles are present, depend not only upon dispersion forces, but also upon electrostatic induction and dipole interactions. We may write c_{11}, c_{12}, and c_{22} as sums of such terms, taken from Chapter IV:

$$c_{11} = \tfrac{3}{4}\alpha_1^2 I_1 + 2\alpha_1 \mu_1^2 + \frac{2\mu_1^4}{3kT} \quad (21a)$$

$$c_{12} = \frac{2\alpha_1 \alpha_2 I_1 I_2}{3(I_1 + I_2)} + (\alpha_1 \mu_2^2 + \alpha_2 \mu_1^2) + \frac{2\mu_1^2 \mu_2^2}{3kT} \quad (21b)$$

$$c_{22} = \tfrac{3}{4}\alpha_2^2 I_2 + 2\alpha_2 \mu_2^2 + \frac{2\mu_2^4}{3kT} \quad (21c)$$

As we have seen in Chapter IV, the induction forces are always small compared with the other two, so in a first approximation we neglect them and consider only the first and last terms of Equations 21abc. Further, as we have done in Chapter VII, we neglect the slight difference between the harmonic mean and geometric mean of the ionization potentials. To this approximation, we may write for the c's:

$$c_{11} = \delta_1^2 + \omega_1^2 \quad (22a)$$

$$c_{12} = \delta_1 \delta_2 + \omega_1 \omega_2 \quad (22b)$$

$$c_{22} = \delta_2^2 + \omega_2^2 \quad (22c)$$

In these equations the δ's signify the contribution of the dispersion forces and the ω's the orientation (dipole forces).

Substituting from Equations 23abc into Equation 21, we obtain for the heat of mixing:

[22] A. E. van Arkel and S. E. Vles, *Rec. trav. chim.*, **55**, 407 (1936); A. E. van Arkel, *Trans. Faraday Soc.*, **42B**, 81 (1946).

$$\Delta H^M = (x_1 V_1 + x_2 V_2)\left[(\delta_1 - \delta_2)^2 + (\omega_1 - \omega_2)^2\right]\varphi_1 \varphi_2 \tag{23}$$

and for the partial molal heats:

$$\Delta \overline{H}_1 = V_1 \left[(\delta_1 - \delta_2)^2 + (\omega_1 - \omega_2)^2\right]\varphi_2^2 \tag{24a}$$

$$\Delta \overline{H}_2 = V_2 \left[(\delta_1 - \delta_2)^2 + (\omega_1 - \omega_2)^2\right]\varphi_1^2 \tag{24b}$$

In considering Equations 24 and 25ab, we must remember that the δ's no longer have their usual meaning as the square roots of the cohesive energy densities or internal pressures but rather that:

$$\frac{\Delta E^V}{V} = \delta^2 + \omega^2 \tag{25}$$

The derivation of Equations 24 and 25ab implies spherical force fields such that the dipole is buried at the center of a more or less spherical molecule and that the hindered rotation discussed earlier in this chapter is not serious. We would therefore expect this treatment to hold, at best, only for solutions where the g-factor is not very different from unity.

The important feature is that equality of cohesive energy densities or internal pressures does not suffice to guarantee a zero heat of mixing and ideal solution. For this to be true, both the component parts of $\Delta E^V/V$ must be the same for both components. That is, not only must $\left(\frac{\Delta E^V}{V}\right)_1 = \left(\frac{\Delta E^V}{V}\right)_2$, but also $\delta_1 = \delta_2$ and $\omega_1 = \omega_2$. Further one may show that:

$$(\delta_1 - \delta_2)^2 + (\omega_1 - \omega_2)^2 \geq \left[\left(\frac{\Delta E^V}{V}\right)_1^{\frac{1}{2}} - \left(\frac{\Delta E^V}{V}\right)_2^{\frac{1}{2}}\right]^2 \tag{26}$$

Consequently, the heat of mixing will normally be equal to or greater than that calculated from the internal pressures. Furthermore, for a solution of one polar and one nonpolar component, ideal solutions are impossible; even if $\delta_1 = \delta_2$, a residual ω_1^2 term will remain (since $\omega_2 = 0$).

Actually for most substances (except for water, ammonia the alcohols, etc. — where g is large and hydrogen bonding important), the ω's are small compared with the δ's and represent a small correction term. It should be recalled that ω is proportional to the square of the dipole moment, and ω^2 to μ^4, so the effect will increase rapidly with increasing dipole moment. In addition, buried dipoles (as in chloroform) produces smaller ω's than exposed ones (as in acetone).

The heat of mixing according to the above picture is always positive. The only exception to such a rule is to be found when both components are polar and a specific interaction between the different dipoles is possible; this phenomenon will be discussed in Chapter XI.

Equations 24 and 25ab are useful for qualitative interpretation of solutions of polar molecules, but they have not yet been applied to specific systems. However, Stockmayer[23] has used a similar formulation with considerable success in treating mixtures of polar gases.

---

[23] W. H. Stockmayer, *J. Chem. Phys.*, **9**, 398, 864 (1941).

CHAPTER X

Hydrogen Bonding

The dipoles in which hydrogen occurs linked to N, O or F exert effects upon each other far beyond those which would be expected from the magnitude of their moments alone. Everyone is familiar with the fact that the boiling points of H_2O, NH_3 and HF are remarkably high for molecules of such low molecular weight, and yet their dipole moments are not particularly high, being 1.85, 1.48 and 1.91 Debye units, respectively. C_2H_5Br, with a dipole moment as large as that of water, 1.83 and a molecular weight six times as great, has a much lower boiling point, 38° C., and SO_2 with a dipole moment of 1.6 and a molecular weight of 64 boils at —10°C. The reason for such differences is that the bare proton of hydrogen compounds with strongly negative atoms is so small that it can come very close to a second negative atom, forming a "hydrogen bond" or "hydrogen bridge"[1]. The latter term seems to the authors slightly preferable but the former is in more common use, therefore we retain it in the following discussion.

It is not essential to the purpose of this book to review in detail the history and theory of the hydrogen bond, which have been well covered in work easily accessible[1,2]. Suffice it to say, as to theory, that it seems now to be generally agreed that the bonding hydrogen does not participate in two covalent bonds but that the interaction is essentially electrostatic, the exceptional nature of the bond being due to the closeness of approach of the two dipoles made possible by the small size of the proton, as stated above. This greatly hinders molecular rotation as revealed by high values of the parameter, g, of the Kirkwood treatment described in the preceding chapter and causes the pure liquid to have a higher dielectric constant than it would otherwise have.

The strengths of hydrogen bonds fall off roughly in the order FHF, OHO, OHN, NHN, CHO, but they are very dependent upon the geometry of particular combinations, upon the nature of neighboring atoms and upon resonance, and upon acid-base characters. The strength of a particular bond is at least approximately indicated by the X—H—X[1] distance, as revealed

[1] M. L. Huggins, "Hydrogen Bridges in Organic Compounds", *J. Org. Chem.*, **1**, 407 (1936). A comprehensive treatment.

[2] *e. g.*, L. Pauling, "Nature of the Chemical Bond", Cornell Univ. Press, 1945, Chapter IX. E. N. Lassettre, *Chem. Rev.*, **20**, 279 (1937).

N. V. Sidgwick, "The Electronic Theory of Valency", Oxford Univ. Press, 1929. "Some Physical Properties of the Covalent Link in Chemistry", Cornell Univ. Press, 1933.

by x-ray or electron diffraction. Table 1 gives representative values. The values for hydrogen bond energy given in the table have been calculated without any attempt to estimate and subtract the contribution of the London forces.

TABLE 1. Hydrogen bond distances and energies.

Bond	Substance		YHX dist., Å	ΔE, kcal.
FHF	KHF_2		2.26[4]	
	HF	gas	2.55[5]	6.2[13]
OHO	CH_3COOH	gas		7.6[14]
	HCOOH	gas	2.67[7]	6.8[15]
	H_2O	solid	2.78[6]	5.7[16]
NHF	NH_4F		2.66[8]	
	NH_4HF		2.82[9]	
NHO	$CO(NH_2)_2$		2.98) 3.03)[10]	
NHN	NH_4N_3		2.97[11]	
	NH_3	solid	3.38[12]	1.8[16]
CHO	$(CH_3)_2CO.HCCl_3$			4.1[17]
CHN	HCN			2.7[18]

A number of investigators have studied the effect of hydrogen bonding upon infra-red absorption. Fox and Martin[19] and Badger and Bauer[20] found proportionality between bond strength and frequency in infra-red shift. Errera[21] and coworkers have studied the association of ethyl alcohol with

[4] R. H. Bozorth, *J. Am. Chem. Soc.*, **45**, 2128 (1923).
[5] S. H. Bauer, J. Y. Beach and J. H. Simons, *Ibid*, **61**, 19 (1939).
[6] W. H. Barnes, *Proc. Roy. Soc.*, **A 125**, 670 (1929).
[7] L. Pauling and L. O. Brockway, *Proc. Nat. Acad. Sci.*, **20**, 336 (1934).
[8] W. H. Zachariasen, *Z. Physik Chem.*, **127**, 218 (1927).
[9] L. Pauling, *Ibid.*, **85**, 380, (1933).
[10] R. W. Wycoff and R. B. Corey, *Z. Krist.*, **89**, 462 (1934).
[11] L. K. Frevel, *Ibid.*, **94**, 197 (1936).
[12] H. Mark and E. Pohland, *Z. Krist.* **61**, 532 (1925).
[13] J. H. Simons and J. H. Hildebrand, *J. Am. Chem. Soc.*, **46**, 2183 (1924).
[14] F. H. MacDougall, *J. Am. Chem. Soc.*, **58**, 2585 (1936).
[15] A. S. Coolidge, *Ibid*, **50**, 2166 (1928).
[16] Calc. from heat of sublimation.
[17] E. A. Moelwyn-Hughes and A. Sherman, *J. Chem. Soc.*, (1936) 101.
[18] W. F. Giauque and R. A. Ruehrwein, *J. Am. Chem. Soc.*, **61**, 2626 (1936).
[19] J. J. Fox and A. E. Martin, *Proc. Roy. Soc.*, **A 162**, 419 (1937).
[20] R. M. Badger and S. H. Bauer, *J. Chem. Phys.*, **5**, 839 (1937). R. M. Badger, *Ibid.*, **8**, 288 (1940).
[21] J. Errera, *Trans. Faraday Soc.*, **33**, 120 (1937); cf. also, *J. Chem. Phys.*, **8**, 63 (1940); Nature **138**, 882 (1936).

itself, with pyridine and with acetone in inert solvents; these are completely dissociated only at less than 0.1 volume percent. Rodebush[22] and coworkers have studied the infra-red shift for water. Gordy[23] and coworkers have observed the shift of the OD bond in CH_3OD and D_2O. They find that the strength of the bond increases in going from esters to aldehydes and from ketones to ethers to amines. The find also an interesting linear relation between the shift in the OD bond both for CH_3OD and D_2O and the logarithms of the basicity constants as measured in water solutions[24].

The structures of the various association complexes are a matter of considerable significance. Aliphatic acids form dimers with closed six-membered rings, excluding the H atoms, as follows:

$$R - C \underset{\displaystyle O \cdots\cdots H - O}{\overset{\displaystyle O - H \cdots\cdots O}{}} C - R$$

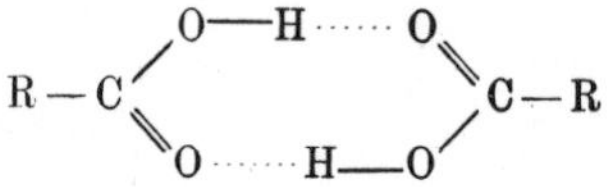

as indicated by molecular weight determinations in both vapor and solution, by low dipole moment[25], by x-ray and electron diffraction[26]. Many hydroxy acids form intra-molecular hydrogen bonds which operate to prevent intermolecular association[2]. This type of bonding has been extensively studied by Hilbert, Wulf, Hendricks and Liddel[27], who used as evidence the disappearance of the infra-red absorption of OH at approximately $7100\,cm^{-1}$. The work of these authors can be profitably studied by anoyne dealing with the complexities of hydrogen bond formation.

In ice, and to a variable extent in water, depending upon temperature, each oxygen is surrounded by four labile hydrogen bonds[28]. The molecules of the alcohols, ammonia, HF and HCN, can form only two hydrogen bonds, therefore the polymers consist of molecular chains. The arrangement of hydrogen bonds in crystalline substances is an interesting topic, but beyond the scope of this book.

The type of polymerization has an important bearing upon the validity of formulas often ascribed to solvates. For example, we see hydrogen ion

[22] L. B. Borst, A. M. Buswell and W. H. Rodebush, *J. Chem. Phys.*, **6**, 61 (1938); A. M. Buswell, V. Dietz and W. H. Rodebush, **5**, 84, 501 (1937).

[23] W. Gordy, *Phys. Rev.*, **50**, 1151 (1936); **51**, 564 (1937); with A. H. Nielsen, *J. Chem. Phys.*, **4**, 769 (1936); **6**, 12 (1938); **7**, 93 (1939); with S. C. Stanford, *Ibid*, **8**, 170 (1940); **9**, 204, 215 (1941).

[24] See also, L. P. Hammett, *J. Chem. Phys.*, **8**, 644 (1940).

[25] C. P. Smyth and H. E. Rogers, *J. Am. Chem. Soc.*, **52**, 1824 (1930).

[26] W. C. Pierce and D. P. McMillan. *Ibid*, **60**, 779 (1938).

[27] G. E. Hilbert, O. R. Wulf, S. G. Hendricks and U. Liddel, *Nature*, **135**, 147 (1935); *J. Am. Chem. Soc*, **58**, 548, 1991, 2287 (1936).

[28] Chapter IX. ref. 6, 7, 8.

in aqueous solution written as "hydronium ion", H_3O^+, which is evidently an over-simplification in view of the hydrogen bonds linking together an indefinite and changing number of water molecules. Huggins[29] represents this by the more realistic formula:

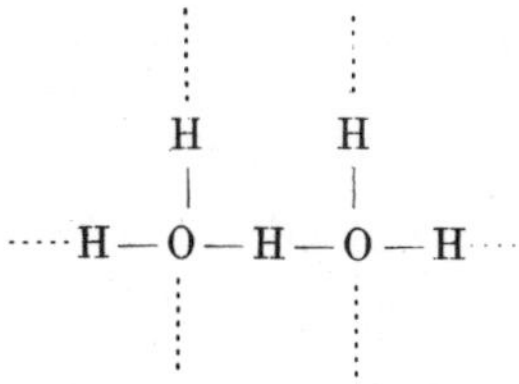

Only where the energy of hydration for a limited number of water molecules is markedly greater than the energy of the hydrogen bond, or where a definite hydrate can be frozen out, as in the case of $H_2O \cdot HF$, $H_2O \cdot 2HF$ and $H_2O \cdot 4HF$[30] does it seem altogether proper to assign a formula with a limited number of water molecules.

The same difficulty applies to association complexes with the alcohols in view of their indefinite chain-like association. Ammonia on the other hand, is but weakly hydrogen-bonded, therefore the strong combination between H^+ and NH_3 can properly be written as NH_4^+, although there is evidence in the high solubility of its salts in liquid ammonia that NH_4^+ and NH_3 are more strongly bonded than NH_3 to NH_3.

The $\equiv C-H$ link is capable of forming hydrogen bonds to oxygen or nitrogen provided the atoms attached to the carbon are such as to increase markedly the polarity of the $C-H$ bond. The evidence for this was first presented by Glasstone.[31] Table 1 contains the examples, HCN and the acetone-chloroform complex. Ether-chloroform is another. Copley, Zellhoefer and Marvel[32] in an important series of papers, have reported the enhancement of solubility over the Raoult's law values for such substances as haloforms, monofluoromonochloromethane, and methylene chloride in a number of solvents, such as ethers, esters and amines; low solubilities in highly associated solvents such as alcohols, and amides; nearly normal solubilities in dimerized solvents such as the fatty acids.

When we are interested in comparing the attraction of the solvent for different solutes using liquid solutes, it is necessary to take into account differences in vapor pressure of the different solute liquids, for a liquid of

---

[29] M. L. Huggins, *J. Phys. Chem.*, **40**, 723 (1936),

[30] G. H. Cady and J. H. Hildebrand, *J. Am. Chem. Soc.*, **52**, 3843 (1930).

[31] S. Glasstone, *Trans. Faraday Soc.*, **33**, 200 (1937).

[32] M. J. Copley, G. F. Zellhoefer and C. S. Marvel, *J. Am. Chem. Soc.*, **60**, 1337, 1343 2666, 2714 (1938); *Ind. Eng. Chem.*, **29**, 584 (1937).

lower vapor pressure will be less soluble than one of higher vapor pressure, other things being equal. We do not have figures for the vapor pressures of the three substituted benzenes in Table 2 at 20°C but their boiling points are so near together as to indicate that the order would not be changed by reducing their solubilities in water to the same vapor pressure by means of Henry's law. Benzene, at the same vapor pressure as phenol, would have a far smaller solubility than that given in the table.

TABLE 2. Solubility in water, 20°C.

	Boil. pt.	$\mu \cdot 10^{18}$ e.s.u.	Mole percent in water
Benzene	80	0	0.013
Nitrobenzene	208	4.2	0.028
Aniline	184	1.5	0.70
Phenol	182	1.7	1.7

The greater strength of the OHO bond over the OHN bond, seen in Table 1, can account for the positions of phenol and aniline in Table 2.

The increase in the solubility of water in benzene caused by the addition of a third substance has been discussed by Staveley, Jeffes and Moy.[33]

TABLE 3. Increment in Solubility of Water in Benzene at 25°C caused by Addition of a Third Substance.

Added substance	$\frac{\text{Incr. in mole fraction of water}}{\text{Mole fraction of added substance}}$
Phenol[34]	200
Acetic acid[35]	160
Ethyl alcohol[36]	125
Methyl alcohol[36]	80
Aniline	40
Nitrobenzene	9
Anisole	6
Bromobenzene	0+
Chloroform	0+

[33] L. A. K. Staveley, J. H. E. Jeffes and J. A. E. Moy. *Trans. Faraday Soc.*, **39**, 5 (1943).
[34] S. Horiba, *Mem. Coll. Sci. Kyoto Imp. Univ.*, **1**, 49 (1914).
[35] J. Barbaudy, *Rec. Trav. Chim. Pays-Bas*, **45**, 207, (1926); *Compt. Rend.* **182**, 1279, (1926.)
[36] J. Waddell, *J. Phys. Chem.*, **2**, 233 (1898).

CHAPTER XI

Specific Interactions: "Solvation" and "Association"

Among the earliest interpretations of deviations from Raoult's law was the attempt by Dolezalek[1] to correlate departures from ideality with chemical reactions between either like molecules or unlike pairs. According to his view, the actual molecular species present obey Raoult's law; the only problem is to correctly identify the various species present and their amounts. Although we now realize that this is a very oversimplified picture, it seemed very plausible at the time, following as it did Arrhenius' successful treatment of dilute electrolyte solutions in terms of ionic dissociation. Dolezalek was led to his "chemical" treatment of nonideal solutions by an erroneous assumption about the nature of intermolecular forces; namely, that the potential energy between two unlike molecules is always the *arithmetic mean* of those between like pairs. If this were so, the heat of mixing is necessarily zero, and a "physical" interpretation of nonideal solutions is thereby excluded. We have seen in Chapter IV that van der Waals', London or dispersion forces between molecules follow approximately a *geometric mean*, permitting the simple physical explanation of positive heats of mixing set forth in Chapter VII. But Dolezalek and his followers, writing twenty years before London's treatment of dispersion forces, guessed wrong and were led to their entirely chemical treatment of solvation and association in solutions. Even in those days, however, the geometric mean and a physical interpretation had its champions, notably the Dutch school of van der Waals and van Laar[2] and the literature of the period is full of some very harsh polemic between the opposing points of view.[3]

While the Dolezalek picture of chemical interactions in solution is certainly oversimplified and often unnecessary, if not obviously wrong, it remains a partial basis or jumping-off place for a discussion of the specific interactions between molecules which undoubtedly exist in certain cases.

SPECIFIC INTERACTIONS BETWEEN UNLIKE MOLECULES

Chemical combinations between the components. If the molecules of A and B in a binary mixture unite to form a compound, such as AB, it is

---

[1] F. Dolezalek, *Z. physik. Chem.*, **64**, 727, (1908).

[2] J. J. van Laar, *Z. physik. Chem.*, **72**, 723 (1910); **83**, 599 (1913).

[3] For a discussion of the controversy see J. Timmermans, *J. chim. phys.*, **19**, 169 (1921) and G. Scatchard, *Chem. Revs.*, **8**, 321 (1931).

evident that the number of uncombined molecules of each species, and hence the escaping tendencies of the species, will be reduced. If the combination is complete, only those molecules of the components which are present in excess of those forming the compound will be able to escape as such. If N_1 moles of A mix with N_2 (less than N_1) moles of B, then the number of moles of AB is N_2 and the number of moles of A remaining uncombined is $N_2 - N_1$. The total number of moles present in the solution is N_2, so that the true mole fraction[4] of A, $x_A = (N_2 - N_1)/N_2$, and if all three species are sufficiently alike to obey Raoult's law (Dolezalek's assumption), then the activity is equal to the true mole fraction[5]:

$$a_1 = x_A \frac{N_2 - N_1}{N_2} = \frac{x_2 - x_1}{x_2} \tag{1}$$

If this is plotted against the apparent mole fraction of A, a curve is obtained which is shown in Fig. 1, marked $K = \infty$.

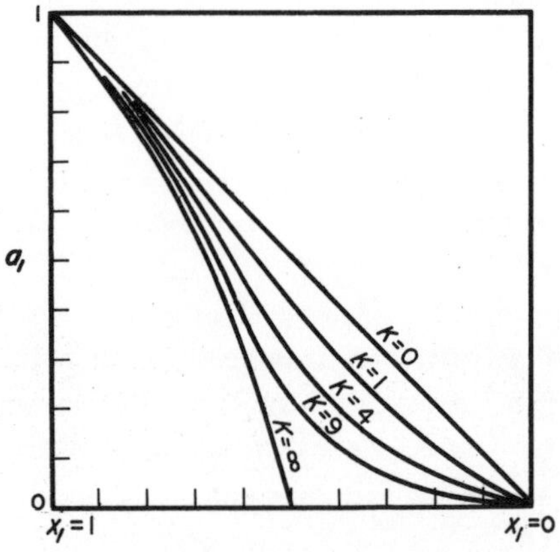

Fig. 1 Effect of binary compound formation on activity.

If B is not completely used up, A, B, and the compound AB being all present in equilibrium in the solution, then the actual mole fractions present can be seen easily from the following scheme:

4 Throughout this discussion, we shall use numerical subscripts for stoichiometric quantities, alphabetic subscripts for the "true" species present. Thus N_1 is the number of moles of A put into the mixture, while N_A is the number of moles of uncombined A; x_1 and x_2 are "apparent" mole fractions, while x_A, x_B and x_{AB} are "true" mole fractions.

5 Simple thermodynamic considerations show that in this case the "apparent" and "true" activities are identical: $a_1 = a_A$.

Reaction	A	+	B	=	AB
Moles taken	N_1		N_2		
Moles present at equilibrium	$N_A = N_1 - N_{AB}$		$N_B = N_2 - N_{AB}$		N_{AB}

The total number of moles being $N_1 + N_2 - N_{AB}$, the true mole fractions and again, assuming Raoult's law for the true species, the activities are related by the equations:

$$a_1 = x_A = \frac{N_1 - N_{AB}}{N_1 + N_2 - N_{AB}} \tag{2a}$$

$$a_2 = x_B = \frac{N_2 - N_{AB}}{N_1 + N_2 - N_{AB}} \tag{2b}$$

$$a_{AB} = x_{AB} = \frac{N_{AB}}{N_1 + N_2 - N_{AB}} \tag{2c}$$

These three activities are connected by an equilibrium constant:

$$K = \frac{a_{AB}}{a_1\, a_2} \tag{3}$$

and if we substitute from Equations 2abc, we obtain:

$$K = \frac{N_{AB}\,(N_1 + N_2 - N_{AB})}{(N_1 - N_{AB})\,(N_2 - N_{AB})} \tag{4}$$

Equation 4 may be used to eliminate N_{AB} from Equations 2abc. If we eliminate N_{AB} and express the activities in terms of the stoichiometric mole fractions, we obtain:

$$a_1 = \frac{x_1 - x_2 + (1 - kx_1\, x_2)^{\frac{1}{2}}}{1 + (1 - kx_1\, x_2)^{\frac{1}{2}}} = \frac{kx_1 - 2 + 2\,(1 - kx_1\, x_2)^{\frac{1}{2}}}{kx_1} \tag{5a}$$

$$a_2 = \frac{x_2 - x_1 + (1 - kx_1\, x_2)^{\frac{1}{2}}}{1 + (1 - kx_1\, x_2)^{\frac{1}{2}}} = \frac{kx_2 - 2 + 2\,(1 - kx_1\, x_2)^{\frac{1}{2}}}{kx_2} \tag{5b}$$

$$a_{AB} = \frac{1 - (1 - kx_1\, x_2)^{\frac{1}{2}}}{1 + (1 - kx_1\, x_2)^{\frac{1}{2}}} = \frac{2 - kx_1\, x_2 - 2\,(1 - kx_1\, x_2)^{\frac{1}{2}}}{kx_1\, x_2} \tag{5c}$$

where the new constant $k = 4\,K/(K + 1)$. Where the formation of the compound is complete, $K = \infty$ ($k = 4$), and Equation 5a reduces to Equation 1, while if $K = 0$ ($k = 0$), no combination takes place and the equations becomes the simple expression for Raoult's law, $a_1 = x_1$. By assigning a series of values to K there is obtained the family of curves illustrated in Fig. 1.

The first application of equations such as 5 abc was Dolezalek's[1] interpretation of the negative deviations from Raoult's law in the system acetone-chloroform. Table 1 gives the partial pressures of acetone and chloroform in their solutions according to Zawidski's[6] measurements (see Fig. 2, Chapter III) compared with the values calculated by the method just outlined, assuming $K = 1.25$ ($k = 2.22$).

Table 1. System Acetone-Chloroform

Mole Fraction Chloroform	Partial Pressure Acetone p_1 (mm. Hg)		Partial Pressure Chloroform p_2 (mm. Hg)	
x_2	Observ.	Calc. (Eqn. 5a)	Observ.	Calc. (Eqn. 5b)
0.000	345	(345)	0	0
0.060	323	323	9	8
0.184	276	274	32	30
0.263	241	241	50	47
0.361	200	198	73	73
0.424	174	170	89	92
0.508	138	134	115	120
0 581	109	106	140	147
0.662	79	78	170	177
0.802	38	38	224	229
0.918	13	14	266	268
1.000	0	0	293	(293)

Dolezalek and Schulze[7] applied the same method to calculating the total pressures ($p_1^\circ a_1 + p_2^\circ a_2$) of solutions of chloroform and ether. Table 2 gives the calculated values, assuming $K = 2.36$ ($k = 2.89$), compared with the measured values of Kohnstamm and Dalfsen[8] at 33.25°C.

Table 2. Total Pressures of Chloroform-Ether Solutions at 33.25°.

Mole Fraction of Chloroform.		0	0.102	0.305	0.500	0.705	0.920	1.000
Total Pressure	Observed	731	661	499	355	281	270	276
	Calculated	(731)	657	500	355	294	276	(276)

[6] J. v. Zawidzki, *Z. physik. Chem.*, **35**, 129 (1908).
[7] F. Dolezalek and A. Schulze, *Z. physik. Chem.*, **83**, 45 (1913).
[8] P. Kohnstamm and B. M. van Dalfsen, *Proc. Acad. Wet.*, **29**, 156 (1901).

More complicated types of solvation can be treated according to the same principles as those just outlined. For example, if the compound formed in the solution consists of two molecules of B to one of A, the equation for its formation and the number of molecules of each species present at equilibrium would be as follows:

Reaction	A	+	2B	$\rightleftarrows$	AB_2
Moles taken	N_1		N_2		
Moles present at equilibrium	$N_A = N_1 - N_{AB_2}$		$N_B = N_2 - 2N_{AB_2}$		N_{AB_2}

The total number of moles being $N_1 + N_2 - 2N_{AB_2}$, the activities, if equal to the respective mole fractions, would be

$$a_1 = \frac{N_1 - N_{AB_2}}{N_1 + N_2 - 2N_{AB_2}} \tag{6a}$$

$$a_2 = \frac{N_2 - 2N_{AB_2}}{N_1 + N_2 - 2N_{AB_2}} \tag{6b}$$

$$a_{AB_2} = \frac{N_{AB_2}}{N_1 + N_2 - 2N_{AB_2}} \tag{6c}$$

The equilibrium constant would be

$$K = \frac{a_{AB_2}}{a_1 a_2^2} = \frac{N_{AB_2}(N_1 + N_2 - 2N_{AB_2})^2}{(N_1 - N_{AB_2})(N_2 - 2N_{AB_2})^2} \tag{7}$$

which could be used to eliminate the variable N_{AB_2} in the three preceding equations[9]. One should note that these more complex compounds do not always produce negative deviations from Raoult's law over the whole concentration range. For example, in the case of the compound AB_2, the activity of B, a_2, is less than x_2 at all concentrations, but the activity of A, a_1, is greater than x, when $x_1 > \frac{1}{2}$ and less when $x_1 < \frac{1}{2}$. The total excess free energy of mixing ΔF^E is always negative.

Compound formation (or its equivalent) is of special importance in the field of solubility, for as we have seen in Chapter III, negative deviations from Raoult's law enhance the solubility of gases or solids in liquids over the ideal solubility and makes liquid-liquid immiscibility impossible.

The "physical" interpretation of negative deviations. Before discussing the validity of Dolezalek's treatment of deviations from ideality in terms of the formation of new chemical species in solution, let us first con-

[9] Expressions of this sort were used by J. H. Hildebrand and E. D. Eastman, *J. Am. Chem. Soc.*, **37**, 2452 (1915) in connection with thallium amalgams.

sider an alternative "physical" interpretation of the same phenomena.

We have seen in Chapter VII, that a very general formulation of the heat of mixing of regular solutions leads to an equation:

$$\Delta H_1^M = V_1 (c_{11} + c_{22} - 2 c_{12}) \varphi_2^2 \tag{8}$$

where c_{11}, c_{22} and c_{12} represent the energies of interaction (per cc.) for like and unlike pairs. When the interaction between unlike molecules is given by the geometric mean, $c_{12} = (c_{11} c_{22})^{\frac{1}{2}}$, the term $(c_{11} + c_{22} - 2 c_{12})$ reduces to $(c_{11}^{\frac{1}{2}} - c_{22}^{\frac{1}{2}})^2$ or replacing $c^{\frac{1}{2}}$ by δ, to $(\delta_1 - \delta_2)^2$, the square of the difference in solubility parameters.

$$\Delta \bar{H}_1^M = V_1 (\delta_1 - \delta_2)^2 \varphi_2^2 \tag{9}$$

Since the difference term is squared, such an equation can lead only to zero or positive heats of mixing. If, however, we remove the restrictions from c_{12}, the whole range of positive or negative heats of mixing is attainable. The failure of c_{12} to follow the geometric mean rule for dispersion forces we shall ascribe to "specific interactions" between either like or unlike pairs as the case may be. For example, if c_{12} is not the *geometric mean* of c_{11} and c_{22}, but the *arithmetic mean* (as Dolezalek assumed), then the heat of mixing is exactly zero. If there is a strong specific interaction between the different components, c_{12} may exceed even the arithmetic mean, and then $\Delta \bar{H}_1$ is negative.

If the entropy of mixing is ideal as is assumed for regular solutions, then, as we have seen in Chapter VII, we may write for the activity coefficient γ_1:

$$RT \ln \gamma_1 = \Delta \bar{H}_1 = V_1 (c_{11} + c_{22} - 2 c_{12}) \varphi_2^2 \tag{10}$$

or simply

$$\ln \gamma_1 = k_1 \varphi_2^2 \tag{11 a}$$

$$\ln \gamma_2 = k_2 \varphi_1^2 \tag{11 b}$$

where

$$\frac{k_1}{k_2} = \frac{V_1}{V_2} \tag{12}$$

It is instructive to try to apply Equations 11 a and 11 b to the same acetone-chloroform system which Dolezalek treated by Equations 5 a and 5 b (Table 1).

Table 3 compares the activity coefficients calculated both ways. For acetone ($V_1 = 74$) $k_1 = -.82$; for chloroform ($V_2 = 81$) $k_2 = -.90$.

Table 3. Activity Coefficients in Acetone-Chloroform System.

Mole Fraction Chloroform	Activity Coefficients					
x_2	γ_1 (acetone)			γ_2 (chloroform)		
	Obs.	Eqn. 5a	Eqn. 11a	Obs.	Eqn. 5b	Eqn. 11b
0.000	1.00	1.00	1.00	. . .	.44	.41
0.060	.99	.99	.99	.51	.48	.46
0.184	.98	.98	.98	.59	.56	.56
0.263	.95	.95	.94	.65	.61	.63
0.361	.91	.90	.88	.69	.69	.71
0.424	.88	.86	.85	.72	.74	.76
0.508	.82	.79	.79	.77	.81	.82
0.581	.75	.73	.74	.82	.86	.86
0.662	.68	.67	.68	.88	.91	.91
0.802	.56	.56	.58	.95	.97	.97
0.918	.46	.50	.49	.99	.99	.99
1.000	. . .	.44	.44	1.00	1.00	1.00

The two equations fit about equally well, frequently agreeing with each other better than with the experimental data; so that here there is no basis for a choice between the two. It will be seen that Equations 5ab are symmetrical, while Equations 11ab permit asymmetry when the volumes are unequal; to obtain asymmetric relations from the "chemical" formulation, we need to assume more complex compounds[10], such as AB_2. The acetone-chloroform system is in fact slightly asymmetric, as seen in Fig. III-5, but the asymmetry is in the opposite direction to that predicted by the volume ratios. If we define generalized or "effective" volumes q_1 and q_2, as in Chapter VII, and rewrite Equations 11ab in terms of "effective" volume fractions or q-fractions, we have (cf. Equation VII-49):

$$\ln \gamma_1 = k'_1 \left[\frac{q_2 x_2}{q_1 x_1 + q_2 x_2} \right]^2 \tag{13a}$$

$$\ln \gamma_2 = k'_2 \left[\frac{q_1 x_1}{q_1 x_1 + q_2 x_2} \right]^2 \tag{13b}$$

[10] Variation of the type of compound makes the "chemical" treatment a two parameter theory, just as varyng the volume ratio makes Equations 11ab two parameter equations.

where

$$\frac{k'_1}{k'_2} = \frac{q_1}{q_2} \tag{14}$$

The acetone-chloroform system can be fitted quantitatively with Equations 13ab by assuming a greater "effective" volume for the acetone such that $q_1/q_2 = 1.2$. The physical meaning of such an assumption is not entirely clear, but is probably related to the effective surfaces of the molecules (cf. Langmuir's treatment in Chapter IX). Regardless of the uncertain theoretical justification, equations of the type of 13ab, loosely called "van Laar equations", are widely used since they afford additional flexibility. The vapor pressures of cadmium amalgams at 322°C. can be accounted for either by assuming[11] partial formation of a solvate having the simple formula CdHg, putting k in Equation 5a equal to 3 (corresponding to $K = 3$), or by the "physical" Equation 11a by assuming $k_1 = -1.5$ (since the molal volumes differ by less than ten percent, we ignore the difference and use mole fractions in Equation 11a). Table 4 shows the comparison with the observed activities of Hg, as well as with the more general Equation 13a assuming $k'_1 = -4.37$, $q_1/q_2 = 1.90$ (cf. Chapter III pp. 36–37).

Table 4. Cadmium Amalgams at 322°C.

Mole fraction of Mercury x_1	0.931	0.861	0.738	0.623	0.488	0.418	0.331
Observed a_1	0.921	0.850	0.688	0.525	0.322	0.232	0.148
Calc. Eqn. 5a	0.928	0.847	0.682	0.513	0.317	0.235	0.154
Calc. Eqn. 11a	0.924	0.839	0.665	0.504	0.332	0.253	0 169
Calc. Eqn. 13a	0.927	0.845	0.680	0.522	0.323	0.235	0.148

In this case, the "chemical" Equation 5a is decidedly better than Equation 11a, although the empirical Equation 13a, with two unrestricted parameters, fits the data better than either.

Causes of the specific interaction. We shall postpone until the end of the chapter further comparison of these two methods of approach to the specific interaction problem, but it is important to consider the causes of these effects. We have seen that negative deviations from Raoult's law, corresponding to enhanced solubilities, tend to occur when the components of a solution have an abnormally great attraction for each other; this fact seems clear whether one formulates it in a "chemical" or a "physical" terminology. Since the interaction is a spezific one, it is easier to discuss

[11] J. H. Hildebrand, A. H. Foster, and C. W. Beebe, *J. Am. Chem. Soc.*, **42**, 545 (1920)

its causes in terms of the specific chemical nature of the molecules involved and their capacity for chemical combination. (The usefulness of such a treatment, however, is not of itself evidence for actual chemical bonds.)

The prediction of chemical combination is, however, the main goal of chemistry, and until it is reached this problem will remain more or less unsolved. We must, therefore, be content to note a few guiding principles, together with a number of actual behaviors which may serve by analogy to predict others.

1. **Polarity**. From the discussion of polarity in Chapter IX it is evident that chemical combination should be more frequent between molecules of high polarity than between those of low polarity, and examination of the experimental facts shows this to be the case. For example, the highly polar water molecules show this tendency in a great degree, forming a great variety of hydrates, especially with the highly polar salt molecules. Other polar molecules, such as NH_3, furnish frequent instances of the same sort, for we have ammonia complexes both in solution and in the solid state. The highly polar salts combine in great variety to form complex or double salts. Sulfuric and hydrofluoric acids enter into frequent combination with their salts.

As polarity diminishes this tendency diminishes also. "Alcohol of crystallization" occurs much less frequently than "water of crystallization", "benzene of crystallization" is known in comparatively few cases, while the nearly non-polar paraffin molecules almost never form addition compounds with other molecules[12].

We may feel reasonably certain that the intermolecular attraction which yields solid "addition compounds" operates also in the liquid state to cause negative deviations from Raoult's law, so that the abundant existing evidence of the sort above cited justifies the statement that negative deviations from Raoult's law and abnormally great solubilities occur most frequently when the components are highly polar.

2. **Formation of hydrogen bonds**. A particular kind of polarity which is likely to result in the formation of "compounds" is that which may produce hydrogen bonds, as discussed in Chapters IX and X. Although the dipoles involved are apparently of the same nature as in other polar molecules, the small size of the hydrogen atom permits such a close approach that large electrostatic forces come into play. An example of this is the acetone-chloroform interaction; Moelwyn-Hughes and Sherman[13] assign to the C-H... O interaction in this "compound" an energy of 4.1 kilocalories.

3. **Differences in positive and negative character of the components.** High polarity is not in itself sufficient to cause chemical combination. It is

[12] G. N. Lewis *J. Am. Chem. Soc.*, **35**, 1448 (1913); **38**, 762 (1916).
[13] E. A. Moelwyn-Hughes and A. Sherman, *J. Chem. Soc.*, 101 (1936).

necessary for the substances to differ in the sense implied by the contrasting terms acidic and basic, or positive and negative. Thus, we usually think of water as a neutral substance, ammonia as positive or basic and HF as negative or acidic. Accordingly we find the affinity between H_2O and NH_3 or H_2O and HF to be much weaker than that between NH_3 and HF. Again, liquid NH_3 and liquid HCl, on mixing, would combine completely, giving the extreme negative deviation from Raoult's law. With ammonia and acetic acid the deviation is small, and with aniline and phenol it is very slight.

The diversity in character which determines the tendency to addition or solvation may be interpreted in the sense of the "dualistic" theory of Davy and Berzelius, restated in modern terms. In the case of the elements the greatest tendency to form stable compounds occurs when one element is highly positive, readily losing electrons, and the other element highly negative, readily adding electrons. Arranging the elements according to decreasing tendency to lose electrons gives us the familiar "replacement series" of the elements, starting with the alkalie metals and ending with the highly negative nonmetallic elements.

Many examples of this sort are given by Kendall[14] and collaborators in a series of very useful studies of the solubilities of polar substances, where in it is shown that the tendency of various salts to combine with or dissolve in their free acids is closely related to the separation of their metals from hydrogen in the potential series of the elements. It is shown, further, that a weak acid can act as a "base" towards a strong acid, the combination being stronger the greater the diversity in strength between the two acids. The strength of the combination may thus be regarded as dependent upon the negativity of the acid radicals.

Kendall, Crittenden and Miller[15], in their rather extensive studies of compound formation in fused salt mixtures, have noted the great difference between antimony trihalides and aluminum trihalides in respect to the formation of compounds with other halides, the former being almost barren, the latter, particularly rich in this respect. This difference is beautifully correlated by the Lewis theory, with the difference in the charge of the atomic kernels of Al and Sb, which are 3 and 5, respectively, corresponding to their groups in the Periodic System. The electron structures of the trichlorides would accordingly be indicated as follows:

$$
\begin{array}{cc}
\overset{\cdot\,\cdot}{:Cl:} & \overset{\cdot\,\cdot}{:Cl:} \\
\overset{\cdot\,\cdot}{:Cl:Al} & \overset{\cdot\,\cdot}{:Cl:Sb:} \\
\overset{\cdot\,\cdot}{:Cl:} & \overset{\cdot\,\cdot}{:Cl:}
\end{array}
$$

[14] J. Kendall, A. W. Davidson and H. Adler, *J. Am. Chem. Soc.*, **43**, 1481 (1921)
[15] J. Kendall, E. D. Crittenden and H. K. Miller, *J. Am. Chem. Soc.*, **45**, 963 (1923).

The Sb has its complete octet of electrons, and both it and the chlorine atoms are saturated. On the other hand, the Al has but 6 electrons and can attach 2 more. For example, with KCl it forms the compound

$$
\begin{array}{c}
: \overset{\cdot\cdot}{\underset{}{Cl}} : \\[2pt]
: \overset{\cdot\cdot}{\underset{\cdot\cdot}{Cl}} : \overset{\cdot\cdot}{\underset{\cdot\cdot}{Al}} : \overset{\cdot\cdot}{\underset{}{Cl}} : K \\[2pt]
: \underset{\cdot\cdot}{Cl} :
\end{array}
$$

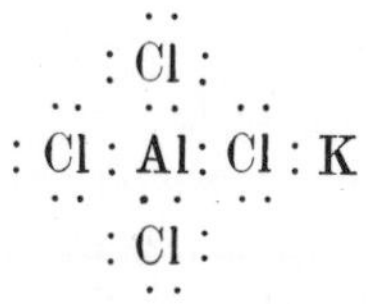

which, in the fused state, would doubtless contain the anion $AlCl_4^-$.

Compounds containing more $AlCl_3$ can be formed by a union of $AlCl_3$ molecules, which may be represented as follows:

$$
\begin{array}{c}
: \overset{\cdot}{Cl} \qquad : \overset{\cdot\cdot}{Cl} \qquad : \overset{\cdot\cdot}{Cl} : \\[2pt]
: \overset{}{Cl} : \overset{}{Al} : \overset{}{Cl} : \overset{}{Al} : \overset{}{Cl} : \overset{}{Al} \\[2pt]
: \underset{\cdot\cdot}{Cl} : \qquad : \underset{\cdot\cdot}{Cl} : \qquad : \underset{\cdot\cdot}{Cl} :
\end{array}
$$

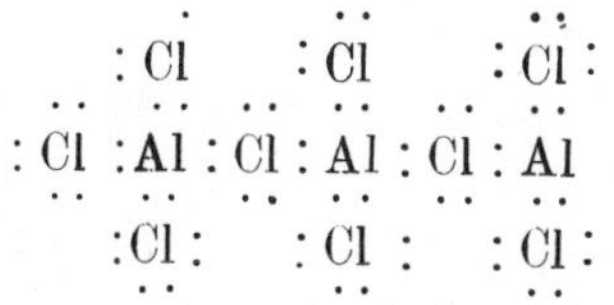

This union may be continued indefinitely in pure $AlCl_3$, fixing the positions of the $AlCl_3$ molecules, and giving a solid rather than a liquid, on account of the orienting forces, although one which is volatile, on account of the weakness of these forces.

In $SbCl_3$, the orienting forces are weaker, so that it can exist as a liquid through a considerable temperature range, and, for similar reasons, it shows but little tendency to form double salts. We might expect this difference between the halides of Al and Sb to cause many differences in solubility. We would probably find, for example, that solid $AlCl_3$ would be more soluble in chlorobenzene than would solid $SbCl_3$, if the solids were compared at temperatures at which their activities with respect to their liquid forms are equal.

Certain solutions of iodine, discussed in Chapter XVII, afford interesting examples of acid-base interaction in the electron donor-acceptor sense. The iodine molecule may be regarded as acidic in its reaction with iodide ion, a base or donor, to form I_3^-. Iodine adds strongly to ether and acetone, both basic, to form brown solvates. It adds likewise, although weakly, in solution to benzene. This has long been rather puzzling, but it can be explained as due to a weak basic character in benzene, indicated by its combination with such acids as BCl_3, BF_3 and, reversibly, with H_2SO_4. The substitution of methyl groups in the benzene ring increases basic character and causes stronger interaction with iodine; the color of the solutions shifts increasingly from red to brown in the order, benzene, toluene, xylene, mesitylene, and α-methyl naphthalene[16].

[16] H. A. Benesi and J. H. Hildebrand, *J. Am. Chem. Soc.*, **70**, 2832 (1948).

SPECIFIC INTERACTIONS BETWEEN LIKE MOLECULES

Association of one component. In order to account for positive deviations from Raoult's law Dolezalek[1] assumed that one of the components is associated, containing a certain proportion of double molecules which are dissociated into single molecules as this component is diluted with the other, each molecular species present, however, obeying Raoult's law when the "true" mole fraction rather than the apparent mole fraction is considered. If we consider a solution made up of N_1 moles of A and N_2 moles of B, the latter being partly associated to form N_{BB} moles of double molecules B_2. the number of moles of single molecules remaining in solution would be $N_1 - N_{BB}$ and their mole fraction $N_B = (N_2 - N_{BB}) / (N_1 + N_2 - N_{BB})$. If we assume an equilibrium constant K for the reaction $2B \rightleftarrows B_2$, we may eliminate N_{BB} from the equations in a way analogous to the case of compound formation, bearing in mind that the experimental activity a_2 of B is referred not to the hypothetical liquid of single molecules, but to the actual pure liquid which contains some B_2 molecules. The results of this calculation[17] are given in Equations 15 ab:

$$a_1 = \frac{2kx_1}{(2k-1)x_1 + kx_2 + (x_1^2 + 2kx_1 x_2 + kx_2^2)^{\frac{1}{2}}} \tag{15a}$$

$$a_2 = \left(k^{\frac{1}{2}} + 1\right) \frac{-x_1 + (x_1^2 + 2kx_1 x_2 + kx_2^2)^{\frac{1}{2}}}{(2k-1)x_1 + kx_2 + (x_1^2 + 2kx_1 x_2 + kx_1^2)^{\frac{1}{2}}} \tag{15b}$$

where $k = 4K + 1$

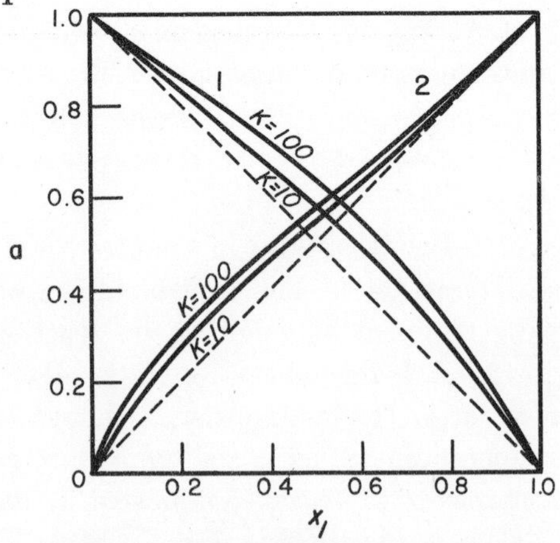

Fig. 2 Deviations from Raoult's law assuming association of one component.

Equations 15ab can be used to calculate vapor pressures of solutions of the type under consideration by assigning appropriate values to K. Fig. 2

[17] For the details of this development, readers are referred to the second edition of this book, or to the original papers of Dolezalek.

shows the activities of the two components in such systems for values of $K=10$ and $K=100$. Dolezalek[1] has carried out such calculations for the systems benzene-carbon tetrachloride, and ether-methyl salicylate, assuming the second named component of each pair to be partly associated with $K=0.207$ and 2.9 respectively; his equations reproduce the small positive deviations fairly well. Reference to Fig. 2 shows, however, that even large values of K are insufficient to account for the large deviations from Raoult's law that are found with many solutions, such as acetone-carbon disulfide (Fig. III-1.4) and carbon disulfide-methylal[6] as shown in Fig. 3. The curves

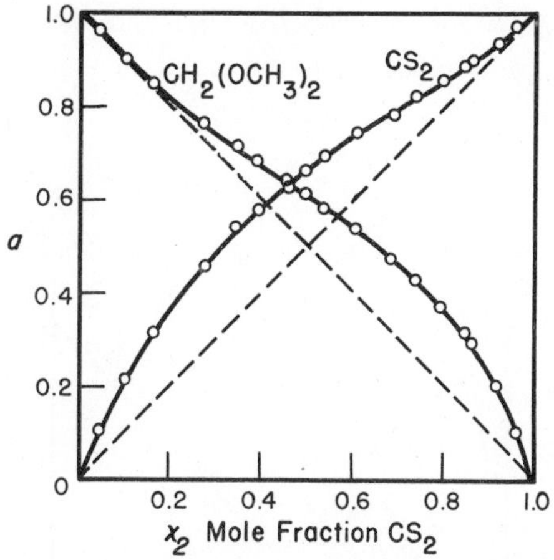

Fig. 3. Activities in methylal-carbon disulfide solutions.

in the latter figure also are more symmetrical than those in Fig. 2 where K is large. Möller[18] has derived expressions for more complicated reactions assumed in order to reproduce certain curve-pairs. For example, the solution ethyl iodide-ethyl acetate is assumed to contain triple molecules of the former and double molecules of the latter, while both components of solutions of carbon tetrachloride-ethyl acetate are assumed to form double molecules. In none of the systems he considers, however, are the deviations very large, and the disciples of Dolezalek have discreetly avoided such systems as acetone-carbon disulfide.

A still greater difficulty with this picture is presented by mixtures which form two liquid phases. Keyes and Hildebrand[19], who investigated the system aniline-hexane, have pointed out that even the assumption of very complex molecules of aniline is insufficient to account for the extreme deviations here encountered. Fig. 4 shows the known points on the actual partial pressure curve of the hexane, the complete theoretical curve, corresponding to Fig. III-19, being indicated by a dotted line. If the aniline is

[18] H. G. Möller, *Z. physik. Chem.*, **69**, 449 (1909).

[19] D. B. Keyes and J. H. Hildebrand *J. Am. Chem. Soc.*, **39**, 2126 (1917).

assumed to be *completely* associated to form molecules of $(C_6H_5NH_2)_n$ where n is an integer, then one single molecule forms $1/n$ associated molecules. Assuming the activity is equal to the "true" mole fraction, we obtain for the hexane:

$$a_2 = \frac{x_2}{x_2 + \frac{x_1}{n}} \tag{16}$$

Fig. 4 shows a series of curves corresponding to a series of values of n. It would be expected, of course that any such complex molecules would dissociate as the percentage of hexane increased, giving lower values of the

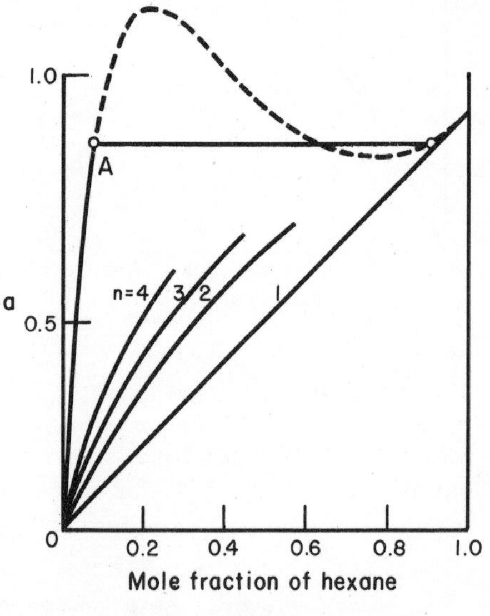

Fig. 4. Activity of hexane in solution with aniline; A- experimental; compared with values calculated for assumed aniline polymers $n = 1$—4.

activity at the upper end than the curves represent, so that the curves represent maximum values. It is obvious that no reasonable value of n comes anywhere near explaining the actual behavior of this or any other system. If the cause of the behavior lies in the "association" of the aniline, it is evident that a very different kind of association must be pictured, an association not into relatively simple complexes which are able to mix with the other component so as to obey Raoult's law, but rather an association of the whole mass of aniline molecules to form a liquid in which the internal pressure or attractive force between the aniline molecules is so great as to resist dispersion into the hexane.

The difficulty of interpreting two-phase liquid mixtures by any purely "chemical" theory of this kind has been clearly stated by Washburn[20], as indicated in Chapter II. Since the partial pressure or activity of each component must be the same in the two liquid phases, the mole fractions, if Raoult's law held, would have to be the same. It is impossible to manipulate the mole fractions to give such a result without making the two phases identical in composition; *i. e.* there is only one phase.

The advocates of the Dolezalek theory are often led to assume association in liquids which according to all other criteria are entirely normal ("unassociated"). Thus, Schulze and Hock[21] explain the positive deviation of the total vapor pressures of benzene-stannic chloride solutions by assuming the formation of double molecules $(SnCl_4)_2$ to the extent of 81% in the pure liquid. At room temperature, this association would have to be still greater in absolute conflict with abundant evidence that stannic chloride is a perfectly normal liquid[22]. The most striking example of the absurdities to which supporters of the "chemical" interpretation of all deviations from ideality were led is Dolezalek's[23] explanation of nitrogen-argon solutions by assuming polymerization of the argon to double molecules.

The "physical" interpretation of positive deviations: internal pressures. We have seen the fantastic conclusions to which Dolezalek was led by his unfortunate assumption (which we now know to be erroneous) of the arithmetic mean. When we replace this mistaken assumption by the more nearly valid one of the geometric mean, we are lead to the development of the internal pressure treatment of heats of mixing (See Chapter VII), resulting in Equation 9. Most of the difficulties arising in the Dolezalek treatment disappear, and most of the positive deviations he attributed to "association" are explained equally well by the non-specific interactions inherent in differences in internal pressure or solubility parameters. Moreover, this "physical" treatment permits explanation of greater deviations such as those in acetone-carbon disulfide or those producing two liquid phases, as we have seen in Chapter III and will see further in subsequent chapters.

It must not be forgotten in considering such a matter that the fact that a formula which has a theoretical basis can be made to fit the fact by a proper choice of constants is not proof of the correctness of the underlying theory, especially when the formula is very elastic. Although equations such as 15ab contain but a single constant, elasticity equivalent to a second adjustable parameter is obtained by assuming *ad libitum*, as Möller did, other forms of association. It would be strange indeed, if such a procedure did not yield satisfactory equations for the moderate deviations

---

[20] E. W. Washburn, *Trans. Am. Electrochem. Soc.*, **22**, 333 (1912); *J. Am. Chem. Soc.*, **32**, 653 (1910).

[21] A. Schulze and H. Hock, *Z. physik. Chem.* **86**, 445 (1914).

[22] J. H. Hildebrand, *J. Chem. Phys.*, **15**, 727 (1947).

[23] F. Dolezalek, *Z. physik. Chem.* **93**, 585 (1918).

from ideality which were considered by Dolezalek and his followers, but while failure of an equation is damaging evidence against a theory, its success by no means constitutes a "proof". The same system may often be treated by several different formulas, as we have seen in the cases of acetone-chloroform and cadmium amalgams; thus the same data may serve to "prove" two theories regarded by their authors as so utterly conflicting as to call for some very harsh polemic[2,3,24].

Considerations such as these led the senior author to a position of considerable scepticism concerning his earlier conclusions regarding the constitution of certain amalgams[25]. The positive deviations shown by zinc[26], lead[11], tin[11], bismuth[27] and silver[28] amalgams may be explained either by assuming association of one component or on the basis of differences in internal pressure. The gradual accumulation of evidence on this point is now strongly in favor of the latter assumption, while still admitting the validity of assuming some kind of specific interaction (such as solvation) to account for negative deviations such as occur with cadmium[11] and thallium[28] amalgams. The isolation of a solid compound of thallium and mercury[29] is evidence for the basic assumption of such interactions. The chief obstacles to regarding the metals as associated to definite polymers such as Zn_2 are, first, the normal behavior of most of them with respect to vaporization[30], and second, the difficulty of making the same assumption regarding the type of association of a given metal in various solutions. A fuller discussion of metallic solutions will be found in Chapter XIX.

Some further objections to the simple "chemical" theory. In addition to the difficulties cited in the preceding section, namely the inadequacy of the "chemical" theory in explaining large positive deviations and phase separation, and the obviously absurd nature of some of the polymeric molecules assumed, two further objections of a more theoretical nature might be cited:

1. The assumption of Raoult's law for the "true" species in solution is incorrect on at least two scores. First, we now know that the entropy of mixing of double or triple molecules with single molecules is not ideal, but that sizeable negative deviations from Raoult's law may be ascribed to differences in molecular size. Secondly, it is hard to imagine an interaction between two substances strong enough to produce a compound AB, but having no effect on the heat of mixing of the three species A, B and AB. To this, one may reply that these effects are absorbed in the equilibrium constant

---

24 F. Dolezalek, *Z. physik. Chem.*, **83**, 40 (1913).
25 J. H. Hildebrand, *J. Am. Chem. Soc.*, **35**, 501 (1913).
26 J. H. Hildebrand, *Trans. Am. Electrochem. Soc.*, **22**, 319 (1912).
27 E. D. Eastman and J. H. Hildebrand, *J. Am. Chem. Soc.*, **36**, 202 (1914).
28 J. H. Hildebrand and E. D. Eastman, *J. Am. Chem. Soc.*, **37**, 2452 (1915).
29 T. W. Richards and F. Daniels, *J. Am. Chem. Soc.*, **41**, 1732 (1919).
30 J. H. Hildebrand, *J. Am. Chem. Soc.*, **37**, 2452 (1915), **40**, 45 (1918).

K, but to argue so is to practically admit the formal equivalence of the "physical" and "chemical" treatments.

2. Without the introduction of an additional parameter, the "chemical" theory gives no information concerning the temperature dependence of the equilibrium constant K, and hence of the activities. In the "physical" theory, if we make the plausible approximation that the heat of mixing is independent of temperature, a fairly adequate interpretation of the temperature dependence of solubilities is obtained, as we shall see in subsequent chapters.

It is evident from the preceding discussions that recourse to what we have called "specific" interactions is necessary only when the interaction between unlike species deviates from the expected *geometric mean*. "Association", if it plays a role at all, is important only when the interaction between like pairs of one or more components is abnormally great leading to the breakdown of the *geometric mean* law. Such a behavior might be expected from components which strongly hydrogen bond in the pure state, water, the alcohols, and the amines, for example. If the "chemical" treatment is to have any validity, it must be superimposed not upon Raoult's law, but upon a normal internal pressure treatment, assuming reasonable positive deviations from Raoult's law for the "true" species.

Modern treatments of "association". The Dolezalek treatment was improved at an early date by van Laar[31], who trenchantly criticized the arithmetic mean hypothesis and replaced it with one in which an association effect is added to the van der Waals — van Laar treatment of ordinary solutions in which the geometric mean was assumed. His application of the equation to water solutions for which he assumed an equilibrium $2H_2O = (H_2O)_2$ was unfortunate since we now know the "association" of water to be far more complex, but this early work represents a marked advance over that of the Dolezalek school.

With the accumulation of more information about the structure of hydrogen-bonded liquids, (see Chapter X), it became apparent that if their properties were to be described in terms of a chemical association, they must be assumed to be capable of almost limitless polymerization, the actual liquids consisting of an equilibrium mixture of polymers of all degrees of polymerization. In addition, one must distinguish between a three dimensional polymer network such as water which is able to form four tetrahedral bonds per molecule and the linear (or cyclic) polymerization to which molecules with capacity for only two bonds per molecules (such as HCN, HF, and the alcohols) are restricted.

With the development of the statistical theories of solutions of linear high polymers (for the details, see Chapter XX), an attempt to treat solutions of "associated" liquids with high polymer equations was in order, and such a treatment has been formulated by Tobolsky and Blatz[32], and in

[31] J. J. van Laar, *Proc. K. Akad. Wetensch. Amsterdam*, **7**, 517 (1905).

[32] A. V. Tobolsky and P. J. Blatz, *J. Chem. Phys.*, **13**, 379 (1945).

a slightly different manner, but with identical results, by Flory[33]. They assume that a given substance is capable of associating by the reactions:

$$A + A = A_2 \qquad K_1$$

$$A_2 + A = A_3 \qquad K_2$$

$$A_n + A = A_{n+1} \quad K_n$$

and that the equilibrium constant K for each step in the association is the same, i. e. $K_1 = K_2 = K_n$.

If we define a "degree of association" p as the ratio of the number of association "bonds" formed to the total possible if the liquid were completely polymerized to one huge molecule, then for the pure substance:

$$\frac{\mathrm{p}}{(1-\mathrm{p})^2} = K \tag{17}$$

or in solutions, where the association effect is diluted:

$$\frac{\mathrm{p}}{(1-\mathrm{p})^2} = K\varphi_2 \tag{18}$$

where φ_2 is the volume fraction of the associating component.

From the same assumptions we deduce that the number average degree of polymerization $\overline{\mathrm{m}}_n$ is given by:

$$\overline{\mathrm{m}}_n = \frac{1}{1-\mathrm{p}} \tag{19}$$

Substitution of this into the free energy equations for mixed polymer solutions obtained by Flory[34] and Scott and Magat[35] (Equations XX-15ab), we obtain for the activity of the non-associating component:

$$\ln a_1 = \frac{\Delta \overline{F}_1}{RT} = \ln \varphi_1 + \mathrm{p}\,\varphi_2 + \mu\,\varphi_2^2 \tag{20}$$

where μ is the familiar high polymer constant depending partly upon the difference of internal pressure. To the approximation that the monomers 1 and 2 are the same size, we can substitute the stoichiometric mole fractions

[33] P. J. Flory, *J. Chem. Phys.*, **14**, 49 (1945).
[34] P. J. Flory, *J. Chem. Phys*, **12**, 425 (1944).
[35] R. L. Scott and M. Magat, *J. Chem. Phys.*, **13**, 172 (1945).

for the volume fractions and obtain for the activity coefficient:

$$\ln \gamma_1 = \mathrm{p} x_2 + \mu x_2^2 \tag{21}$$

If we expand Equation 18 in powers of $K\varphi_2$, we obtain for p:

$$\mathrm{p} = K\varphi_2 - 2(K\varphi_2)^2 + 5(K\varphi_2)^3 - \ldots \tag{22}$$

Substituting into Equation 21 and replacing φ_2 by x_2 we obtain:

$$\ln \gamma_1 = (\mu + K)\, x_2^2 - 2K^2 x_2^3 + 5K^3 x_2^4 - \ldots \tag{23}$$

For small values of the equilibrium constant K, or in dilute solution, only the first term of Equation 23 is important, and it, we see, is identical in form with the physical formulation. The constant is enhanced by an additive factor K quite equivalent to the assumption in the physical theory of an abnormally large value for the interaction constant c_{22} in Equation 8. Only for large values of K, when the x_2^3 becomes important, would it be possible to distinguish between the two equations[36]. Redlich and Kister[37] have assumed a slightly different model for association phenomena, and obtain for the activity coefficient of the non-associating component[38]:

$$\ln \gamma_1 = (\mu + K)\, x_2^2 - 2K^2 x_2^3 + (\tfrac{9}{2}K^3 + 2K^2)\, x_2^4 - \ldots . \tag{24}$$

We see that this differs from the Tobolsky-Blatz-Flory Equation 23, only in the x_2^4 and higher terms. Redlich and Kister have fitted the data for several systems in which methanol is the associating component; the results[39] are shown in Table 5.

From the values of K at 25° C. and 64° C., they calculate the reasonable value of 3.3 kcal for the heat of association, the right order of magnitude for hydrogen bonding. The non-agreement of the K-values for hexane and heptane is attributed to experimental errors.

---

[36] Even for large values of K, a choice between the two formulations is difficult, because for large positive deviations from Raoult's law, (a) the quasi-chemical treatment of ordering effects in non-associated solutions produces a negative term in x_2^3 not unlike that in Equation 23, and (b), phase separation may occur, making determination of γ_1 for large x_2's impossible.

[37] O. Redlich and A. T. Kister, *J. Chem. Phys.*, **15**, 854 (1947).

[38] This form is not given in the Redlich-Kister paper, but expansion of their Equation 33 leads to our Equation 24.

[39] Redlich and Kister use parameters B and K; our μ is related to them by the equation $\mu = 2.3\ [B - \log\ (1 + K)]$

Table 5. Associating Systems

	Temperature	B	K	μ
methanol-benzene	35° C	1.050	6.1	.20
methanol-carbon tetrachloride	35° C	1.105	6.1	.25
methanol-n-hexane	45° C	1.71	30	.22
methanol-n-heptane	58° C	1.25	6.6	.37
methanol-toluene	64° C	0.95	3.8	.27

CRITIQUE OF THE CHEMICAL AND PHYSICAL APPROACHES

We have seen in the preceding pages how two quite different methods of formulating the specific interactions which produce abnormal deviations from Raoult's law lead in many cases to equations which, while mathematically different, are hardly distinguishable when applied to experimental data. This leads to the suspicion that the difference between the physical and chemical approaches may be largely a matter of viewpoint, and that when properly formulated (as Dolezalek's certainly was not), they might prove to be identical. If this be true, then adecision between the two is a matter of personal choice and the question is devoid of any real substance. Before drawing such a conclusion, however, let us examine further the possibility of distinguishing the two approaches.

Chemical species in solution. An early suggestion for recognizing chemical species in solution was that of determining the molecular weight by measurement of the colligative properties of solutions: vapor pressure lowering, osmotic pressure, depression of the freezing point, elevation of the boiling point. Properly carried out, however, this is effective only for determining the chemical species at infinite dilution, and while important for electrolytes is of no importance here. In concentrated solutions, determination of apparent molecular weights obviously begs the question as to whether deviations from Raoult's law are due to physical or chemical effects. Other criteria have been discussed by Timmermans[40], but are primarily methods for demonstrating the purity of a compound rather than its existence in a mixture. For example Roscoe[41] has shown that the azeotropic mixture of water and nitric acid is not a pure compound by demonstrating that the composition of the maximum boiling mixture changed when the temperature and pressure were varied; this demonstration does not however eliminate the possibility of a ternary mixture of H_2O, HNO_3, and a compound, but merely shows that the compound, if it exists at all, is not the only species present.

It is evident that we must look beyond thermodynamics to find a useful method of distinguishing "physical" and "chemical" effects. Other physical

[40] J. Timmermans, "Chemical Species", translated by R. Oesper (Chemical Publishing Company, New York, 1940).

[41] H. E. Roscoe, *J. Chem. Soc.*, **13**, 146 (1861).

properties afford considerable evidence for abnormal effects in solutions. An example would be the appearance of colors in solutions of colorless components, or more generally, the absorption of light in frequency ranges not attributable to either component. The difference between the color of solutions of iodine in benzene or ether and the color of "normal" iodine solutions is strong evidence (as we shall see in Chapter XVII) for specific interaction between the iodine and the solvent molecules. Other properties may be equally important, such as the measurements of dipole moments in solutions of non-polar substances or the shift of Raman frequencies.

These abnormal phenomena, even though they may possibly be explained without explicit reference to "chemical" effects, are surely evidence for very specific interactions between the molecules, and are widely used in the study of many systems.

The criterion of saturation. A primary feature of the normal covalent bond is its uniquely saturated character. Two separated hydrogen atoms have a strong tendency to combine to form a hydrogen molecule H_2 with the evolution of a large amount of energy, but having done so, there is virtually no tendency to add a third atom to form a molecule H_3. The strong forces tending to form the H—H bond have been satisfied and the bonding tendency is "saturated". This is not true of coulombic forces; the positive Na^+ ion in the NaCl crystal exerts its electrostatic attraction (or repulsion, as the case may be) indiscriminately on all other ions, depending only on the distance of separation. Nor are the London dispersion forces of a "saturated" type; the energy of a normal liquid is the sum over all pairs of molecules, the existence or non-existence of one pair has little or no effect on the energy of another pair, as we have seen in Chapter IV. This non-additivity is characteristic of the "chemical" bond.

An example taken from real gases may be instructive. The deviations from ideality in the gas phase may be attributed[42] to the formation of transitory clusters of molecules; the probability of forming molecular pairs accounts for the second virial coefficient, the higher terms are dependent in large part upon the formation of clusters of three or more molecules. If the forces between molecules are not saturated, the tendency to form these larger clusters is of the same order of magnitude (save for the concentration dependence) as that to form pairs. Where, however, there are strong forces which are saturated by the formation of a pair, then any relation between the probability of pairs and triplets is lost. For example, in argon vapor at normal pressures, there will be only a few pairs and a very few triplets; increasing the pressure will increase the concentration of both species. In acetic acid vapor[43], however, the hydrogen bonding in the dimer is so strong that at room temperature and one atmosphere pressure the gas is almost

---

[42] See for example, J. E. Mayer and S. G. Harrison, *J. Chem. Phys.*, **13**, 276 (1945).

[43] F. H. MacDougall and D. R. Blumer, *J. Am. Chem. Soc.*, **55**, 2236 (1933); F. H. MacDougall, *Ibid*, **58**, 2585 (1936).

completely dimerized (see Chapter X); on the other hand, there seems to be no reason to believe that the higher clusters are any more prevalent than in argon vapor. We may speak of the intermolecular forces as "saturated" in this case[44]. A similar case of saturation exists in the equilibrium between gaseous NO_2 and N_2O_4[45].

An analogous situation prevails in solutions, except that sizeable numbers of the larger clusters (triplets, etc.) are possible because of the higher concentrations. This may be used to distinguish qualitatively between the "chemical" and "physical" approaches. The physical formulation (Equations 8 and 11) assumes that the interaction between all adjacent pairs may be described by three parameters, one for each type. This would mean that in the case of the system acetone-chloroform, when an acetone molecule has interacted with one adjacent chloroform, it is still capable of the same interaction with any other chloroform molecules which are nearest neighbors. This is implausible, since by the nature of the molecule, it seems likely that the interaction is a saturated one. The agreement between the "chemical" and "physical" equations for this system must be attributed to the relative weakness of the interaction; for stronger interactions Equations 5 and 11 diverge.

On the other hand, it is much less likely that the intermetallic "compounds" show saturation; the approximately spherical force fields of the metals suggest an interaction much different, and in fact, order-disorder transitions in the β-brasses (CuZn, etc) have been treated with a large degree of success by purely "physical" formulations similar to Equations 8 and 11 (Metallic solutions and intermetallic "compounds" are discussed further in Chapter XIX).

The "associated" liquids such as the alcohols and water fall in an intermediate class. With the alcohols, saturation is reached only when two hydrogen bonds per molecule are formed, and we may expect divergence between a "physical" theory and a "chemical" formulation involving linear polymers only at concentrations where an alcohol molecule will have *three* or more alcohol molecules as nearest neighbors. With water, of course saturation is reached only when four hydrogen bonds per molecule are formed, a situation to be found only in fairly concentrated solutions.

While it is clear that "chemical" treatments were badly misapplied when used for certain systems, it is equally clear that there are systems where "chemical" or "saturation" effects are important.

The discussion of the preceding pages is intended only to give a picture of the various effects possible in solutions where specific interactions be-

[44] The quantum-mechanical interpretation of "saturation" involves resonance or exchange forces. We use "saturation" in a more general sense to include cases (like the above where electrostatic forces are "saturated" by virtue of steric effects preventing close approach of a third molecule to the dipole.

[45] W. F. Giauque and J. D. Kemp, *J. Chem. Phys.*, **6**, 40 (1938).

tween molecules play a role. It is apparent that all of the existing treatments of such effects, whether "chemical" or "physical", leave something to be desired, at least so far as their theoretical basis and general applicability are concerned, and that further attention to such solutions is merited. It is to be hoped that in the next few years we will see significant advances in the direction of an adequate treatment of specific interactions in solutions.

CHAPTER XII

Systems of Three or More Components.

While most of the interest in mixtures and solutions centers around binary systems involving only two components, many problems involve more complex mixtures of three or more components. While the previous chapters have dealt exclusively with binary mixtures, it is interesting as well as important to extend the treatment of regular solutions to ternary systems and higher. As we shall see, no new assumptions need to be introduced, and the mathematical treatment is entirely straightforward.

Entropy in multicomponent systems. While the entropy of complex systems of n components may be derived any of the ways discussed in Chapter VI perhaps the simplest way to view it is in terms of the free-volume treatment, If, following Hildebrand[1], we regard the mixing process as equivalent to the sum of n expansions, one for each component, the free volume available to component 1 is initially, only its own free volume $N_1 \mathrm{v}_1^f$, but after mixing, the free volumes of all the other components are available. Thus, we may write for the entropy of mixing:

$$\Delta S^{\mathrm{M}} = - R \left[N_1 \ln \frac{N_1 \mathrm{v}_1^f}{N_1 \mathrm{v}_1^f + \ldots . N_n \mathrm{v}_n^f} + \ldots . + \right.$$

$$\left. N_n \ln \frac{N_n \mathrm{v}_n^f}{N_1 \mathrm{v}_1^f + \ldots . + N_n \mathrm{v}_n^f} \right] \tag{1}$$

We have seen that in a binary system, we obtain the ideal entropy of mixing when the free volumes are all equal. If we set $\mathrm{v}_1^f = \mathrm{v}_2^f = \ldots = \mathrm{v}_n^f$, the arguments of the logarithms become mole fractions, and we have:

$$\Delta S^{\mathrm{M}} = - R \left[N_1 \ln x_1 + N_2 \ln x_2 + \ldots + N_n \ln x_n \right] \tag{2}$$

As in the binary case, differentiation leads to ideal partial molal entropies:

$$\Delta \bar{\mathrm{S}}_1 = - R \ln x_1 \tag{3a}$$

$$\Delta \bar{\mathrm{S}}_2 = - R \ln x_2 \tag{3b}$$

....

$$\Delta \bar{\mathrm{S}}_n = - R \ln x_n \tag{3n}$$

[1] J. H. Hildebrand, *J. Chem. Phys.*, **15**, 225 (1947).

This is to be expected, since the increase of disorder of component 1, for example, should be independent of the source of the additional free volume, whether it be from many components, one, or none (as in the case of mere expansion of a gas).

The same equations may be derived from a quasi-lattice treatment, where the number of indistinguishable configurations Ω_m is merely:

$$\Omega_m = \frac{(n_1 + n_2 + \ldots + n_n)!}{(n_1 !)(n_2 !) \ldots (n_n !)} \tag{4}$$

Where there are differences in size or shape of the different components, the same complications arise which were considered for binary systems in Chapter VI. For the special case of chain molecules occupying a series of sites on a quasi-lattice (such as high polymer mixtures) equations applicable to multicomponent systems have been derived[2,3,4].

Except for the case of such extreme differences of size and shape as are found in high polymer solutions, we shall assume (as in Chapter VI) that the ideal entropies (Equation 3) are good enough approximations for the actual, and hence that the assumption of regular solutions is valid.

The heat of mixing. Any of the more or less equivalent methods of calculating the heat of mixing (see Chapter VII) suffice for multicomponent systems. For simplicity, we use Scatchard's cohesive energy equations[5], rather than the more complex method of distribution functions[6] which leads to the same results; initially we restrict ourselves to a ternary system, and assume that the cohesive energy per mole of a ternary mixture may be represented by an expression analogous to Equation VII — 13:

$$-E_m = (x_1 V_1 + x_2 V_2 + x_3 V_3)(c_{11}\varphi_1^2 + c_{22}\varphi_2^2 + c_{33}\varphi_3^2 + 2c_{12}\varphi_1\varphi_2 + 2c_{13}\varphi_1\varphi_3 + 2c_{23}\varphi_2\varphi_3) \tag{5}$$

where the x's, V's and φ's have their usual meaning of mole fractions, molal volumes, and volume fractions, and the c's, as in Equation VII—13, represent interaction constants or cohesive energy densities. The important feature of Equation 5 is that it is a two subscript equation; the c's are constants of the binary systems, and there are no constants depending upon all three components simultaneously. This is equivalent to the assumption that the energy of any set of three molecules is exactly the sum of the three pairs taken independently; this is presumably true except where the dipole

[2] E. A. Guggenheim, *Proc. Roy. Soc.*, **A 183**, 213 (1944).
[3] P. J. Flory, *J. Chem. Phys.*, **12**, 425 (1944).
[4] R. L. Scott and M. Magat, *J. Chem. Phys.*, **13**, 172 (1945).
[5] G. Scatchard, *Chem. Rev.*, **8**, 321 (1931); *Trans. Faraday Soc.*, **33**, 160 (1937).
[6] J. H. Hildebrand and S. E. Wood, *J. Chem. Phys.*, **1**, 817 (1933).

or steric interaction with a third molecule influences the orientation and hence the energy of the first two[7].

Recalling that $-E_1 = c_1 V_1$, etc., we may derive for the heat or energy of mixing:

$$\Delta H^M = \Delta E^M = E_m - x_1 E_1 - x_2 E_2 - x_3 E_3$$

$$\Delta H^M = (x_1 V_1 + x_2 V_2 + x_3 V_3)(A_{12}\varphi_1\varphi_2 + A_{13}\varphi_1\varphi_3 + A_{23}\varphi_2\varphi_3) \quad (6)$$

where

$$A_{12} = c_{11} + c_{22} - 2c_{12} \quad (7\,a)$$

$$A_{13} = c_{11} + c_{33} - 2c_{13} \quad (7\,b)$$

$$A_{23} = c_{22} + c_{33} - 2c_{23} \quad (7\,c)$$

The A's are of course the coefficients for the three separate binary systems; so we see that the ternary system is completely described if all three two-component systems are known.

Differentiation leads to the partial molal heats of mixing:

$$\Delta\bar{H}_1 = V_1\left[A_{12}\varphi_2^2 + A_{13}\varphi_3^2 + (A_{12} + A_{13} - A_{23})\varphi_2\varphi_3\right] \quad (8\,a)$$

$$\Delta\bar{H}_2 = V_2\left[A_{12}\varphi_1^2 + A_{23}\varphi_3^2 + (A_{12} + A_{23} - A_{13})\varphi_1\varphi_3\right] \quad (8\,b)$$

$$\Delta\bar{H}_3 = V_3\left[A_{13}\varphi_1^2 + A_{23}\varphi_2^2 + (A_{13} + A_{23} - A_{12})\varphi_1\varphi_2\right] \quad (8\,c)$$

If, in addition, we assume that the interaction energy between unlike pairs is the geometric mean of those between like pairs, then, as we recall from Chapter VII, the A's are simple functions of the solubility parameters δ:

$$A_{ij} = (\delta_i - \delta_j)^2 \quad (9)$$

Then Equations 8abc simplifiy:

$$\Delta\bar{H}_1 = V_1\left[(\delta_1 - \delta_2)\varphi_2 + (\delta_1 - \delta_3)\varphi_3\right]^2 \quad (10\,a)$$

[7] This is not the same as the more general conclusion that, given the molecular distribution functions, the energy is the sum over all pairs. Equation 5 implies further an independence of the distribution functions (as assumed by Hildebrand and Wood) such that the orientations of molecular pairs are not coupled. In reality, of course, they are, and this would show up in different actual distribution functions.

$$\Delta\overline{H}_2 = V_2 \Big[(\delta_2 - \delta_1)\varphi_1 + (\delta_2 - \delta_3)\varphi_3 \Big]^2 \tag{10b}$$

$$\Delta\overline{H}_3 = V_3 \Big[(\delta_3 - \delta_1)\varphi_1 + (\delta_3 - \delta_2)\varphi_2 \Big]^2 \tag{10c}$$

Each of these equations may be rearranged in a form which shows that the partial molal heat of mixing of liquid 1 with liquids 2 and 3 is equivalent to the heat of mixing of liquid 1 with a hypothetical new liquid whose δ is the volume fraction average of 2 and 3.

$$\Delta\overline{H}_1 = V_1 (\delta_1 - \delta_o)^2 \varphi_o^2 \tag{11}$$

where $$\delta_o = \frac{\varphi_2 \delta_2 + \varphi_3 \delta_3}{\varphi_2 + \varphi_3} \qquad \varphi_o = \varphi_2 + \varphi_3$$

Such a transformation may always be made and is frequently useful in dealing with one phase systems, as we shall see.

An alternative transformation leads to the partial molal heat of mixing as a function of the δ of the pure substance and the average δ of the ternary mixture:

$$\Delta\overline{H}_1 = V_1 \Big[\delta_1 (1 - \varphi_1) - \varphi_2 \delta_2 - \varphi_3 \delta_3 \Big]^2 = V_1 (\delta_1 - \overline{\delta})^2 \tag{12}$$

where $$\overline{\delta} = \varphi_1 \delta_1 + \varphi_2 \delta_2 + \varphi_3 \delta_3$$

For the general case of n components, we obtain an entirely similar set of equations:

$$- E_m = V_m \left(\sum_{i=1}^{n} \sum_{j=1}^{n} c_{ij} \varphi_i \varphi_j \right) \tag{13}$$

$$V_m = \sum_{i=1}^{n} x_i V_i \tag{14}$$

$$\Delta H^M = \frac{V_m}{2} \sum_i \sum_j A_{ij} \varphi_i \varphi_j \tag{15}$$

(Remember that $A_{ii} = 0$)

$$\Delta\overline{H}_k = V_k \Big[\sum_i \sum_j (A_{ik} - A_{ij}) \varphi_i \varphi_j \Big] \tag{16}$$

If Equation 9 (*i. e.*, the geometric mean law) holds, then we may write $\Delta\overline{H}_k$ in terms of the δ's:

$$\Delta\overline{H}_k = V_k \left[\sum_i (\delta_k - \delta_i)\, \varphi_i \right]^2 \tag{17}$$

Equations 11 and 12 remain unchanged except for the obvious extension of the meanings of δ_o, φ_o, and $\overline{\delta}$.

Activity coefficients in regular ternary systems. For regular solutions the entropy is ideal, and we have seen that the activity coefficients are directly related to the partial molal heats of mixing. We may therefore use Equations 10abc and 12 to write:

$$\ln \gamma_1 = \frac{\Delta\overline{H}_1}{RT} = \frac{V_1}{RT}(\delta_1 - \overline{\delta})^2 \tag{18a}$$

$$\ln \gamma_2 = \frac{\Delta\overline{H}_2}{RT} = \frac{V_2}{RT}(\delta_2 - \overline{\delta})^2 \tag{18b}$$

$$\ln \gamma_3 = \frac{\Delta\overline{H}_3}{RT} = \frac{V_3}{RT}(\delta_3 - \overline{\delta})^2 \tag{18c}$$

where, as before

$$\overline{\delta} = \varphi_1 \delta_1 + \varphi_2 \delta_2 + \varphi_3 \delta_3 \tag{19}$$

We see from Equations 18abc that the activity coefficient varies with the term under the square, *i. e.*, with the average solubility parameter $\overline{\delta}$. Consequently the line of constant γ will be the line of constant $\overline{\delta}$, and most important, *it is the same line for all three components*, although of course γ_1, γ_2 and γ_3 have different values. Analysis of Equation 19 shows further that on a volume fraction scale all such lines are parallel. Figures 1abc show the activity coefficient contours for a typical case ($\delta_1 = 10$, $\delta_2 = 9$, $\delta_3 = 7$; for simplicity, we assume equal molal volumes $V_1 = V_2 = V_3 = 120$; $V/RT = 0.2$). Of special interest is the fact that for component 2, with a δ-value lying between the other two, there is a line clear across the diagram for which $\gamma_2 = 1$ and for which the partial molal heat is zero and the partial molal free energy is ideal; for the other two components, of course, no such line exists. This is a perfectly general phenomena for all systems for which Equation 9 holds; we should expect it to be valid for all nonpolar ternary systems and probably for other systems where orientation effects are not serious. Actually it holds with surprising accuracy even in the systems phenol-toluene-iso-octane[8], and phenol-toluene-methylcyclohexane[8] (except at very high phenol concentrations); toluene is the intermediate component, as would be expected from the solubility parameters.

Figures 1abc also show the activity contours calculated from the activity coefficients by the formula $a = \gamma x$.

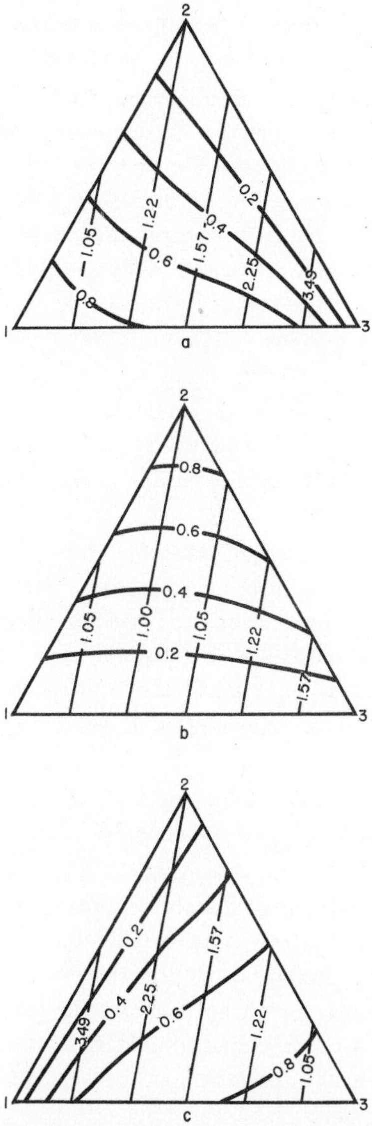

Fig. 1. Activities and activity coefficients in three component systems. The activity contours are the heavy lines; the activity coefficient contours are the thin straight lines, a) a_1 and γ_1, b) a_2 and γ_2, b) a_3 and γ_3.

[8] H. G. Drickamer, G. G. Brown, and R. R. White, *Trans. Am. Inst. Chem. Engrs.*, **41**, 555 (1945).

More general treatments of ternary systems: While Equations 18 abc will fit many ternary systems with a fair degree of accuracy, it is necessary to utilize more general expressions to correlate much of the ternary data accurately. Part of this is due to the fact that few systems in which all three components are nonpolar have been studied since the system of importance to the engineering problems of extraction equilibria usually involve such substances as alcohol, water, or acetone. The simple equations discussed in the preceding section may be modified in several ways:

(1) Instead of assuming a dependence upon the volume fraction as in Equations 5-19, White[9] adopted a semi-empirical form of the van Laar equation (cf. Chapter III), using the a's and b's not in the van der Waals sense but as adjustable parameters involving a sort of generalized volume fraction (cf. Chapter VII). He however retained a relation between the a's analogous to Equation 9, and required the a's and b's to be consistent in the three binary systems and the ternary system. With such equations, White was able to fit data for systems methanol-ethanol-water, benzene-ethanol-water, and ethanol-water-cellosolve.

(2) Where an equation such as Equation 9 is no longer valid, we may fall back on the more general Equations 8 abc, which do not involve the geometric mean assumption. In such a case A_{12}, A_{13}, and A_{23} are independent parameters.

(3) Even more general treatments are obtained by introducing higher powers and three- and four-subscript parameters into the equations. A four subscript twelve parameter equation was used by Benedict and coworkers[10] to correlate data on *n*-heptane-methanol-toluene mixtures. Such elaborate equations are useful only when quantitative interpolation of data is necessary for engineering design purposes and have little or no theoretical justification.

An excellent review of the various methods of evaluating thermodynamic data for binary and ternary liquid systems has been given by Wohl[11].

Phase equilibria in ternary systems: We have seen in Chapter III how the free energy equations of regular solutions may be used to explain separation into two liquid phases, and to calculate the approximate concentrations of the conjugate phases as well as the critical solution temperature. The appropriate equations for three components may be used to calculate the phase boundary in a ternary diagram. Here however the calculations are more difficult, because three equations must be solved simultaneously in order to obtain two conjugate points and the connecting tieline. The conditions are that the activities of each component be the same in both phases, or in a similar way, the free energies:

---

[9] R. R. White, *Trans. Am. Inst. Chem. Engrs.,* **41**, 539 (1945).

[10] M. Benedict, C. A. Johnson, E. Solomon, and L. C. Rubin, *Trans. Am. Inst. Chem. Engrs.,* **41**, 371 (1945).

[11] K. Wohl, *Trans. Am. Inst. Chem. Engrs.,* **42**, 215 (1946).

$$\Delta\bar{F}_1' = \Delta\bar{F}_1'' \tag{20 a}$$

$$\Delta\bar{F}_2' = \Delta\bar{F}_2'' \tag{20 b}$$

$$\Delta\bar{F}_3' = \Delta\bar{F}_3'' \tag{20 c}$$

Solution of such equations is tedious, even in the simplest cases. One may however derive the coordinates of the plait point or "critical phase" in terms of the parameters of the equations. In practice, however, this has seldom been done, since most ternary systems showing phase separation which have been studied to date involve anomalous components such as hydrogen bonding substances or metals, for which the reliability of the equations is uncertain. An exception is found in the treatment of ternary systems involving high polymers, to be discussed in a subsequent chapter. The development of the fluorocarbons, with the resulting expansion of the solubility parameter spectrum fororganic liquids, makes possible interesting future studies of phase separation at room temperatures in systems where all three components are nonpolar.

Thermodyamic relations in ternary systems and the various phase diagrams resulting therefrom have been treated qualitatively in books by Marsh[12] and Masing[13].

Partition of solutes between immiscible liquids. The problem of calculating phase equilibria in a ternary system is enormously simplified when two of the components are essentially immiscible. We may then treat the ternary system as two binary systems in equilibrium; then only the activity of the component capable of existing in both phases needs to be considered.

When two liquids are practically immiscible in each other it is evident, as explained in Chapter III, that they deviate enormously from Raoult's law. If, then, a solute is introduced which distributes itself between the two solvents, it is evident, further, that its deviations from Raoult's law with respect to the two solvents may be quite different. For example, if the solute obeys Raoult's law with one of the liquids it will deviate greatly from it with respect to the other liquid.

Let this behavior be represented by Figure 2, in which the two curves represent the activity of the solute, 2, in the respective solvents, 1 and 3.

---

[12] J. S. Marsh, "Principles of Phase Diagrams", Alloys of Iron Research, Monograph Series (McGraw-Hill, New York, 1935).

[13] G. Masing, "Ternary Systems", translated by B. A. Rogers, (Reinhold, New York, 1944).

If sufficient of the solute is introduced so that its activity is a_2 when distributed at equilibrium between the two liquids, the ratio of its mole fractions in 1 and 3 is ab/ac. If mole fractions are substituted by concentrations, by the aid of the molecular weights and densities, we have the ordinary "partition coefficient", which has been found so useful in getting the activity of one of the components of a complex equilibrium mixture. If, now, we add more 2 so as to raise its activity in the system to a'_2, the ratio of its mole fractions becomes ad/ae, but inspection of Figure 2 shows

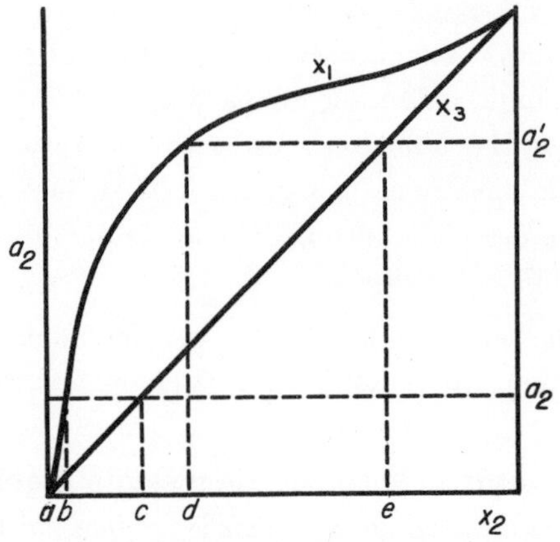

Fig. 2. Activities of a solute in two different solvents, in relation to partition.

that this ratio is by no means the same as at the lower concentration, but that the partition coefficient rises in a way quite predictable from a knowledge of the activity-composition curves. In so far, therefore, as we can determine the latter, we can predict the partition coefficient and its variation with the concentration. The figure also shows that if we restrict ourselves to sufficiently small concentrations so that the activity curves may be regarded as straight (*i. e.* where Henry's Law is valid) the partition coefficient will remain constant within the same limit.

Since the total activity of an electrolyte does not vary linearly with the concentration, even in dilute solutions, partition coefficients yield the same kind of evidence for ionization as do all other properties which measure activity.

It is not unlikely that the solute is itself only partially miscible with one of the liquids. In such a case, there is a maximum and minimum in the activity curve (cf. Figs. III-18-21), and we have relations similar to those shown schematically in Figure 3. Here we see that the partition coefficient will fall off with increasing concentration, since the activity in the good solvent (3) shows more curvature in the region of interest than does that

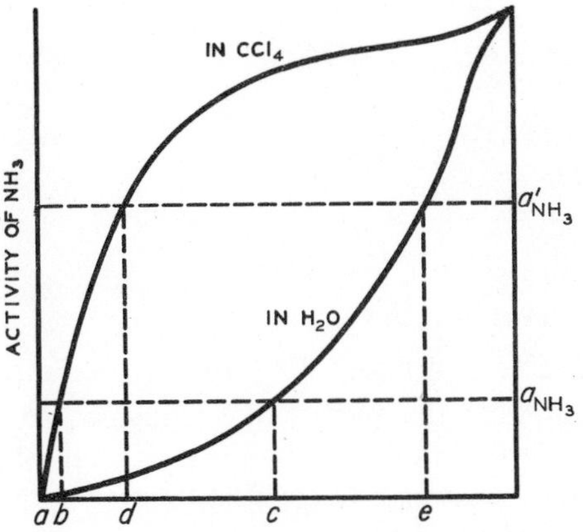

Fig. 3. Activities of a solute (2) in two different solvents in one of which it is only slightly soluble.

in the poor solvent (1), a reversal of the situation in Figure 2. We see that the direction of the shift of the partition coefficient with concentration will depend upon the relative curvature of the two activity curves of the system in question.

A few examples will serve to illustrate the correlation between partition coefficients and the general principles used throughout this volume. The solubilities of iodine give us a knowledge of its activities in various solvents, which serve to predict the general facts regarding its partition between two solvents. Let us consider its partition between water and carbon disulfide, bromoform, carbon tetrachloride, respectively, for which we have data by Jakowkin[14]. Like nearly all data upon partition coefficients these refer to amount of solute in unit volume of solution, so that in the absence of densities of the solutions it is impossible to recalculate to mole fractions. However, the conclusions stated above are sufficiently well illustrated by the original figures. Since water is only partially miscible with liquid iodine, even at 150°C (See Fig. XVII-1), it evidently corresponds to the

[14] A. A. Jakowkin, *Z. physik. Chem.*, **18**, 585 (1895).

solvent 1 in Fig. 3. We therefore expect that the concentration in water divided by the concentration in iodine should decrease with increasing concentration; Table 1 shows that this is the case.

Table 1.

Conc. of Iodine, g./liter		Ratio
in H_2O	in CS_2	$\frac{\text{Conc. in } H_2O}{\text{Conc. in } CS_2}$
0.0518	30.36	.00171
0.1104	65.81	.00168
0.1743	108.3	.00161
0.2571	167.6	.00153

A similar effect is shown for the other solvents.

When enough iodine is present to saturate the solution the ratio of the two solubilities should give the partition coefficient, except in so far as the solubilities of the two liquids in each other affect the results. This relation was first pointed out by Berthelot and Jungfleisch[15] who, however, failed to substantiate it experimentally due to errors in their figures. Jakowkin, however, later showed it to be true by the aid of the figures here reproduced in Table 2.

Table 2.— Partition in Saturated Iodine Solutions.

	Solubility, 25°; g./liter	Ratio found	Ratio calc.
Water	0.3387	. . .	. . .
Carbon disulfide . .	230.0	679	685
Bromoform	189.6	559	559
Carbon tetrachloride. .	30.33	89.6	89.7

The ratios in the last column were got by extrapolation to saturation of the partition coefficients such as are given in Table 1 for unsaturated solutions.

If we turn to a polar solute, such as ammonia, we find a state of affairs illustrated in Figure 4, where the activity of the ammonia in water is less than that demanded by Raoult's law while in carbon tetra-

[15] M. Berthelot and E. Jungfleisch, *Ann. chim et phys.*, 4, 26, 400 (1872).

chloride it is greater, due to the great difference in polarity. Accordingly, the partition coefficient expressed with the concentration in the carbon

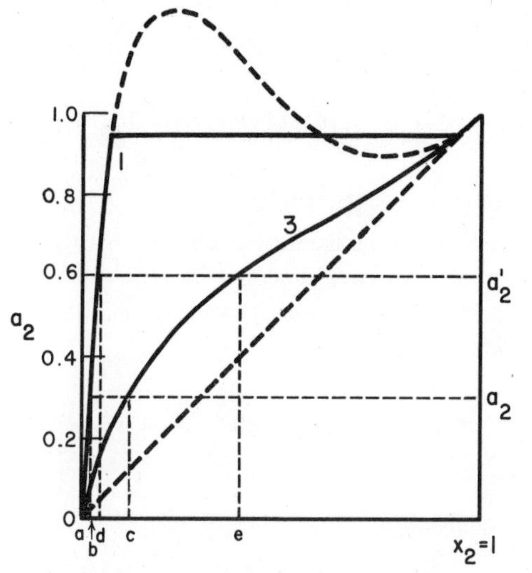

Fig. 4. Relation of partition coefficient of NH_3 between CCl_4 and H_2O to its activities in these solvents.

tetrachloride in the numerator is less than unity and increases with increasing concentration as shown in Table 3, which gives partial data by Hertz and Lewy[17].

Table 3.—Molal Concentration of NH_3.

in H_2O	in CCl_4	Ratio
1.73	0.0079	0.00456
2.35	0.0118	0.00502
5.70	0.0357	0.00626
6.86	0.0464	0.00677
8.59	0.0735	0.00856

Since the ionization of the ammonia in the water layer is insufficient to have any marked effect upon the partition ratio, it is usual to attempt to explain the inconstancy of a ratio of this sort by assuming that the solute forms complex molecules in the nonpolar liquid. Objections to this practice of ascribing all discrepancies from the ideal solutions laws to molecular changes have been given in Chapter XI, and apply with equal force here.

[16] W. Hertz and M. Lewy, *Jahresber. Schles. Ges. vaterl. Kult., Naturw. Sekt.* **1906: 1**. See also H. W. Smith, *J. Phys. Chem.*, **26**, 256 (1922).

CHAPTER XIII

Vapor Pressure of Binary Liquid Solutions

Approximately ideal solutions are formed, in harmony with theory, by a number of pairs of nonassociated liquids whose solubility parameters differ by only small amounts. The same is true of a pair of closely related associated liquids such as methyl and ethyl alcohols. Table 1 gives a number

Table 1. Approximately ideal solutions.

Liquid 1.	Liquid 2.	t°C	$\frac{100\,\Delta P}{Pi}$	$(\delta_1 - \delta_2)^2$	Ref.
n-Heptane	2, 2, 4-Trimethyl pentane	97.2	−0.05	0.25	1
n-Heptane	Methyl cyclohexane	97.2	∼0	0.1	1
n-Heptane	*n*-Octane	97.2	−0.6	0.01	1
n-Heptane	*n*-Hexane	67.5	−0.9	0.03	1
n-Heptane	3-Heptene	97.2	0.5		1
n-Octane	2, 2, 4-Trimethyl pentane	98.1	−0.5	0.36	1
Benzene	Toluene	79.6	∼0	0.06	1
Toluene	Ethylbenzene			0.01	2
Benzene	Ethylene chloride	50.0	∼0		3
Propylene bromide	Ethylene bromide	85.1	∼0		3
Methyl iodide	Chloroform	35.	0.5	0.42	4
Methyl iodide	Benzene	35	3	0.55	4
Benzene	Methylal (Dimethoxymethane)	25	−2.4		4
n-Hexane	Hexadecane	20	−3		5,6
Ethyl alcohol	Methyl alcohol	25	∼0		7
Ethyl alcohol	*n*-Propyl alcohol	25	1		8
Carbon disulfide	Carbon tetrabromide				9

[1] H. A. Beatty and G. Calingaert. *Ind. Eng. Chem.*, **26**, 504 (1934).
[2] S. Young and E. C. Fortney, *J. Chem. Soc.*, **83**, 45 (1903).
[3] J. v. Zawidski, *Z. physik. Chem.*, **35**, 129 (1900).
[4] N. D. Litvinov, *J. Phys. Chem.*, *U.S.S.R.*, **14**, 782 (1940).
[5] J. H. Hildebrand and J. W. Sweny, *J. Phys. Chem.*, **43**, 109, 297 (1939).
[6] J. N. Brønsted and J. Koefoed, *Kgl. Danske Videnskab. Selskab, Matemat.-Fysiske Meddelelsen*, Bd. XXII, No. 17 (1946).
[7] G. C. Schmidt, *Z. physik. Chem.*, **99**, **71**, (1921).
[8] G. S. Parks and J. R. Schwenck, *J. Phys. Chem.*, **28**, 720 (1924).
[9] A. E. Korvezee, *Rec. trav. chim.*, **53**, **464** (1934).

of nearly ideal solutions by way of illustration, with the percent deviations in total pressure, $100\ \Delta P/P^i$, at $x = 0.5$, and the square of the difference in their solubility parameters, $(\delta_1 - \delta_2)^2$, taking the values from Appendix I for 25° C, since it would not be worth while to go to the trouble of recalculating them to the temperatures at which the vapor pressures were measured, in each case. It is likewise not worth while to attempt to correct vapor pressures for deviations from the gas laws.

The case of hexane-hexadecane is an interesting one, and we discussed it in Chapter VI in connection with the problem of entropy of molecules of very different length arranged in approximately parallel array. The analysis there given would appear to be the more realistic one for a component whose molecules depart so far from spherical symmetry as do those of normal hexadecane. The small departures from ideality found by Brønsted and Koefoed[6] could be explained on the basis of nonideal entropy of mixing of molecules of different length[10]. It is regrettable that these investigators did not repeat their measurements at a different temperature so as to learn whether the entropy is ideal, which was found to be the case in the somewhat less precise measurements of Hildebrand and Sweny[5].

Carbon disulfide solutions. Turning to nonideal solutions, carbon disulfide solutions offer more illuminating cases than most others by reason of the fact that its internal pressure is higher than the internal pressures of most of the common volatile liquids; therefore, in the absence of association or solvation, the departures from ideal behavior should theoretically increase in order of increasing difference in the solubility parameters. Table 2 gives,

Table 2. — Carbon disulfide solutions.

	t °C	$\frac{100\ \Delta P}{P i}$	$\delta_1 - \delta_2$ from sol'ns	$\delta_1 - \delta_2$ from pure components	Ref.
Methyl alcohol	36.5	2 liq.			
Acetone	29.2	56			12
Dimethoxy methane	35.2	28	2.8		5
i-Pentane	17.	24.5	2.4	3.15	12
i-Butyl chloride	20.	20.0			12
Ether	29.2	15.8	2.0	1.45	12
Cyclohexane	19.8	14.0		1.7	12
Chloroform	20.	14	1.9	1.0	12
Benzene	25.	12.5	1.8	.85	12, 13
Carbon disulfide		0	0	0	

[10] J. H. Hildebrand, *J. Am. Chem. Soc.*, **59**, 794 (1937).
[12] J. Hirshberg, *Bull. Soc. chim. Belg.*, **41**, 163 (1932).
[13] J. Sameshima, *J. Am. Chem. Soc.*, **40**, 1503 (1918).

in the second column of figures, the per cent excess of the total pressure over the ideal total pressure for a number of pairs reported in the literature. We see, first, that methyl alcohol forms two liquid phases with carbon disulfide below 36.5 °C. This extreme deviation from ideality is in accord with the difficulty encountered by most nonpolar molecules in penetrating into a liquid held together by strong hydrogen bonds. We shall see in Chapter XV, for example, that it is an exceptionally poor solvent for nonpolar gases. Acetone has such a high dipole moment, 2.8 Debye units, that its solvent powers cannot be deduced from its δ-value of 9.9 derived from energy of vaporization. Its poor solvent power for phosphorus, P_4, (cf. Chapter XVII) is in accord with its behavior here.

The deviations in total pressure for the other solutions increase approximately in order of increasing difference between the δ-values of the components except in the case of the moderate reversal with chloroform. We shall see evidence in Chapter XVII that the solvent power of chloroform for three solid solutes of high internal pressure is in accord with a solubility parameter, $\delta \sim 9.0$, a little less than that of benzene, instead of the value 9.3, derived from energy of vaporization. That such an empirical adjustment is iecessary is not difficult to understand in view of its dipole moment, 1.05 Debye units; that a parameter can be so assigned as to account for different solutions is gratifying.

The fact that the data referred to in Table 2 were obtained at somewhat different temperatures and by different observers, and also that some of them bear internal evidence of experimental errors in the determination of partial pressures, makes difficult a strict correlation between the deviations and the solubility parameters.

We shall begin with an examination of the solution of carbon disulfide with isopentane. The deviations in this case are large, minimizing experimental errors; the data are internally consistent; and the molal volumes are considerably different, 60.7 cc. and 117.5 cc., respectively, at 25 °C, so that volume fractions, φ, differ considerably from mole fractions, x. In Fig. 1 A are plotted points for this system calculated from the data of Hirshberg[12]. As ordinates are plotted 4.575 $T \log \gamma_1/V_1$ against φ_2^2, the circles referring to CS_2 in this and the following figures, and the points, with subscripts reversed, to i-C_5H_{12}. The slope of the line drawn through these points gives the value of $(\delta_1 - \delta_2)^2$ for this solution. We see, first, that all the points all close to one line drawn through them; second that $(\delta_1 - \delta_2)^2 = 5.65$ when $\varphi_2^2 = 1.0$ and therefore $\delta_1 - \delta_2 = 2.4$. This is to be compared with the values of δ derived from energy of vaporization, given in Table 2, $\delta_1 - \delta_2 = 9.9 - 6.75 = 3.15$. Line B, in Fig. 1, is drawn through the points for solutions with methylal (dimethoxymethane) from the classic paper of Zawidski[5]. The plot shows that the data conform excellently with our equation with $(\delta_1 - \delta_2)^2 = 4.0$. The slight scattering of the points at the upper ends

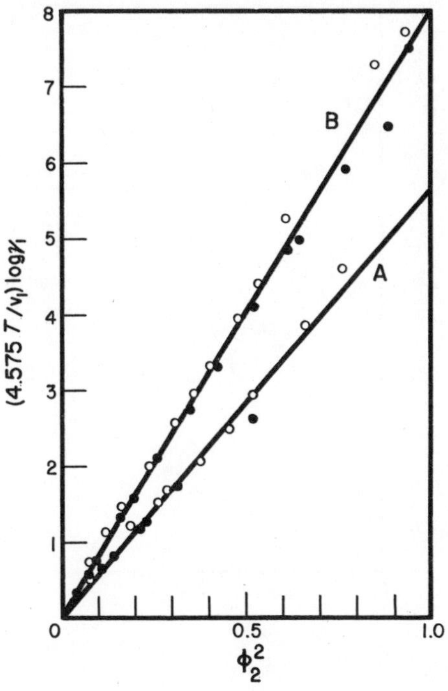

Fig. 1. Solutions of carbon disulfide with isopentane, A; and, with dimethoxymethane, B.

of such a line is not significant as they represent very small partial pressures where errors can have large effects.

Next, let us compare Fig. 1 A, with Fig. 2, where log γ_1 is plotted against x_2^2 and log γ_2 against x_1^2 for the same data. The two sets of points do not fall on the same line and the two lines are curved. This is an excellent illustration of the importance of using volume-fractions instead of mole fractions.

Fig. 3 shows a plot like that of Fig. 1 for the experimental data reported for CS_2-$CHCl_3$, also by Hirshberg[12]. We see that a common line suffices for both activity coefficients but that the data are evidently less accurate. In the case of carbon disulfide with ether, Fig. 4, the points for CS_2 are evidently considerably in error. The points for carbon disulfide with benzene, by Sameshima[13], fall rather well on two straight lines of slightly differing slope, Fig. 5. This may be attributed either to a systematic error or to volume changes on mixing or to some degree of specific interaction between the components. The fact that the slopes of these lines are considerably greater than would be predicted from the δ-values of the two components lends plausibility to such a guess.

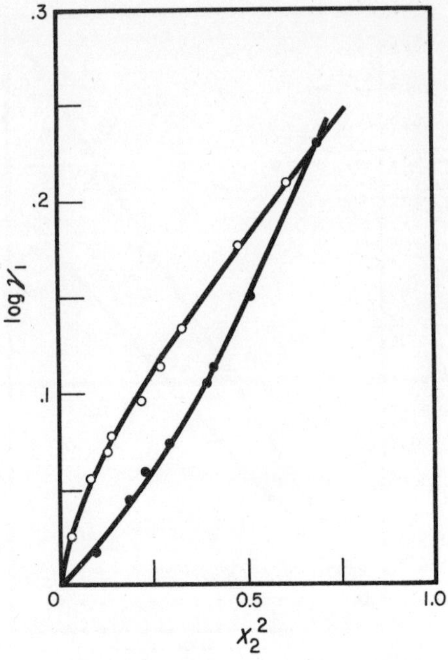

Fig. 2. Carbon disulfide-iso-pentane solutions. Result of plotting log γ_1 against square of mole fraction, x_2.

The discrepancies between the values of δ for the second component given in the fourth and fifth columns of figures are samples of the shortcomings of theory or experiment, or inadequate data or all three. Further consideration of disturbing factors will be found below.

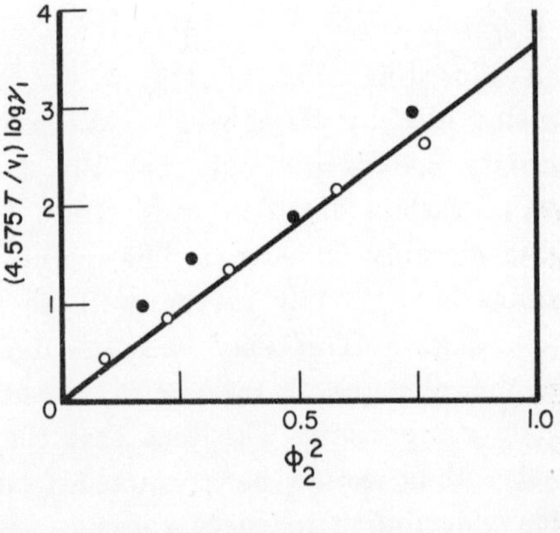

Fig. 3. Carbon disulfide-chloroform solutions.

It is an interesting fact that the data of Zawidzki for CS_2-acetone solutions shown in Chapter III, Fig. 1, give, when plotted in the manner here shown in Figs. 1-5, an excellent straight line, as in Fig. 1. The

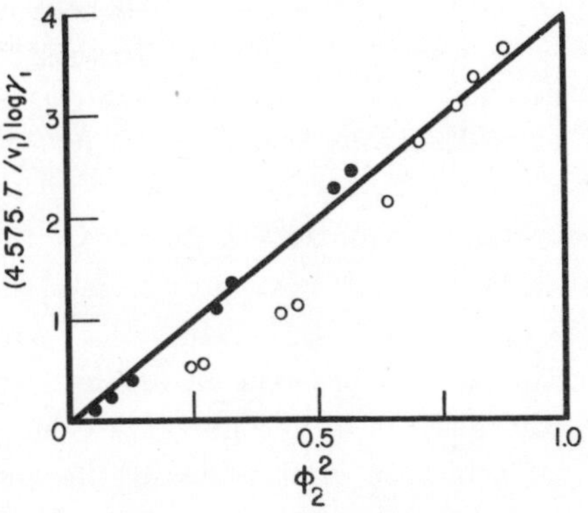

Fig. 4. Carbon disulfide-ether solutions.

intercept gives an empirical value for $\delta_1 - \delta_2$ from which a δ_2-value for acetone can be obtained, but which of course, does not agree with its $(\Delta E^V/V)^{\frac{1}{2}}$. It would be interesting, nevertheless, to see whether solutions of acetone with other nonpolar components would yield the same value.

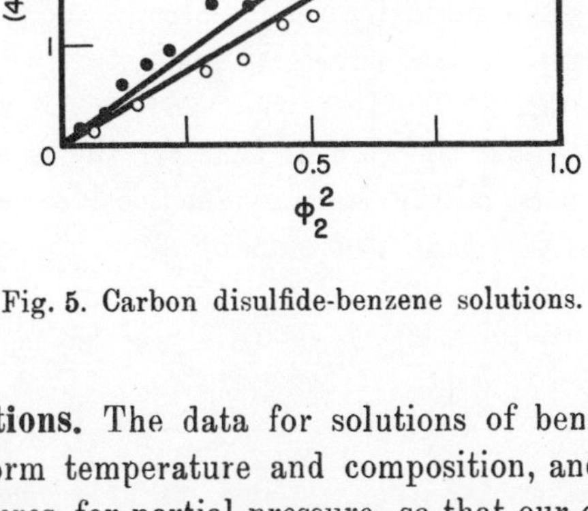

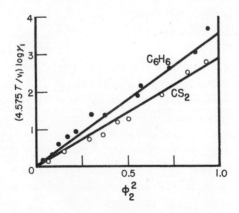

Fig. 5. Carbon disulfide-benzene solutions.

Benzene Solutions. The data for solutions of benzene have not been determined at uniform temperature and composition, and we have, in many cases, no direct figures for partial pressure, so that our comparisons between deviations from ideal behavior and differences in internal pressure cannot be made as directly as we should like. The internal pressure of benzene is so near to that of other common liquids such as carbon tetrachloride, chloroform and ethylene chloride, that the deviations from Raoult's law are small, and the effects of volume changes, deviations from gas laws, and experimental errors more or less obscure the effect of internal pressure differences. Butane and hexane, however, differ sufficiently from benzene to cause considerable increases in activity coefficients, as shown by the measurements of Calingaert and Hitchcock[14]. For benzene in butane, for example, at 25° C, $p_2 = 737$ mm. and $p_2^\circ = 1823$ mm. at $x_2 = 0.20$. Accordingly, $4.575\, T \log \gamma_2 = 418.5$ cal. Also, $v_1 = 102.0$ cc. and $v_2 = 89.3$ cc. and $\delta_1 - \delta_2 = 2.6$. The solubility parameters in Appendix I give $9.15 - 6.6 = 2.55$.

Benzene and ether obey Raoult's law very closely, according to Schmidt[15], despite the difference $\delta_1 - \delta_2 = 9.15 - 7.45 = 1.7$. An explanation may be found in the contraction of 0.6 per cent on mixing instead of the small expansion expected in the absence of recognizable chemical effects. This may be another instance of acid-base interaction in the electron acceptor-donor sense, such as is suggested in Chapter XV to account for the action of benzene solutions of iodine.

An additional example is furnished by the negative deviation from Raoult's law of the partial pressure of HBr over its solution in benzene reported by Kapustinskii and Mal'tsev[16].

Solutions of benzene with cyclohexane have been investigated with great precision and comprehensiveness by Scatchard, Wood and Mochel[17a] and Wood and Austin[18], and the results compared with similar studies of benzene with carbon tetrachloride[17b] and of the latter with cyclohexane[17c]. These important results are summarized in Table 3. The largest deviation from ideality is that between benzene and cyclohexane, as it should be from the δ-values, but the deviation is too great in terms of the simple equation. However, by taking account of the comparatively large increase of volume on mixing by the method developed by Scatchard[19], the agreement is improved. The extra large excess entropy of mixing these components was at first explained as due to "an abnormally small entropy in one of the liquids, probably caused by incomplete randomness of orientation which becomes complete in the mixtures. If this explanation were correct, the excess entropy of the first system should equal the sum of that for the other two if there were no lack of randomness in the more symmetrical carbon tetrachloride, and would in general be less than this sum by twice the effect for carbon tetra-

[14] G. Calingaert and L. H. Hitchcock, *J. Am. Chem. Soc.*, **49**, 750 (1927).

[15] G. C. Schmidt, *Z. physik. Chem.*, **121**, 122 (1926).

[16] A. F. Kapustinskii and V. A. Mal'tsev, *J. Phys. Chem.*, (U.S.S.R.), **14**, 105 (1940).

[17] G. Scatchard, S. E. Wood and J. M. Mochel, (a) *J. Phys. Chem.*, **43**, 119 (1939) (b) *J. Am. Chem. Soc.*, **62**, 712 (1940); (c) *Ibid.*, **61**, 3206 (1939).

[18] S. E. Wood and A. E. Austin, *J. Am. Chem. Soc.*, **67**, 480 (1945).

[19] G. Scatchard, *Trans. Faraday Soc.*, **33**, 160 (1937).

chloride. From Table 3 we see that the excess entropy for benzene-cyclohexane is almost four times as great as the sum of the other two systems. Barring the very improbable case of a large negative entropy in one of the mixtures giving compensation, most study of the two systems with carbon tetrachloride shows that the most of the excess entropy cannot arise from an abnormally low entropy in either of the components."[17b]

Table 3. Properties of Equimolal Mixtures.

	$C_6H_6-C_6H_{12}$	$C_6H_{12}-CCl_4$	$C_6H_6-CCl_4$
$100\Delta V^M/\sum xV$	0.65	0.16	0.003
$100\Delta P/P^i$ at 70°	9.73	2.17	2.75
" " " 40°	12.32	2.63	3.15
Difference	2.59	0.46	0.40
Difference from vol. regular solution	0.88	0.06	0.16
ΔH^M cal./mole	175.8	34.2	30.2
$\Delta F^M - \Delta F^i = \Delta F^E$	74.4	16.7	19.5
$T(\Delta S - \Delta S^i) = T\Delta S^E$	101.4	17.5	10.7
ΔE^M	120.0	20.7	29.0
" calc.	26.0	3.8	9.2
$100\,(c_{12} - \sqrt{c_{11}\,c_{22}})/c_{12}$	2.5	0.5	0.5

Evidence of some degree of ordered arrangement in the two pure liquids was found by Hildebrand[20] in their extra entropy of vaporization. The above facts may find a qualitative explanation in the different shapes of the two molecular species, flat *vs.* puckered hexagons, so that the order possible in each of the separate liquids breaks down.

Ward[21] measured the x-ray diffraction of benzene-cyclohexane solutions and interpreted his results as indicating a sub-microscopic emulsion structure, a most improbable situation in view of the small deviation of these solutions from ideality. But the difference between the peaks is only 0.41 Å and Warren and Murray[22] repeated the observations and showed that such a small difference is incapable of revealing an emulsoid structure even if it existed.

Direct calorimetric measurements of the heat of mixing of carbon tetrachloride with benzene, silicon tetrachloride, and normal heptane were carried out by Vold[23]. His figures for the first pair are somewhat smaller, 20.8 cal. per

[20] J. H. Hildebrand, *J. Chem. Phys.*, **7**, 233 (1939).
[21] H. K. Ward, *J. Chem. Phys.*, **2**, 153 (1934).
[22] G. E. Murray and B. E. Warren, *J. Chem. Phys.*, **7**, 141 (1939).
[23] R. D. Vold, *J. Am. Chem. Soc.*. **59**, 1515 (1937).

mole of mixture at $x = 0.5$, than those calculated from internal pressures. In the case of carbon and silicon tetrachlorides, the components with most nearly spherical symmetry, his measured and calculated values agreed within the experimental error, 32 and 29 cal./mole. A remarkable feature of his work is that although the difference in the δ-values for the other two solutions, calculated from the heat of mixing, do not agree very closely with the values derived from energy of vaporization, $\delta_1 - \delta_3$ from the heats of mixing is exactly equal to $(\delta_1 - \delta_2) - (\delta_3 - \delta_2)$.

Carbon tetrachloride and bromine show a large positive deviation from Raoult's law, in harmony with the large difference in internal pressure, which according to Appendix I is 2.9. Lewis and Storch[24] found $p_2/p_2^\circ = 0.048$ for bromine at $x_2 = 0.025$ and 25°C. This gives $\gamma_2 = 1.92$. We will calculate $\delta_2 - \delta_1$, from Equation VII-46. For this purpose we use $V_1 = 97.1$ cc. and $V_2 = 51.2$ cc. and obtain $\delta_2 - \delta_1 = 2.79$, which agrees well with the above value from the internal pressure difference. We might suppose that the similarity in the electron systems of these molecules would give a more normal interaction than in most cases. It is worth noting, also, that the experimental data are more accurate in this case than in most of the others we are discussing in this chapter.

Alcohols in solution with a nonpolar component show large positive deviations from ideality, sufficient to give two liquid phases in such cases as carbon disulfide-methanol. Wolf[25] discussed the solutions, methanol-cyclohexane; ethanol with hexane, cyclohexane, and benzene; *t*-butanol in hexane; carbon disulfide in methanol, ethanol, *i*-propanol, *i*-butanol and *sec*-butanol. Scatchard, Wood and Mochel[26] made one of their comprehensive surveys of methanol with benzene and with carbon tetrachloride, and Wood extended the same methods to methanol-cyclohexane. Scatchard and Raymond[27] studied the system ethanol-chloroform. It is worthwhile to give here the authors' own summary interpretation of their findings.

"The unusual behavior of the ethanol-chloroform system was attributed[27] to the interactions between the hydrogens of the hydroxyl and of chloroform with the oxygen of ethanol and the chlorine of chloroform. The positive enthalpy and excess entropy of mixing in solutions dilute in ethanol were attributed to dissociation of the aggregates of alcohol molecules, and the negative values in solutions rich in alcohol were attributed to an interaction between alcohol and chloroform to give aggregates each of which contains more molecules of alcohol than does an aggregate without chloroform. Since interaction of the chloroform hydrogen with the alcohol oxygen cannot account for this excess, it was assumed that the alcohol

---

[24] G. N. Lewis and H. Storch, *J. Am. Chem. Soc.*, **39**, 2544 (1917).

[25] K. L. Wolf, *Trans. Faraday Soc.*, **33**, 179 (1937).

[26] G. Scatchard, S. E. Wood and J. M. Mochel, *J. Am. Chem. Soc.*, **68**, 195 (1946); S. E. Wood, *ibid.*, 1963 (1946).

[27] G. Scatchard and C. L. Raymond, *ibid.*, **60**, 1278 (1938).

hydrogens react with the chloroform chlorines. This interaction seems to be the only explanation for the negative enthalpy change in ethanol-carbon tetrachloride mixtures rich in ethanol.

"We expected in methanol-carbon tetrachloride mixtures a similar tendency to negative excess entropies and enthalpies in solutions rich in methanol, without being able to predict that the effect would be so different on the two functions that the enthalpy becomes negative only in mixtures very rich in methanol while the excess entropy is negative for all mixtures.

"We were surprised, however, to find a similar asymmetry with methanol-benzene mixtures, although it is less marked than with carbon tetrachloride. Thus the enthalpy, though less positive in alcohol rich mixtures, is never negative, and the entropy changes from negative to positive as the methanol fraction becomes less than thirty per cent. In these mixtures there can be no parallel collinear dipoles such as that formed in methanol-carbon tetrachloride by the four atoms C-Cl H-O. There is a possibility of interaction between the hydrogen of benzene and the oxygen of methanol, but it does not seem probable that it can involve much energy and we know no other cases of strong interaction of aromatic hydrogen with oxygen. We believe that the most probable interaction is that of the hydroxyl hydrogen with the electrons within, and on both sides of the benzene ring. These electrons should be easily polarizable, but we know no other examples of this type of interaction.

"The mutual energy of unit volumes of the components may be calculated from the equation [our symbols]

$$c_{12} = \frac{1}{2}\left(\frac{-\Delta E^M}{\varphi_1 \varphi_2 V_m} + c_{11} + c_{22}\right)$$

by approximating the value of ΔE^M by ΔH^M at half mole fraction and 35°. The absolute value of c_{12} is 5% greater than $\sqrt{c_{11} c_{22}}$ for benzene-methanol and about 8% greater than $\sqrt{c_{11} c_{22}}$ for carbon tetrachloride-methanol. This shows that there must be a strong interaction between molecules of the two components corresponding to the association of the alcohol molecules."

Redlich[28] has considered the thermodynamic properties of systems composed of an associated with a non-associated component taking account of the variable association of one component. This treatment of the problem has been described in Chapter XI.

Osmium tetroxide and carbon tetrachloride solutions present an instructive case. Anderson and Yost[29] determined the partial vapor pressure of CCl_4 and showed that it agreed well with the assumption of an equilibrium

[28] O. Redlich and A. T. Kister, *J. Chem. Phys.*, **15**, 854 (1947).
[29] L. H. Anderson and D. M. Yost, *J. Am. Chem. Soc.*, **60**, 1822 (1938).

between OsO_4 and $(OsO_4)_4$, although they mention the other type of explanation, *i. e.*, that the molecular field strengths or internal pressures of these two substances are sufficiently different to cause departure from Raoult's law without the presence of any definite polymer of either species. Polymerization in solution is contraindicated by the evidence that even in the pure liquid state osmium tetroxide behaves as a normal liquid.

The vapor pressure has been measured by Ruff and Tschirch[30], by von Wartenberg[31], and by Ogawa[32]. Plotted in the usual way, log p against $1/T$, the values agree rather well, those of Ogawa appearing most consistent, and give a molal heat of vaporization of about 9040 cal. at the boiling point (130 °C.), corresponding to a Trouton quotient of 22.4. This test and the more rigid test by the aid of the "Hildebrand rule" indicate a normal liquid. This conclusion is further confirmed by surface tension measurements by Ogawa.

We can show that the extent of the departure of the solutions of the tetroxide in carbon tetrachloride from Raoult's law is approximately what could have been predicted from the difference in their internal pressures. For carbon tetrachloride at 25 °C., $\delta_1 = 8.6$. The vapor pressures of the osmium tetroxide just cited give $\Delta H^V = 9800$, extrapolated to 25 °C. The liquid densities observed by Ogawa give a molal volume of 58.0 cc. extrapolated to 25 °C. from the melting point, (40 °C.), hence $(\Delta E^V/V)^{\frac{1}{2}} = 12.6$.

Table 4. Data for the system osmium tetroxide-carbon tetrachloride, 25 °C.

x_2	p_1	a_1	γ_1	φ_2	$\delta_2 - \delta_1$
0.000	11.46	1.000	1.000	0.000	
0.395	7.86	0.686	1.133	0.278	3.13
0.599	6.19	0.540	1.344	0.471	2.84
0.693	5.39	0.470	1.530	0.574	2.81
				Mean	2.93

Table 4 gives the values for several solutions sufficiently concentrated in the tetroxide to show deviations from Raoult's law. Substituting these values in the general equation gives the values of $\delta_2 - \delta_1$ recorded in the last column, with a mean of 2.9. Since $\delta_2 > \delta_1$ in this case, $\delta_2 = 2.9 + 8.5 = 11.4$, sufficiently close to the value, 12.6, given above to indicate that the departures from Raoult's law are adequately accounted for by this means and do not require ann chemical explanation.

[30] O. Ruff and F. W. Tschirch, *Ber.*, **46**, 929 (1913).
[31] H. von Wartenberg, *Ann.*, **440**, 97 (1924).
[32] E. Ogawa, *Bull. Chem. Soc. Japan*, **6**, 302 (1931).

Constant boiling mixtures-minimum boiling points. When the two components of a binary mixture have nearly equal vapor pressures it takes little positive deviation from Raoult's law to yield a maximum in the vapor pressure composition curve, which is a condition of great practical significance, since it limits the possibility of separation by fractional distillation. Where the components differ considerably in internal pressure or in polarity, a mixture with a minimum boiling point may be found, even when the boiling points of the pure components differ considerably.

A large number of liquid mixtures have been examined by Lecat for maxima and minima in boiling points, and his own observations, together with a remarkably complete record of similar observations by others are to be found in his book, "La Tension de Vapeur des Mélanges de Liquides: L'Azéotropisme"[33], a work indispensable to anyone concerned with the problems of distillation. Table 5 gives several examples from these collected data.[33a]

Table 5. Minimum Boiling Liquid Mixtures.

	b. pt.		b. pt.	Min. b. pt. of mixture
Cyclohexane	80.8°	Hexane	69.0°	None
Cyclohexane		Carbontetrachloride	76.8°	76.5°
Cyclohexane		Toluene	110.7°	None
Cyclohexane		Benzene	80.2°	77.5°
Cyclohexane		Methylethyl ketone	79.6°	72. °
Carbontetrachloride	76.8°	Diethyl ketone	102.2°	None
Carbontetrachloride		Cyclohexane	80.8°	76.5°
Carbontetrachloride		Ethyl acetate	77.2°	74.8°
Mesitylene	164.0°	Benzene	78.0°	None
Mesitylene		Chlorotoluene	161.3°	160.5°
Mesitylene		Bromobenzene	156.1°	None
Mesitylene		Propionic acid	140.7°	139.3°

Cyclohexane is not far enough from hexane to yield a minimum boiling mixture in view of the difference of 12° in their boiling points, but carbon tetrachloride, farther from cyclohexane in internal pressure and nearer in boiling point gives a mixture boiling with a slight minimum. Toluene with its much higher boiling point shows no minimum, although the deviation from Raoult's law is doubtless equally large. Benzene, differing still more

[33] Brussels, Lamertin, 1918, Cf. Subsequent data in various issues of the *Ann. Soc. Sc.*, Brussels.

[33a] For a more recent summary of azeotropic data, see L. H. Horsley, *Anal. Chem.* **19**, 508—600 (1947).

in internal pressure and with nearly the same boiling point, shows a pronounced minimum. Methyl ethyl ketone on account of its polarity shows a still more pronounced minimum, while diethyl ketone, though nearly as polar and undoubtedly deviating almost as much from Raoult's law, has a boiling point so much higher that no minimum appears.

Carbon tetrachloride differs but little in boiling point from the three other liquids mentioned with it in Table 5, but the cyclohexane and ethyl acetate differ enough from it in internal pressure (and the latter probably in polarity as well) to give minimum boiling mixtures, while benzene, which it resembles more closely, does not.

Mesitylene and chlorotoluene have boiling points close together, so that their small difference in internal pressure is sufficient to give a minimum. Bromobenzene, though having larger internal pressure, boils enough lower than mesitylene to give no minimum boiling mixture, while propionic acid, though boiling still lower, is so polar a substance that a minimum again appears.

The boiling point diagram for acetone-carbon disulfide solutions[34] is given in Fig. 6 (cf. Chapter III. Fig. 1).

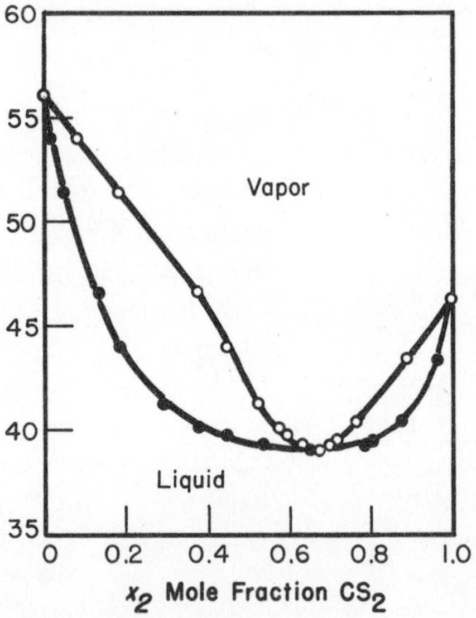

Fig. 6. Boiling point diagram of the acetone-carbon disulfide system, showing the minimum boiling point.

Constant boiling mixtures - maximum boiling points. Negative deviations from Raoult's law result from tendency towards chemical union, and when this is sufficiently marked to counteract any difference in boiling points of the pure components it may give rise to a minimum in the vapor pressure curve and a maximum in the boiling point curve. The following

[34] M. A. Rosanoff and C. W. Easley, *J. Am. Chem. Soc.*, **31**, 953 (1909).

cases of negative deviation have already been mentioned: chloroform-acetone, chloroform-ether. The former gives a maximum boiling point[34], as shown in Table 6 and Fig. 7 (cf. Chapter III, Fig. 2), while the latter, by reason of the difference of 26.4° in the boiling points of the pure constituents, is not able to show a maximum.

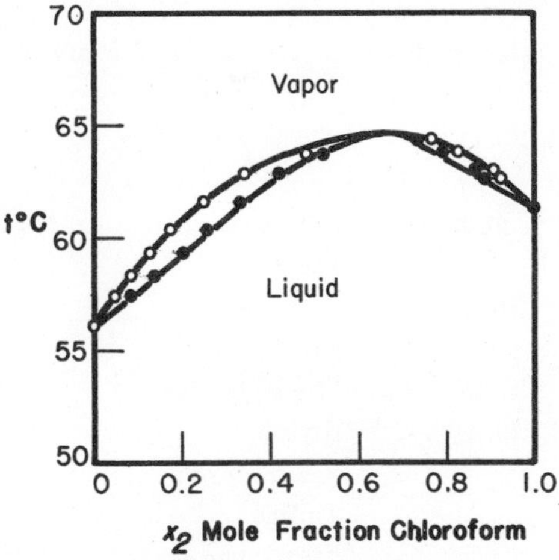

Fig. 7. Boiling point diagram for the acetone-chloroform system, showing the maximum boiling point.

Further examples from Lecat are given in Table 6, which illustrate certain of the principles outlined in the earlier chapters. They illustrate the fact that negative deviations from Raoult's law occur almost exclusively with polar substances, and also that a pronounced difference in acidic and basic character promotes such deviation. Thus, aniline and hydrogen chloride give a very great maximum in boiling point, while aniline and the weaker acetic acid, in spite of the much smaller difference in their boiling points, do not give a maximum boiling mixture. Propionic acid with pyridine, a stronger base than aniline, shows a maximum 10° higher than the boiling point of the acid. It should be noted that not all the substances showing this evidence of combination are commonly regarded as acidic and basic respectively, for the list contains such polar substances as ketones, esters and aldehydes.

Fractional distillation. The method for constructing the boiling point composition curve from the vapor pressure curves of the pure components and upon the assumption of Raoult's law has alread been described (Chapter III). When deviations from ideality occur they give rise to corresponding deviations in the boiling point curve, causing greater separation between the two curves. The deviation may be sufficient, provided the difference in boiling points is not too great, to give a minimum, in which case the vapor tends to approach the composition of the minimum boiling mixture and no complete separation of the components is possible unless the minimum can be destroyed by distilling under a different pressure or perhaps by adding a third component.

Table 6. Maximum boiling liquid mixtures.

	b. pt.		b. pt.	Max. b. pt. of mixture
Chloroform	61.0°	Acetone	56.3°	63.4°
Chloroform		Ether	34.6°	None
Water	100.0°	Hydrogen chloride	80.0°	110.0°
Water		Nitric acid	86.0°	120.5°
Pyridine	115.5°	Propionic acid	140.7°	150.8°
Phenol	181.5°	Glycol	197.4°	199.0°
Phenol		Benzaldehyde	179.2°	185.6°
Phenol		Aniline	184.4°	186.2°
Phenol		Ethyl butyrate	178.6°	185.6°
Phenol		Benzyl alcohol	205.5°	206.0°
Formic acid	100.8°	Acetone	56.2°	None
Formic acid		Diethyl ketone	102.2°	105.0°
Aniline	184.4°	Hydrogen chloride	80.0°	244.8°
Aniline		Acetic acid	118.5°	None

Conversely, when the deviation from Raoult's law is negative, the boiling point-composition curve may show a maximum, in which case the distillate will contain an excess of one component or the other, depending upon which side of the maximum the mixture lies. In either case, the residue will approach in composition the maximum boiling mixture and no complete fractionation will be possible unless the maximum can be destroyed.

It should ordinarily be possible to destroy a maximum or minimum in the boiling point of a solution by adding a third component which can be subsequently separated. Let us consider a mixture such as carbon disulfide-acetone mixtures, whose vapor pressures, partial and total, are shown in Chapter III, Fig. 1. The following considerations may serve to select a suitable third component. First, it should have a relatively high boiling point to facilitate the distillation of the first two components, and to avoid any new azeotrope. Second, it may well have a small negative deviation in vapor pressure with one of the components, if possible, so as to destroy the convexity of the three dimensional surface which would represent the total vapor pressure of the three component mixture. This is illustrated in Fig. 8, where the vapor pressures of the binary systems A—B, B—C, and C—A, are plotted. If these are folded into a triangular prism, the negative deviation of the curve for B—C might be expected to destroy the positive deviation

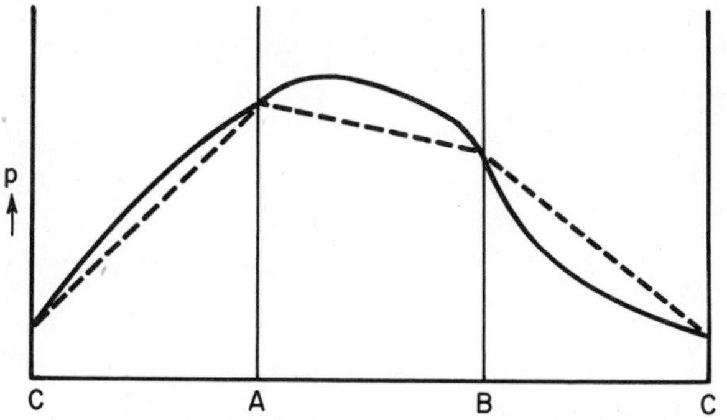

Fig. 8. Method of destroying an azeotropic mixture of A and B by adding a third component, C.

of the curve for the mixture to be separated, A—B, provided enough of component C is added. A suitable third component for the solution carbon disulfide-acetone might be a high boiling, somewhat polar liquid. For further consideration of three component systems, see Chapter XII.

Molecular weight from rise in boiling point. The rise in the boiling point of a solvent per mole of solute has been extensively used to determine the molecular weight of the solute. In most cases, however, there is found a departure from the normal value as the concentration of the solute is increased in spite of care taken to express the concentration in the most favorable way. This departure has invited calculations of the "degree of association", and so great has been the faith of most investigators in the validity of the boiling point law that it has seldom occured to them to put the onus for any departure upon it rather than upon the molecular weight. The theories outlined in this volume do not lead us to expect that many substances will form wholly ideal solutions or give constant and normal values of molecular weight, even though their molecular weights as pure liquids are quite normal.

The rise in boiling point of an infinitely dilute ideal solution is given by the familiar equation,

$$\frac{dT}{dx_2} = \frac{RT^2}{\Delta H_1^V} \qquad (1)$$

where ΔH_1^V is the heat of vaporization of the solvent. Deviations from this equation for actual solutions arise, first, from the simplifications made in its derivation and, second, from depatures from ideality. The problem is essentially the same as that connected with the lowering of the freezing point, which is treated later, and we will pause here only to give one illustration, using the rise in boiling point of carbon disulfide produced by naphthalene and phosphorus, according to data by Beckmann[35]. The values of ΔH^V for the solvent given in the literature[36] are 6670, 6420, 6380, 6600, the mean of which is 6520. This gives $RT^2/\Delta H^V = 30.8$. Table 7 gives part of the original data, together with values of x_2 and of $\Delta T/x_2$. It will be noted that the molal rise in boiling point with naphthalene solutions is but little less than the normal value, whereas with phosphorus it is considerably less for similar concentrations. This difference is in harmony with the internal pressure differences and with data mentioned elsewhere

Table 7. Rise in boiling point of carbon disulfide.

Solute	$(\Delta E^V/V)^{\frac{1}{2}}$ at 25°	x_2	ΔT	$\Delta T/x_2$	Apparent Molec. wt.
Ideal	10.0			30.8	
Naphthalene	9.9	0.0438	1.293	29.5	1.04 · 128
		0.0762	2.268	29.8	1.03 · 128
Phosphorus	14.3	0.0339	0.980	28.8	1.07 · 124
		0.0681	1.810	26.6	1.16 · 124
		0.1032	2.630	25.4	1.21 · 124

upon the solubilities of these same solutes in carbon disulfide. If the molal weight of the solute, instead of the molal rise, is calculated from the data, we obtain the values in the last column of the table, which might be interpreted to mean that naphthalene is slightly associated in carbon disulfide while phosphorus is considerably so. Such an assumption must be regarded as without foundation, for the components of the solution are so unlike that they form two liquid phases below — 6.5° and must also be far from ideal at the boiling point of carbon disulfide. It is the equation, therefore, not the molecular weight of phosphorus, which needs correction.

We may further object to the frequent practice of making the molecular weight of the solute bear the brunt of the entire alteration required to make the data fit the ideal equation, even in cases where the solvent is polar and the solute nonpolar, and where association of the former might

[35] E. Beckmann, *Z. physik. Chem.*, **6**, 437 (1890); **5**, 76 (1890).

[36] H. V. Regnault, *Mem. Acad.*, **26**, 1, 262 (1862); A. Winkelmann, *Ann. Physik.*, **[2]**, **9**, 2-8, 368 (1880); K. Wirtz, *Ibid*, **40**, 446 (1890); T. Andrews, *Pogg. Ann.* **75**, 501 (1848).

more properly be assumed. It should be remembered, as pointed out in Chapter XI, that association of either component would cause both to deviate in a positive direction from Raoult's law, and hence the fact that such deviation may be found should not be taken as evidence that the solute is associated rather than the solvent. For example, one observer has concluded that anthracene is associated in solution in fused cinnamic acid, although the latter should undoubtedly be regarded as the associated component.

CHAPTER XIV

Mixtures of Gases

Although gases are infinitely miscible and hence raise no problems of solubility, it is interesting to consider the thermodynamics of their mixtures in relation to the solution properties of the substances in their condensed phases. First, however, it is desirable to consider briefly the various equations of state used to represent pressure-volume-temperature relations for gases.

Equations of state for pure gases. The first significant attempt to interpret the deviations of a real gas from the perfect gas laws was the equation of state which van der Waals[1] proposed in 1873.

$$P = \frac{RT}{\mathrm{V} - \mathrm{b}} - \frac{\mathrm{a}}{\mathrm{V}^2} \tag{1}$$

In the quasi-theoretical justification of this equation, the term a/V^2 represents a correction for the attractive forces between molecules, while b corrects for the finite volume occupied by the molecules.

A slightly different equation of state, which yields a somewhat better agreement with experiment, was proposed by Dieterici[2]:

$$P = \frac{RT}{\mathrm{V} - \mathrm{b}}\, e^{-\frac{\mathrm{a}}{RT\mathrm{V}}} \tag{2}$$

A third equation with two adjustable parameters[3] was proposed by Berthelot[4]:

$$P = \frac{RT}{\mathrm{V} - \mathrm{b}} - \frac{\mathrm{a}}{T\mathrm{V}^2} \tag{3}$$

Equation 3 is not, however, the one usually referred to as the "Berthelot equation", which is an empirical expression for low pressures in which the constants a and b are related to the critical constants:

---

[1] J. D. van der Waals, "Over de continuet van den gas-en vloeistoftoestand" (Leiden, 1873); German translation, "Die Continuität des gasförmigen und flüssigen Zustandes" (Leipzig, 1881).

[2] C. Dieterici, *Ann. Phys. Lpz.*, **69**, 685 (1899); **5**, 51 (1901).

[3] Since R is an experimental quantity, we may regard the van der Waals, Dieterici, and Berthelot equations as having three parameters, one of which is universal.

[4] D. Berthelot, *Trav. Bur. Int. Poids. Mes.*, **13**, (1907).

$$PV = RT + \left(b - \frac{a}{RT^2}\right) P \tag{4}$$

where $R = 32 P_c V_c / 9 T_c$; $a = 16 P_c V_c^2 T_c / 3$; $b = V_c/4$. (Cf. Chapter I, p. 10)

Since none of these two parameter equations is overly successful in representing the experimental data, more complex equations of state have been advanced; that of Keyes[5] involving four adjustable constants; that of Beattie and Bridgeman[6], five; and a more recent equation of Benedict, Webb and Rubin[7], as many as eight. Of these, the most frequently used is the Beattie-Bridgeman five parameter equation:

$$P = \frac{RT}{V^2}\left[1 - \frac{c}{V T^3}\right]\left[V + B_o\left(1 - \frac{b}{V}\right)\right] - \frac{A_o}{V^2}\left(1 - \frac{a}{V}\right) \tag{5}$$

As we have seen in Chapter I, a very useful and completely general medium for expressing the behavior of real gases is the virial equation of state, first used by Kamerlingh Onnes[8].

$$\frac{PV}{RT} = 1 + \frac{B}{V} + \frac{C}{V^2} + \frac{D}{V^3} + \ldots \tag{6}$$

In such a formulation, the constants B, C, D, etc. are functions only of the temperature. Of special interest is the second virial coefficient B, to which we will return later. The van der Waals, Dieterici, and Keyes equations of state all give the same functional form for B, namely:

$$B = b - \frac{a}{RT} \tag{7}$$

Berthelot's equation depends upon the inverse second power of the temperature:

$$B = b - \frac{a}{RT^2} \tag{8}$$

while the Beattie-Bridgeman and Benedict-Webb-Rubin equation give the same three-term expression for B.

$$B = B_o - \frac{A_o}{RT} - \frac{c}{T^3} \tag{9}$$

[5] F. G. Keyes, *Proc. Nat. Acad. Sci.*, **3**, 323 (1917).

[6] J. A. Beattie and O. W. Bridgeman, *J. Am. Chem. Soc.*, **49**, 1665 (1927); **50**, 3133 (1928); *Proc. Am. Acad. Arts. Sci.*, **63**, 229 (1928).

[7] M. Benedict, G. V. Webb. and L. C. Rubin, *J. Chem. Phys.*, **8**, 334 (1940).

[8] H. Kamerlingh Onnes, *Commun. Phys. Lab. Univ. Leiden*, No. 71 (1901).

Equations of state for gas mixtures. When one turns from pure gases to mixtures, it seems intuitively reasonable to retain an equation of state of the same form, a procedure which can be justified theoretically unless the gases react chemically. The problem of treating gas mixtures reduces therefore to one of computing values of the parameters for the mixture from those of the pure substances, preferably without the introduction of any new constants.

Van der Waals suggested that for his equation of state (and for any similar one), the parameters a and b for a binary mixture might be expressed in the following equations:

$$a = a_1 x_1^2 + 2a_{12} x_1 x_2 + a_2 x_2^2 \tag{10a}$$

$$b = b_1 x_1^2 + 2b_{12} x_1 x_2 + b_2 x_2^2 \tag{10b}$$

where a_1 a_2, b_1 and b_2 are the parameters for the pure gases, while a_{12} and b_{12} are interaction constants for the pair of substances comprising the mixture. It is obviously highly desirable to relate a_{12} and b_{12} to the a's and b's of the pure substances.

At an early date Lorentz[9] pointed out that collision diameters are additive for rigid spheres; hence a volume function such as the co-volume b should be written as:

$$b_{12} = \left[\frac{1}{2}(b_1)^{\frac{1}{3}} + \frac{1}{2}(b_2)^{\frac{1}{3}}\right]^3 \tag{11}$$

While this expression is certainly theoretically preferable, and was used by van der Waals in his book[1], it has usually been replaced in practice by the simple linear relation of the arithmetic mean:

$$b_{12} = \frac{1}{2}(b_1 + b_2) \tag{12}$$

Galitzine[10] was apparently the first to use a geometric mean law applying it to both a and b in an attempt to interpret nitrogen-carbon dioxide mixtures. Subsequently Berthelot[11] suggested for the binary mixture van der Waals equations, an arithmetic mean for b_{12} (Equation 12) and a geometric mean for a_{12}:

$$a_{12} = (a_1 a_2)^{\frac{1}{2}} \tag{13}$$

---

[9] H. A. Lorentz, *Wied. Ann.*, **12**, 127, 660 (1881).
[10] B. Galitzine, *Wied. Ann.*, **41**, 770 (1890).
[11] D. Berthelot, *Compt. rend.*, **126**, 1703, 1857 (1898).

Only much later was it shown (as we have seen in Chapters IV and VII) that the quantum mechanical theory of intermolecular forces in large measure justifies this assumption. It was these two relations (Equations 12 and 13), then entirely empirical, which van Laar[12] used in his extensive theoretical work on mixtures of gases and liquids, leading as we have seen in Chapter VII to the "van Laar equation" for liquid solutions. One of the most impressive uses of the van der Waals equation for gas mixtures is van Laar's[13] exhaustive mathematical treatment of the very complex liquid-gas phase relations in binary systems.

Similar combining rules were developed for the Keyes equation[14]. For the Beattie-Bridgeman equation, Beattie[15] suggested the geometric mean for A_o, and the arithmetic mean (linear combination) for the other four, B_o, a, b, c. More recently, Beattie, Stockmayer, and Ingersoll[16] have made computations of methane-n-butane mixtures which indicate that use of the geometric mean for A_o and c, the arithmetic mean for a and b, and the Lorentz relation (Equation 11) for B_o give somewhat better agreement with experiment.

For the virial equation of state (Equation 6) Mayer[17] has shown that the nth virial coefficient is a polynomial of nth order in the mole fractions, the coefficients being functions only of the temperature. Thus we may write for B and C:

$$B = B_1 x_1^2 + 2B_{12} x_1 x_2 + B_2 x_2^2 \tag{14}$$

$$C = C_1 x_1^3 + 3C_{112} x_1^2 x_2 + 3C_{122} x_1 x_2^2 + C_2 x_2^3 \tag{15}$$

where B_1, B_2, C_1, and C_2 are the virial coefficients of the pure gases, and B_{12}, C_{112}, and C_{122} are properties of the mixture.

At this point, it is interesting to consider two general "laws" for mixtures which do not depend upon particular equations of state. The first is Dalton's law that pressures are additive at constant volume and temperature. This is generally made true by defining the partial pressure as the mole fraction times the total pressure ($p_1 = x_1 P$). However if we calculate the pressure each component would have separately with the same volume and temperatures, Dalton's law is a possible method for computing the properties of gas mixtures. Reference to Equation 6 shows that for this to be true for all volumes each of the virial coefficients B, C, D, etc. must be a linear combination of the coefficients for the pure substances. This can

[12] J. J. van Laar "Sechs Vorträge über das Thermodynamische Potential" (Braunschweig, 1907).

[13] J.J. van Laar, *Proc. K. Akad. Wetenschapp*, **7**, 646; **8**, 33, 578 (1905); **9**, 226 (1906). *Archives Musee Teÿler*, Ser. **2**, **10**, 109 (1905).

[14] F. G. Keyes, *J. Am. Chem. Soc.*, **49**, 1393 (1927); F. G. Keyes and H. G. Burks, *J. Am. Chem. Soc.*, **50**, 1100 (1928).

[15] J. A. Beattie *J. Am. Chem. Soc.*, **51**, 19 (1929).

[16] J. A. Beattie, W. H. Stockmayer, and H. G. Ingersoll, *J. Chem. Phys.*, **9**, 871, (1941).

[17] J. E. Mayer, *J. Phys., Chem.* **43**, 71 (1939).

only be true if B_{12}, C_{112} and C_{122} (we ignore the D's and higher coefficients) in Equations 14 and 15 satisfy the conditions:

$$B_{12} = \frac{1}{2}(B_1 + B_2) \tag{16a}$$

$$C_{112} = \frac{1}{3}(2C_1 + C_2) \tag{16b}$$

$$C_{122} = \frac{1}{3}(C_1 + 2C_2) \tag{16c}$$

Dalton's law was shown to be of only approximate validity and in place of it, Amagat[18] proposed that volumes are additive at constant pressure and temperature. The significance of this assumption is best seen by transforming Equation 6 into the corresponding power series in pressure:

$$\frac{PV}{RT} = 1 + \frac{BP}{RT} + \frac{(C - B^2)}{(RT)^2}P^2 + \frac{(D - 3BC + 2B^3)}{(RT)^3}P^3 + \dots \tag{17}$$

Amagat's law can only be true if the coefficients of each of the terms in Equation 17 are linear combinations of those for the pure substances. This leads to a set of conditions for B and C analogous to those for Dalton's law:

$$B_{12} = \frac{1}{2}(B_1 + B_2) \tag{18a}$$

$$C_{112} = \frac{1}{3}(2C_1 + C_2) - (B_1 - B_2)^2 \tag{18b}$$

$$C_{122} = \frac{1}{3}(C_1 + 2C_2) - (B_1 - B_2)^2 \tag{18c}$$

The Amagat law was studied by Leduc[19], with whose name the law is sometimes coupled, who claimed it was exact for mixtures of the permanent gases, but more recent work, as we shall see, has shown this to be incorrect.

We see that Equation 18a is the same as 16a; so the parameter B_{12} must be a linear combination of B_1 and B_2 for either Dalton's or Amagat's law to be valid. In the next section we will consider the second virial coefficient of gas mixtures in some detail.

---

[18] E. H. Amagat, *Ann. chem. phys.*, [5], **19**, 384 (1880); *Compt. rend.* **127**, 88 (1898).
[19] A. Leduc, *Compt. rend.*, **126**, 218 (1898).

Beattie and Stockmayer[20] have reviewed equations of state for pure gases and mixtures, with respect to work prior to 1940. Another review, relating primarily to gas mixtures, is that of Gillespie[21].

The second virial coefficient of gas mixtures. Before considering several theoretical interpretations of the second virial coefficient, it is worthwhile to summarize some of the experimental data for mixtures. Table 1 gives values for B_1, B_2 and the interaction constant B_{12} for some of the mixtures which have so far been investigated. We have seen that both the Dalton and Amagat laws require B_{12} to be the arithmetic mean; therefore we represent the deviation from this assumption by a difference function $\Delta = 2B_{12} - B_1 - B_2$, also shown in Table 1.

Table 1. Second virial coefficients for gas mixtures.
(Units — cm^3/mole)

System	Reference	Temperature (°C)	B_1	B_2	B_{12}	Δ
He — H_2	22,23	25	11.4	14 7	17.2	4.1
He — Ne	24,25	100	11.4	11.8	13.9	4.6
He — A	23	25	11.4	—16.4	18.4	41.8
H_2 — A	23	25	14.7	—16.4	8.1	17.9
H_2 — N_2	27,25	20	14.5	— 6.2	13.7	19.1
H_2 — CO	28	25	14.6	— 9.8	12	19
N_2 — O_2	24,26	50	—0.38	—11.0	— 7.1	2.8
H_2O — CO_2	29	90	—503	—64.6	—111	346
CH_4 — n-C_4H_{10}	16,30	200	—4.0	—254.2	—60.4	137.4

We see that in no case is the difference Δ zero, although it is small for the systems He — H_2, He — Ne, and N_2 — O_2. In every case it is positive, as would be expected. An oversimplified but useful interpretation of Δ is obtained by substituting the Berthelot-van Laar assumptions (Equations 12 and 13) into Equation 7 for the second virial coefficient of the van der Waals gas. The b's, having been combined linearly, vanish, and we obtain:

$$\Delta = \frac{\left(a_1^{\frac{1}{2}} - a_2^{\frac{1}{2}}\right)^2}{RT} \qquad (19)$$

[20] J. A. Beattie and W. H. Stockmayer, *Reports. Prog. Phys.*, **7**, 195, (1940).
[21] L. J. Gillespie, *Chem. Rev.* **18**, 359 (1936).
[22] C. W. Gibby, C. C. Tanner, and I. Masson, *Proc. Roy. Soc.*, **A122**, 283 (1929).
[23] C. C. Tanner, and I. Masson, *Proc. Roy. Soc.*, **A126**, 268 (1930).
[24] L. Holborn and J. Otto, *Z. Physik.*, **23**, 77 (1924).
[25] J. E. Lennard-Jones and W. R. Cook. *Proc. Roy. Soc.*, **A115**, 334 (1927).
[26] L. Schames, *Physik. Z.*, **32**, 16 (1931).
[27] T. T. H. Verschoyle, *Proc. Roy. Soc.*, **A111**, 552 (1926).
[28] G. A. Scott, *Proc. Roy. Soc.*, **A128**, 330 (1929).
[29] W. H. Stockmayer, *J. Chem. Phys.*, **9**, 398 (1941).
[30] J. A. Beattie and W. H. Stockmayer *J. Chem. Phys.*, **10**, 473 (1942).

Expressions of the form of Equation 19 are already familiar to the reader from Chapters VII and XIII, the difference of the $\sqrt{a}$'s being analogous to that of the solubility parameters δ. Like the heat of mixing of regular solutions, in the absence of specific interactions, Δ must always be positive, leading to curves of B versus composition which are always concave downward. (Cf. Figure 1, in which the data of Beattie and Stockmayer[30] on methane-n-butane are plotted).

While Equation 19 is wholly inadequate to explain the temperature dependence of Δ, (unless we assume temperature dependence of the a's) it is nevertheless interesting to test its consistency by comparing the values for three interlocking pairs in the same manner as the consistency of the solubility parameter theory was tested in Chapter VII. The triangle He—H_2—A (Table 1) offers such a test. For He—H_2, $\Delta^{\frac{1}{2}} = 2.0$, while for H_2—A, $\Delta^{\frac{1}{2}} = 4.2$. The sum of these is 6.2, while $\Delta^{\frac{1}{2}}$ for the third pair He—A is 6.5, a more than satisfactory agreement for as crude a representation as that of Equation 19.

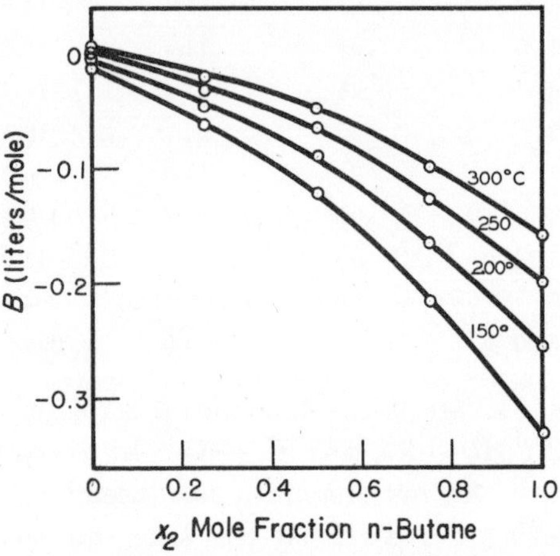

Fig. 1. The second virial coefficient of methane-n-butane mixtures at different temperatures.

For a satisfactory representation of the second virial coefficient at various temperatures, a functional form at least as complex as that derived from the Beattie-Bridgeman equation (Equation 9) is required. Beattie and Stockmayer[30] have obtained the following expressions for mixtures of methane and n-butane (Fig. 1):

$$B_1 = 0.05587 - 27.75/T - 12.83 \times 10^4/T^3 \tag{20a}$$

$$B_2 = 0.16020 - 152.1/T - 975 \times 10^4/T^3 \tag{20b}$$

$$B_{12} = 0.1102 - 78/T - 54 \times 10^4/T^3 \tag{20c}$$

$$\Delta = 0.0043 + 24/T + 854 \times 10^4/T^3 \tag{20d}$$

Several different methods are possible for combining constants: square root combination (geometric mean), linear combination (arithmetic mean) or Lorentz combination (Equation 11). Beattie and Stockmayer showed that a good fit for Equations 20 was obtained by using Lorentz combination for the first term (B_o) and square root combinations for the other two (A_o and c). This equation yields the theoretical curve I of Figure 2. (Curve II results from linear combinations of B_o and c, retaining the square root combination for A_o).

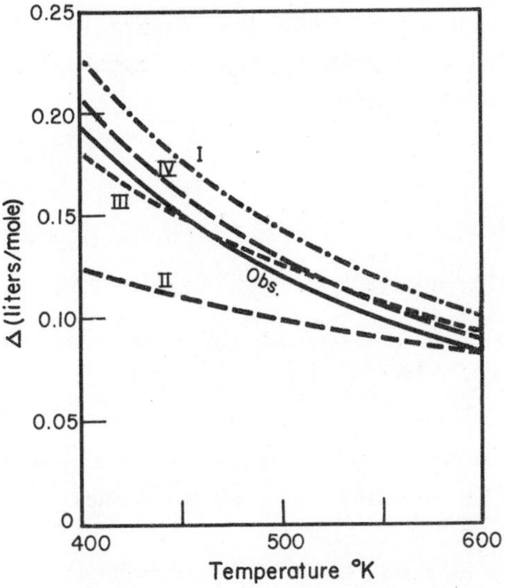

Fig. 2. The difference function $\Delta = 2B_{12} - B_1 - B_2$ for methane-*n*-butane mixtures. The solid curve is the measured one. The dashed curves are calculated in various ways (see text).

Theoretical treatments of the second virial coefficient have been extensive[31], and will be discussed here only briefly. It can be shown by means of classical statistical mechanics that the second virial coefficient may be represented by the integral:

$$B = \frac{N}{2V} \int (1 - e^{-\varepsilon/kT}) \, d\tau_1 \, d\tau_2 \qquad (21)$$

where ε is the intermolecular potential energy of a pair of molecules as a function of their space coordinates, and the integration is performed over the whole volume of the containing vessel. For molecules of essentially

[31] For a detailed discussion, see Fowler and Guggenheim, "Statistical Thermodynamics", (Cambridge, 1939), Chapter VII, and the original papers of Ursell, Lennard-Jones, Buckingham, Mayer, and others.

spherical symmetry (such as the rare gases), ε is a function of r only, and Equation 21 reduces to:

$$B = 2\pi N \int_0^\infty \left(1 - e^{-\varepsilon(r)/kT}\right) r^2 dr \tag{22}$$

These results are valid either for pure gases or for mixtures (for B_{12}, ε_{12} is the potential energy of an unlike pair), provided special quantum mechanical effects are negligible.

For an intermolecular potential of the Lennard-Jones type (see Chapter IV Equations 16-27), the integration may be carried out explicitly. If we assume for the potential function:

$$\varepsilon = -\frac{k}{r^6} + \frac{j}{r^{12}} \tag{23}$$

we may rewrite it in the form:

$$\varepsilon = 4\varepsilon^* \left[\left(\frac{d^*}{r}\right)^{12} - \left(\frac{d^*}{r}\right)^6\right] \tag{24}$$

where d^* is the collision diameter (where $\varepsilon = 0$) and $-\varepsilon^*$ is the minimum potential energy at the equilibrium distance, defined by:

$$(d^*)^6 = k/j \qquad \varepsilon^* = k^2/4j$$

If we substitute Equation 24 for ε into Equation 22, and integrate, we obtain for B:

$$B = \frac{2\pi N (d^*)^3}{3} \sqrt{2} \left(\frac{\varepsilon^*}{kT}\right)^{\frac{1}{4}} \left[\Gamma\left(\frac{3}{4}\right) - \sum_{n=1}^{\infty} \frac{2^{n-2}}{n!} \Gamma\left(\frac{2n-1}{4}\right)\left(\frac{\varepsilon^*}{kT}\right)^{n/2}\right] \tag{25}$$

The terms in ε^* and d^* are separable, and Stockmayer and Beattie[32] have tabulated values of B/β (where $\beta = 2\pi N (d^*)^3/3$) for values of ε^*/kT from 0.20 to 1.00.

Equation 25 has been frequently used in treating pure gases. By using a linear combination for d^* and a square-root combination for ε^*, Beattie and Stockmayer[30] obtained excellent agreement in computing the properties of methane-*n*-butane mixtures (See curve III, Figure 2). The success of this result suggested a fourth form of combination for equations of the type of 20 a b c. If the Beattie-Bridgeman equation for B is written in the form:

[32] W. H. Stockmayer and J. A. Beattie, *J. Chem. Phys.*, **10**, 476 (1942).

$$B = B_\circ \left[1 - \frac{A_\circ}{B_\circ RT} - \frac{c}{B_\circ T^3}\right] \tag{26}$$

and B_{12} is computed by using the Lorentz combination for the $B_\circ$ outside the bracket and square root combination for $A_\circ/B_\circ$ and $c/B_\circ$, we obtain Curve IV of Figure 2, and Equation 27 for Δ:

$$\Delta_{IV} = -\ 0.0180 + 43.7/T + 754/T^3 \tag{27}$$

This, they conclude, is the best of the combination rules for computing B_{12} from the equation of state.

Stockmayer[33] has treated the virial coefficient for mixtures of polar gases by splitting the term (or terms) for the intermolecular attraction into two parts, one for the dispersion forces, the other for the orientation force, and applying to each *separately* a geometric mean combination law. (Cf. the discussion at the end of Chapter IX). He has shown that this gives fairly satisfactory agreement with data for H_2O-CO_2, N_2-NH_3, and N_2-H_2O.

The free energy of mixing. In conclusion, it is interesting to consider the thermodynamic functions in gas mixtures. For the free energy of mixing per mole at constant pressure, we may write:

$$\Delta F^M = RT\ [\ln f_m - x_1 \ln f_1^\circ - x_2 \ln f_2^\circ + x_1 \ln x_1 + x_2 \ln x_2] \tag{28}$$

Expressing the fugacities in terms of the virial coefficients, we obtain (Cf. Equation 17, as well as Chapter I, Equation 30):

$$RT \ln f = \int V dP = RT \ln P + BP + \frac{(C - B^2)\,P^2}{2RT} + \ldots \tag{29}$$

If these are substituted into Equation 28, the final result is:

$$\begin{aligned}\Delta F^M &= RT\,(x_1 \ln x_1 + x_2 \ln x_2) + (2B_{12} - B_1 - B_2)\,x_1 x_2 P \\ &+ \frac{1}{2RT}\Big[(3C_{112} - 2C_1 - C_2)\,x_1 + (3C_{122} - 2C_2 - C_1)\,x_2 \\ &+ 2B_1\,(B_1 - B_{12})\,x_1^2 + \{(B_1 - B_2)^2 - B_{12}^2\}\,x_1 x_2 \\ &+ 2B_2\,(B_2 - B_{12})\,x_2^2\Big]\,x_1 x_2 P^2 + \ldots\end{aligned} \tag{30}$$

[33] W. H. Stockmayer, *J. Chem. Phys.*, **9**, 863 (1941).

The first term in Equation 30 is merely the ideal free energy of mixing; so, neglecting terms in P^2 and higher, we can write for the excess free energy ΔF^E:

$$\Delta F^E = \Delta F^M - \Delta F^i = x_1 x_2 P\Delta \tag{31}$$

For the partial molal free energies, we obtain:

$$\Delta \bar{F}_1 = RT \ln x_1 + x_2^2 P\Delta \tag{32a}$$

$$\Delta \bar{F}_2 = RT \ln x_2 + x_1^2 P\Delta \tag{32b}$$

and for the fugacities:

$$\ln f_1 = \ln x_1 f_1^\circ + \frac{P\Delta}{RT} x_2^2 \tag{33a}$$

$$\ln f_2 = \ln x_2 f_2^\circ + \frac{P\Delta}{RT} x_1^2 \tag{33b}$$

In an early treatment of gas mixtures, Lewis and Randall[34] suggested that the fugacity of a gas in a mixture was the mole fraction times the fugacity of the pure substance at the same total pressure (*i. e.*, $f = xf^\circ$). This ideal solution assumption proved very useful, but we see it can strictly be true only if $\Delta = 0$, a situation possible only between substances with very similar force fields. Gillespie[35] has shown that the Lewis and Randall law is actually the same as the Amagat law, which we have discussed earlier.

[34] G. N. Lewis and M. Randall, "Thermodynamics and the Free Energy of Chemical Substances", (McGraw-Hill, 1923) Chapter XIX, pp. 225—227.

[35] L. J. Gillespie, *J. Am. Chem. Soc.*, **47**, 305, 3106 (1925).

CHAPTER XV

Solubility of Gases in Liquids

The ideal solubility of a gas below its critical temperature can be calculated from its saturation pressure, p_2°, by aid of the ordinary form of Raoult's law, $p_2 = p_2^\circ x_2$, where p_2 is the partial pressure of the gas over the solution, usually taken as 1 atmosphere when $x_2 = 1/p_2^\circ$. Accordingly, since the saturation pressure of a gas increases with temperature, its ideal solubility decreases. Also, the higher the saturation pressure of a gas or the lower its boiling point or critical temperature, other factors being equal, the less soluble it is.

Fugacity correction. Since we are concerned with substances whose saturation pressures are above one atmosphere, often considerably, it is pertinent to inquire into the error made by using p_2/p_2° instead of f_2/f_2°. Table 1 gives the saturation pressures of Cl_2 at 0°, 20°, and 40° C. from which we calculate the mole per cent of it in any ideal solution at each of these temperatures at 1 atmosphere, obtaining the values in columns 5 and 6.

Table 1. Ideal Chlorine Solubilities.

				Mole percent Cl_2		
t° C	p°, atm.	f at $p = 1$	f° at p°	From $1/p$°	From f/f°	Diff. %
0	3.66	0.984	3.44	27.3	28.6	5
20	6.62	0.986	6.04	15.1	16 3	7
40	11.50	0.989	10.10	8.7	9.8	12

The difference between the two figures for ideal solubility in this case is seldom great enough, in view of uncertainty regarding deviation from Raoult's law in a particular case, to justify the labor of calculating the fugacities. This deviation may be expected to be small when the solvent is not greatly different from chlorine in internal pressure and in molal volume. Let us consider its solution in CCl_4 at 0° C. The energy of vaporization of chlorine at 0° we have extrapolated from the measurements of Giauque and Powell[1] to be 4070 cal. per mole. Its liquid molal volume at 0° is 48.3 cc., and $\Delta E^V/V$ is 84.2 cal./cc. For CCl_4 at this temperature[2]

[1] W. F. Giauque and T. M. Powell, *J. Am. Chem. Soc.*, **61**, 1970 (1938).
[2] cf. R. D. Vold, *Ibid.*, **59**, 1515 (1937).

the values are 93.0 cc. and 80.7 cal./cc., so near to the value for Cl_2 as to make the term $V_2 \varphi_1^2 (\delta_1 - \delta_2)^2$, in Equation VII-46 almost negligible, indicating that this solution should conform closely to Raoult's law. This is indeed the case, as shown by the measurements of Taylor and Hildebrand[3] reproduced in Table 2.

Table 2. Solubility of Cl_2. Mole percent at 1 atmos. and 0° C.

	Heptane	$SiCl_4$	CCl_4	Ideal (f_2/f_2°)
$(\Delta E^V/V)^{\frac{1}{2}}$	7.65	7.81	8.98	9.24 (Cl_2)
$100\,x_2$	27.0	28.8	29.8	28.6

The figures for the solubility of Cl_2 in CCl_4 at 0° C and low pressures of Cl_2 obtained by Jakowkin[4] show poorer agreement with Raoult's law in the form $p_2/f_2^\circ = x_2$, with $f_2^\circ = 3.44$ atm. as shown in Table 3.

Table 3. Solubility of Cl_2 in CCl_4 at 0° C.

p_2 (mm)	2.56	5.68	11.40	18.70
$10^5 p_2/f_2^\circ$	98	218	438	718
$10^5 x_2$	105	251	506	829

Correction for ratio of liquid volumes. The question naturally arises whether the discrepancy in liquid volumes is sufficient to affect the theoretical solubility in the sense of Equation VII-47. Using the value of f_2/f_2° from Table 1, and the molal volumes given above, and solving by the method of successive approximation gives $N_2 = 0.462$ when $N_1 = 1.000$ and $x_2 = 0.316$ to compare with the experimental value, 0.298. The values of the several terms in the equation are as follows:

$$\log \frac{f_2}{f_2^\circ} = \log \varphi_2 + 0.4343\, \varphi_1 \left(1 - \frac{V_2}{V_1}\right) + \frac{V_2 \varphi_1^2 (\delta_1 - \delta_2)^2}{4.575 T}$$

$$-0.544 = -0.719 + 0.172 \qquad + 0.002.$$

We see that the heat term, the last on the right, is nearly negligible, in accord with our earlier statement, and that the first two terms on the right add to give $-$ 0.547, little different from $\log x_2$. In other words, the extra labor involved in using the more complicated procedure was practically wasted.

[3] N. W. Taylor and J. H. Hildebrand, *J. Am. Chem. Soc.*, **45**, 682 (1923).
[4] A. A. Jakowkin, *Z. physik. Chem.* **29**, 613 (1899).

Gases above their critical temperatures. It was mentioned in Chapter II that Raoult's law can be used to obtain a fair estimate of the solubility of a gas even above its critical temperature, where p_2° has no clear physical meaning, by extrapolating the plot of log p° vs. $1/T$, which is practically a straight line, right up to the critical point, as illustrated in Figure 1 for the vapor pressure of methane. That this should be true

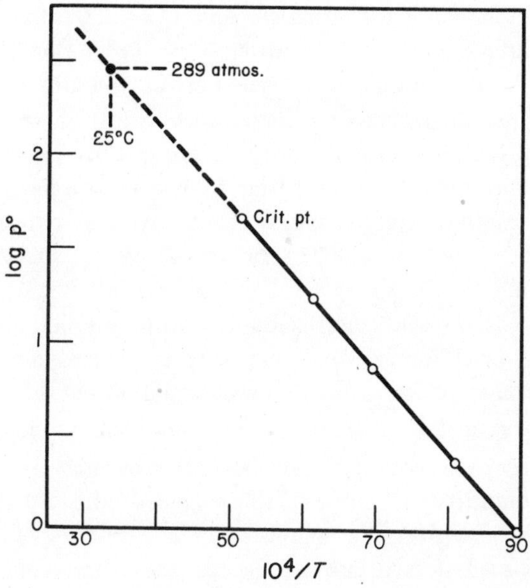

Fig. 1 Vapor pressure of methane.

at lower pressures is obvious if we write the Clausius-Clapeyron equation in the form

$$\frac{d \log p^\circ}{d(1/T)} = \frac{\Delta H^V}{2.3R} \qquad (1)$$

or its integrated form, with p° expressed in atmospheres,

$$\log p^\circ = \frac{\Delta H^V}{4.575}\left(\frac{1}{T_b} - \frac{1}{T}\right) \qquad (1a)$$

which, combined with Raoult's law, gives:

$$\log x_2 = \log p - \frac{\Delta H^V}{4.575}\left(\frac{1}{T_b} - \frac{1}{T}\right) \qquad (2)$$

That it holds so closely between the boiling point and the critical point is evidently due to compensating variations in ΔH^V and $V^g - V^l$ in the pure thermodynamic equation

$$\frac{dp}{dT} = \frac{\Delta H^V}{T(V^g - V^l)} \tag{3}$$

from which Equation 1 is derived by neglecting V^l and setting $V^g = RT/p^\circ$. It is a simple matter to extrapolate linearly to 25° C., where, in the case of methane, $\log p^\circ = 2.45$, and $p^\circ = 289$ atm. This value may be used to calculate x in the equation $x = p/p^\circ$. For the solubility of methane in an ideal solution when the partial pressure of methane above the solution is one atmosphere we have, accordingly, $x_2 = 1/289 = 0.0035$. As a matter of fact, and surprisingly enough, this gives more than the right order of magnitude, for, according to the measurements of McDaniel, the solubility of methane in hexane, in which we may expect it to approach Raoult's law fairly well, is 0.0031. In xylene it is 0.0026. The values of $1/p_2^\circ$ given in Table 4 for the several gases have all been obtained in this way, and we see there that their solubilities in any one solvent not only increase regularly with increase in $1/p_2^\circ$, as was pointed out in Chapter II[5], but also, in the case of solvents of low internal pressure, at the top of the table, agree approximately with the values obtained for $1/p_2^\circ$.

As we proceed to consider solvents of progressively higher internal pressure, the solubility of any of these gases falls off rather regularly, hence we may expect that the solubility of a given gas in a new solvent could be interpolated if it is inserted in the table according to its internal pressure, provided that neither hydrogen bonding nor chemical combination occurs. That such a semiquantitative procedure suffices for many purposes can be inferred from the degree of uniformity in the order for the different gases seen in Table 4. The imperfections there evident are not all due to imperfections in the procedure, for the accuracy of the data themselves leaves much to be desired. For example, the Ostwald coefficient of nitrogen in acetone at 25° C is 0.1794 according to Horiuti[6] and 0.1460 according to Just[6]; McDaniel[7] reported 3.288 for ethane in hexane at 25° and 4.500 in heptane, an incredible difference; Lannung[6] has cited the discrepancy between four published values for the Ostwald coefficient for helium in water at 25° C, Estreicher[8] 0.0150, von Antropoff[9] 0.0109; Cady, Elsey and Berger[10] 0.0094; Lannung 0.0095.

[5] cf. J. H. Hildebrand, *J. Am. Chem. Soc.*, **38**, 1452 (1916); F. Körösy, *Trans. Faraday Soc.*, **33**, 416 (1937).

[6] See references to Table 4, p. **243**.

[7] A. S. McDaniel, *J. Phys. Chem.*, **15**, 587 (1911).

[8] T. Estreicher, *Z. physik. Chem.* **31**, 176 (1899).

[9] A. v. Antropoff, *Z. Electrochem.* **25**, 269 (1919).

[10] H. P. Cady, H. M. Elsey and E. V. Berger, *J. Am. Chem. Soc.*, **44**, 1456 (1922).

Table 4 – Solubilities of Nonpolar Gases
Mole fraction · 10^4 at 25°C and 1 atmosphere

	δ	$\mu \times 10^{18}$	He	H_2	N_2	CO	O_2	A	CH_4	C_2H_4	C_2H_2	C_2H_6
"Ideal"		0		8	10	12,8	13,2	16	35	152	208	250
n-Hexane	7,29	0		6,5 [G]	12,5 [G]		19,3 [G]		31,5 [MC] 42 4 [G]	161 [MC]		177 [MC]
Ethyl ether	7.45	1.1		5,52 [H]	12,52 [H]	16,9 [H]	19,8 [H]		45,3 [H]			
Cyclohexane	8,20	0	1,22 [L]	3,80 [G]	7,22 [G]			14,8 [L]	28,3 [G]			
Carbon tetrachloride	8,64	0		3,27 [H]	6,42 [H]	8,86 [H]	12,0 [H]		28,6 [H]	147 [H]	111 [H]	213 [H]
m-Xylene	8,82	0,5		4,13 [J]	6,14 [J]	9.12			25,8 [MC]			
Methyl acetate	(9,44)	1,7		3,07 [H]	5,97 [H]	8,65 [H]	9,08 [H]		20,0 [H]	117 [H]	706 [H]	108 [H]
Acetone	(9,86)	2,8	1,08 [L]	2,31 [J]	5,92 [H]	8,54 [H] 6,73 [J]	9,25 [H]	9,06 [L]	22,3 [H]	75 [MC]	726 [H]	
Benzene	9,16	0	0,77 [L]	2,61 [H]	4,40 [H]	6,63 [H] 6,24 [J]	8,16 [H]	8,85 [L]	20,7 [H]	124 [H] 107 [MC]	176 [H]	151 [H]
Chloroform	9,25	1,1		2,20 [M]	4,45 [J]	6,45 [J]	7,38 [LV]					
Chlorobenzene		1,6		2,66 [H]	4,31 [H]	6,32 [H]	7,91 [H]		20,8 [H]	121 [H]	150 [H]	148 [H]
Nitrobenzene		4,1		1,56 [J]	2,63 [J]	3,94 [J]						
Methyl alcohol	(14,4)	1,7	0,60 [L]	1,57 [J]	2,35 [J]	3,25 [J]	3,18 [LV]	4,44 [L]	7,1 [LV]			
Carbon disulfide	10,0	0		0,93 [J]	1,45 [J]	2,06 [J]						
Aniline		1,5		1,07 [J]	1,15 [J]	2,00 [J]						
Water		1,9	0,070 [L]	0,15 [J]	0,12 [J]	0,18 [J]	0,23 [W]	0,25 [L]	0,24 [W]	0,88 [W]	7,53 [W]	0,33 [W]

G) D. Guerry Jr., Thesis, Vanderbilt Univ, 1944.
H) J. Horiuti, *Science Papers, Inst. phys. chem. Research, Tokio*, **17**, no. 341, p. 125 (1931).
J) G. Just. *Z. physik. Chem.*, **37**, 342 (1901).
L) A. Lannung, *J. Am. Chem. Soc.*, **52**, 68 (1934).
LV) G. Levi, *Gazz. chim. ital.*, **31** II, 513 (1901).
W) L. W. Winkler, cf. Int. Crit. Tables, III, pp. 255—261 (McGraw Hill Book Co, 1928).
M) E. B Maxted and C. H. Moon, *Trans. Faraday Soc.*, **32**, 769 (1936).
MC) A. S. Mc Daniel, *J. Phys. Chem.* **15**, 587 (1911).

The position in the table of strongly polar solvents, such as methyl acetate and acetone, as might be expected, does not accord with the values of their internal pressure as calculated from the energy of vaporization per cc.; their solvent powers for the different gases agree rather well, however, in fixing their places in the table. On the other hand, those polar solvents which are not particularly hydrogen bonding, such as chloroform and chlorobenzene, are correctly placed by their internal pressures, presumably because the energy of vaporization per cc. includes the contribution of the dipoles, and the geometry of the molecules is such that the dipoles do not orient them very strongly. One should expect, of course, that if both gas and solvent are markedly polar, the departures from the order in the table could be considerable.

The enormous solubilities of acetylene in acetone and in methyl acetate are the result of chemical combination. McIntosh[11] reported crystalline compounds of acetylene with acetone, ether, and ethyl alcohol. The solubility of acetylene in water is similarly enhanced by solvation; a crystalline hydrate $C_2H_2 \cdot 6H_2O$ has been reported by Villard[12].

A semi-quantitative treatment of solubilities in solvents of higher internal pressure is possible by combining Equations VII-46 and 1a and setting $\varphi_1 = 1$, since, for pressures of the order of 1 atmosphere or less $N_2 \ll N_1$. We then write,

$$-\log\ x_2 = \log p_2^\circ + \mathrm{V}_2\,(\delta_1 - \delta_2)^2/4.58\,T \qquad (4)$$

The senior author showed, in the previous edition of this book, how value of V_2 and δ_2 could be selected, illustrated in the case of argon, which correlated its solubilities in different solvents and therefore could serve to calculate its solubility in other solvents. Gonikberg[13] has applied this treatment to solubilities of hydrogen, using for V_2 the molal volume of liquid hydrogen, 28.6 cc., and for $\log\ p_2^\circ$, the expression (Equation 1a)

$$\log\ p_2^\circ = \frac{57}{4.58}\left(\frac{1}{T_b} - \frac{1}{T}\right).$$

The test of the equation is seen in the degree of uniformity of the values of δ_2 for hydrogen. His calculated values are shown in Table 5.

The agreement in the values for δ_2 is all that could be expected, except in the case of CS_2, and that may be due to experimental error, for the values obtained by Just, as was this one, are generally different from those of Horiuti. We may therefore place some confidence in a calculation of the solubility in a new solvent using a mean value of $\delta_2 = 2.1$.

[11] D. McIntosh, *J. Phys. Chem.*, **11**, 306 (1907).

[12] P. Villard, *Compt. rend.*, **106**, 1602; **107**, 395 (1888); **120**, 1262 (1895).

[13] M. G. Gonikberg, *J. phys. Chem.*, USSR, **14**, 582 (1940).

Table 5. Values of δ for H_2 calculated from solubilities at 20° C.[13a]

	$x_2 \times 10^4$	δ_1	δ_2
Ether	6.05	7.45	2.10
m-Xylene	4.0	8.10	2.02
Carbon tetrachloride	3.2	8.54	2.11
Toluene	3.7	8.32	2.10
Benzene	2.5	9.00	2.17
Carbon disulfide	0.84	9.98	1.7

A rigorous thermodynamic approach which avoids the difficulty of referring to vapor pressures of substances above their critical temperature is as follows:

We assume a gas at pressure p and temperature T in equilibrium with a solution in which its mole fraction is x_2. We wish to relate the heat ΔH and the entropy ΔS of transferring one mole of the substance from the gas at pressure p to the solution at concentration x_2 to the corresponding quantities at the temperature T_A at which the pure substance 2 has the vapor pressure p. At this temperature, the heat involved in going from the gas to the solution at mole fraction x_2 is the sum of the heat of condensation $(-\Delta H_A^V)$ and the partial molal heat of mixing $\Delta \bar{H}_2^M$. We may write[14] for ΔH at temperature T:

$$\Delta H = -\Delta H_A^V + \Delta \bar{H}_2^M - \int_{T_A}^{T} (\bar{C}_p - C_p^g)\, dT \tag{5a}$$

where $\bar{C}_p$ is the partial molal heat capacity of 2 in the solution at temperature T, pressure p and mole fraction x_2 and C_p^g is the corresponding heat capacity of the gas.

Similarly the entropy may be written as:

$$\Delta S = -\Delta S_A^V + \Delta \bar{S}_2^M - \int \frac{(\bar{C}_p - C_p^g)}{T}\, dT \tag{5b}$$

ΔS_A^V is of course $\Delta H_A^V / T_A$ and for regular solutions $\Delta \bar{S}_2^M = -R \ln x_2$.

[13a] The δ-values for the solvents in Table 5 are those which Gonikberg took from the second edition of this book. If the revised δ-values given in Appendix I are used, the agreement is not quite so satisfactory.

[14] The whole cycle must be carried out at constant pressure, p. At temperatures below T, this requires putting the solution under an external pressure, such as a mercury piston. Note that at temperature T_A, x_2 is not the equilibrium solubility.

Substituting and equating $T\Delta S$ to ΔH at equilibrium, we obtain:

$$\ln x_2 = \frac{-\Delta \overline{H}^M}{RT} + \frac{\Delta H_A^V}{R}\left(\frac{1}{T} - \frac{1}{T_A}\right) - \frac{1}{RT}\int_{T_A}^{T} (\overline{C}_p - C_p^g)\, dT$$

$$+ \frac{1}{R}\int_{T_A}^{T} (\overline{C}_p - C_p^g)\, d\ln T \tag{6}$$

The second term on the right is nothing but $\ln p/p°$, where $p°$ is the fictitious vapor pressure of the gas based upon a linear extrapolation. We may then write Equation 6 in a more compact form:

$$\ln x_2 = \ln \frac{p}{p°} - \frac{\Delta \overline{H}_2^M}{RT} - \frac{1}{RT}\int \Delta C_p\, dT + \frac{1}{R}\int \frac{\Delta C_p}{T}\, dT \tag{7}$$

If we neglect the two terms involving ΔC_p, we obtain the simple Equation 4 used in the preceding pages. Since the heat capacity in the solution is certainly greater than that of the gas, the solubility of the gas is enhanced over the value obtained from Equation 4. This is confirmed by values at the top of Table 4. The ΔC_p involved here, unlike that between the solid and liquid, is probably strongly dependent on temperature and should not be taken outside the integral, but where the necessary data exist, the exact Equation 7 could be used. Note that $\Delta \overline{H}_2^M$ is properly that at the temperature T_A where both substances are normal liquids.

An alternative approach. In Chapter VII, Equation 20, which may be rewritten as

$$-E = 2\pi (N^2/V)(N_1^2 \textstyle\int_{11} + N_2^2 \int_{22} + 2N_1 N_2 \int_{12}) \tag{8}$$

was developed for the potential energy of a solution with reference to two gaseous components. $\int_{11}$ denotes the integral $\int \varepsilon_{11}\, \varrho_{11}\, r^2\, dr$, where ε_{11} is the potential energy between molecular $1-1$ pairs and ϱ_{11} is the distribution function of pure 1. If component 2 is a gas at ordinary temperature, so that its solubility is small, $N_2 \ll N_1$ and there are virtually no solute molecules near enough to each other to interact, therefore the term $N_2^2 \int_{22}$ may be omitted. The partial molal energy of the gas is obtained by $(\partial E/\partial N_2)_{N_1}$. The resulting expression can be further simplified in view of the fact that $N_2 \ll N_1$ and $\overline{V}_1 \simeq V_1$, giving

$$\overline{E}_2 = 2\pi N^2 \left(\frac{\overline{V}_2 \int_{11}}{V_1^2} - \frac{2\int_{12}}{V_1}\right), \tag{9}$$

and, since $\Delta E_1/V_1 = 2\pi (N^2/V_1^2)\int_{11} = \delta_1^2$,

$$\overline{E}_2 = \overline{V}_2\, \delta_1^2 - 4\pi N^2 \textstyle\int_{12}/V_1. \tag{10}$$

The evaluation of the terms $\overline{V}_2$ and $\int_{12}$ in this equation we shall discuss below, but first let us note that since the gas is in equilibrium with its solution the free energy of solution is zero and therefore $\overline{E}_2 = T\Delta\overline{S}_2 - PV^g$. We may express $\Delta\overline{S}_2$ by $R\ln(V_2^g/V_2^f)$, where $V_2^g = RT/p_2$ and V_2^f is the free volume available to 1 mole of the gas in the solution. The number of moles of solvent per mole of solute is essentially $1/x_2$ and its volume per mole of solute is V_1/x_2. We may assume that the free volume is equally available to both solvent and solute, so that $V_2^f = V_1^f/x_2$. For $p_2 = 1$ atmos. we can then write

$$\overline{V}_2\, \delta_1^2 - 4\pi N^2 \int_{12}/V_1 = RT(\ln 0.082\, T - \ln V_1^f + \ln x_2 - 1). \qquad (11)$$

We are not prepared at this writing to attempt a sufficiently definite evaluation of the terms $\overline{V}_2$, $\int_{12}$ and V_1^f in this equation to apply it to experimental data and offer only the following comments. First, it might have been expected that the partial molal volumes of such solutes as H_2, He, A, etc., would be of the order of magnitude of their volumes in their own pure liquid states, or even less, due to the higher internal pressures of the solvents we ordinarily consider; it is extraordinarily interesting to find, however, that the former are much greater than the latter, as shown by the data of Horiuti in various solvents and by Kritchevsky and Ilinskaya[15] in water and methanol. They are so interesting as to merit the reproduction here, in Table 6, of the values for 25° C.; we have rounded them to 2 significant figures.

Table 6. Partial Molal Volumes of Gases, 25° C.

	H_2	N_2	CO	O_2	CH_4	C_2H_2	C_2H_4	C_2H_6	CO_2	SO_2
Ethyl ether	50	66	62	56	58					
Acetone	38	55	53	48	55	49	58	64		68
Methyl acetate	38	54	53	48	53	49	62	69		47
Carbon tetrachloride	38	53	53	45	52	54	61	67		54
Benzene	36	53	52	46	52	51	61	67		48
Methanol	35	52	51	45	52				43	
Chlorobenzene	34	50	46	43	49	50	58	64		48
Water	26	40	36	31	37				33	
Pure liquid at b. pt.	28	35	35	28	39	42	50	55	40	45

[15] I. Kritchevsky and A. Ilinskaya, *Acta Physiochimica*, *U.R.S.S.*, **20**, 327 (1945).

One striking comparison is that between the partial molal volumes and the molal volumes of the pure liquids at their boiling points, the former being much larger. Another is the same regular decrease in $\overline{V}_2$ for all the liquids in the order given in the table, the only significant exceptions being C_2H_2 and SO_2 in solutions where there is solvation. We may interpret this expansion as the combined result of the kinetic energy of the solute and the smaller attraction which one of these solute molecules exerts upon the surrounding solvent molecules.

These high values of $\overline{V}_2$ must be taken into account in any attempt to evaluate $\int_{12}$ in terms of the relation of the attraction constants k_{11} and k_{12} and the distribution function $\varrho_{11}(r)$ and $\varrho_{12}(r)$. The proper evaluation of the free volume per mole of solvent is still a matter calling for further study, as set forth in Chapter V.

Carbon dioxide and nitrous oxide present cases of specific chemical interactions with many solvents like those seen in Table 4 only in the case of acetylene in acetone and methyl acetate. Nitrous oxide has a dipole moment

Table 7. - Solubility of CO_2 and N_2O at 1 atmos., 0° C. Mole fraction × 10^4

	CO_2(J)	CO_2(K)	N_2O
$1/p°$	178		202
$1/f°$	257		
Amyl acetate	270	283	312
Acetone	209	211	185
Pyridine	129	129	120
Benzaldehyde	128	125	134
Ethylene chloride	125		115
Acetic acid	121	124	
Chloroform	123	121	182
Nitrobenzene	113		
Toluene	107		
m-Xylene	102		
Carbon tetrachloride	100		
Benzene	91		
i-Amyl alcohol	87	87	111
Ethylene bromide	82	82	100
Propyl alcohol	77		
Ethyl alcohol	70	69	72
Methyl alcohol	71	60	53
o-Toluidine	66		
Aniline	55	53	56
Carbon disulfide	22		
Water	7	7	5

of 0.17 Debye units[16]; carbon dioxide is nonpolar but is an "electron-acceptor" acid as shown by its reactions with water and other oxides. Table 7 contains data for these gases obtained by Just[17] and by Kunerth[18] arranged, as in Table 4, in order of decreasing solubility. One may see first, that the order for N_2O parallels approximately that for CO_2; second, that it is roughly the same as the order in Table 4 for a number of solvents; but, third, there is abundant evidence of solvation, particularly with solvents containing the carbonyl group. Many of the solvents are so close together that the evident minor uncertainties regarding the experimental data could permit some shifts in the order. CO_2 being an acid in the sense of "accepting" electrons from such molecules as H_2O and other bases, exhibits solubilities in such solvents greater than would otherwise be expected. We note the increase in solubility in order in aniline, toluidine and pyridine, the order of increasing basic strength as revealed by their basic ionization constants in aqueous solution[19]. Further, its solubility in water, although small, is enhanced by the formation of H_2CO_3. Even if we did not know this to be case, the fact of hydration would be evident from the figures in Table 8.

Table 8. Effect of Hydration on Solubility of CO_2. Ratios of solubility in water to solubility in non-reacting solvents.

	C_6H_6	CCl_4	CS_2
CO_2	0.077	0.070	0.315
CO	0.037	0.049	0.115
N_2	0.037	0.054	0.121

The chemical nature of N_2O is less familiar than that of CO_2, and the data available less abundant, but its solubilities seem to follow rather closely from the assumption that it is similar to CO_2, but slightly less prone to form addition compounds. It is, accordingly, somewhat less soluble than CO_2 in the more polar solvents, but distinctly more soluble in the non-polar solvents, both by reason of its smaller solvating power and the larger value for the ideal solubility.[20]

[16] H. E. Watson, G. G. Rao, and K. L. Ramaswamy, *Proc. Roy. Soc.* (*London*) **A 143**, 558 (1934).
[17] G. Just, *Z. physik. Chem.*, **37**, 342 (1901).
[18] W. Kunerth, *Phys. Rev.*, **19**, 519 (1922).
[19] cf. N. F. Hall and M. R. Sprinkle, *J. Am. Chem. Soc.*, **54**, 3469 (1932).
[20] Kunerth has used his own data and those of Just as a basis for a denial of any connection between solubility and internal pressure for gases. He has, however, neglected to make the distinction previously insisted upon by the present author between liquids of low and high polarity. The reader can see that if the more polar liquids are omitted from Table 7 the others fall in the same order, within the limits to be expected, as was found in Table 4 and also throughout this volume for a variety of solubilities and other properties. Cf. Hildebrand, *Phys. Rev.*, **21**, 46 (1923).

The ideal solubilities of these gases at 1 atmosphere based upon the relation $x = 1/p^\circ$ can be calculated from their saturation pressures at 20° which, according to Villard[21], are 56.3 atm. for CO_2 and 49.4 atm. for N_2O, giving for x, 0.0178 and 0.0202, respectively. Since the above pressures are very high, making the gases deviate considerably from the gas laws, it may be preferable to calculate x from $1/f^\circ$. Roth[22] has given data for the ratio of the volume of CO_2 at 18.5° under various pressures, to the volume at 0° and 1 atm., from which the volume per mole is found to be 22.34 liters. Using this value, we give in Table 9 the actual molal volumes instead of the relative volumes given by Roth.

Table 9.

p	V	V^i	$a = V^i - V$
15	1.350	1.492	142
25	0.729	0.896	167
40	0.398	0.560	162
		Av.	157

The ideal volumes at the same pressures are given in the 3rd column while the 4th gives their difference a in Equation I-24. We find $f = 38.9$ atm. and the "ideal solubility" would be $1/38.9 = 0.0257$.

Dolezalek has "corrected" the saturation pressure by substituting for it $p + a/V^2$, which, taking $a = 0.0070$, gives 120 atm., which gives for the solubility $1/120 = 0.00835$, a very different figure from either $1/p^\circ$ or $1/f^\circ$. Of course $p + a/V^2$ would represent the ideal pressure only if b were zero, which is by no means the case.

Ammonia is a substance whose solubilities are strongly affected by its high dielectric constant, its basic nature and its hydrogen bonding power. The influence of these factors is seen in the data in Table 10. In the liquid state, it is incompletely miscible with toluene so that its small gas solubility in that solvent is in accord with a large positive deviation from Raoult's law. Ether is somewhat hydrogen bonding and the alcohols and water more strongly so, in the order given.

Table 10. Mole Fraction of NH_3 Gas Dissolving at 1 Atmos. and 0°.

$1/p^\circ$[23]	Toluene[17]	Ether[24]	Ethyl[25] alcohol	Methyl[26] alcohol	Water[27]
0.238	0.0026	0.079	0.398	0.439	0.481

[21] P. Villard, *Ann. chim. phys.*, 7, 10, 387 (1897).
[22] W. Roth, *Wied. Ann.*, 11, 1 (1880).
[23] From $x = 1/p^\circ$, taking $p^\circ = 4.19$ atm.
[24] Calculated from data by Hantzsch and Vagt.
[25] C. A. L. De Bruyn, *Rec. trav. chim.*, 11, 112 (1892).
[26] J. W. Mallet, *Am. Chem. Journ.*, 19, 807 (1897).
[27] E. P. Perman, *J. Chem. Soc.*, 83, 1168 (1903).

Inert gases in water. Lange and Watzel[28] in 1938, and Eley[29] in 1939, attacked the problem of the solubility of the inert gases in water by splitting the energy and entropy of solution into two parts, the formation of cavities and the introduction of the gas molecules into them. Lange and Watzel estimated the energy of cavitation by aid of the heat of vaporization, while Eley used Equation I-7, with I-9 for the entropy. These give for the energy of N cavities, $\Delta E^c = T\overline{V}_2 (\partial P/\partial T)_V$, and for the entropy, $\Delta S^c = \overline{V}_2 (\partial P/\partial T)_V$. Now the striking thing about water is that $(\partial P/\partial T)_V$ is negative at 0° C, zero at 4° C and increases with rising temperature, giving 1.2 kcal. at 80° C for $\overline{V}_2 = 10$ cc. This makes the partial molal energy and entropy of solution at 4° C depend only on the energy and entropy of introduction of the solute molecules. Relative values of the energy depend mainly upon the polarizability of the solute molecules. At high temperatures, the large energy required to form the cavities outweighs the solvent-solute attraction. Eley calculated values for these quantities for the inert gases in water and in the second paper pointed out the difference in these respects between water and typical organic solvents.

The ease with which small molecules, such as those of helium, can find free volume for themselves in cold water despite their small attractive force, assists helium to dissolve in cold water to a far greater extent than would be expected by analogy with other gases. This is related to the ability of helium to diffuse through quartz glass, for the channels through ice are approximately the same size as those through quartz. This can be illustrated by the aid of figures from Table 4, calculating the ratio of the solubilities in water to that in another solvent, shown in Table 11. We see that the ratios for A and N_2 in the same solvent are nearly identical, but much greater for He, particularly at 0° C. In other words, although He is less soluble in any one solvent than any other gas, the decrease is least in water.

The relative insolubility of helium is responsible for its use in preventing the affliction known as the "bends", or "caisson disease". The development of this use by the U. S. Bureau of Mines and later by the U. S. Navy was initiated by the senior author[30].

---

[28] E. Lange and R. Watzel, *Z. physik. Chem.* **(A) 182,** 1 (1938).

[29] D. D. Eley, *Trans. Faraday Soc.*, **35**, 1281, 1421 (1939).

[30] R. R. Sayers, W. P. Yant and J. H. Hildebrand, *Bur. Mines, Serial No.* 2670, Feb., 1925.
Nature, **121**, 577 (1928). See also.
J. H. Hildebrand, *Science*, **45**, 324 (1927).
E. End, *Am. J. Physiol.* **120**, 712 (1937).
E. End and M. E. Nohl, *Marquette Med. Rev.*, **2**, 53 (1938).
L. E. Dodd, *Am. J. Phys.* **8**, 181 (1940).
J. A. Hawkins and C. W. Shilling, *J. Biol Chem.*, **113**, 649 (1936).
Report on Use of Helium-oxygen Mixtures for Deep Diving, Exptl. Diving Unit, Navy Yard, Wash., D. C., April, 1939.
A. R. Behnke and T. L. Willmon. "U.S.S. Squalus", *U. S. Navy, Med. Bull.*, **37**, No. 4. (1939).

When compressed air is breathed by divers working at considerable depth, a good deal of nitrogen dissolves in the body fluids and tissues which may effervesce, unless a long time is spent in ascending, causing stoppages of circulation or of nerve impulses which are at least very painful and at worst very dangerous. By substituting helium for nitrogen to withstand the hydrostatic pressure—the partial pressure of oxygen must be kept below

Table 11. Solubility in water divided by solubility in other solvent (Bunsen coefficients in the case of olive oil).

	Benzene		Cyclohexane	Olive oil[31]
	0°	25°	25°	22°
He	0.35	0.091	0.057	0.58
A	0.053	0.028	0.017	0.29
N_2		0.027	0.017	0.25

about 1 atmosphere — much less inert gas dissolves and the incidence of bends is greatly reduced. The figures in Tables 4 and 11 show that the advantage of helium over nitrogen is greater at body temperature than it would be at lower temperatures, and, further, that it is even greater in organic solvents, including the body lipoids, than in water and hence in the blood stream.

Another advantage of helium, discovered by Behnke[32], is that it does not have the narcotic effect shown by concentrated nitrogen. Lawrence[31] and his associates have shown that the heavier inert gases exert strong narcotic effects, argon excceding nitrogen, and 80 percent krypton with oxygen at 1 atmosphere having as great an effect as air at 6 atmospheres. It is significant that this anaesthesia must be a purely physical phenomenon, depending chiefly upon the molar quantity, not the nature of the dissolved gas.

[31] J. H. Lawrence, W. F. Loomis, and C. A. Tobias and F. H. Turpin, *J. Physiol.* **105**, 197, (1946).

[32] A. R. Behnke and O. D. Yarbrough, *Amer. J. Physiol*, **126**, 409 (1939).

References.

Solubility of Gases in Liquids, A. E. Markham and K. A. Kobe, *Chem. Rev.*, **28**, 519 (1941).

Solubilities of Gases and Surface Tension, H. H. Uhlig, *J. Phys. Chem.* **41**, 1215 (1937).

CHAPTER XVI

Solubility of Liquids in Liquids

It was pointed out in Chapter III that at a critical consolute temperature T_c, $\partial a/\partial x = 0$ and $\partial^2 a/\partial x^2 = 0$ for both components. A pair of components with equal molal volumes which obey the simple, symmetrical Equation III-14, $RT \ln (a_1/x_1) = Bx_2^2$, would break into two liquid phases for values of $B > 2RT$. The more general equation for regular solutions, upon applying the above conditions, gives

$$RT_c = \frac{2x_1 x_2 V_1^2 V_2^2}{(x_1 V_1 + x_2 V_2)^3} (\delta_1 - \delta_2)^2 \tag{1}$$

and, at T_c,

$$x_1 = 1 - x_2 = \frac{(V_1^2 + V_2^2 - V_1 V_2)^{\frac{1}{2}} - V_1}{V_2 - V_1} \tag{2}$$

For liquids of equal molal volumes Equation 1 reduces to

$$2RT_c = V(\delta_1 - \delta_2)^2 \tag{3}$$

All of these equations are to be regarded as only approximate, in view of neglect of departures from additivity on mixing, clustering in the critical region, and sensitivity of T_c thus calculated to small variations in the δ-values used. Two practical approximations are possible when $V_1 \neq V_2$, (1) to use Equation 3 instead of Equation 1 with V taken as the arithmetic mean of V_1 and V_2, and (2) to calculate x_1 and x_2 by assuming the critical composition to lie at $\varphi_1 = \varphi_2 = 0.5$.

The composition of the liquid phases in equilibrium below the critical point is given by applying the conditions that at any one temperature $a_1 = a_1'$ and $a_2 = a_2'$, the primes indicating the second phase. The resulting simultaneous equations are troublesome to solve; the solution is best carried out graphically.

Let us see the magnitudes involved in Equations 1 and 3. In order to obtain unmixing no lower than 25° C, in the case of two liquids with equal molal volumes of 100 cc., $\delta_1 - \delta_2$ would have to be at least 3.4; if the second component has $V_2 = 60$ it would have to be 3.6. Now normal pentane, whose δ-value at 25° C, 7.05, is one of the lowest known till recently, would be incompletel miscible at this temperature only with a nonpolar liquid whose δ-value is about 10.4 to 10.6, or more. Reference to the table of δ-values, Appendix I, shows how scarce such substances are among those liquid at room temperatures. Active phosphorus, P_4, $\delta = 14.3$, which can easily be supercooled far below its melting point, 44° C, furnishes an almost lone example. It yields a number of two-liquid systems, to be discussed below. In order to find nonpolar two-liquid systems, it has been necessary to melt such other substances with high internal pressure as SnI_4, I_2 and S_8, also discussed below. Quite recently, however, the fluorocarbons, with δ-values of 5.5 to 6.1, have been found to yield two phases with many ordinary liquids, since the latter need δ-values of only about 8.8. It is easy to see, in the light of the above discussion, why most of the familiar two-liquid systems contain one component, such as water or methanol, in which strong association contributes to the unlikeness of the two species. Examples include, beside the well known water systems, methanol-carbon disulfide, methanol-hexane, aniline-hexane, nitrobenzene-hexane, phenol-hexane, sulfur dioxide-cyclohexane.

But before dealing with systems having an associated component, let us first consider the relatively few solutions of nonpolar components which are amenable to semiquantitative treatment as regular solutions.

Phosphorus solutions. The nonpolar liquid of highest internal pressure at room temperature is active phosphorus, P_4. Although its freezing point is 44° C, it is easily supercooled below 0° C. It yields two liquid phases with a number of substances. Hildebrand and Buehrer[1] determined the critical consolute temperatures shown in Table 1. In view of the variety of temperatures involved, we have not undertaken the labor of computing the corresponding internal pressures, but merely point out the at least rough correspondence with the relative values at 25°C. The solubility relations of phenanthrene and anthracene show them to have nearly equal internal pressures, and the solubilities of iodine in p-$C_6H_4Br_2$ and in 1,2 $C_2H_4Br_2$ plotted in Fig. 1, Chapter XVII, show them to have practically identical internal pressures.

We can add the evidence furnished by the solubilities of P_4 plotted in Fig. 4 Chapter XVII, which show that it forms two liquids with benzene, carbon tetrachloride, and n-heptane, and evidently also with ether and acetone. The order is the order of internal pressures. The relation between the solid-liquid and supercooled liquid-liquid curves for P_4 and CS_2 is particularly interesting and instructive. These two curves result from the substitution of the same solubility parameters and molal volumes in the appropriate regular solution equations. The solubility parameter, δ_2, for P_4 derived from vapor pressures, 13.3, as set forth in the following chapter, is too small to give the experimental value of T_c for P_4 in CS_2 but the value 14.5 accounts well for such diverse figures as T_c for P_4-CS_2 and solid P_4 in CCl_4.

[1] J. H. Hildebrand and T. F. Buehrer, *J. Am. Chem. Soc.*, **42**, 2213 (1920).

Table 1. Critical Solution Temperatures of Liquid Phosphorus, P_4

	t_c	δ_1 at $t°$ C	
n-Decane	300	6.0	175
Chlorobenzene	264	7.8	130
Naphthalene	202	8.8	200
Phenanthrene	200	8.8	200
Anthracene	198		
1.2-Dibromoethane	165	9	130
p-Dibromobenzene	163	9	130
Carbon disulfide	−6	10.0	0
P_4		14.3	0

Stannic Iodide is a nonpolar substance with a high internal pressure, melting at 143.5° C. It forms two-liquid systems with liquids of sufficiently low internal pressures, such as the paraffins and silicon tetrachloride for which data are given in Table 2 and plotted in Fig. 1, also in another

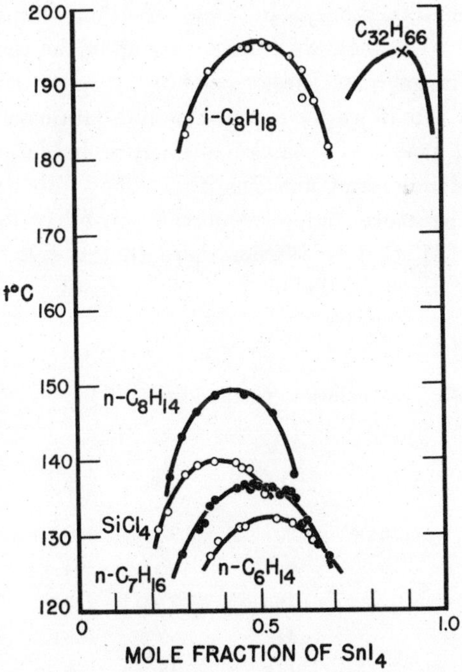

Fig 1. Liquid-liquid solubilities of stannic iodide

way correlated with the solid-liquid systems in Chapter XVII, Fig. 2. The figure for dicetyl solutions was obtained by Hildebrand and

Wachter[2]; that for silicon chloride solutions by Hildebrand and Negishi[3]; the others by Dice and Hildebrand[4]. Here, as with phosphorus solutions, the data do not easily permit a rigid quantitative check of the general question, nor is it to be expected, in view of the shapes of the normal paraffins, that the equation would permit accurate calculations of the critical temperatures. We shall therefore merely call attention to the following:

1. The critical temperatures of the paraffin solutions are in the order of their solubility parameters for 25° C, an order which is certainly maintained at higher temperatures.

2. The calculated and observed mole fractions at the critical points agree within the limits of error of both the theory and the experimental determinations of the flat maxima of the solubility curves. This is particularly striking in the case of dicetyl, where the critical composition lies so far from 50 mole percent. This system illustrates the general fact that the component with the larger molecules is less soluble on a mole fraction basis than the one with the smaller molecules.

3. The solutions SnI_4 with $SiCl_4$ conform most closely to the assumption of spherical symmetry implicit in Equation 2 and offer, therefore, the fairest test of of the general theory. In view of other simplifications introduced in the theoretical treatment, we cannot rely upon the temperature coefficients of the relatively large quantities δ_1 and δ_2, to give correctly that of the smaller $(\delta_1 - \delta_2)^2$. But if we have experimental data over a sufficient range of temperature it is possible to make a fairly reliable extrapolation by the method used by Hildebrand and Negishi[3]. They calculated values of $\delta_2 - \delta_1$ over a long temperature range from the solubility data themselves, solid SnI_4 from 0° to 131° C, liquid from there to the critical point at 139.9° C. Their figures are given in Table 3.

Table 2. Critical Solution Temperatures of Liquid Stannic Iodide

	V_1 25°C	δ_1	t_c°C	x_2 obs.	x_2 calc.
2,2,4-Trimethyl pentane	207	6.95	195.3	50	54
Dicetyl	615		194	90	85
n-Hexane	163	7.3	149.4	42	
Silicon chloride	115	7.55	139.0	39	44
n-Heptane	174	7.45	136.8	48	50
n-Octane	188.5	7.55	132.0	52	53

[2] J. H. Hildebrand and A. Wachter, *J. Am. Chem. Soc.*, **57**, 866 (1935).
[3] J. H. Hildebrand and G. R. Negishi, *Ibid*, **59**, 339 (1937).
[4] M. E. Dice and J. H. Hildebrand, *Ibid*, **50**. 3023 (1928).

Table 3. Values of $\delta_2 - \delta_1$ for SnI_4 in $SiCl_4$ calculated from solubility data.

t°C	$-\log x_2$	$-\log x_2^i$	V_1, cc.	V_2, cc.	φ_1		$\delta_2 - \delta_1$
0	2.810	1.142	111.5	148.3	0.998		3.77
25.0	2.414	0.886	115.4	151.1	.995		3.74
40.0	2.208	.747	117.2	153.0	.992		3.71
81.3	1.628	.413	127.4	157.6	.970		3.64
88.0	1.536	.362	129.4	158.8	.964		3.62
112.1	1.191	.203	137.2	161.6	.925		3.55
115.6	1.131	.175	138.6	162.0	.917		3.53
131.0	0.185	.079	145.0	163.7	.313		3.49
		$-\log x_2'$				φ_2'	
132.0	0.642	0.256	145.4	163.8	0.750	0.416	3.35
							3.46
136.0	.577	.292	147.2	164.2	.713	.463	3.32
							3.29
139.9	.409	.409	149.0	164.7	.586	.586	3.25

A plot of $\delta_2 - \delta_1$ against temperature is shown in Fig. 2. It is evident that the points for the liquid-liquid system, shown by solid circles, are only slightly off the line for the solid-liquid system and that the trend of the latter, being nearly linear, could have been used to predict the behavior of the former from the latter. This was actually done for the system $I_2 - CCl_4$, described below.

It is significant, also, that a treatment which ignores both volume changes and the clustering, or fluctuations in density actually visible by light scattering close to the critical point, is nevertheless able to correlate as well as it does the behavior of the system near the critical point with its behavior far away, where the concentration of the SnI_4 is so low as to make any clustering negligible. Experiment thus unites with theory [5] to indicate that clustering falls of, rapidly in departing from the critical point either in temperature or composition.

Iodine-carbon tetrachloride solutions. The parameters in the solubility equation which fit the experimental points for solid I_2 in CCl_4 from 0° to 50 °C indicated that at higher temperatures the curve should have the S-shape shown in Chapter XVII, Fig. 1, with two compositions for one temperature where a liquid-liquid curve cuts it. An extrapolation with some allowance for expected curvature and rough calculation by successive approximations by aid of Equations 2 and 3 indicated a liquid-liquid solubility

[5] M. V. Schmoluchowski, *Ann. Physik.*, [4], **25**, 205 (1908); A. Einstein, *Ibid*, **33**, 1275 (1910); Wo. Ostwald, *Ibid.*, **36**, 848 (1911). R. S. Krishnan. *Kolloid Z.*, **84**, 8 (1938).

curve with t_c somewhere between 150° and 170 °C and at 71 mole per cent of iodine. It was not possible to verify this prediction by visual observation because of the opacity of concentrated iodine solutions, therefore the appearance of an iodine-rich liquid phase upon cooling a sealed tube of the homogeneous solution was detected by the torque produced when it was held balanced in an inclined position. In this way were obtained the points of the liquid-liquid curve shown in Fig. 2, according to which $t_c = 160.5°$ with 68 mole per cent of I_2.

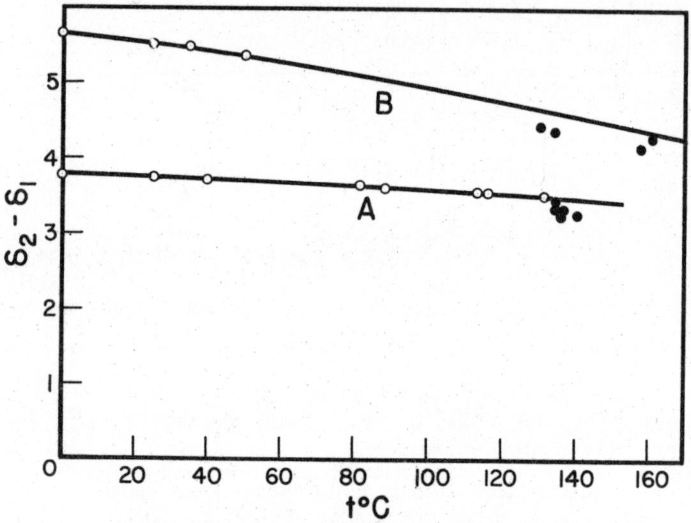

Fig. 2. Trend of $\delta_2 - \delta_1$ with temperature. Curve A, SnI_4—$SiCl_4$; curve B, I_2 — CCl_4.

Molten sulfur solutions. Sulfur-λ, which, like rhombic and monoclinic solid sulfur, contains zig-zag octagonal molecules of S_8, has a high internal pressure, $\delta = 11.7$ from solubility data at 25 °C, and forms two-liquid systems above its melting point with a number of other substances as shown in Table 3.

The critical temperatures of mixing with the nonpolar second components accord qualitatively with their internal pressures. But sulfur also shows higher, unmixing temperatures, as indicated in the table. This is, of course, connected with the transition of S_λ to S_μ in which the octagonal molecules break up into string molecules of variable length. These are so unlike each other that although they do not quite separate into two liquids, the addition of a second component causes the separation when the proportion of S_μ becomes sufficiently large. The presence of some S_μ in S_λ even down to the melting point introduces a complication which discourages much expectation of quantitative agreement.

Table 4. Solubilities of Molten Sulfur.

	Critical Solution Temperatures, °C	
	of mixing	of unmixing
Paraffin[6]	not reached	
Xylene[6]	not reached	
Ethyl benzene[6]	190°	
Toluene[6, 7]	180°	222°
Benzene[6, 7]	163°	226°
Triphenylmethane[8]	147°	199°
β-Dichloroethyl sulfide[9]	143°	
Aniline[7]	138°	
Benzyl chloride[10]	134°	
Chlorobenzene[2]	116°	
Phenanthrene[6]	below melting point of sulfur.	
Diphenyl[6]	below melting point of sulfur.	
Naphthalene[6]	below melting point of sulfur.	
p-Dibromobenzene	below melting point of sulfur.	
Methylene iodide	below melting point of sulfur.	

Fluorocarbons. As mentioned earlier, the fluorocarbons, with their low δ-values, are able to form two-liquid systems with a number of ordinary liquids, even similar hydrocarbons, a fact that seemed quite surprising until analyzed in the light of the general theory of regular solutions. Scott[11] has calculated the solubility parameters for a number of them and reviewed in the light of theory the meager solubility data available at the time of writing.

Let us see what these parameters would give for the system *f*-methyl cyclohexane-carbon tetrachloride at 25 °C, where $\delta_2 - \delta_1 = 2.6$. This and the mean value of $V = 146$ cc. substituted in Equation 3 gives $T_c = 248°$, that is, complete miscibility at 25 °C. This is in accord with experiment. Moreover, the fluorocarbon is also reported as completely miscible with ethyl ether and "petroleum ether", for which $\delta_1 - \delta_2$ values are still smaller. But benzene, for which $\delta_2 = 9.15$, and $\delta_2 - \delta_1 = 3.15$ gives $T_c = 353°$, or 80 °C, corresponding to limited miscibility at 25 °C.

[6] H. R. Kruyt, *Z. physik. Chem.*, **64**, 486 (1909).
[7] W. Alexejeff, *Wied. Ann.*, **28**, 305 (1886).
[8] A. Smith, W. B. Holmes and E. S. Hall, *Z. physik. Chem.* **52**, 602 (1905).
[9] J. A. Wilkinson, C. Neilson and H. M. Wylde, *J. Am. Chem. Soc.*, **42**, 1377 (1920).
[10] J. Boguski and W. Jakubowski, *J. Russ. Phys. Ges.*, **37**, 92 (1905); *Chem. Zentr.*, (1905) I, 1207.
[11] R. L. Scott, *J. Am. Chem. Soc.*, **70**, 4090 (1948).

Table 5. Thermodynamic Properties of Fluorocarbons.

Formula	Name	Melt. pt.	Boil. pt.	25 °C: V cc./mole	25 °C: ΔH^V kcal/mole	δ
C_5F_{12}	*f*-*n*-Pentane*		29.5	183	6.0	5.5
C_6F_{14}	*f*-*n*-Hexane		58	205	7.1	5.6
C_7F_{16}	*f*-*n*-Heptane	—52.8	82.4	227	8.1	5.7
C_8F_{18}	*f*-*n*-Octane		104	253	8.9	5.7
C_5F_{10}	*f*-Cyclopentane		23.7	152	5.9	5.9
C_6F_{12}	*f*-Cyclohexane	$>$58.2	subl.	170	6.8	6.0
C_7F_{14}	*f*-Methylcyclohexane	77.5	195	195	7.7	6.0
C_8F_{16}	*f*-Dimethylcyclohexane		~102	~ 215	8.6	6.1

* We use the prefixed letter *f* to denote the "perfluoro"-compound.

As this book goes to press, Mr. D. R. F. Cochran[11a], at our suggestion, has just obtained the necessary points for constructing the solubility curve for *f*-methyl cyclohexane and benzene. His results are shown in Fig. 3. The consolute point

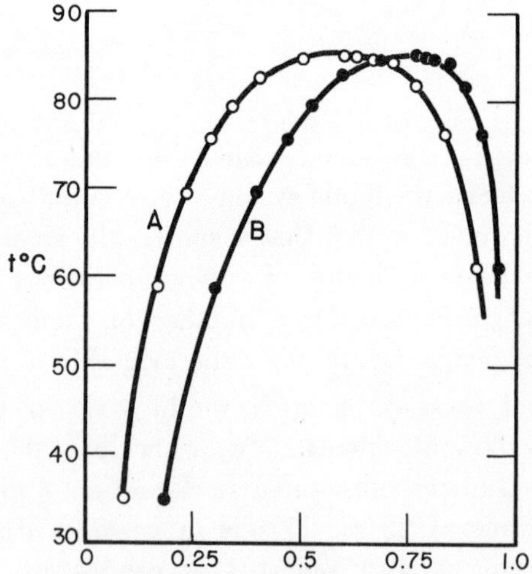

Fig. 3. Solubility of perfluoromethyl cyclohexane with benzene. Curve A, volume fraction, curve B, mole fraction of benzene.

is 85.3 °C and the mole fraction of benzene at this point, located by a rectilinear diameter, is 0.75. The discrepancy in molal volumes is largely responsible for its considerable displacement from 0.5, as shown by plotting against volume fraction. Let us see how Equations 2 and 3 correspond to

[11a] J. H. Hildebrand and D. R. F. Cochran, *J. Am. Chem. Soc.*, **71**, 22 (1949).

the experimental figures. We have no data on the temperature dependence of the two molal volumes, but we may assume for this rough calculation that they vary in the same way and use the densities and δ-values at 25 °C. Substituting the molal volumes in Equation 2 gives 0.75 for the mole fraction of benzene at the consolute point, in agreement with experiment, and Equation 3 gives $t_c = 80$ °C (Equation 1 gives 87 °C). This is a far closer agreement than one would have any right to expect, in view of all the approximations involved.

Critical solution temperatures of the paraffin hydrocarbons. Because of the importance of characterizing the various paraffin hydrocarbons, especially in the petroleum industry, a large amount of data on their critical temperatures with other substances has been accumulated. Of particular interest are the "aniline points", the critical solution temperatures of the hydrocarbons with aniline[12], which are used extensively to characterize petroleum fractions.

In Table 6, critical solution temperatures for aniline[13], nitrobenzene[14] and $\beta - \beta'$ dichloroethyl ether ("chlorex")[14] with the normal paraffins are listed. From these, we may calculate the δ-values of aniline, nitrobenzene and chlorex using Equations 1 and 2. (The δ-values are for 25 °C; correcting them for temperature involves only trivial corrections).

Table 6. Critical Solution Temperatures of Normal Paraffins.

			Aniline ($V_2 = 92$)		Nitrobenzene ($V_2 = 103$)		Chlorex ($V_2 = 117$)	
	δ_1	V_1	t	δ_2	t	δ_2	t	δ_2
n-butane	6.70	101.4	84.1	10.54	41	10.21		
n-pentane	7.05	116.1	71.5	10.68	25.15	10.35	10.85	10.16
n-hexane	7.29	131.6	69.1	10.78	20.60	10.43	12.70	10.34
n-heptane	7.43	147.5	70.0	10.79	19.48	10.47	16.50	10.36
n-octane	7.55	163.5	72.0	10.80	20.68	10.49	20.67	10.43
n-nonane	7.65	179.7	74.6	10.81	21.78	10.51	24.00	10.45
n-decane	7.73	196	77.5	10.79				
n-hexadecane	8.0	295	95.1	10.69	38.52	10.42	47.93	10.46
Average				10.73		10.41		10.37

The initial effect of the increasing chain length is primarily that of decreasing $\Delta\delta$, and so decreases the temperature. As the molecules get larger the increase in volume overshadows the increase in δ, and the

[12] Technically the "aniline point" is the solution temperature for equal volumes of hydrocarbon and aniline, but the difference between these and actual critical solution temperatures is extremely small.

[13] A. W. Francis, *Ind. Eng. Chem.* **33**, 554 (1941).

[14] H. M. Woodburn, K. Smith and H. Tetewsky, *Ind. Eng. Chem.*, **36**, 588 (1944).

temperature increases again. As indicated by the constancy of the calculated δ_2's, the agreement is remarkable, for the maximum variation in the calculated δ_2-values is only 0.3 units, even for aniline which is a hydrogen-bonding solvent, while the hydrocarbons vary from 6.7 to 8.0. Of course the close similarity in structure of the paraffins accounts for part of this We may compare these calculated δ-values with those obtained in other ways. The heat of vaporization of aniline yields a δ-value of 9.8, while from the swelling of vulcanized rubber, Scott and Magat[15] estimate 9 9 for nitrobenzene, a satisfactory agreement considering the nature of the solvents.

When we consider the branched-chain isomers, the agreement is not nearly so good; for example, from the critical solution temperature of the system iso-octane nitrobenzene (30.40°), we calculate a δ_2 of 9.83 for nitrobenzene; if we use 10.41, we obtain much too high a temperature (114°). Qualitatively, we find a rough agreement between the critical solution temperatures and the δ-values of isomeric hydrocarbons of the same carbon content, but a somewhat better correspondence exists between them and the molal volumes or the refractive indices, as Francis[13] pointed out.

Table 7 compares the critical solution temperatues for aniline and nitrobenzene with the δ's, molal volumes and refractive indices of the isomeric hexanes and heptanes.

Table 7. Critical Solution Temperatures for Paraffin Isomers

	Aniline	Nitrobenzene	δ_1	V_{25}	n_D^{20}
n-hexane	69.1	20.60	7.29	131.6	1.3750
3-methyl pentane	69.3	21.4	7.15	130.6	1.3765
2,3-dimethyl butane	72.0	24.1	6.99	131.2	1.3750
2-methyl pentane	74.3	25.61	7.04	132.9	1.3716
2,2-dimethyl butane	81.0	33.50	6.73	133.7	1.3689
3-ethyl pentane	66.3		7.36	144.4	1.3934
2,3-dimethyl pentane	68.1		7.24	145.0	1.3920
3,3-dimethyl pentane	69.7		7.09	145.4	1.3910
n-heptane	70.0	19.48	7.43	147.5	1.3876
3-methyl hexane	70.6		7.29	146.7	1.3882
2,2,3-trimethylbutane	72.3	23.08	6.95	146.1	1.3895
2-methyl hexane	73.8		7.21	148.6	1.3850
2,2-dimethyl pentane	78.0		6.92	149.7	1.3824
2,4 dimethyl pentane	78.8		6.96	149.9	1.3820

An entirely satisfactory explanation of these phenomena remains to be found.

[15] R. L. Scott and M. Magat, *J. Polymer Sci.*, **4**, 555 (1949).

Liquid-liquid systems with water as one component. Molecules whose mutual attraction is enhanced by hydrogen bonding resist penetration by molecules of a nonpolar liquid. Water, with more of this kind of attraction per cubic centimeter than has any other liquid, has a minimum of internal pressure arising from London forces; consequently, the solubility of a second component in water is influenced strongly by its ability to form hydrogen bonds or else to ionize. The alcohols furnish familiar examples. Methanol, ethanol and propanol are completely miscible with water, but the higher alcohols, beginning with the butanols, are partly miscible with water, their solubility falling off with increasing size of the alkyl group. The branched isomers are drawn into water more easily than the corresponding normal isomers.

But if we wish to use figures for the relative solubilities in water, which we may distinguish as component 1, of two other similar substances, 2 and 2′, for the purpose of inferring the relative attractions of their respective molecules for water molecules, we must remember that the mutual solubility of two condensed phases is not a function only of the 1-2 forces but of the 1-1 and the 2-2 forces as well. By using water as the common solvent for both, we cancel the 1-1 forces but the 2-2 forces and the 2′-2′ forces are in general different, and their difference should be allowed for in some way. It should not be difficult to see that the greatly different solubilities of solid anthracene and solid phenanthrene in any solvent are chiefly the result of the very different energies of their solid phases; their nearly identical boiling points indicate that they would cause substantially the same lowering of the vapor pressure of a common solvent. The 1-2 and the 1-2′ attractions are doubtless nearly the same; it is the difference between the 2-2 and the 2′-2′ forces in the solid crystals that is chiefly rensponsible for their different solubilities.

The same distinction should be made in comparing the solubilities of two different slightly soluble liquids in water if we are trying to compare the 1-2 with the 1-2′ forces. One should allow for the different vapor pressures of the two liquids by calculating their solubilities, assuming Henry's law, at the same vapor pressure, just as we do when comparing gaseous solutes.

This is illustrated in Table 8. We see, first, that liquid *n*-butyl alcohol dissolves in water at 20 °C to an extent nearly 4 times as great as *i*-amyl alcohol, and that the solubility of ethyl propionate is only a little less than that of *i*-amyl alcohol. But these three liquids have very different vapor pressures, so that we are not introducing them into water at the same fugacity. In the last column are given the solubilities to be expected of the vapors at 1 mm. pressure, assuming Henry's law. We see, first, that the amyl alcohol is only half as soluble as the butyl alcohol; second, that liquid ethyl propionate is only a little less soluble than liquid *i*-amyl alcohol, but at the same vapor pressure the latter is vastly more soluble, in harmony with its far greater hydrogen bonding ability.

Table 8. Solubility in Water, 20°C.

	Dipole moment Debye units	Vapor pressure mm.	Moles/1000 g H_2O at vapor pressure	at 1 mm. pressure
n-Butyl alcohol	1.66	4.4	1.15	.26
i-Amyl alcohol	1.66	2.3	.32	.14
Ethyl propionate	1.8	27.8	.23	.0084
n-Propyl chloride	2.0	280.3	.0255	.00009
n-Propyl iodide	1.9	35.1	.0054	.00015

Palit[16], for example, has attributed the different solubilities of isomeric alcohols in water to different effects of the hydroxyl group upon electron displacements in the hydrocarbon chain. The differences in solubility are largely accounted for by their different vapor pressures, as shown by the examples in Table 9. It should be obvious that the minor effects of the shape of the alkyl radical should be investigated *after* correcting the solubilities for these differences in vapor pressure, or, what would be equivalent, using their partial vapor pressures at the same solubility.

Table 9. Solubilities of isomeric alcohols in water in relation to their vapor pressures. 20°C.

Butyl alcohols	Wt. %	p (mm.)	Amyl alcohols	Wt. %	p (mm.)
Normal	6.4	5.0	Normal	2.4	2.8
Iso.	8.5	8.6	Iso.	2.9	2.3
Secondary	12.5	12	Methyl propyl	4.9	4.
	20		Tertiary	12.2	12.
	22.5				
Tertiary	∞	30			

Similarly, liquid *n*-propyl chloride is five times as soluble in water as liquid *n*-propyl iodide, but on correcting for the discrepancy of their vapor pressures, the iodide is really more soluble, in harmony with the greater force field of the iodine atom over the chlorine atom.

Next, we should note that although propyl iodide and propyl alcohol have almost the same dipole moments, 1.66 and $1.60 \cdot 10^{18}$ e. s. u., the former is but slightly soluble in water while the latter is completely miscible. This is a striking instance of the inadequacy of dipole moments alone to explain intermolecular forces, as discussed in Chapters IV and IX.

[16] S. Palit, *J. Phys. Coll. Chem.* **51**, 837 (1947).

Table 10. Solubility in Water. 20°C.

	Dipole moment Debye units.	Moles / 1000 g H_2O	Boil. pt.
Benzene	0	0.0073	80
Nitrobenzene	4.2	0.0155	211
Aniline	1.5	0.435	184
Phenol	1.7	0.95	182

Similar examples are furnished by the solubility in water of benzene and its substitution products, shown in Table 10. We have no figures for the vapor pressures of the three benzene derivatives at 20 °C, but these cannot be so different, in view of their boiling points, as to alter the relative solubilities significantly; if we applied the correction in the case of benzene, its relative solubility would be even smaller. The table shows clearly that it is the hydrogen bonding character rather than the dipole moment which determines the ability of the substance to dissolve in water; nitrobenzene, with by far the highest dipole moment, is far less soluble than aniline or phenol. The fact that the hydroxyl group forms stronger bonds than the amino group is well known.

Sulfur dioxide solutions introduce the disturbing factors of both polarity and acidic character. Its dipole moment is 1.61 Debye units. With *n*-hexane[17] it gives two liquid phases with a consolute temperature of 71 °C.; with cyclohexane, whose internal pressure is a little higher, the consolute temperature is 55.6 °C., with benzene it is completely miscible and with cyclohexene **and** cyclohexadiene it reacts. Sulfur dioxide gives two-liquid systems with tetrahalides[18] with the consolute temperatures shown in Table 11, arranged in order of the δ-values of the latter at 25 °C.

Table 11. Consolute Temperatures of Sulfur Dioxide with Tetrahalides.

	$SiCl_4$	$GeCl_4$	CCl_4	$SnCl_4$	$TiCl_4$	$SnBr_4$	$TiBr_4$
T_c	268	268	244	228	285	322	377
δ(25°C)	7.6	8.1	8.6	8.7	9.0	9.6	...

The consolute temperatures increase in both directions from a minimum at $SnCl_4$, which might be interpreted as indicating a practical solubility parameter for SO_2 in the neighborhood of that for $SnCl_4$, about 8.7, but this would not accord with the two liquid phases for SO_2 with cyclohexane. Such discrepancies illustrate the uncertainties involved in prediction based only upon internal pressures when substances capable of specific interactions are involved. Although the solubility relations of the fourth group tetrahalides with each other accord reasonably well with their internal pressures[19],

[17] W. F. Seyer and E. G. King, *J. Am. Chem. Soc.*, **55**, 3140 (1933).
[18] P. A. Bond and collaborators, *Ibid.*, **48**, 348 (1926); **51**, 2910 (1929); **56**, 2028 (1934).
[19] J. H. Hildebrand, *J. Chem. Phys.*, **15**, 727 (1947).

the presence of SO_2 may serve to enhance the effects of different degrees of ionic or acidic character.

Solubility of water in hydrocarbons. Black, Joris, and Taylor[20] have measured the solubility of water in the various hydrocarbons shown in Table 12, using tritium oxide as a tracer. Their experimental errors are estimated to be of the order of a few percent. The temperature range was between 5°C to 25°C; the values for 20°C are given in the table. They called attention to the following comparisons: the rapid increase in solubility in going from the lower to the higher normal paraffins; the small increase from a normal to a branched isomer; the very large increase from a paraffin to the corresponding olefine. In this connection they say, "It will be noted, that the solubilities of water are not additive in the sense of there being a solubility in the hydrocarbon portion of the molecule plus one to be attributed to the attraction of the double bond for the water. Instead, the double bond acts more nearly as though it multiplied the solubility of water in the hydrocarbon by some factor".

Table 12. Solubility of water in hydrocarbons, mole fraction, x_2 at 20°C.

	$10^4 x_2$	V_1	$\delta_2 - \delta_1$	δ_1	δ_2
n-C_4H_{10}	2.1	101.4	17.4	6.7	24.1
n-C_5H_{12}	3.6	116.1	17.0	7.05	24.1
n-C_6H_{14}	5.3	131.6	16.7	7.3	24.0
n-C_7H_{16}	7.3	147.5	16.5	7.45	24.0
n-C_8H_{18}	9.0	163.5	16.4	7.55	24.0
i-C_4H_{10}	2.4	101.	17.0	6.25	23.3
i-C_5H_{12}	3.6	117.	17.0	6.75	23.8
cycl. C_6H_{12}	4.65	109	16.6	8.2	24.8
C_6H_6	19.0	89	15.1	9.15	24.2
$C_6H_5CH_3$	22.0	107	15.1	8.9	24.0
1-C_4H_8	12.4	95	15.6	6.7	22.3
2-C_4H_8	14.0	91	15.8	7.0	22.8
1-C_7H_{14}	57.0	141	14.3	7.7	22.0
1,3-C_4H_6	19.0	86	15.1	7.6	22.7
1,5-C_6H_{10}	46.0	119	14.4	8.2	22.6

They tested the applicability to their results of the basic solubility equation (VII-46)

[20] C. Black, G. G. Joris, and H. S. Taylor, *J. Chem. Phys.*, **16**, 537 (1948).

$$RT \ln a_2 = RT \ln x_2 + V_2 \varphi_1^2 (\delta_2 - \delta_1)^2 \tag{4}$$

making the simplifying approximations obvious from the very small magnitude of the mole fraction of water, x_2, that $x_1 \simeq 1$ and $\varphi_1 \simeq 1$, and $a_2 = 1$, approximately. They calculated the ratios of the observed values of x_2 to those calculated from the equation, and found that they fell into four groups for paraffins, olefines, diolefines, and aromatics. Only for benzene is the ratio unity.

They next applied the equation for the entropy of mixing molecules of different size in the approximate form derived by Hildebrand[21] (VI-18). The desirability of some such correction is indicated by the small molal volume of water, 18 cc., compared with all the solvents involved. In the case of octane, for example, the ratio is 1 : 9. They found that this brings all but the olefines into agreement with the latter on a line parallel to the one for the former.

We here present the case in a slightly different but equivalent form. We begin by recalling that the cohesive potential energy of water is due largely to its hydrogen bonds, and only to a minor extent to London forces, which are the only ones operating in the hydrocarbons. The interaction between a water molecule and a hydrocarbon molecule would seem to depend mainly upon the water dipole in the other, to an extent depending upon its polarizability and upon their closeness of approach, it would appear that the water molecule could act only upon the portions of hydrocarbon molecule closest to it, so that the local, not the overall polarizability should be the determining factor. The water is so dilute in saturated solutions that only one of any number of olefine groups in a molecule would thus respond. Also, the smaller number of shielding hydrogen atoms around a double bond should permit a water molecule to approach more closely and polarize the bond more effectively.

It could not be expected that this kind of interaction between two molecules of such different kinds would obey the geometric mean relationship, which is one of those implicit in Equation 4. We might hope, however, that this equation might be made fairly valid by using an empirical value for the solubility parameter of water, δ_2, which might conceivably be very different from the one derived from energy vaporization per cc., $(\Delta E^V/V)^{\frac{1}{2}} = \delta_2$. But the small size of the water molecule compared with those of the solvents under consideration indicates the necessity for a correction for the entropy of mixing molecules of different size, and we turn to Equation VI-18, in spite of the oversimplification involved in setting free volumes proportional to molal volumes. We combine the two equations into the single one give in Chapter VII, Equation 41,

$$\ln a_2 = \ln \varphi_2 + \varphi_1 \left(1 - \frac{V_2}{V_1}\right) + V_2 \varphi_1^2 (\delta_2 - \delta_1)^2 / RT \tag{5}$$

[21] J. H. Hildebrand, *J. Chem. Phys.*, **15, 225 (1947)**.

Making the simplifications referred to above, and substituting $V_2 = 18$ and $\ln \varphi_2 = \ln x_2 + \ln 18 - \ln V_1$, we may calculate the values of $\delta_2 - \delta_1$ given in Table 12, and add to them the respective values of δ_1 for the solvents, get the values for the solubility parameter of water, δ_2, given in the last column. We see that all the substances with double bonds yield values around 22.5, and all the others values around 24. The smaller values for the olefines correspond to greater solubilities, in line with the interaction inferred above. The value $\sim$ 24 for all the paraffins and the two aromatics is surprisingly enough practically identical with $(\Delta E^V/V)^{\frac{1}{2}} = 23.8$. We must regard this as sheer good luck, due to a cancelling of disturbing factors rather than as proof of the strict applicability of the equations to systems of this kind. But having established this much, we may feel some confidence in our ability to calculate the solubility of water in another hydrocarbon using one value or the other for the solubility parameter of water, depending upon the presence or absence of a double bond in the solvent molecule. The uncertainty of the result would be expected to correspond to the uncertainty in δ_1 for the solvent, an uncertainty which is often very real due to lack of knowledge of the heat of vaporization in its dependence upon temperature.

The change in the solubility of water with temperature is accounted for primarily by the T in Equation 5, and secondarily by the change in δ-values and, doubtless also, free volumes. The first of these three effects may be inferred from the temperature coefficient of the vapor pressure of water. When the measured solubilities are plotted as $\log x_2$ vs. $1/T$, they give practically straight lines of nearly uniform slope, only a little less than the slope of the line $\log p_2^\circ$ vs. $1/T$ for water. In other words, the solubility of water increases roughly in proportion to its vapor pressure.

Ammonia as a solvent. Liquid ammonia combines a variety of properties to a degree that makes it a remarkably versatile solvent, taxing, therefore, all the resources of our present theories of solubility. It has a rather high dielectric constant and dipole moment; it can form hydrogen bonds or bridges; it is one of the most basic of solvents; its dispersion forces are considerably larger than those of water, its nearest competitor; and its molecular volume, while much larger than that of water, is smaller than that of most other common ionizing solvents. It is even a solvent for certain metals. An analysis of its solubility relations can serve, consequently, as an almost uniquely instructive example of what can be done by means of existing theory.

We are limited in this by the paucity of quantitative data. Most of the observations to be found in the literature are reported by qualitative and rather subjective adjectives, such as "moderately", "fairly", "appreciably", and some are contradictory, several substances being insoluble according to one observer and soluble according to another. Under these circumstances, our analysis of the general problem must be largely qualitative. This should not be so discouraging as it may sound because, as a matter of fact, we need qualitative information far more often than quantitative. The senior author[22] has elsewhere discussed the solvent power of ammonia not only for nonelectrolytes but for electrolytes and metals as well, but only the first group fall within the scope of this book.

The dipole moment of ammonia is 1.49 Debye units, which is to be compared with that of water, 1.85 units, acetone, 2.8 units, etc. Its hydrogen bonding capacity, discussed in Chapter X, is weaker than that of H_2O or HF. Its molal volume is 26.55 cc. at 0 °C, much larger than that of H_2O, 18.0 cc. at 4 °C. The heat of vaporization gives $(\Delta E^V/V)^{\frac{1}{2}} = 13$ for NH_3, which is to be compared with 23.8 for H_2O, 7.5 for ether, etc. Its position among solvents arranged according to increasing basic character is about as follows: SO_2, H_2O, $(C_2H_5)_2O$, $C_6H_5NH_2$, NH_3, CH_3NH_2. We may expect some degree of basic reaction even toward acids which are weaker than NH_4^+, such as C_6H_5OH. Such interaction may often be indistinguishable from hydrogen bond formation, but the alternative ways of thinking of it are likely both to be serviceable.

Let us examine a few typical substances in order to see how well their solubilities conform to these properties.

The aliphatic hydrocarbons, in view of their nonpolarity and low internal pressure, are rather insoluble in ammonia but more soluble than in water, as would be expected.

The aromatic hydrocarbons, with their higher internal pressures, have a distinct but limited solubility, well illustrated by toluene. The vapor pressures of this system were measured by Kraus and Zeitfuchs.[23] The two liquid phases have a consolute temperature of 14.7 °C. The substitution of any strongly hydrogen-bonding group, — OH, — NH_2, etc., enormously enhances solubility; phenol and aniline are miscible with ammonia in all proportions. The contrast with water is what would be expected.

These same groups suffice to draw even aliphatic radicals to which they are attached into ammonia, as shown by all the lower alcohols and amines, even glucose and sucrose. Acetone is sufficiently hydrogen-bonding to form solid $(CH_3)_2CO \cdot NH_3$ and iodoform gives $CHI_3 \cdot NH_3$.

The solubility of NH_3 gas in several solvents, discussed in Chapter XV, may be here recalled as additional evidence of its behavior, with reference to its molecular properties.

[22] J. H. Hildebrand, *J. Chem. Education*, **25**. 74 (1948).

[23] C. A. Kraus and E. H. Zeitfuchs, *J. Am. Chem. Soc.* **44**, 1279 (1922).

CHAPTER XVII

Solubility of Solids in Liquids

It was pointed out in Chapter II how the solubility of a solid whose solution obeys Raoult's law can be calculated from its heat of fusion and the heat capacities of the solid and the supercooled liquid, the latter ordinarily extrapolated from its values above the melting point, using Equations I-36 or 40, with x_2^i substituted for a_2^s. If the solution is not ideal, but regular, the correction for the partial molal heat of mixing the supercooled liquid solute with the solution can be applied, as developed in Chapter VII and expressed in Equation VII-35, yielding Equation VIII-62, which, for the solubility of a solid, becomes

$$\log \frac{x_2{}^i}{x_2} = \frac{V_2 \varphi_1^2 (\delta_1 - \delta_2)^2}{4.575\, T} \tag{1}$$

An alternative derivation, closely parallel to that given in Chapter II, may be instructive. At equilibrium the free energy of the solid F_2^s must equal its partial molal free energy in the solution $\bar{F}_2$. This is equivalent to setting equal to zero the sum of the free energies of the hypothetically separate processes of melting the solid to the super-cooled liquid and mixing the liquid with the solvent to the equilibrium concentration:

$$\Delta F^F + \Delta \bar{F}^M = 0 \tag{2}$$

We have seen in Chapter I that the heat of fusion at any temperature may be expressed in terms of the heat of fusion at the melting point ΔH_m^F and the difference ΔC_p between the heat capacities of solid and liquid:

$$\Delta H^F = \Delta H_m^F + \int_{T_m}^{T} \Delta C_p \, dT \cong \Delta H_m^F - \Delta C_p (T_m - T) \tag{3}$$

Similarly the entropy of fusion may be written as:

$$\Delta S^F = \Delta S_m^F + \int_{T_m}^{T} \frac{\Delta C_p}{T} \, dT \cong \frac{\Delta H_m^F}{T_m} - \Delta C_p \ln \frac{T_m}{T} \tag{4}$$

Combining, we obtain ΔF^F:

$$\Delta F^F = \Delta H_m^F \left(1 - \frac{T}{T_m}\right) - \Delta C_p (T_m - T) + T\Delta C_p \ln \frac{T_m}{T} \tag{5}$$

Combining this with Equation VIII-62 for the partial molal free energy of the solute, we obtain:

$$\Delta H_m^F \left(1 - \frac{T}{T_m}\right) - \Delta C_p (T_m - T) + T\Delta C_p \ln \frac{T_m}{T} + RT \ln x_2 + V_2 (\delta_1 - \delta_2)^2 \varphi_1^2 = 0 \tag{6}$$

Converting to common logarithms, we obtain for $\log \frac{1}{x_2}$:

$$\log \frac{1}{x_2} = \frac{\Delta H_m^F}{4.575} \frac{(T_m - T)}{T_m T} - \frac{\Delta C_p}{4.575} \frac{(T_m - T)}{T} + \frac{\Delta C_p}{1.987} \log \frac{T_m}{T} + \frac{V_2}{4.575\,T} (\delta_1 - \delta_2)^2 \varphi_1^2 \tag{7}$$

Where $\delta_1 = \delta_2$, the heat of mixing is zero and Equation 7 reduces to Equation II-24 for the ideal solubility of a solid. The terms in ΔC_p are frequently not known and can be omitted with only moderate error.

It should be noted, also, that for solids well below their melting points $x_2 \ll 1$ and φ_1 and x_1 run so nearly parallel that the simple Equation VII-11,

$$RT \ln \frac{x_2^i}{x_2} = Bx_1^2 \tag{8}$$

where B is a constant, often holds very well over a considerable range of temperature, as illustrated in Chapter VII, Table 1.

In cases where the molal volumes of solvent and solute are very different it may be worthwhile to introduce the entropy correction developed in Chapter VI. (See Chapter VII, Equation 47). This is quite essential in dealing with solutions of high polymers. (see Chapter XX).

That equation is here repeated for convenience:

$$\log x_2^i = \log \varphi_2 + V_2 \frac{\varphi_1^2 (\delta_2 - \delta_1)^2}{4.575T} + 0.434\, \varphi_1 \left(1 - \frac{V_2}{V_1}\right) \tag{9}$$

Some of the solutes dealt with in the following pages, such as iodine, sulfur and phosphorus, have much higher internal pressures than the solvents and the question naturally arises whether thermal agitation is sufficient to overcome such great discrepancies in internal pressure which might vitiate the assumption of maximum randomness of distribution required for behavior as regular solutions. That this is not the case is well attested by the data and is undoubtedly due to the relatively small concentrations of the solutes in such solutions. Solute molecules in, say, 1 mole per cent solutions are too far apart to form clusters, even if they do so in the immediate neighborhood of the liquid consolute point.

Iodine. The solutions of iodine are very interesting from a theoretical standpoint: first, because they offer many examples of large deviation from Raoult's law; second, because the cases which involve solvation[1] are readily distinguished from the regular, violet solutions by their red, yellow or brown colors; third, because the ease with which iodine can be determined analytically has contributed both to the abundance and accuracy of the data; and fourth, because iodine at ordinary temperature undoubtedly possesses sufficient rotational energy in its violet solutions to give it spherical symmetry and hence justify the application of the quantitative theory developed in Chapter VII.

A survey of practically all of the data in existence which are significant for our study is given in Fig. 1, where the logarithm of the mole fraction of iodine is plotted against the reciprocal of the absolute temperature. The data are taken from the following sources: solubility in hexane from Hildebrand, Ellefson and Beebe[2]; in benzene and carbon disulfide from Arctowski[3]; in chloroform and glycerine from Hantzsch and Vagt[4]; in carbon tetrachloride and bromoform from Jakowkin[5]; in molten sulfur from Smith and Carson[6]; in benzene, carbon tetrachloride and heptane by Hildebrand and Jenks[7]; in titanium and silicon tetrachlorides, ethylene bromide and 2,2,4 trimethylpentane by Negishi, Donnally and Hildebrand[8], in water from the data in International Critical Tables and in fluoroheptane by Benesi and Hildebrand[9].

The curve for liquid iodine in carbon tetrachloride was obtained by Hildebrand[10].

---

[1] Cf. (a) J. H. Hildebrand and B. L. Glascock. *J. Am. Chem. Soc.*, **31**, 26 (1909); (b) P. Waentig, *Z. physik. Chem.*, **68**, 513 (1909); (c) J. H. Hildebrand *Ibid.*, **74**, 679 (1910), (d) W. Brill and W. Ellerbrock, *Z. anorg. allgem. Chem.* **216**, 353 (1934); (e) J. Groh, *Ibid.*, **162**, 287 (1927); (f) M. Chatelet, *Ann. chim.* (**11**), **2**, 5 (1934).

[2] J. H. Hildebrand, E. T. Ellefson and C. W. Beebe, *J. Am. Chem. Soc.*, **39**, 2301 (1917).

[3] H. Arctowski, *Z. anorg. Chem.*, **6**, 392 (1894).

[4] A. Hantsch and A. Vagt, *Z. physik. Chem.* **38**, 728 (1901).

[5] A. A. Jakowkin *Ibid.*, **18**, 590 (1895).

[6] A. Smith and C. M. Carson, *Ibid.*, **61**, 200 (1907).

[7] J. H. Hildebrand and C. W. Jenks, *J. Am. Chem. Soc.*, **42**, 2180 (1920).

[8] G. R. Negishi, L. H. Donnally and J. H. Hildebrand, *Ibid.*, **55**, 4793 (1933).

[9] H. Benesi and J. H. Hildebrand, *Ibid.* **70**, 3978 (1948).

[10] J. H. Hildebrand, *J. Am. Chem. Soc.*, **59**, 2083 (1937).

The ideal solubility of iodine we calculate by the aid of the figures for its heat of fusion and heat capacities as determined by Frederick and Hildebrand[11], $\Delta H^F = 3740$ cal.; C_p (liquid) $= 19.5$ cal, C_p (solid) $= 13.07 + 3.21 \cdot 10^{-4} (t - 25°)^2$. These values in Equation I-40 give $x_2^i = 0.258$ at 25 °C.

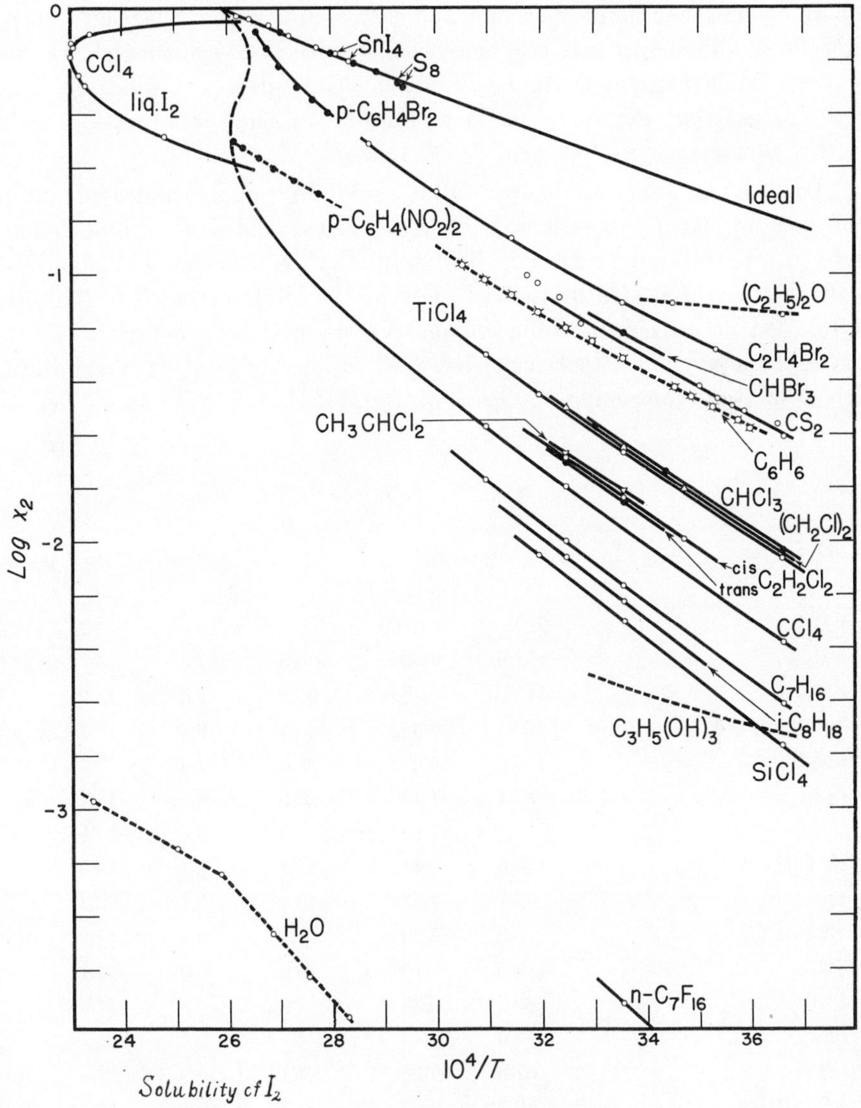

Fig. 1. Solubility of I_2

The violet solutions are indicated in Fig. 1 by solid, the red and brown ones by broken lines. The former quite evidently form a family of curves whose position is determined by simpler factors than those operating with

[11] K. J. Frederick and J. H. Hildebrand, *J. Am. Chem. Soc.*, **60**, 1436 (1938).

the brown solutions. It was this particular family of curves which suggested the designation "regular solutions", whose characteristics were discussed in Chapter VII. Departures from regularity are shown by the non-violet solutions in ether, arsenic trichloride, benzene, dinitrobenzene, glycerine, alcohol, and water, all of which with the exception of benzene, have dipole moments; but dipole moment alone does not suffice to explain the solvation, because chloroform, bromoform and ethylene bromide with strong moments give violet solutions while benzene, with no dipole moment, gives red solutions. These facts suggest that the solvation is essentially an acid-base reaction, in the electron donor-acceptor sense of G. N. Lewis[12].

Benzene is basic, as shown by its solubility in concentrated sulfuric acid and by its combinations with $AlCl_3$, BCl_3 and BF_3, while iodine is acidic in its reaction with I^-. The solubility in benzene is enhanced by small solvation indicated by the red color of the solution, but it is diminished by solution of benzene in solid iodine. We do not have a figure for this, but Beckmann[13] and Stock reported 1.28 g I_2 in 100 g. C_6H_6 in equilibrium with a solution containing 3.39 g I_2 in 100 g. C_6H_6.

Table 1. Iodine Solutions, 25°C.

Solvent	Mol. vol. cc.	Mole % I_2	x_2^i/x_2	δ_1	δ_2	δ_2
n-C_7F_{16}	227	0.0185	1400	5.7	14.2	14.6
n-C_6H_{14}	131.6	0.456	56.6	7.3	13.7	13.8
$SiCl_4$	115.3	0.499	51.8	7.6	13.9	
"*iso*"$-C_8H_{18}$	166.1	0.592	43.6	6.9	13.1	13.4
n-C_7H_{16}	147.5	0.679	38.0	7.4	13.4	13.6
CCl_4	97.1	1.147	22.5	8.6	14.2	
trans-$C_2H_2Cl_2$	77.4	1.417	18.2	9.0	14.5	
cis-$C_2H_2Cl_2$	75.8	1.441	17.1	9.1	14.5	
1,1-$C_2H_4Cl_2$	84.7	1.531	16.9	9.1	14.4	
1,2-$C_2H_4Cl_2$	79.5	2.20	11.7	9.8	14.9	
$TiCl_4$	110.5	2.15	12.0	9.0	14.1	
$CHCl_3$	80.7	2.28	11.3	9.3	14.3	
CS_2	60.6	5.46	4.73	9.9	14.1	
$CHBr_3$	87.8	6.16	4.19	10.5	14.1	
1,2-$C_2H_4Br_2$	86.6	7.82	3.30	10.4	14.1	
					Av. 14.1	
I_2	59.0	25.8	1.00		13.6 = $(\Delta E^V/V)^{\frac{1}{2}}$	

[12] G. N. Lewis, "Valence and the Structure of Atoms and Molecules" *Chem. Catalog Co.*, New York, 1923; *J. Franklin Inst.* **226**, 293 1938). See also, W. F. Luder and S. Zuffanti, "Electronic Theory of Acids and Bases", John Wiley and Sons, New York, 1946.

[13] E. Beckmann and A. Stock, *Z. physik. Chem.*, **17**, 107 (1895).

The effect of solvation is, of course, to increase solubility, as illustrated by ether, which, if there were no solvation, should be only about as good a solvent as hexane. It should be noted that the diminution of solvation with rising temperature makes the temperature coefficients of brown solutions less than those of neighboring violet solutions.

A convenient quantitative check on Equation 1 at a single temperature can be made by inserting the experimental solubilities and molal volumes and solubility parameters, δ_1 for the solvents, and observing the degree of uniformity of the δ_2 values for iodine obtained with the different solvents. The results of such calculations are shown in Table 1, and the agreement with minor exceptions, is all that could be expected in view of the assumptions made in deriving Equation 1. The somewhat smaller values for the larger paraffins raise the question whether the disparities in molal volumes are responsible; their ratio in the case of iodine and "*iso*"-octane is nearly 1 to 3. We have therefore included in Table 1 values of δ_2' calculated by aid of Equation 9 for several solutions in solvents with particularly large molal volumes. It can be seen that the agreement is improved.

Stannic Iodide molecules are tetrahedral, the tin-iodine bonds are largely covalent, and its internal pressure is high; consequently it lends itself well to tests of the theories of regular solutions. Dorfman and Hildebrand[14] determined the solubility of solid SnI_4 over a range of temperature in carbon disulfide, ethylene bromide, *m*-xylene, toluene, benzene, chloroform, carbon tetrachloride, ether and heptane. They also made two determinations of the solubility of stannic iodide in molten sulfur by the aid of cooling curves. The mixture was contained in a test-tube surrounded by a larger tube immersed in a bath of glycerol. By slow cooling, stirring and seeding at the proper time, the initial break in the curve was obtained with an accuracy of 1°. The results are included in Table 1.

McDermott[15] has given values for the solubility of stannic iodide in carbon tetrachloride, chloroform and benzene; Retgers[16] has given a single value for the solvent methylene iodide. There exist data by Arctowski[17] for carbon disulfide between −58° and −114.5° but they appear to be rather inaccurate and we shall not further consider them.

Reinders and de Lange[18] and also van Kloosters[19] have determined melting points for the system stannic iodide-iodine. The two sets of data agree well. Hildebrand and Negishi[20] determined the solubility of SnI_4, both liquid and solid, in $SiCl_4$, and Dice and Hildebrand[21], its liquid-liquid solubility with

---

[14] M. E. Dorfman and J. H. Hildebrand, *J. Am. Chem. Soc.*, **49**, 729 (1927).
[15] F. A. Mc Dermott, *J. Am. Chem. Soc.*, **33**, 1963 (1911).
[16] J. W. Retgers, *Z. anorg. Chem.*, **3**, 343 (1893).
[17] H. Arctowski, *Ibid.*, **11**, 272 (1896).
[18] W. Reinders and S. de Lange, *Ibid.*, **79**, 230 (1912).
[19] H. S. van Klooster, *Ibid.*, **79**, 223 (1912).
[20] J. H. Hildebrand and G. R. Negishi, *J. Am. Chem. Soc.*, **59**, 339, (1937).
[21] M. E. Dice and J. H. Hildebrand, *Ibid.*, **50**, 3023 (1928).

normal hexane, heptane and octane, and "iso"-octane, 2,2,4-trimethyl pentane. All of these are plotted in the usual fashion in Fig. 2. The relation is shown between the curves for solid and liquid SnI_4 in $SiCl_4$, a relation like that previously shown for I_2 and CCl_4.

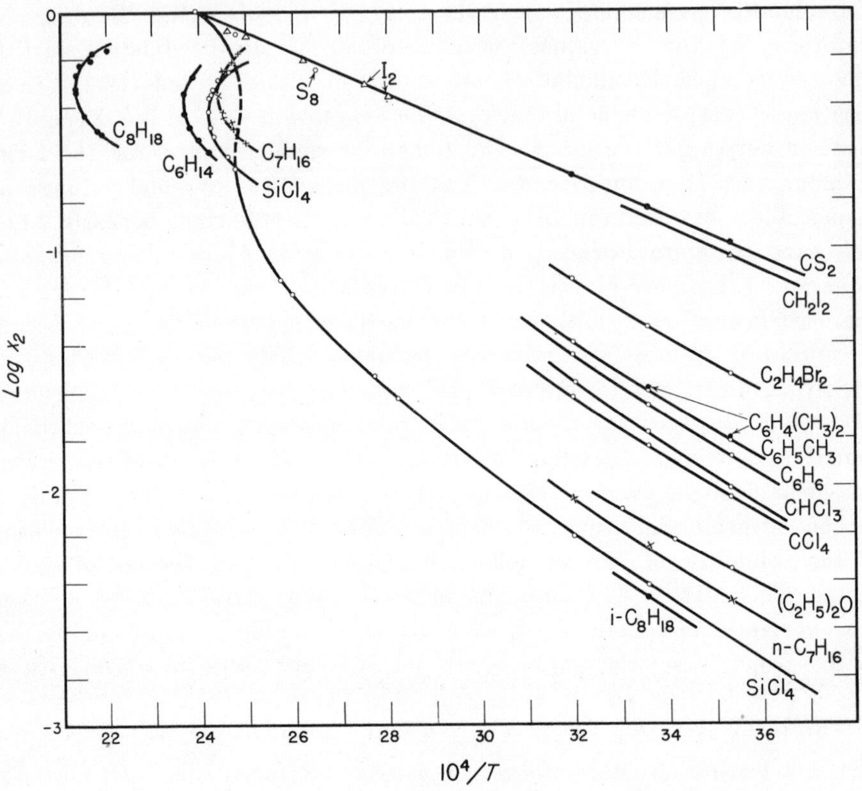

Fig. 2. Solubility of SnI_4

The quantitative relation between the solubilities in the different solvents at 25 °C is shown in Table 2 in the way used for I_2, in Table 1. In the second edition of this book, the heat of fusion of SnI_4 could only be estimated from a comparison of entropies of fusion of tetrahalides; since then, it has been measured by Negishi[22] and found to be 4600 cal. at the melting point, 144.5 °C, with heat capacities for solid, $19.4 + 0.036T$, and for liquid, 40.1 cal. per mole. The activity of the supercooled liquid at 25°, which is x_2^i, is calculated from these figures to be 0.130, subject, of course, to the uncertainty involved in considering C_p for the liquid to remain constant from 144.5 ° to 25° with $\Delta C_p = 5.7$ cal. per mole. But the measured solubility

[22] G. R. Negishi. *J. Am. Chem. Soc.*, **58**, 2293 (1936).

of SnI_4 in CS_2 is 0.146, slightly greater than the above figure. There is no reason to suppose that the ideal solubility actually exceeds the latter figure, so we shall set $x_2^i = 0.146$. The values of $\delta_2 - \delta_1$ in Table 2 have been calculated upon this assumption. Adding the values of δ_1 derived from ΔE^V gives calculated values for δ_2 for SnI_4, the departures of which from their mean, 11.6, are to be ascribed to uncertainties in the data and the necessary extrapolations, to the simplifications involved in deriving the formula to the neglect of volume changes, or to specific solvation interactions such as were more easily recognized in the case of iodine by alterations in color. The fact that the solubilities in benzene, toluene and xylene are in the reverse order of their internal pressures is interesting, in view of the fact that the solubilities of gases accord with that order. The order is the same as in the case of sulfur, however, set forth below, and is doubtless to be explained by the decreasing partial molal volume of sulfur in going from benzene to xylene. The solubilities in chloroform and benzene are also in reverse order, as is the case also with iodine and sulfur in these solvents. This is not strange, in view of the dipole moment of chloroform, 1.1 Debye units. We shall see below that, instead of using the solubility parameter of chloroform derived from energy of vaporization per cc., it is possible to assign a slightly different parameter derived from and consistent with all solubility data for all three solutes.

The relation of the solubility curves for solid and liquid SnI_4 in the same solvent was discussed in Chapter XVI.

Table 2. Stannic Iodide Solutions at 25°.

$V_2 = 151$ cc.

Solvent	Dipole Moment $\times 10^{18}$ e.s.u.	Mole per cent SnI_4	$(\Delta E^V/V)^{\frac{1}{2}}$ Solvent	$(\Delta E^V/V)^{\frac{1}{2}}$ SnI_4
$SiCl_4$	0	0.382	7.55	11.4
n-C_7H_{16}	0	0.553	7.45	11.1
$(C_2H_5)_2O$	1.1	0.690	7.45	(11.0)
CCl_4	0	1.459	8.6	11.6
$CHCl_3$	1.1	1.692	9.3	(12.2)
C_6H_6	0	2.181	9.15	11.9
$C_6H_5CH_3$	0.4	2.507	8.9	11.7
m-$C_6H_4(CH_3)_2$	0.3	2.538	8.8	11.6
CH_2Br-CH_2Br	1.0	4.714	10.4	(12.6)
CS_2	0	14.64	9.9	
			Mean	11.6
			Calculated from vapor pressure	11.7

To derive a figure for the solubility parameter at 25 °C from the vapor pressure measurements of Negishi between 160° and 250° involves an assumption regarding ΔC_p. We may use the expression given by Kelley[23], $\Delta H = 25{,}000 - 18\,T$, which gives $\Delta H = 19{,}630$ and $\delta_2 = 11.7$ at 25 °C. This agrees remarkably well with the value derived from solubilities.

Sulfur. The solubilities of sulfur have been the subject of frequent investigation. We have data by Etard[24] for hexane, benzene, ethylene bromide and carbon bisulfide; by Gerardin[25] for stannic chloride in the neighborhood of the melting point of sulfur; by Aten[26] for sulfur monochloride; by Smith and Carson[27] for iodine; by Cossa[28] for chloroform, ethyl ether, benzene, carbon disulfide and toluene; by Retgers[29] for methylene iodide; by Brønsted[30] for benzene, iodobenzene and chloroform; by Hoffmann[31] for carbon tetrachloride, dichloroethylene, ethylene chloride, pentachloro-ethane, perchloro-ethylene, trichloro-ethylene and tetrachloro-ethane. There are other data for more or less polar solvents, including phenol[32], naphthol[32], alcohols[33], and ammonia[34].

Some of these referred to are obviously not very accurate, and many of the determinations were made only at one temperature. Accordingly it has been desirable to check certain portions and to supplement others, and Hildebrand and Jenks[35] have measured solubilities in carbon tetrachloride, benzene, toluene, *m*-xylene, heptane and ethylene chloride. It seems unnecessary to take up the space that would be required for the tabulation of this mass of data, as our purpose is better served by graphic representation in Fig. 3. The line corresponding to the ideal solubility is calculated from the melting point and the heat of fusion of rhombic sulfur, using data given in a paper by Lewis and Randall[36], and corresponds to an ideal solubility for S_8 of mole fraction 0.282 at 25°. The heat of solution of sulfur in such a solvent is the same as its heat of fusion, or, in other words, such a solvent would mix with molten sulfur with no heat effect.

The vapor pressure curve for sulfur varies in slope in the interval when S_λ is changing into S_μ, so that the low-temperature portion must be used

---

[23] K. K. Kelley, *Bull.U.S.Bur.Mines.*, **383**, (1934).
[24] A. Etard, *Ann. chim. phys.*, [7] **2**, 571 (1894).
[25] A. Gerardin, *Ibid.*, [4], **5**, 129 (1865).
[26] A. H. W. Aten, *Z. physik Chem.*, **54**, 86, 124 (1905).
[27] A. Smith and C. M. Carson, *Ibid.*. **61**, 200 (1909).
[28] A. Cossa, *Ber.*, **1**, 38 (1868).
[29] J. W. Retgers, *Z. anorg. Chem.*, **3**, 347 (1893).
[30] J. N. Brønsted, *Z. physik. Chem.* **55**, 371 (1906).
[31] K. A. Hofmann, H. Kirmreuther, and A. Thal, *Ber.*, **43**, 188 (1910).
[32] A. Smith, W. B. Holmes and E. S. Hall, *J. Am. Chem. Soc.*, **27**, 805 (1905).
[33] C. A. L. De Bruyn, *Z. Physik. Chem.*, **10**, 781 (1892).
[34] O. Ruff and L. Hecht, *Z. anorg. Chem.*, **70**, 61 (1911).
[35] J. H. Hildebrand and C. A. Jenks, *J. Am. Chem. Soc.*, **43**, 2172 (1921).
[36] G. N. Lewis and M. Randall, *J. Am. Chem. Soc.*, **36**, 2468 (1914).

to obtain the heat of vaporization. We have calculated $\Delta H^V = 19{,}100$ cals. per mole from the measurements of Ruff and Graf[37], which gives $\Delta E^V = 18{,}500$ at 25°. The molal volume of supercooled liquid sulfur may be calculated by the aid of measurements by Toepler[38] and others as 135 cc. at 25°. The internal pressure is, accordingly, $(\Delta E^V/V)^{\frac{1}{2}} = 11.7$. Table 3 gives the values of $(\Delta E_2^V/V_2)^{\frac{1}{2}}$ calculated from the solubilities insofar as permitted by knowledge of ΔE for the solvents.

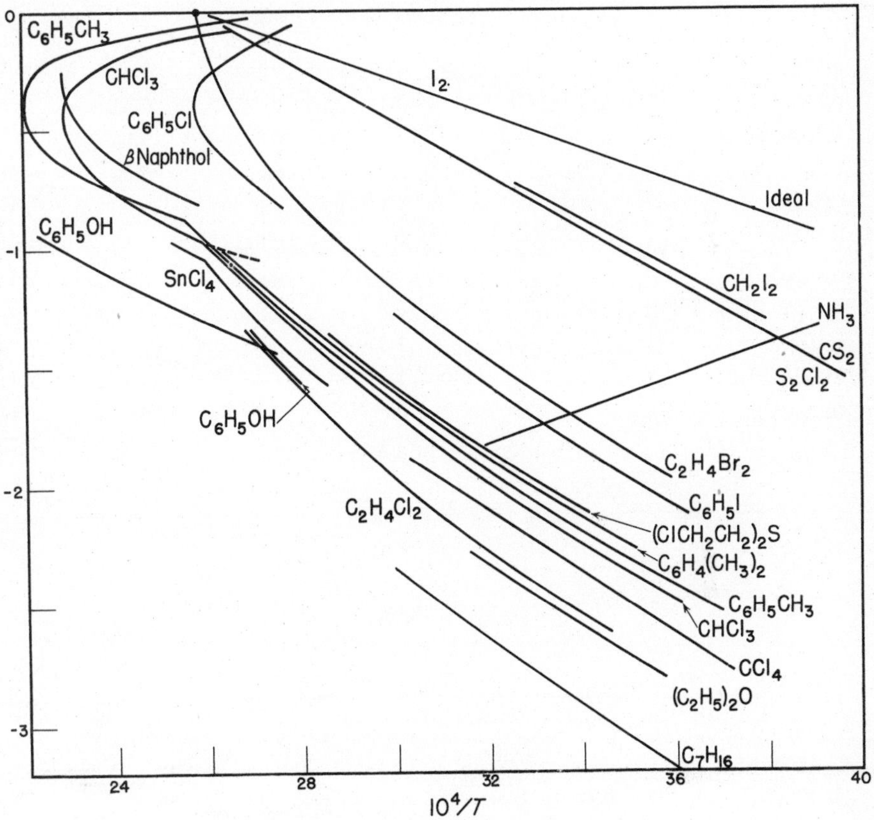

Fig. 3. Solubility of S_8

Phosphorus. We have data for solutions of active phosphorus, whose molecules are P_4, according to both solubility and x-ray findings[39], in carbon disulfide by Cohen and Inouye[40], in benzene and ether by Christomanos[41],

[37] O. Ruff and H. Graf, *Ber.*, **40**, 4199 (1907).
[38] M. Toepler, *Wied. Ann.*, **47**, 169 (1892).
[39] C. D. Thomas and N. S. Gingrich, *J. Chem. Phys.*, **6**, 659 (1938).
[40] E. Cohen and K. Inouye, *Z. physik. Chem.*, **72**, 411 (1910).
[41] A C. Christomanos, *Z. anorg. allgem. Chem.* **45**, 132 (1905).

and in carbon tetrachloride, normal heptane and acetone (approximately onl by Groot and Hildebrand[42]. These data are plotted in Fig. 4 and smooth out for certain temperatures in Table 4.

Table 3. Sulfur Solutions at 25°.

$V_2 = 135$ cc.

Solvent	Dipole moment $\times 10^{18}$ e.s.u.	Mole per cent sulfur	δ_1 Solvent	δ_2 Sulfur
n-C_7H_{16}	0	0.141	7.45	12.3
$(C_2H_5)_2O$	1.1	0.295	7.45	12.0
CH_2Cl-CH_2Cl	1.2	0.321	9.95	(14.5)
CCl_4	0	0.500	8.65	12.9
$CHCl_3$	1.1	0.570	9.25	13.4
C_6H_6	0	0.641	9.15	13.3
$C_6H_5CH_3$	0.4	0.735	8.9	12.9
m-$C_6H_4(CH_3)_2$	0.3	0.825	8.8	12.5
C_6H_5I	1.3	1.66	9.4	12.9
CH_2Br-CH_2Br	1.0	1.95	10.4	12.6
CS_2	0	13.8	9.9	(11.5)
Ideal	0	28.2	Mean	12.7
		Calc. from vapor pressure		11.7

Table 4. Solubility of P_4.

	100 x_2					δ_1	δ_2 (P_4)	
	0°	25°	40°	50°	75°	25°	25°	0°
$(C_2H_5)O$	0.32	0.83	1.34	....	....	7.45	13.9	....
n-C_7H_{16}	0.72	1.24	1.73	2.09	3.02	7.43	13.5	....
CCl_4	0.84	1.58	2.19	2.63	3.80	8.6	14.5	15.0
C_6H_6	....	2.27	3.27	4.07	5.62	9.15	14.9	....
CS_2	72.2	89.	....	....	....	9.9	14.6	15.0

The ideal solubility has been calculated from data by Young a Hildebrand[43], who gave $\Delta H^F = 601$ cal./mole, C_p (solid) $= 21.46 + 2.87$ $10^{-2}t$ and C_p (liquid) $= 24.47 - 9.52 \times 10^{-3}t - 3.93 \times 10^{-5}t^2$. The figures give $x_2^i = 0.865$ at 0 °C and 0.941 at 25 °C.

[42] C. Groot and J. H. Hildebrand, *J. Am Chem. Soc.*, **70**, 3815 (1948).
[43] F. E. Young and J. H. Hildebrand *J. Am. Chem. Soc.*, **64**, 839 (1942).

The points by Christomanos for benzene and ether do not fall very closely upon the curves and the slopes for solid phosphorus are steeper than the slopes of our curves for carbon tetrachloride and heptane. Now the curves for solid P_4 should fall below the extrapolated curves for liquid P_4 by about the amount of log x_2^i, where x_2^i is the ideal solubility, indicated at the top of Fig. 4. One suspects that Christomanos did not take pains to get his solutions saturated; indeed his low points for 0 °C show evidence

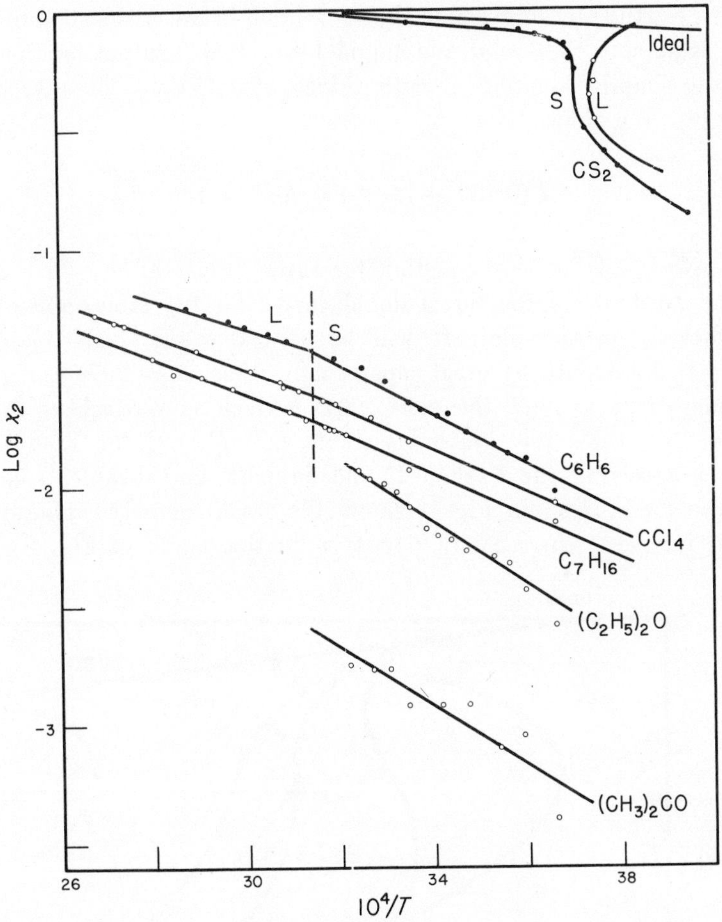

Fig. 4. Solubility of P_4.

that this was the case. His original data are curiously reported, the number of presumably significant figures varying between two and five.

We may note, first, that the solvent powers of the nonpolar solvents for P_4 increase in the order of their internal pressure as measured by their δ-values, added to Table 4. Ether is a poorer solvent by reason of its polarity and acetone very much poorer, for the same reason.

Table 4 contains values for the solubility parameter of phosphorus δ_2 at 0 °C, 25 °C, and at 25 °C with the correction for volume entropy, Equation 9. The agreement between δ_2 values derived from CS_2 and CCl_4 solutions is particulary striking in view of the enormous difference between the solubilities thus accounted for, 72.7 mole per cent and 0.84 mole per cent. It is noteworthy, also, that the unusual S-shaped curve for the CS_2 solutions is itself given by Equation 9 with these particular parameters, along with the liquid-liquid curve nearly tangent to it.

It is worthwhile to examine the connection between the solubility curves for the same solute in solid and liquid form. It will suffice for this purpose to use the simple Equation 8, with values of $a_2 = x_2^i$ close to those of phosphorus. We shall write:

$$T(0.430 - \log x_2) = Kx_1^2 + 136.$$

Fig. 5 gives plots of this equation for three values of K, 207, 233, and 270. The positions of the liquid-liquid curves for the same values of K are also indicated on the plot. It will be seen that the liquid-liquid system could be realized only by great supercooling when $K = 207$. For $K = 233$ the liquid curve touches the solid curve, which is vertical at this point. For $K = 270$, the liquid system is stable through a large range of composition intersecting the S-shaped, and in part unrealizable, solid curve. The curve for benzene in Fig. 4 shows the break where the solid and liquid branches intersect, corresponding in type to this curve in Fig. 5.

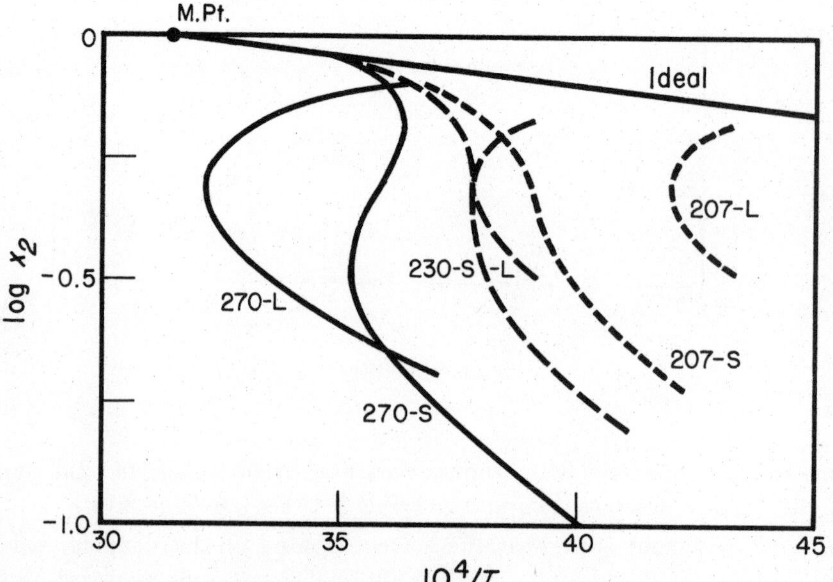

Fig. 5. Relation between solubility curves for solid and liquid forms for different degrees of deviation from Raoult's law.

Naphthalene. Scatchard[44] has compared the measured solubilities of naphthalene at 20° with values calculated by the methods herein described. These figures are reproduced in Table 5 (his values of $\Delta E^V/V$).

Table 5 Solubility of Naphthalene at 20°.

Solvent	$\Delta E^V/V$ calories per cc.	V cc.	Solubility, x_2 Measured	Calculated
Naphthalene (ideal)	101.5	123	0.261	0.261
Chlorobenzene	93.4	101.63	0.256	0.256
Benzene	83.9	88.89	0.241	0.240
Toluene	81.0	106.31	0.224	0.228
Carbon tetrachloride	76.1	96.45	0.205	0.210
Hexane	54.2	130.47	0.090	0.067
Aniline	154.5	91.06	0.130	0.110
Nitrobenzene	143.1	101.95	0.243	0.158
Acetone	97.0	73.34	0.183	0.260
n-Butyl alcohol	123.7	91.45	0.0495	0.232
Methyl alcohol	213.7	40.44	0.0180	0.00075
Acetic acid	172.6	57.23	0.0456	0 0540

If we examine the solubility of naphthalene in the more polar solvents, which have been segregated from the others at the bottom of Table 5, we may observe some rather significant differences. It is evident that dipole moment alone cannot account for the departure from ideal behavior. Of the three similar molecules, chlorobenzene, nitrobenzene and aniline, the one possessing the largest dipole moment, nitrobenzene, is not the one showing the largest diminution in solvent power for the nonpolar solute, naphthalene; on the contrary, this solvent, together with chloroform and chlorobenzene, are nearly ideal solvents for naphthalene, while aniline, with a dipole moment of only 1.51, is the poorest. This may be taken as further evidence for the role of the hydrogen bond as a factor in intermolecular action. Phenol, like aniline, is a comparatively poor solvent. No figure for it has been included in the table, for the eutectic point of this solution lies above 25°, however a plot of the data[45] shows that its solvent power for naphthalene is less than that of aniline. Ethyl alcohol, in which the hydrogen bond is strong, is a still poorer solvent. Ether and chloroform, in spite of their dipole moments in excess of 1 Debye unit, do not lose in solvent power on that account. The relations show that the hydrogen bond is a more important factor than dipole moment in "squeezing out" nonpolar molecules, as was pointed out in Chapter X. Fig. 6 gives certain curves for the solubility of naphthalene

[44] G. Scatchard, *Chem. Rev.*, **8**, 329 (1931).
[45] W. H. Hatcher and F. W. Skirrow, *J. Am. Chem. Soc.*, **39**, 1939 (1917).

in the region near the melting-point, "the freezing point lowering" for naphthalene, which illustrate further the above contrasting behaviors attributable to the hydrogen bond. It is of particular interest to note that the type of curve shown by naphthalene and hexane, which form regular solutions

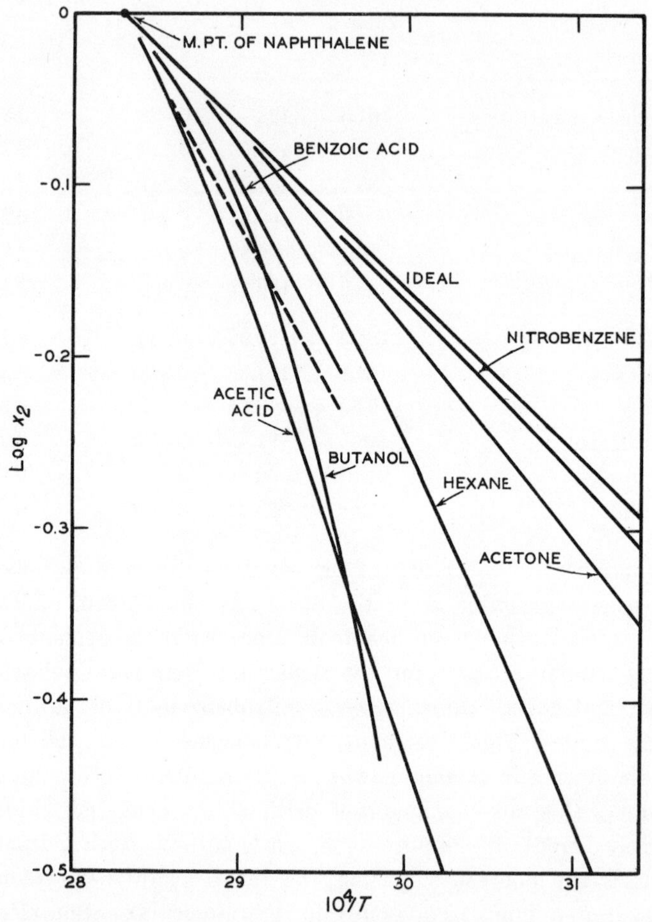

Fig. 6. Freezing point lowering of naphthalene by associated and non-associated substances.

is very different from the curves for acetic and benzoic acids and butyl alcohol, where true association occurs through bonds. The complete formation of double molecules at all concentrations with no other source of deviation from Raoult 's law would give the dotted curve. Dissociation of the dimers of acetic acid evidently occurs only at very low concentrations; dissociation of benzoic acid occurs more easily, and the molecular complexes of the alcohol are evidently more indefinite as to type, in accord with the facts set forth in Chapter X.

Phenanthrene, anthracene, p-dibromobenzene. Solubility data for these substances[46] are given in Table 6. The order indicates that all three solutes have δ_2-values between those of benzene and carbon disulfide as shown below. We discuss these figures in the following paragraphs.

Table 6. Solubility[46], mole percent at 25°

	Phenanthrene	Anthracene	p-Dibromobenzene
Hexane	4.2	0.18	8.6
Ether	15.1	0.59	18.3
Carbon tetrachloride	18.6	0.63	19.3
Benzene	20.7	0.81	21.7
Carbon disulfide	25.5	1.12	22.4
Ethyl alcohol	1.25	0.09	2.0
Ideal	22.1	1.07	24.8

The consistency of the data for solubilities of the preceding solutes in the same solvents can be tested by comparing the order of $\delta_2 - \delta_1$ values for these solutes calculated from the solubility data themselves. This procedure avoids uncertainties connected with certain parts of the process, such as the extrapolation of heat of vaporization. The results are shown in Fig. 7. It can be seen that the solid lines, giving the relative positions of the solvents are approximately parallel, showing that their true solubility parameters have nearly the same relative values with the different solutes. For example, the solvent power of benzene exeeds that of chloroform by an amount corresponding to an excess of 0.2 in its δ-value, contrary to a difference of -0.15 between the values derived from heats of vaporization. Consequently, if $\delta = 9.15$ for benzene we should use $\delta = 8.95$ for chloroform, not 9.3.

Next, the figure makes evident the irregularities due to chemical effects; thus iodine in ether gives $\delta_2 - \delta_1 = 3.4$, whereas, if this solution were regular, we would expect about 5.8 and correspondingly much lower solubility.

Ethylene chloride and bromide evidently exert slightly specific effects, as indicated by moderate departures from parallelism. The point for S_8 in CS_2 is very sensitive to the extrapolation of ΔH^F for S_8, where we have no figures for ΔC_p. The positions of the points for S_8 and SnI_4 in CS_2 are very sensitive to the values assigned to these solvents, hence the slope of that line shown in the figure carries little weight.

Finally, it is evident that values of $\delta_2 - \delta_1$ for S_8 are about 1.3 less and for SnI_4 are about 2.5 less than for I_2. Therefore, if we assume that

[46] J. H. Hildebrand, E. T. Ellefson and C. W. Beebe, *J. Am. Chem. Soc.*, **39**. 2301 (1917)

the heat of vaporization of CCl_4 gives its correct solubility parameter, 8.6 then, since $\delta_2 - \delta_1 = 5.6$ for I_2 in CCl_4, $\delta_2 = 14.2$ for I_2 and about the same for P_4. The value for S_8 would accordingly be 12.9 and for SnI_4 11.7

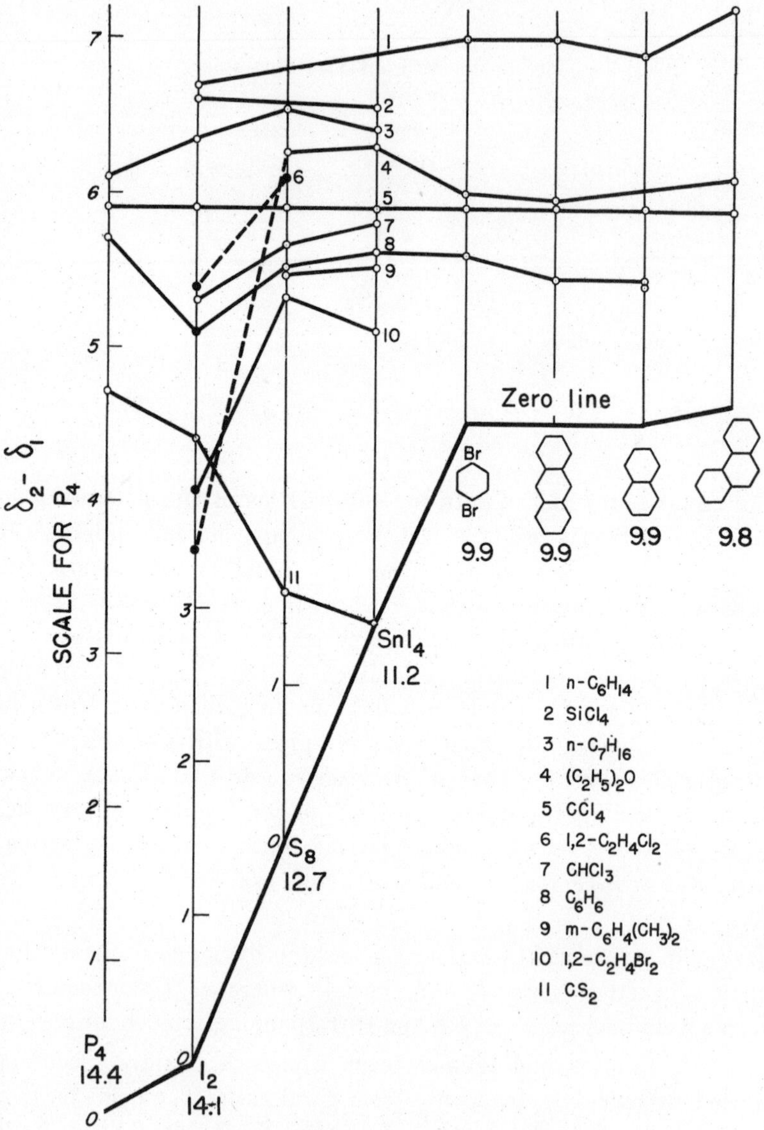

Fig. 7. Test of the consistency $\delta_2 - \delta_1$ values calculated from a variety of solubilities.

The parameter for P_4 appears to be a little greater than for I_2, say 14.4. By assigning parameters to the other solvents in accord with their positions with respect to CCl_4, we are in a position to reproduce the solubility relaions of all these substances and to fill in any gaps. We would fail only n cases where specific interactions occur, as illustrated by the displaced oint for I_2 in ether.

At the same time, the departures from parallelism give an obvious ndication of the errors likely to be encountered in calculating solubilities rom parameters. For example, in order for the $\delta_2 - \delta_1$ values of I_2 and -$C_6H_4Br_2$ to be the same in both CCl_4 and C_6H_{14}, the δ_1-value in the latter vould have to be decreased from 7.0 to 6.7. Reversing the calculation, vith other figures unchanged, would give 0.115 mole per cent for p-$C_6H_4Br_2$ n C_6H_{14} instead of the measured 0.086. It should be remembered, in judging his result, that a variety of factors could contribute to a discrepancy of his magnitude: not only all the approximations introduced in deriving the quation but also uncertainty in the heat of fusion and heat capacities of he solute, and in some cases, although not in this one, the entropy corection for unequal sizes. It might be possible to achieve better correlation y taking fuller account of one or more of such factors, particulary of partial nolal volumes, but a calculation which becomes too complicated, or which equires measurement of other properties of the solution had better be relaced by a direct measurement of solubility. It is well to remember in this onnection that there is no point to knowing solubility within narrow limits nless temperature is to be controlled within corresponding limits.

Paraffins. Ralston, Hoerr and Crews[48] have published valuable data n the solubilities of normal paraffins ranging from octane to dotriacontane nd in a common group of solvents. Their results were obtained over a large ange of temperature and were expressed and plotted as weight percent *vs.* temerature. These data can serve as a useful guide to anyone interested in the ehavior of these or similar substances. Unfortunately, our knowledge of eats of fusion of these paraffins is so meager that we cannot at present se the solubilities for a searching test of the questionable degree of conormity of these long molecules to equations derived upon the assumption f spherical symmetry. We have, however, plotted part of their data for ormal hexadecane in our usual form, log x_2 vs. $1/T$, but without a line or ideal solubility, in Fig. 8. One may see in the pronounced drop in the urves for the solvents with dipole moments evidence of their inability to ause induced dipoles in the paraffin.

In the case of **dotriacontane** (dicetyl), however, we do possess a sufficient body of data for a rather comprehensive examination of the behavior f this extraordinarily large, long molecule. The case is particularly instrucive as an example of the presence of an unusual variety of factors. We ave solubility measurements by Seyer[49] in paraffin solvents ranging from

48 A. W. Ralston, C. W. Hoerr, and L. T. Crews, *J. Org. Chem.*, **9**, 319 (1944). In the same volume are to be found similar data for normal aliphatic amines, alcohols and saturated fatty acids.

49 W. F. Seyer, *J Am. Chem. Soc.*, **58**, 2029 (1936); **60**, 827 (1938).

propane to dodecane, by Ralstón, Hoerr and Crews and by Hildebrand and Wachter[50], both sets in a number of solvents. Hildebrand called attention to the fact that a curve for the ideal solubility should be drawn with due regard to the transition occuring at 63.5 °C. The melting point is 70 °C

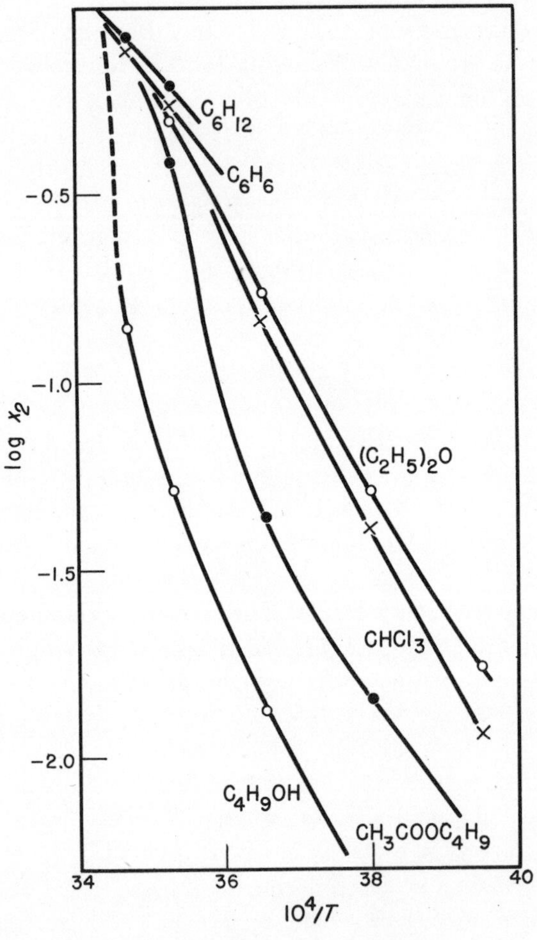

Fig. 8. Solubility of normal hexadecane

Garner, van Bibber and King[51] determined the heats of transition and fusion of normal paraffin hydrocarbons with 22, 26, 30, 34 and 35 carbon atoms from which we have interpolated for dotriacontane the molal heats of transition and fusion as 10.4 kcal. and 17.6 kcal., respectively. The slope of the ideal solubility line for the higher temperature α-form, as drawn in Fig. 8, corresponds, therefore, to 17.6 kcal., whereas, the slope of the

[50] J. H. Hildebrand, *J. Am. Chem. Soc.*, **56**. 794, (1937); J. H. Hildebrand and A. Wachter *J. Phys. & Colloid Chem.* **53**, 886 (1949).

[51] W. E. Garner, K. van Bibber and A. M. King, *J. Chem. Soc.*, **1931**, 1533.

line for the β-form downward from the transition point corresponds to 28.0 kcal. The latter line must not be drawn through the melting point for the α-form, because its melting point, if it could be reached, would be lower. Both of these "ideal" lines are drawn on Fig. 9, in which are

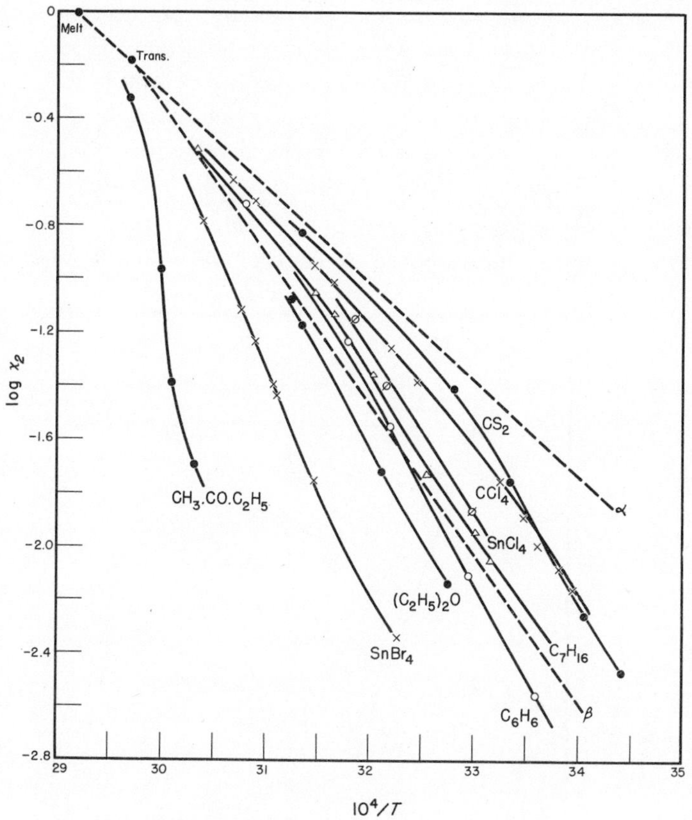

Fig. 9. Solubility of normal dotriacontane.

represented, likewise, a number of the solubility points obtained by Wachter and Hildebrand. Their points for solutions in carbon tetrachloride and benzene agree satisfactorily with those of Ralston et al. for the same solvents, although their points for ether are lower. Fig. 9 includes points for one very polar solvent, 2-butanone, measured by Ralston et al.

Now we see that, although the solubilities in $SnBr_4$, with its high internal pressure, and in methyl-ethyl ketone, with its high dipole moment, are considerably less than Raoult's law solubilities for the β-form, the points for the other solvents fall above that line. Bondi[52] has explained this situation as due to the entropy of mixing molecular species of such different size, calculated by aid of the formula of Guggenheim[53], which

[52] A. Bondi, *J. Phys. Coll. Chem.*, **52**, 248 (1948).
[53] E. A. Guggenheim, *Proc. Roy. Soc. Lond.*, **A 183**, 206, 213 (1944). See also Chapter VI.

raises the Raoult's law solubility by an amount depending upon the rat of molal volumes in each solution. Incidentally, Bondi did not allow f the transition point, so that his ideal line was too low, making th discrepancies appear worse than they actually are.

But it is not at all certain that the entropy of solution is to be calc lated in this way for at least some of these solutions. Hildebrand show that if the molecules of two normal paraffins retain in the solution th parallel orientation they have in the solid, the entropy of mixing is th Raoult's law entropy, despite different molecular lengths. Evidence that no mal hexane and hexadecane behave in this way was presented in Chapter XI

Further evidence may be seen in the solubilities of dotriacontane hexane and in dodecane reported by Seyer and plotted here in Fig. 1

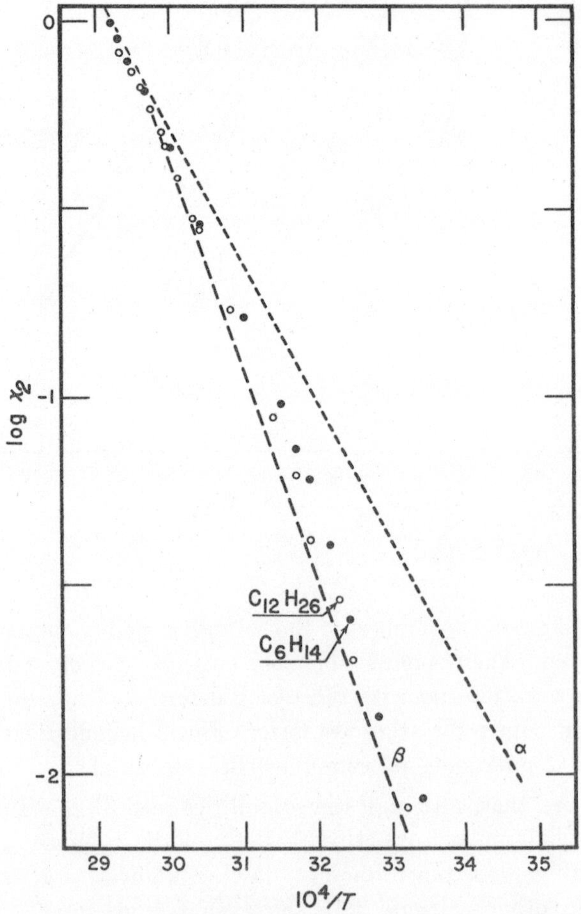

Fig. 10. Solubilities of dotriacontane in hexane and dodecane (Seyer[49]).

Although the ratio of chain lengths is twice as great in the former, th two sets of points differ by scarcely more than the limit of error; furthe nore, they are hardly off from the ideal β-line by more than the uncer-ainty of the latter.

The higher solubilities in carbon disulfide, carbon tetrachloride and, ccording to the data of Ralston, cyclohexane, may be interpreted as due o the volume-entropy effect, for these solvents would presumably interfere nore than the normal paraffin solvents with a quasi-parallel order n dicetyl; however, there is another possible interpretation of the high olubilities, *i. e.*, that the solid phase is the α-form. It is easy to imagine hat the solid, having been obtained, in the method used, by crystallizing ut of the solution, could easily have sufficient of the solvent entangled to nake it more difficult for the dicetyl chains to coalesce to the non-rotating -form. The downward shift in the CS_2 points from near the α-line towards he β-line may be evidence that the solid is finally altering in the direction f the β-form. The fact that the transition is not sharp at 63.5 °C indicates hat rotation does not suddenly set in for the full length of the molecules.

The above facts have been analyzed in some detail because they furnish n excellent example of the variety of factors that may have to be consid-red before reaching conclusions and the errors that can be made by neglect f any one of them. We see in this case the necessity of considering (1) he actual nature of the solid phase; (2) the alteration of the ideal line aused by a transition; (3) the dependence of a nonideal entropy upon the pproximate arrangements of molecules of different size and shape; (4) the ccuracy of the figure for the heat of fusion; (5) the possible curvature in he line for the Raoult's law solubility due to difference in heat capacities f solid and liquid; (6) the accuracy in the solubility data themselves; (7) the olubility parameters; (8) the possible effects of non-additive solution volumes.

Biphenyl. Many years ago, Washburn and Read[54] reported -5.8 °C. or the eutectic point of benzene-biphenyl mixtures, citing it as an example f a system obeying Raoult's law, according to which they calculated -6.1 °C. Revised values for the heats of fusion[55] alter this to -7.1 °, still n good agreement, considering the fact that biphenyl melts at 69.1 °C. Varner, Scheib and Svirbely measured[56] the solubility of biphenyl in the olvents given in Table 7. From their figures we have extrapolated over a mall temperature range to obtain the figures for mole fractions given in Table 7. The deviations from the ideal solubility[56] are small, except for eptane and carbon tetrachloride, and correspond approximately to the sol-bility parameters, δ, but it is evident that the solubility in the last three olvents is too close to the ideal solubility in view of the differences in heir δ-values. This suggested to Tompa[55] an investigation of the system enzene-biphenyl which is a model of care and thoroughness.

[54] E. W. Washburn and J. W. Read, *Proc. Nat. Acad. Sci.*, **1**, 191 (1915); *J. Am. Chem. Soc.*, **41**, 729 (1919).
[55] H. Tompa, *J. Chem. Phys.*, **16**, 292 (1948).
[56] J. C. Warner, R. C. Scheib and W. J. Svirbely, *Ibid*, **2**, 590 (1934).

He set out to determine whether the volume ratio of approximately 2 : 1 introduces a modification of the entropy of the mixture to account for the behavior of the system. Careful measurements of the vapor pressure of benzene solutions gave for $p_1/p_1^0 x_1$ approximately 1.03 at $x_1 = 0.7$. The heat of diluting one mole of solution, $x_1 = 0.665$, with 1.23 moles of benzene was 22.5 cal. absorbed.

Table 7. Solubility of biphenyl 25°C.

	n-C_7H_{16}	CCl_4	CS_2	Benzene	Dioxane	p-$C_6H_4Cl_2$	Ideal
Mole %	12.9	34.0	37.1	38.9	38.6	39.8*	39.4
δ_1	7.45	8.6	9.9	9.15			11.0

* Extrapolated below the eutectic point 27.7°C.

Using this experimental value of the heat of dilution, and correcting for gas imperfections, the formula of Guggenheim (VI-26) with z anywhere between 6 and 12 yields values of $p_1/p_1^0 x_1$ for benzene which agree with the experimental points within their limits of error.

Aluminum bromide furnishes an interesting example of a substance which dimerizes and is broken down only in solvents capable of forming solvates with it. Heldmann and Thurmond[57] determined its solubility in normal butane and discussed its solubilities in other solvents from the standpoint of the theories presented in this book, and Boedeker and Oblad[58] have measured its solubility in normal hexane. The dimer forms obviously regular solutions with these paraffins, also with $AsBr_3$, toluene, and p-xylene. There is evidence of compound formation with benzene, nitrobenzene and its derivatives, and CS_2 (color change). The strongly acidic nature of Al_2Br_6 overshadows internal pressure differences in determining its solubility relationships in all but essentially inert solvents; in these it forms approximately regular solutions. Its solubilities in n-butane and hexane show fair agreement with the equation for regular solutions, using δ-values for Al_2Br_6 derived from its heat of vaporization.

Molecular weight by the freezing point method. When the molecular weight of a dissolved substance is determined by the depression of the freezing point of a solvent, it is the latter which separates, and we essentially determine the temperature at which the solution of a particular composition is saturated with the pure solvent. The "solvent" accordingly plays the role of the "solutes" in the cases discussed earlier in this chapter. Since the solubility curves shown in Figs. 1 — 4 become tangent to the ideal line at the melting point, the lowering of the freezing point can be used to

[57] J. D. Heldmann and C. D. Thurmond, *J. Am. Chem. Soc.*, **66**, 427 (1944).
[58] E. R. Boedeker and A. G. Oblad, *Ibid.*, **69**, 2036 (1947).

determine molal weight of the substance ordinarily considered as the solute, provided the solution is sufficiently dilute. It is obviously desirable to select a solvent with an internal pressure reasonably close to that of the solute in order to avoid the necessity of going to extremely high dilutions.

It is appropriate here to object to the practice of attributing all departures from the ideal freezing point lowering to some chemical effect or other. For example, it would be quite improper to account for the freezing point lowering of $CHBr_3$ by I_2 by assuming higher polymers of I_2; the smaller freezing point lowering is simply the result of difference in internal pressures. Any chemical effects should be assessed in some such manner as was used above for solutions of I_2 in ether.

Mortimer's method of calculating solubilities. Mortimer[59] considered all solubility curves, plotted as log x_2 vs $1/T$, to be approximately straight lines and that the steepness of their slopes can be used as a measure of the internal pressure difference. He has given rules for combining the internal pressures to give a factor, which multiplies ΔH^F in the ideal solubility equation to give the actual slope. He compiled a table of relative internal pressures by consideration of a large body of solubility data, including many polar substances. Although this method of treatment has proved to be of some practical value, the uncertainties introduced by so many polar substances are considerable and the straight line drawn through data that are in reality reverse S-shaped, as Mortimer himself pointed out, is theoretically objectionable. Deviations are proportional not to $[\delta_1^2 - \delta_2^2]$ but to $(\delta_1 - \delta_2)^2$.

The choice of a solvent for recrystallization is a matter of such practical importance that a few words on the subject are appropriate. The object is to choose a solvent in which any impurities likely to be present are very soluble and in which the temperature coefficient of solubility of the substance to be purified is high, so as to permit of good recovery without excessive temperature changes. Since it is the percentage change, not the absolute change in solubility, that is important, the slopes of the logarithmic curves, illustrated in Figs. 1—4, should be as great as possible. Among the solvents for iodine, Fig. 1, the steepest curves are given by solvents of low internal pressure, such as heptane, and the steepness is greater at higher temperatures. It is evident that heptane would be a far more effective solvent than ether for recrystallizing iodine. Of course, any special affinity of a solvent for an impurity likely to be present is a valuable consideration. To purify naphthalene, cf. Fig. 4, an alcohol would be vastly superior to benzene, not only because of the larger temperature coefficient of solubility but also because any polar impurities in the naphthalene might more readily remain in solution. A liquid that solvates with the substance to be recrystallized is a poor choice, because the solubility curve is flattened by such behavior, as illustrated by the curves for the brown iodine solutions.

[59] F. S. Mortimer, *J. Am. Chem. Soc.*, **44**, 1416 (1922); **45**, 633 (1923).

Effect of pressure upon the solubility of solids.[60] When pressure is applied to both the solid and liquid phase of a solution in equilibrium with a solid the composition of the solution is in general altered so as to keep the fugacity of the substance in the solid the same as in the solution i. e.,

$$\frac{d\ln f^s}{dP} = \frac{d\ln f}{dP} \tag{10}$$

Now, the change of the fugacity of the solid with pressure is given by the equation

$$\frac{d\ln f^s}{dP} = \frac{V^s}{RT} \tag{11}$$

where V^s is the molal volume f the solid. The fugacity of this component of the solution is altered not only by the increased pressure but also by the changing composition of the solution. We may write, therefore.

$$\frac{d\ln f}{dP} = \left(\frac{\partial \ln f}{\partial P}\right)_x + \left(\frac{\partial \ln f}{\partial \ln x}\right)_P \frac{d\ln x}{dP} \tag{12}$$

The first term in the right-hand member is given by

$$\left(\frac{\partial \ln f}{\partial P}\right)_x = \frac{\overline{V}}{RT} \tag{13}$$

where $\overline{V}$ is the partial molal volume of this component in the solution. Substituting Equations 11, 12 and 13 in 10 gives

$$\frac{V^s}{RT} = \frac{\overline{V}}{RT} + \left(\frac{\partial \ln f}{\partial \ln x}\right)_P \frac{d\ln x}{dP}$$

or transposed,

$$\frac{d\ln x}{dP} = \frac{V^s - \overline{V}}{RT\left(\frac{\partial \ln f}{\partial \ln x}\right)_P} \tag{14}$$

If Raoult's law holds

$$\left(\frac{\partial \ln f}{\partial \ln x}\right)_P = 1,$$

and $\overline{V}$ then usually equals V^l, the molal volume in the pure liquid state

[60] Cf. H. C. Sorby, *Proc. Roy. Soc.*, **12**, 358 (1863); F. Braun, *Ann. Phys. Chem.*, [2], **30**, 250 (1887)

(cf. Chapter III), so that we may simplify Equation 14 for such a case to

$$\frac{d\ln x}{dP} = \frac{V^s - V^l}{RT} \tag{15}$$

Since most substances expand on melting, V^l is usually larger than V^s, and hence $V^s - V^l$ is negative and the solubility decreases with pressure.

If there is a positive deviation from Raoult's law $\bar{V}$ is usually greater than V^l so that $V^s - \bar{V}$ in Equation 14, will be an even larger negative quantity than $V^s - V^l$, in Equation 15. In such a case, also,

$$\frac{\partial \ln f}{\partial \ln x} < 1,$$

which will tend to increase the right hand member of Equation 14, and accentuate the diminution of solubility with increasing presssure.

If there is a negative deviation from Raoult's law, $\bar{V}$ is usually less than V^l, and if it is also less than V^s the right hand member of Equation 14 will be positive, giving an increase in solubility with pressure. In such a case

$$\frac{\partial \ln x}{\partial \ln P} > 1,$$

which tends to diminish the effect of pressure.

We may summarize by saying that with systems which obey Raoult's law or which deviate from it in a positive direction, the usual effect of increasing the pressure upon the system will be to decrease the solubility, while with systems which deviate in the negative direction from Raoult's law increasing the pressure may cause an increase in solubility in some cases. Of course, if the quantities in the righthand member of Equation 14 are known by experiment, the effect of pressure upon solubility can be calculated exactly. It should be emphasized that these effects of pressure are very small; for example, if $\Delta V = 10$ cc, it would require a pressure of 250 atmospheres to change the ideal solubility by ten percent.

If the pressure is applied to the solid phase only, as in the familiar experiment of drawing a wire through a block of ice without cutting the latter in two, then the effect is always to melt the solid, or increase its solubility, the increase being given by the equation,

$$\frac{d\ln x}{dP} = \frac{V^s}{RT\left(\frac{\partial \ln f}{\partial \ln x}\right)_P} \tag{16}$$

Experimental data upon the effect of pressure upon solubility have been obtained by Deffet[61].

Solid solutions. Cases arise sometimes, frequently among the metals-when the solid phase in equilibrium with a solution is itself a solution, rather than one of the components in the pure solid state. The fugacity of component 2 from a solid solution, f_2', will, of course, be less than from its pure solid form, f^s, at the same temperature, so that the amount of 2 in the liquid will also be less, or the temperature at which solid would separate from the solution will be higher than if the solid separating were pure[62]. This subject will be discussed at length in the following Chapters (XVIII and XIX).

Eutectic mixtures. In the preceding pages, we have considered the solubility of one solid component only. As we study the solubility at lower and lower temperatures, however, we finally reach temperatures below the melting point of the other component, that which we generally regard as the solvent. Below this temperature this solid may also separate out from the solution. When no solid solutions are formed, the complete phase diagram consists of two separate solubility curves, one for each component. These two curves eventually cross, and below such a temperature, called the "eutectic temperature", no liquid phase is stable. This phenomenon is of considerable importance because of the change in the crystallization at this point. Suppose we cool a solution of A and B, richer in A than the eutectic mixture. First crystals of pure solid A appear and as the solution is cooled further more and more A crystallizes out and the solution becomes richer in B. When the eutectic temperature is reached, however, the remaining solution crystallizes out, a micro-crystalline mixture of pure A and pure B, differing markedly at least in superficial characteristics from either of the pure solids. A typical eutectic diagram is afforded by the system naphthalene-phenanthrene[63] shown in Figure 11. The two liquidus curves are essentially the ideal solubility curves for the two substances, since they differ but slightly in internal pressure, as we have seen (Fig. 7).

The effect of compound formation on the solubility of solids. We have seen in Chapter XI how the formation of a chemical compound between the components produces negative deviations from Raoult's law. We should therefore expect that when a substance is capable of such a specific interaction with a solvent, its solubility would be enhanced.

---

[61] L. Deffet, *Bull. soc. chim. belg.*, **47**, 1 (1938).

[62] Lewis and Randall, "Thermodynamics", p. 238, have given a formula for the freezing point lowering involving the distribution coefficient between the solid and liquid phases. See also A. Smits, *Proc. Acad. Sci. Amsterdam*, **23**, 679 (1921) *Verslag. Akad. Wetenschappen Amsterdam*, **29**, 319 (1921); J. Jakob, *Z. Kryst.* **56**, 295 (1921); L. Vegard, *Z. Physik*, **5**, 17 (1921); E. C. Bain, *Trans. Am. Inst. Min. Met. Engr.* 1139 N. (Feb., 1922); C. Wagner and W. Schottky, *Z. physik. Chem.* **B2**, 163. (1930). C. Wagner, *Ibid.* (Bodenstein Festband), 1931. H. Seltz; *J. Am. Chem. Soc.*, **56**, 307 (1934).

[63] E. Rudolfi, *Z. physik. Chem.*, **66**, 705 (1909).

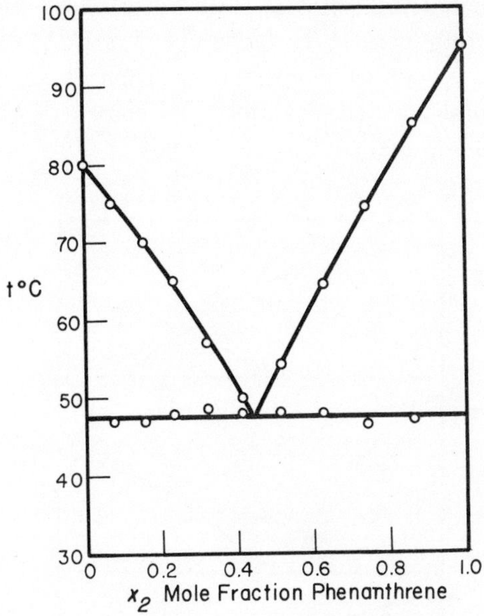

Fig. 11. Solubilities in the naphthalene-phenanthrene system, showing eutectic mixture

The effect of solvation upon the solubilities of solids has been clearly illustrated by Kendall, Davidson and Adler[64]. Figure 12 shows their diagrams for a series of mixtures in which is assumed a gradually increasing formation of the compound AB in the liquid state. "In this diagram, temperature is plotted against the molecular composition of the saturated solution. To facilitate comparison of the curves it is necessary to note that the point A represents the same temperature throughout, the melting point of pure substance A.

"Curve I indicates the ideal system A-B_I, where compound formation is entirely absent. The solubility curve of A in B_I, the line AC," as well as that of B_I in A, the line DB, "represents the ideal solution equation," II-23.

"The stable portions of the two curves end at their point of intersection, E, the eutectic point of the system.

"Curves II to V illustrate the successive changes which occur in the diagram as compound formation increases[65]. In Curve II the compound is so highly dissociated in solution that its solubility curve FGH never enters the stable region of the diagram; in Curve III compound formation is somewhat more extensive and the solubility curve of the compound AB_{III} possesses a

[64] J. Kendall, A. W. Davidson, and H. Adler, *J. Am. Chem. Soc.*, **43**, 1481 (1921).

[65] In curve I, the line AC approaches a vertical line at $x = 1$ asymptotically. In curve V, AC approaches asymptotically a vertical line at $x = \frac{1}{2}$. In the remaining curves AC assumes an intermediate position.

limited stable interval KL; in Curve IV this interval has expanded sufficiently to exhibit a maximum point at G (in other words, the compound AB_{IV} is stable at its melting point); in Curve V, finally the compound AB_V is not dissociated at all into its components in the solution, the system consisting, indeed, of two simple systems of the type shown in Curve I compressed into one composition range.

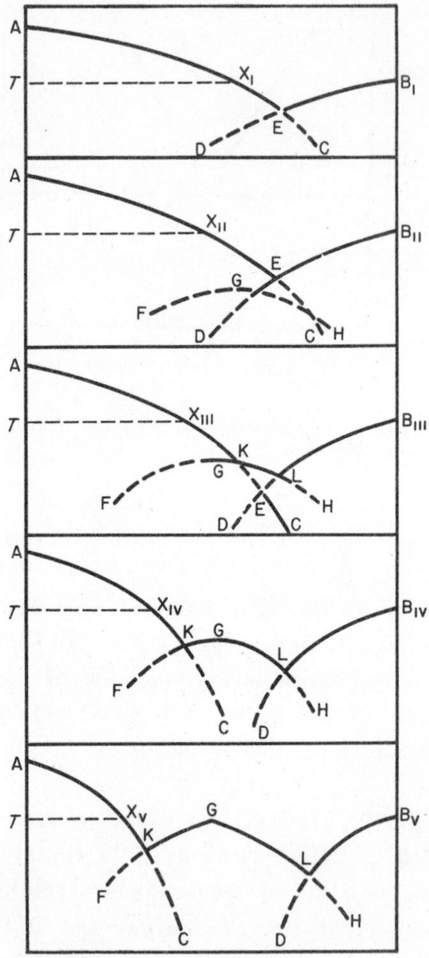

Fig. 12. Effect of compound formation upon melting point and solubility

"The essential point to be noted in these systems is the depression of Curve AC from its ideal position, which compound formation in solution necessitates. If only part of the total A in solution exists as uncombined A then, since the solution of uncombined A reaches the ideal value, the total mole fraction of A in the saturated solution, must exceed this ideal value by an amount depending on the stability of the compound AB in the liquid state. The solubility of A at any fixed temperature T consequently increases regularly as we pass from Curve I to Curve V. This may best be seen by comparing the compositions of the saturated solutions at temperature T (represented by the points X_{I}, X_{II}, X_{III}, X_{IV}, X_{V}, respectively on the various curves.).

"Increasing solubility and increasing compound formation, therefore, for a fixed solute A in a series of different solvents, proceed in parallel."

CHAPTER XVIII

Solid Solutions

Under favorable conditions, two substances will not only be completely miscible in the liquid state but will crystallize together in the same crystal lattice forming a partial or complete series of solid solutions. The most important solid solutions are those between the metals, the homogeneous alloys; for reasons which will be made apparent shortly, solid solutions are the exception rather than the rule among binary systems of organic compounds. However, because of the somewhat special nature of intermetallic forces, discussion of metallic solutions, both liquid and solid, will be postponed to the following chapter: This chapter will be confined to the general principles of solid solution formation, and their application to non-metallic systems.

Ideal or perfect solid solutions: We may visualize a solid solution of two substances which mix with no change of volume and no heat of mixing. For such an ideal solution, the free energy of mixing is merely that arising from the entropy of random mixing.

Equilibrium between solid and liquid phases requires the partial molal free energies to be equal in both phases; using this condition we obtain:

$$RT \ln x_1^s = \Delta F_1^F + RT \ln x_1^l \qquad (1\,a)$$

$$RT \ln x_2^s = \Delta F_2^F + RT \ln x_2^l \qquad (1\,b)$$

where the superscripts s and l refer to the solid and liquid respectively and ΔF_1^F and ΔF_2^F are the heats of fusion of the two pure substances. Recalling Equation XVII-5 for the temperature dependence of the free energy of fusion (neglecting the ΔC_p terms), we obtain partition equations

$$\ln \frac{x_1^l}{x_1^s} = \frac{\Delta H_1^F}{R}\left[\frac{1}{T_1^m} - \frac{1}{T}\right] \qquad (2\,a)$$

$$\ln \frac{x_2^l}{x_2^s} = \frac{\Delta H_2^F}{R}\left[\frac{1}{T_2^m} - \frac{1}{T}\right] \qquad (2\,b)$$

where T_1^m and T_2^m are the melting points of the pure substances, and ΔH_1^F and ΔH_2^F the corresponding heats of fusion.

Equations 2a and 2b may be combined and rearranged to obtain the liquidus and solidus lines, x_1^l and x_1^s as a function of temperature:

$$x_1^l = \frac{1 - k_2 e^{\frac{\Delta H_2^F}{RT}}}{k_1 e^{\frac{\Delta H_1^F}{RT}} - k_2 e^{\frac{\Delta H_2^F}{RT}}} \tag{3a}$$

$$x_1^s = \frac{1 - k_2 e^{\frac{\Delta H_2^F}{RT}}}{k_1 e^{\frac{\Delta H_1^F}{RT}} - k_2 e^{\frac{\Delta H_2^F}{RT}}} \cdot k_1 e^{\frac{\Delta H_1^F}{RT}} \tag{3b}$$

where $k_1 = e^{-\Delta H_1^F/RT_1^m}$ and $k_2 = e^{-\Delta H_2^F/RT_2^m}$.

Seltz[1] has applied Equations 3a and 3b to the calculation of equilibrium phase diagrams for the binary metal systems Cu-Ni, Ag-Pd, and Au-Pt. For the first two, the agreement is satisfactory; the deviation of the Au-Pt curve will be discussed later.

Nitrogen and carbon monoxide, which have equal molal volumes and are iso-electronic, form two complete series of solid solutions corresponding to the two crystal forms, hexagonal and cubic, in which both pure solids exist. From the heats of fusion of the β-phases, we may calculate the

Table 1. N_2-CO System

	N_2	CO
Liquid		
Heat of vaporization ΔH^V (cal/mole)	1333	1444
Boiling point T_b (°K)	77.3	81.6
Molal volume V^l (cm³)	34.6	34.4
Solubility parameter δ_l	5.9	6.1
β-Solid (hexagonal)		
Heat of fusion ΔH^F (cal/mole)	172.3	199.7
Melting point T_m (°K)	63.1	68.1
Molal volume V^β (cm³)	28.5	30.4
Solubility parameter δ_β	6.9	7.0
α-Solid (cubic)		
Heat of transition ΔH^T (cal/mole)	54.7	151
Transition point T_t (°K)	35.6	61.5
Molal volume V^α (cm³)	27.3	26.8
Solubility parameter δ_α	7.2	7.8

[1] H. Seltz, *J. Am. Chem. Soc.*, **56**, 307 (1934).

ideal solidus and liquidus lines, while the heats of transition from the α to the β-phase give a corresponding set of lines. Fig. 1 shows the experimental data of Komarov, Likhter and Ruhemann[2] and the theoretical ideal solution curves. Table 1 gives the necessary data[3].

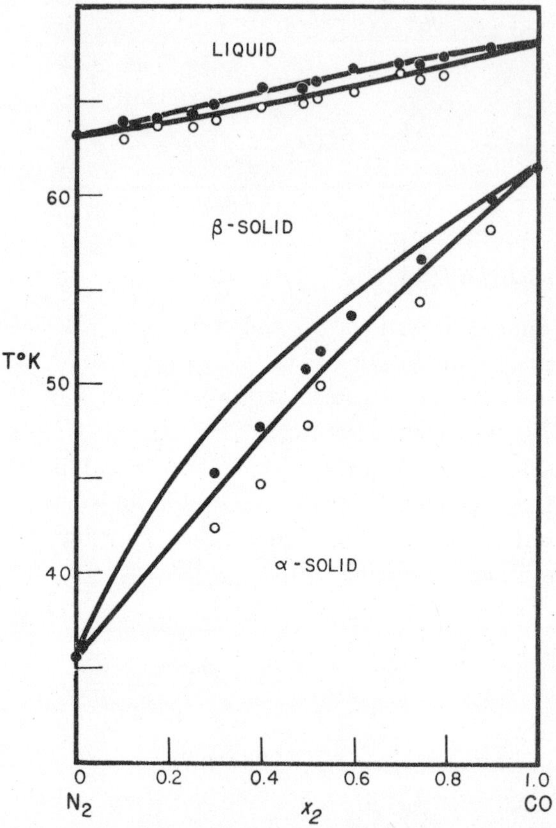

Fig. 1. Solid solutions of nitrogen and carbon monoxide. Solid lines are theoretical curves for ideal solid solutions

The agreement for the fusion curves in Fig. 1 is excellent (except for the somewhat greater separation of the experimental solidus and liquidus curves); the experimental transition curves are depressed somewhat below the ideal solution ones, but the qualitative features are the same.

Nonideal solid solutions. We have seen in earlier chapters that ideal solutions of liquids are the exception rather than the rule and that in nearly every case, sizeable deviations from Raoult's law are found. There

[2] P. Komarov, A. Likhter, and M. Ruhemann, *Zhur. Tekh. Fisiki,* **5,** 1723 (1935).

[3] Thermal data: CO-J.O. Clayton and W. F. Giauque, *J. Am. Chem. Soc.,* **54,** 2610 (1932); N_2-W. F. Giauque and J. O. Clayton, *J. Am. Chem. Soc.,* **55,** 4875 (1933).

is no reason to expect the situation to be different for solid solutions; we may expect differences in internal pressures between the two components to produce a positive heat of mixing and corresponding positive deviations from Raoult's law. A sufficiently large heat of mixing will of course produce segregation and partial miscibility quite analogous to that with liquids.

The heat of fusion is normally a very small percentage of the heat of vaporization; so the difference in the cohesive energies of liquid and solid is small. The combination of this with the small decrease of molal volume on freezing leads to a small increase in the solubility parameter. If these changes are similar for both components, the difference $\delta_1 - \delta_2$ remains almost unchanged, and as a consequence, we may expect the heat of mixing in solid solutions to be of the same order of magnitude as in the corresponding liquid phase.

One complicating feature must now be noted. To this heat of mixing based upon internal pressure considerations, we must add a distortion energy due to differences of size and shape.

The distortion energy. The lack of long range order in liquids permits mixing together without difficulty molecules of very different sizes and shapes. In the crystalline solid, however, the molecules are arranged in a regular lattice of repeating units. In order to form a solid solution, we must replace certain molecules in this lattice by molecules of the second component. When this second molecule is markedly different in size or shape, it is obvious that this substitution can be made only at the price of introducing a considerable amount of strain or distortion into the crystal. Only a limited amount of such a strain can be tolerated; when this is exceeded, a lower free energy is attained by separation into two phases. It is for this reason that solid solutions are rare in systems of organic compounds; even where the internal pressures are equal, differences in size and shape preclude any significant solid solution range. Only where the two substances are very similar in size and shape ("isomorphous") are solid solutions possible.

Calculation of the lattice energy of a solid solution is an involved problem and remains to be solved satisfactorily. Lawson[4] has attempted to calculate the strain energy in a binary solid solution of atoms of different sizes, and by the introduction of admittedly fairly arbitrary assumptions, derives for the distortion energy:

$$\Delta E^D = \frac{4}{3}\left(\frac{G_1}{V_1} x_1 + \frac{G_2}{V_2} x_2\right)(V_1 - V_2)^2 x_1 x_2 \qquad (4)$$

[4] A. W. Lawson, *J. Chem. Phys.*, **15**, 831 (1947).

where G_1 and G_2 are the shear moduli for the pure solids, and V_1 and V_2 the molal volumes.

Scott[5], from a different but equally arbitrary model, obtained (for substances obeying the geometric mean law — Equation VII-45):

$$\Delta E^D = \frac{2\,\delta_1\,\delta_2\,(V_1\,V_2)^{\frac{1}{2}}\,(V_1 - V_2)^2}{(x_1\,V_1^2 + x_2\,V_2^2)}\,x_1\,x_2 \tag{5}$$

Both treatments yield values of ΔE^D of the same order of magnitude and both find the strain energy proportional to the square of the difference in molal volumes.

On substitution of numbers into Equations 4 or 5, we conclude that for differences in volume greater than about 20%, the strain energy is so great that phase separation occurs, and that as the difference in volume becomes greater, the solubility becomes vanishingly small. From the form of Equation 5, we conclude that the solubility of a small atom in a lattice of larger ones is greater than the solubility of the large atom in the small lattice. This physically obvious condition is also the case for liquid-liquid systems as we may recall.

We may expect a treatment for atomic lattices to hold amost equally well for approximately spherical molecules, but extension to other lattices would be almost prohibitively difficult.

Types of solid solution diagrams. Various types of solid-liquid phase diagrams are possible quite analogous to the liquid-gas distillation curves seen in Chapter XIII. Roozeboom[6] gave a qualitative thermodynamic treatment of these in 1899 and his classification into five types remains the standard method of description of solid solution phase diagrams.

Type I. *The two components form a complete series of solid solutions in which the liquidus and solidus curves lie between the two melting points.* This type of diagram, of which the ideal solid solutions are a special case, occurs whenever the deviations from Raoult's law are sufficiently similar in magnitude. For example, when both phases have large and approximately equal positive heats of mixing, we obtain the same lens-type phase boundaries as for ideal solutions, but the two phase region is expanded, the liquidus curve lying above the ideal, the solidus curve, below. This is the explanation of the Au-Pt system (Fig. 2) which troubled Seltz[1,7], but was explained later by Scatchard and Hamer[8]. For equal negative deviations from Raoult's law, the reverse situation applies; the actual two-phase region is compressed into a smaller area than the ideal.

[5] R. L. Scott, to be published.

[6] H. W. B. Roozeboom, *Z. physik. Chem.*, **30**, 385, 413 (1899). See also his book. "Die Heterogene Gleichgewichte".

[7] H. Seltz, *J. Am. Chem. Soc.*, **57**, 391 (1935).

[8] G. Scatchard and W. J. Hamer, *J. Am. Chem. Soc.*, **57**, 1809 (1935).

When the free energy of mixing (in an absolute sense) is less in the liquid phase than in the solid (greater negative deviations in the liquid or greater positive deviations in the solid), the liquidus and solidus curves are depressed below the ideal as in the N_2-CO α-β transition (Fig. 1). For the corresponding case when the absolute deviation is greater in the liquid phase, the curves are raised above the ideal. These conditions are partially discussed by Seltz[7], who gives a graphical method for calculating phase diagrams from activity curves.

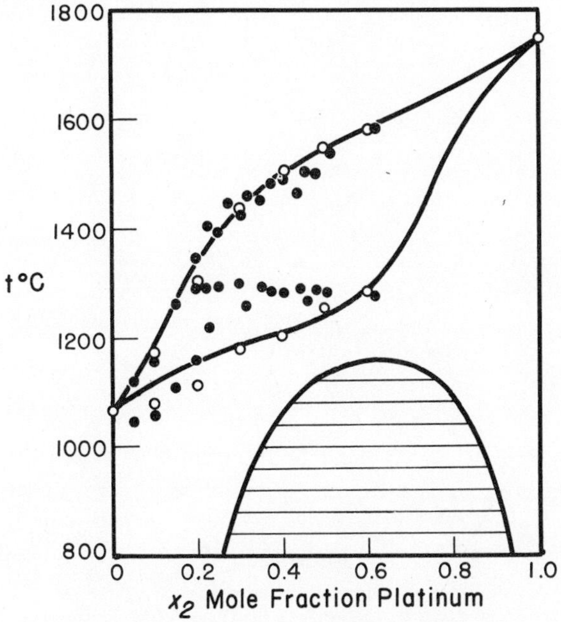

Fig. 2. Solid solutions of gold and platinum. The solidus and liquidus lines are those calculated by Scatchard and Hamer

The kind of free energy curves which give rise to a Type I diagram are shown in Fig. 5 adapted from Roozeboom[6]. Taking the pure liquid phases as the standard states, we may graph $F^s - F^\circ$ and $F^l - F^\circ$ for the liquid and solid phases at different temperatures. As shown in Chapter III a straight line simultaneously tangent to both curves defines the conjugate phases.

Type II. *The components form a complete series of solid solutions and the liquidus and solidus curves have a maximum.* This rare type of diagram occurs only when the deviations from ideality are sufficiently greater in the liquid than in the solid to raise the phase boundary above the melting point of the higher melting substance. The classic example is the system *d*-carvoxime - *l*-carvoxime[9], where the maximum temperature is at the melting point of the racemic mixture (Fig. 3). The existence of this Type II has been the subject of considerable controversy to which we will return in a later section.

[9] J. H. Adriani, *Z. physik. Chem.*, **33**, 453, 469 (1900).

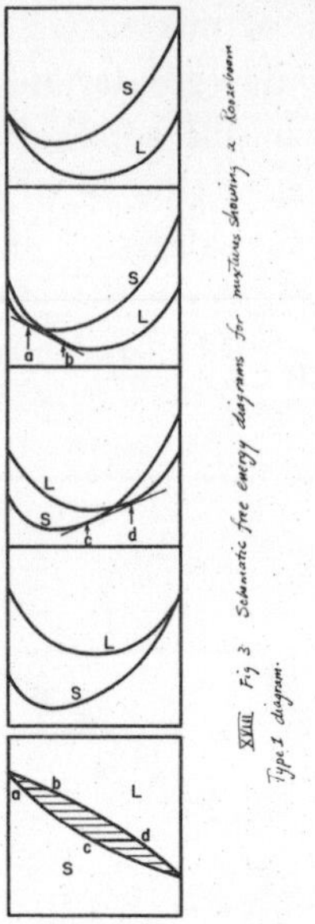

Fig. 3. Solid solutions in the system
d-carvoxime-*l*-carvoxime

Type III. *The components form a complete series of solid solutions, and the liquidus and solidus curves describe a minimum.* When the deviations in the solid exceed those in the liquid, a minimum in the melting point curve is possible. How great the excess of the solid over the liquid must be in order to cause Type III curves rather than Type I depends upon the melting points, heats of fusion, etc. in a similar way as the maximum and minimum boiling points do for gas-liquid equilibria (Chapter XIII).

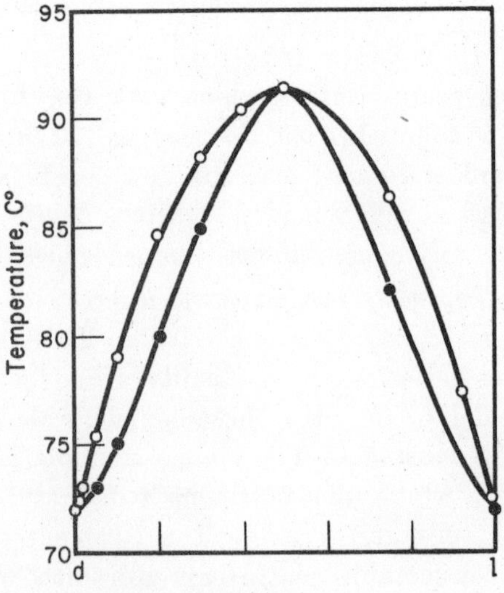

Fig. 4. Solid solutions of bromobenzene
and iodobenzene (Pascal)

A typical example is the system bromobenzene-iodobenzene[10] shown in Fig. 4. The schematic free energy relations are shown in Fig. 6.

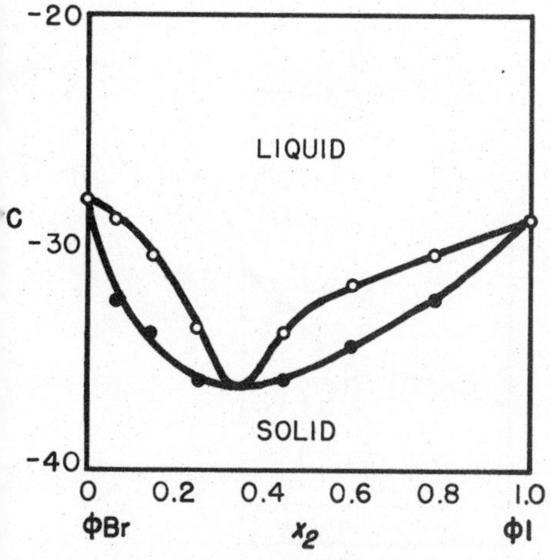

Fig. 5. Schematic free energy diagrams for mixtures showing a Roozeboom Type I diagram

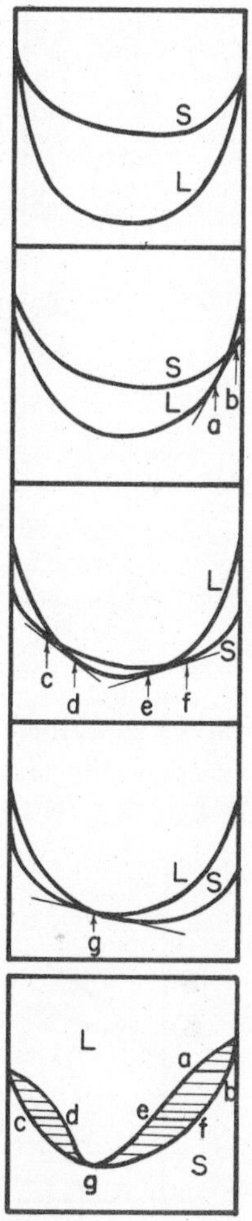

Fig. 6. Schematic free energy diagram for substances showing a Roozeboom Type III diagram

Type IV. *The components form an incomplete series of solid solutions, and the curves pass through a transition (peritectic).* This type of phase diagram represents a Type I modified by a miscibility gap in the solid phase. The system *p*-chloroiodobenzene-*p*-diiodobenzene[11] (Fig. 7) illustrates this type, which may arise when the deviations from ideality are large enough to produce separation in the solid phase, but not quite large enough to produce separation in the liquid. Below the peritectic transition temperature

[10] P. Pascal, *Bull. soc. chim.*, **Ser. 4, 13, 744** (1913).

[11] H. Rheinboldt and M. Kircheisen, *J. prakt. Chem.* **113**, 199 (1926).

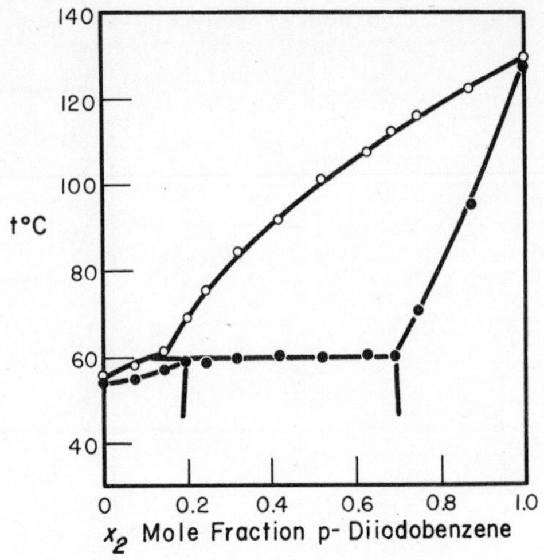

Fig. 7. Solid solutions in the *p*-chloroiodobenzene-*p*-diiodobenzene system, showing a peritectic Type IV diagram

the liquid is in equilibrium with one solid phase, above it with another. One may visualize the transition between Type I and Type IV in a series of schematic diagrams (Fig. 8abcd) representing an increasing solid critical

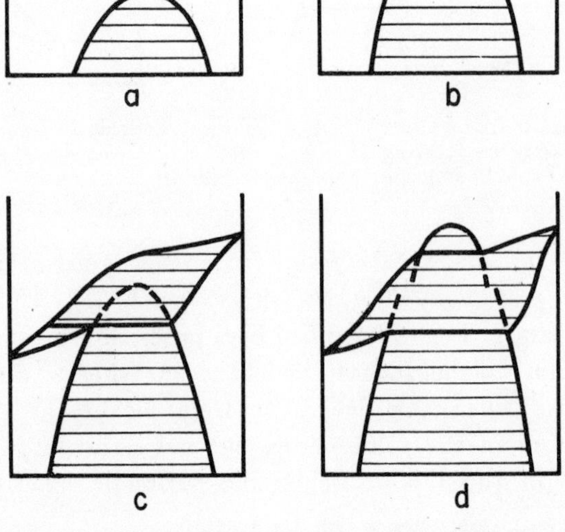

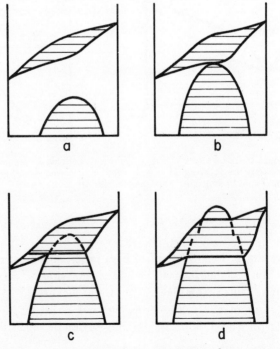

Fig. 8. Transition from Type I to Type IV diagrams

solution temperature. We have seen (Figure 2) that the system Au-Pt is analogous to Fig. 8a. If the miscibility gap persists into the liquid phase, we have Fig. 8d.

Type V. *The components form an incomplete series of solid solutions, and the curves show a eutectic point.* This kind of phase diagram, exemplified by the system azobenzene-azoxybenzene[12] shown in Fig. 9, is the case of incomplete miscibility corresponding to the complete miscibility of Type III. These may arise when very large positive deviations in the solid, sufficient to cause phase separation, are accompanied by much smaller deviations in the liquid phase.

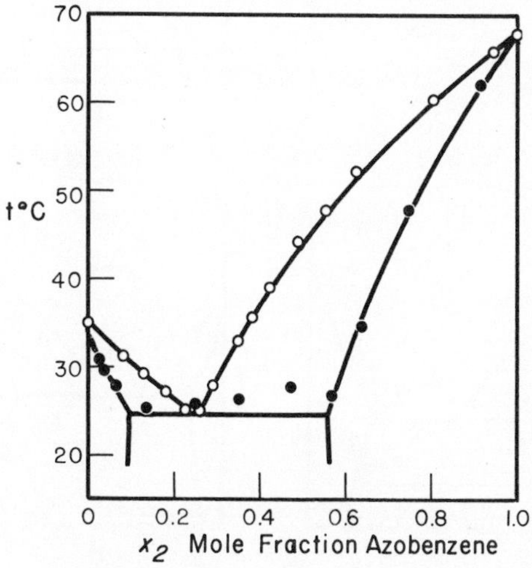

Fig. 9. Solid solutions in the azoxybenzene-azobenzene system, showing a eutectic Type V diagram

Figs. 10 abc show schematically the transition between Type III and Type V. Fig. 10d shows a continuation of phase separation into the liquid phase. Fig. 11 shows the free energy relations which give rise to Type V diagrams. The distortion energy is peculiar to the solid phase and is lost on melting while we expect that part of the heat of mixing arising from internal pressure differences to be much the same in the liquid phase. We may therefore expect systems where the distortion energy is sizeable to exhibit diagrams of Types III or V while those without much distortion energy may have Type I, II or IV diagrams. With substances markedly different in size or shape, solid solution formation is negligible and we get the familiar eutectic diagram in which the liquid solution is in equilibrium with a pure solid phase. Solubility equilibrium in such systems was discussed in Chapter XVII.

[12] H. Hartley and J. M. A. Stuart, *Trans. Chem. Soc. London,* **105,** 309 (1914).

One can imagine combinations of Type II with liquid immiscibility, but in view of the rareness of the ordinary Type II diagram, examples are not likely to be found.

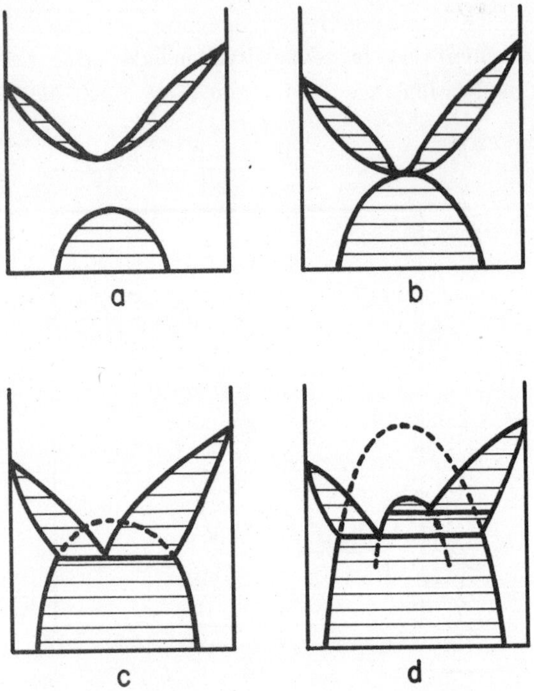

Fig. 10. Transition from Type III to Type V diagrams

Crystallization in different lattices. An alternate cause of incomplete miscibility in the solid phase occurs when the two pure substances crystallize in incompatible crystal lattices. For example, one can imagine two spherical molecules crystallizing in the two close-packed structures; one in the face centered cubic lattice (O_h^5), the other in the hexagonal (D_{6h}^4). Even if the molal volumes and internal pressures are identical, a complete series of solid solutions is precluded by the impossibility of passing continously from one structure to the other without enormous distortion of the crystals. Where the difference in energy between the two lattices is small, the region of solid solution formation may be very great but at least a small miscibility gap is inevitable.

Such differences in crystal structure give rise to Type IV and V diagrams. The free energy relations for such a type V diagram are shown schematically in Fig. 12. The model visualizes a meta stable α-crystal for pure substance 2 and a similar β-crystal for substance 1.

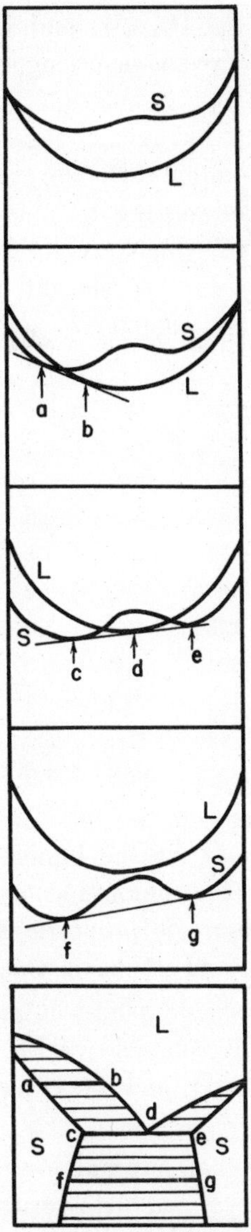

Fig. 11. Schematic free energy relations for substances forming a eutectic mixture (Roozeboom Type V)

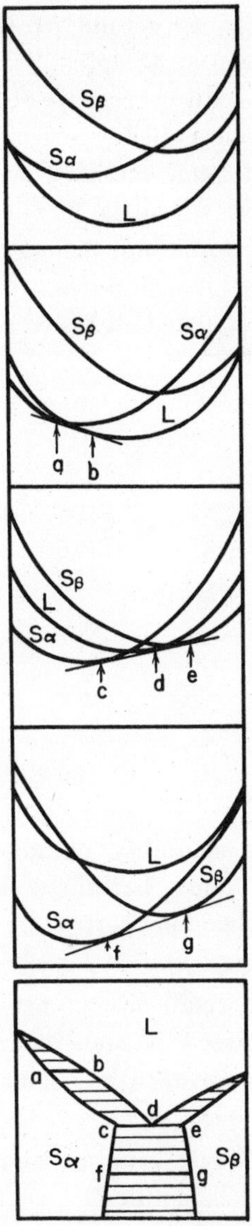

Fig. 12. Schematic free energy diagrams for substances crystallizing in different crystal lattices α and β. (Roozeboom Type V)

The only exceptions to the general incompatibility of different crystal structures might be cases where one structure is a distorted modification of the other. For example metallic indium crystallizes in a tetragonal face centered structure (D_{4}^{17}) which is merely a slightly squashed form of the face-centered cubic (O_h^5). Lead, which crystallizes in the latter structure, was once thought to form a complete series of solid solutions with indium.

The complicated phase diagrams caused by transitions in the solid state have been discussed by Roozeboom [6].

Solid solutions of the rare gases, and N_2, O_2, CO, and CH_4. We have seen in Chapter V that the rare gases (except neon) agree almost exactly with a theory of corresponding states for liquids and solids, and have been called "perfect liquids". In addition nitrogen, oxygen, carbon monoxide and methane exhibit almost perfect liquid behavior, but differ somewhat as solids for obvious reasons. It is interesting to consider solid solution formation among these substances, all of which are solids only at very low temperatures. Table 2 tabulates some of the relevant properties for these, listed in order of decreasing solubility parameters.

Table 2.

	T_m	T_b	V_s	V_l	ΔH_b^V	P_c	δ_b
Xe	161.3	165.1	37.1	42.7	3020	58.2	8.0
Kr	116.0	120.9	29.6	34.1	2160	54.1	7.5
O_2	54.4	90.1	22.4	28.0	1630	49.7	7.2
A	83.8	87.3	24.6	28.1	1560	48.0	7.0
CH_4	90.6	112.5	(30.9)	(38)	2040	45.7	6.8
CO	68.1	81.6	30.4	34.4	1440	34.5	6.1
N_2	63.1	77.3	28.5	34.6	1330	33.5	5.9
Ne	24.6	27.2	13.8	16.6	446	26.9	4.9

The solubility parameters tabulated are those for the liquids at their boiling points, but these should be indicative of the magnitude of those for the solids. For perfect liquids the internal pressure is proportional to the critical pressure, and the correlation between δ_b and P_c bears this out.

The small size of neon precludes any appreciable solid solution formation between it and the other substances. The complete series of solid solutions between α-N_2 and α-CO and between β-N_2 and β-CO has already been noted.

Methane, krypton, and argon, with about equal internal pressures and all crystallizing in face-centered cubic lattices, form complete series of solid solutions. The systems CH_4-Kr[13,14] (Fig. 13a) and A-Kr[14] (Fig. 13b) exhibit Type I diagrams. The system CH_4-A[14] (Fig. 13 c), with a greater discrepancy in volume, shows a Type III minimum.

Argon and oxygen are very similar in molal volume and internal pressure but are incompletely miscible[14], forming a type IV peritectic (Fig. 13 d). The solid phase at the melting point, α-O_2, apparently has a cubic crystal lattice[15], but judging from the phase diagram, it is not isomorphous with argon. The nitrogen-oxygen system[2] exhibits a Type V eutectic diagram (Fig. 14); not only are the crystal structures different (hexagonal for

[13] M. V. Stackelberg, F. Quatram and H. U. Antweiler, *Z. Elektrochem.*, **42**, 552 (1936).
[14] H. Veith and E. Schröder, *Z. physik. Chem.* **A 179**, 16 (1937).
[15] W. H. Keesom and K. W. Taconis, *Physica*, **3**, 141 (1936).

β-N_2) and the internal pressures unequal, but a sizeable difference in molal volume introduces a large strain energy. This distortion of the crystal is clearly indicated by the measurements of the heat of fusion by Komarov, Likhter, and Ruhemann[2]. ΔH^F is 107 calories for pure α-oxygen, but drops steadily to below 50 calories at about 30% N_2 (near the eutectic), and then rises to 171 calories for pure β-N_2; the curve is shown in Fig. 15. The decrease in the heat of fusion, accompanied by a much smaller change in the entropy of fusion, leads to a marked depression of the melting point of the solid solution.

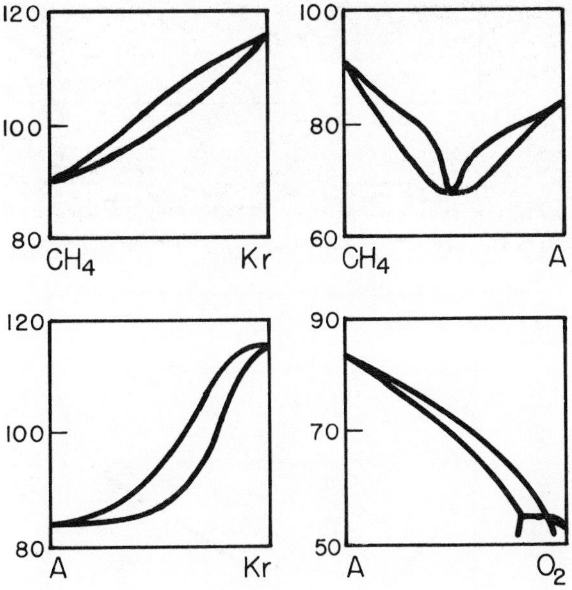

Fig. 13. Solid solutions of methane, krypton, argon and oxygen

Solid solutions of the tetrahalides and related compounds. The tetrahalides, whose tetrahedral symmetry closely approaches the spherical, represent a useful class of polyatomic molecules in which to study solid solutions. Unfortunately the data are fragmentary, and much further work could be done to round out the picture.

The general properties of the tetrahalides have been reviewed by Hildebrand[16] and only those of interest for the known binary systems are given in Table 3.

Tertiary-butyl chloride is listed with the tetrahalides because it forms a complete series of solid solutions with carbon tetrachloride (a Type III diagram).

[16] J. H. Hildebrand, *J. Chem. Phys.*, **15**, 727 (1947).

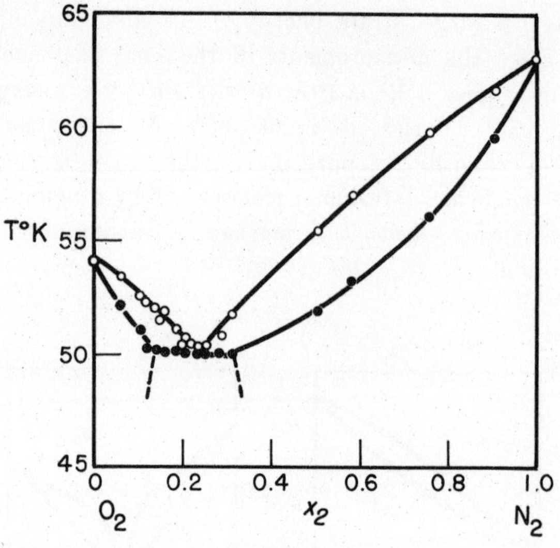

Fig. 14. Solid solutions of oxygen and nitrogen

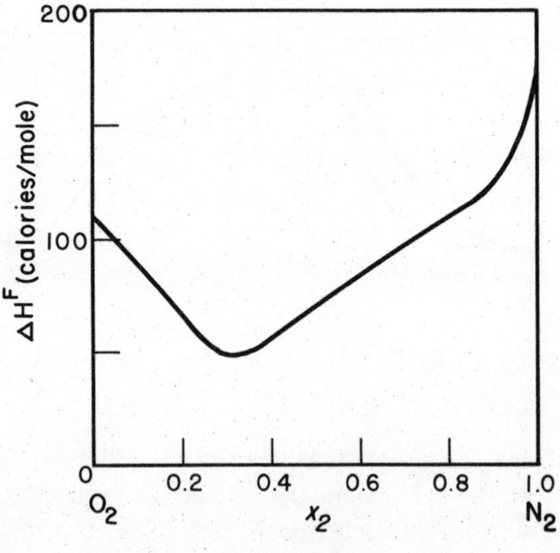

Fig. 15. Heat of fusion of oxygen-nitrogen mixtures

Most of the work on solid solutions of tetrahalides was done by Raeder[17]. With the silicon tetrahalides, he found eutectic diagrams of Type III. The greatest solubility was found in the system $SiBr_4$ - SiI_4 where the two phase region extended only from 4-10% SiI_4. For the system $TiCl_4$ - $TiBr_4$, Raeder found a complete series of solid solutions of Type I.

[17] M. G. Raeder, *Det. Kgl. Norski Videnskabers Selskars Skrifter*, 1929 NR 3; *Z. anorg. allgem. Chem.* **162**, 22 (1927).

Table 3.

	m. p. (°C.)	b. p. (°C.)	V_s	V_l	ΔH^V_{298}	δ_{298}
CCl_4	−23	77		97	7.83	8.6
$(CH_3)_3CCl$	−27	52		109		
$SiCl_4$	−67	57		115	7.19	7.6
$SiBr_4$	5	153	123	127	10.38	8.8
SiI_4	121	288				
$SnCl_4$	−33	113	117	118	9.55	8.7
$SnBr_4$	30	207		131		
$TiCl_4$	−23	136		111	9.62	9.0
$TiBr_4$	38	230	141			

Among the tin tetrahalides, $SnCl_4$ and $SnBr_4$ are sufficiently alike to be completely miscible in the solid phase, as are the pair $SnBr_4$ - SnI_4; both systems exhibiting the minimum of a Type III diagram. On the other hand $SnCl_4$ and SnI_4 are so unlike as to form a eutectic mixture.

Unfortunately the results for the tin and the titanium halides are questionable because of the possibility of exchange of halogen atoms.

Solid solutions among organic compounds. We have noted earlier that two complex organic compounds can form solid solutions only when they are very similar in size, shape and internal pressure. An early investigation of isomorphism was Pascal's [10,18] study of solid solutions of tetraphenyl-silicon, -tin, and -lead; and the corresponding tri-, di-, and monophenyl compounds of Group V, VI and VII elements. The thermodynanic data which are useful for interpretation of his results are shown in Table 4; tetraphenylmethane and tetraphenyl-germane, which Pascal did not use, are included for completeness.

Among the Group IV tetraphenyls, the silicon, tin, and lead compounds (all that were measured) are all mutually soluble in all proportions. The φ_4Sn - φ_4Pb system is virtually ideal, the entire curve (Type I) lying in the two degree range between the melting points. Tetraphenyl-silane differs from the other two in having a smaller molal volume, and the φ_4Si-φ_4Sn and φ_4Si-φ_4Pb systems show Type III minima at 221° and 219 °C. respectively.

The only systems among the Group V triphenyls [18, 18a] showing unbroken solid solutions are φ_3N-φ_3P, φ_3N-φ_3Sb, and φ_3As-φ_3Sb, all with Type III minima. Of the rest, φ_3P-φ_3As and φ_3Sb-φ_3Bi show peritectic transitions (Type IV), while the remaining five show eutectics (Type V). The complete miscibility of triphenylamine with triphenyl phosphine and the arsine with the stibine may be attributed to similarity in internal pressures and molal volumes. Greater disparities in the other systems produce phase separation.

[18] P. Pascal, *Bull. Soc. Chim.*, **Ser.** [**4**], **11**, 321, 595, 1030 (1912); **13**, 744 (1913).
[18a] M. V. Forward, S. T. Bowden, and W. J. Jones, *J. Chem. Soc.*, **1949**, S 26.

Diphenyl sulfide, selenide and telluride are mutually miscible in all proportions, all three systems showing minima (Type III) of which that of the φ_2 Se - φ_2Te is the shallowest, as might have been expected. Diphenyl sulfide and diphenyl ether are only partially miscible, having a wide eutectic zone (Type V); this is attributed to the difference between the oxygen bond angle (110°) and that of sulfur (90°), which produces a sizeable distortion energy in the crystal.

Table 4.

	m. p. (°C.)	b. p. (°C.)	V^s	V^l	δ_l
φ_4 C	282	431			
φ_4 Si	233		288		
φ_4 Ge	236	400			
φ_4 Sn	226	420	284		
φ_4 Pb	228		298		
φ_3 N	127	364	213	297	7.3
φ_3 P	79	384	219	310	7.4
φ_3 As	59	378	234	315	7.6
φ_3 Sb	48	377	234	321	8.0
φ_3 Bi	76		276		
φ_2 O	26	259	159		
φ_2 S	— 22	296		166	
φ_2 Se	2				
φ_2 Te	4				
φ F	— 41	86		94	
φ Cl	— 44	132		101	
φ Br	— 28	156		104	
φ I	— 29	189		111	
φ CN	— 12	191		102	

Of the Group VII phenyls only the system chlorobenzene-bromobenzene exhibits a simple Type I diagram, while the chloride-iodide and bromide-iodide show minima (Type III). Fluorobenzene is incompletely miscible with all the other three (Type V eutectics), due to a combination of internal pressure and volume effects. Chlorobenzene and benzonitrile are similarly only partially miscible.

Another interesting case of isomorphism among complex organic compounds is that of the diphenylene compounds investigated by Cullinane and coworkers[19]. For example, complete series of solid solutions are found in

[19] N. M. Cullinane and C. A. J. Plummer, *J. Chem. Soc.*, **1938**, **63**;
N. M. Cullinane and W. T. Rees, *Trans. Faraday Soc.*, **36**, **507** (1940).

the systems fluorene-diphenylene oxide[20], carbazole-diphenylene oxide, diphenylene oxide-diphenylene sulfide, and diphenylene sulfide-diphenylene selenide, although diphenylene oxide and diphenylene selenide form a eutectic mixture. The complete insolubility of diphenylene dioxide and diphenylene disulfide is attributed to different structure; the former molecule is planar (as evidenced by zero dipole moment); the latter is folded (a large dipole moment).

Compound formation and solid solutions. Many binary solid-liquid diagrams involve more complex liquidus and solidus curves than the five simple types described by Roozeboom. The complications are almost universally attributed to compound formation and almost every maximum in a phase diagram is pounced upon as evidence for a "compound" of that particular composition. The reader will recall from Chapter XI the agnostic view which the authors take with respect to much "compound formation" in solutions. The discussion there applies *a fortiori* to many solid "compounds".

First let us consider one undeniable case of compound formation, that of the iodine-bromine system[21]. Figure 16 shows what is actually two binary systems in juxtaposition, Br_2-IBr and IBr-I_2. The existence of iodine monobromide is beyond question; the equilibrium in aqueous solution[22] is strongly in the direction of IBr, and it may be assumed that the compound is only moderately dissociated even in the gas phase.

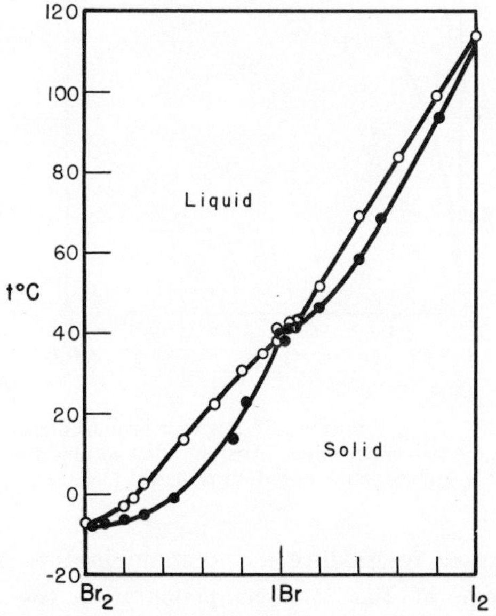

Fig. 16. Solid solutions in the iodine-bromine system

[20] A. Lüttringhaus, *Annalen*, **528**, 229 (1937).
[21] P. C. E. Meerum-Terwogt, *Z. anorg. Chem.*, **47**, 209 (1905).
[22] J. H. Faull, *J. Am. Chem. Soc.*, **56**, 522 (1934).

The general question of "compounds" in the solid phase is illustrated by the controversy over the "existence" of Roozeboom's Type II diagram. As early as 1908, van Laar[23] claimed to have proved impossible a maximum solid-solution diagram; all he actually did was to show that such a diagram was inconsistent with free energy equations derived from the van der Waals equation of state or internal pressure considerations. The contention of more recent exponents of this point of view[24,25] is that in such a diagram as that of *d*-*l*-carvoxime (Fig. 4) the racemic mixture is a compound, and that like the iodine-bromine system, any Type II diagram is actually two Type I diagrams side-by-side.

In opposition to this point of view Timmermans[26] cites other Type II diagrams whose maxima occur at stoichiometric compositions hard to explain as compounds. For example the system 2,4,6, tribromotoluene-2,3,5 tribromotoluene[27] (Fig. 17) shows a maximum at 66% 2,4,6; a 2 : 1 compound is hard to justify physically.

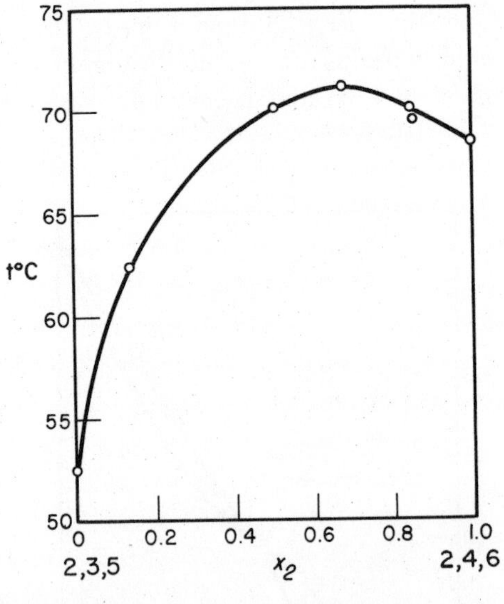

Fig. 17. Solid Solutions of 2,3,5 tribromotoluene and 2,4,6 tribromotoluene (Jaeger). The solidus and liquidus curves were not distinguished

All that is necessary to produce a maximum in the melting curves is a favored arrangement of the two components in the crystal at that composition, resulting in a negative energy somewhat the reverse of the

[23] J. J. van Laar, *Z. physik. Chem.*, **63**, 216 (1908).
[24] E. Jänecke, "*Kurzgefasstes Handbuch aller Legierungen*" (Leipzig, Spamer, 1937).
[25] A. N. Campbell, *Nature,* **153**, **530** (1944).
[26] J. Timmermans, "Les Solutions Concentrées" (Paris, 1936); "Chemical Species" (Paris 1927; New York and London, 1940), pp. 18-24; *Nature*, **154**, 23 (1944).
[27] F. M. Jaeger, *Z. Krist.,* **38**, 583, (1904).

distortion energy discussed in an earlier section. This energy (associated perhaps with a decrease in volume) may be purely physical in source, involving only steric factors and no special "chemical" bonding. On melting, in the disorder of the liquid state, this favored arrangement and its associated energy is lost.

The "compounds" deduced from phase diagrams range all the way from the kind just described to such unquestioned ones as iodine monobromide. The argument is primarily semantic, depending upon how broad a meaning one is willing to give the word "compound". However, since binary diagrams with maxima do exist, and since they may always be described by formal thermodynamics in terms of the initial components, there seems to be no reason to abandon Roozeboom's Type II.

CHAPTER XIX

Metallic Solutions

Metallic solutions offer a particularly inviting field for the application of a theory of solubility because a large amount of data is available, and also because the metals differ among themselves in surface tension, compressibility, expansion, internal pressure and other characteristics far more than the familiar non-metallic liquids, so that they offer a much more severe test of a theory than do most non-metallic solutions. For example, although only a few non-metallic liquids, excluding water, are sufficiently unlike to yield two liquid phases, there are known more than fifty metallic pairs which are incompletely miscible as liquids. In addition the extensive studies of the phase diagrams of solid alloys suggest the extension of solubility theory to solid solutions as we have seen in the preceding chapter.

The experimental investigations of Tammann[1], Meyer[2], Ramsay[3], Richards and coworkers[4], Hulett and De Lury[5], and Hildebrand and coworkers[6], were made with the object of discovering whether the simple laws of non-metallic solutions were applicable or whether the existence of the so-called "free" electrons in the metals affect their thermodynamic properties. Although the deviations from the simple concentration laws of ideal solutions have been found to be great in many cases, it appears that all the systems investigated do approach Raoult's law asymptotically in dilute solutions. The dissolved molecules may be considered as monatomic and departures from the laws of ideal solutions are to be ascribed to causes other than polymerization or dissociation of the atoms into ions and free electrons. It is easy to explain abnormally low activities of the components of the solution on the basis of "compound" formation but there are a number of cases where the activities are much greater than the simple concentration law would re-

[1] G. Tammann, *Z. physik. Chem.* **3**, 441 (1889).

[2] G. Meyer, *Ann. Physik*, [2], **40**, 244 (1890).

[3] W. Ramsay, *J. Chem. Soc.*, **55**, 521 (1889).

[4] T. W. Richards and G. N. Lewis, *Proc. Am. Acad. Arts Sci.*, **34**, 87 (1898).
T. W. Richards and G. S. Forbes, *Carnegie Inst. Pub.*, **56**, 1 (1906).
T. W. Richards and J. H. Wilson and R. N. Garrod-Thomas, *Ibid.*, **118**, 1-72 (1908);
T. W. Richards and F. Daniels, *Trans. Am. Electrochem. Soc.*, **22**, 343 (1912); *J. Am. Chem. Soc.*, **41**, 1732 (1919); T. W. Richards and J. B. Conant, *Ibid.*, **44**, 601 (1922).

[5] G. A. Hulett and R. E. De Lury, *J. Am. Chem. Soc.*, **30**, 1805 (1908).

[6] J. H. Hildebrand, *Trans. Am. Electrochem. Soc.*, **22**, 319, 335 (1912); *J. Am. Chem. Soc.*, **35**, 501 (1913); J. H. Hildebrand and E. D. Eastman. *Ibid*, **36**, 2020 (1914); **37**, 2452 (1915); J. H. Hildebrand, A. H. Foster and C. W. Beebe, *Ibid.*, **42**, 545 (1920).

quire. This type of deviation we are, of course, tempted to explain on the basis of differences of internal pressure, as in the case of non-metallic solutions.

Intermetallic forces. The nature of the intermetallic forces which are responsible for the high cohesive energy of metals is an exeedingly important problem to which no completely satisfactory answer has yet been found. In an attempt to explain the high electrical and thermal conductivity of metals, early metal theory assumed a "free electron" model in which metallic ions were surrounded by a virtual continuum of electrons, the free electron "gas". While initially successful in explaining some phenomena, insuperable difficulties (with respect to the specific heat, for example) arose and the free electron concept has now been replaced by a much more complicated band mechanism for conductivity[7].

More important for our purposes is the development of a satisfactory treatment of metallic binding and structure. A pioneer contribution in this field was made by Hume-Rothery[8] who noted the importance of electron ratios in determining the structure of binary alloys, and deduced the semi-empirical "Hume-Rothery rules". More recently Pauling[9,10] and Engel[11] have attempted to interpret the structure and properties of metals and alloys in terms of their electronic configurations. While their treatments differ in detail, both regard metallic binding as being considerably if not primarily covalent in nature. According to Pauling, these bonds are formed by a hybridization of orbitals involving not only the s and p electrons (the so-called "metallic electrons"), but also part of the d shell as well. Engel, on the other hand distinguishes between the convalent bond formed by the "metallic" s and p electrons and the strong interaction between the uncoupled d electrons; to the latter, he attributes a major part of the large cohesive energy of the transition elements.

These covalent bonds differ however from the usual ones found in non-metallic molecules in that there is a large amount of resonance of the bonds among the various available positions. (For example, in Pauling's view, in a lithium crystal, there is one covalent bond per molecule, resonating among fourteen possible positions). This resonance between a large number of equivalent or almost equivalent positions produces something similar to a spherical force field, the closest approach thereto except for the monatomic rare gases. This condition for the theory of regular solutions is better satisfied by metallic solutions than by solutions of non-metallic polyatomic molecules.

---

[7] Cf. F. Seitz, "The Modern Theory of Solids" (New York, Mc Graw Hill Book Co, 1940).

[8] W. Hume-Rothery, "The Structure of Metals and Alloys" (London, Institute of Metals Monograph, 1936).

[9] L. Pauling, "The Nature of the Chemical Bond", 2nd Edition, (Cornell University Press, 1942), pp. 401-422.

[10] L. Pauling, *Phys. Rev.*, **54**, 899 (1938), *J. Am. Chem. Soc.*, **69**, 542 (1942).

[11] N. N. Engel, *to be published.*

More serious is the problem of the potential between unlike atoms in a metallic solution. We have seen in Chapter VII that the simple internal pressure treatment of the heat of mixing depends upon the approximate validity of a geometric mean law for unlike pairs. We have seen that a geometric mean holds exactly for coulombic and dipole interactions, and to a very good approximation for dispersion forces, but it is very hard to say *a priori* what to expect for intermetallic forces.

Pauling[12,13] has suggested that the energy of a covalent bond between unlike atoms is the geometric mean of the energies of like pairs plus a term for the ionic character of the bond depending upon the square of the difference of the electronegativities. Thus, for two metals in about the same position on the electronegativity scale, we might expect an internal pressure treatment to give reasonable results. On the other hand, where the ionic character of the bond enhances the energy of the unlike pair, we may anticipate smaller heats of mixing than so calculated, and ultimately with large enough discrepancies in electronegativity, the bond between two unlike atoms is so strong that special effects describable as compound formation are observed. In the absence of such specific effects, we actually find a rough correlation.

In addition, we must consider Engel's suggestion that in the transition metals the cohesive energy depends primarily upon an additional type of binding between uncoupled *d* electrons. If this kind of interaction is subject to a geometric mean law, it might explain the fact that alloys between two transition metals show very few compounds and rather better agreement with an internal pressure treatment than do the others. (It should be noted that if the energy between unlike pairs is the sum of terms, each separately the geometric mean of corresponding terms for like pairs, the total energy is less than the geometric mean, leading to a *greater* heat of mixing than that based upon internal pressures - cf. Chapter VII).

For a more detailed discussion of these and other questions, we must turn to a consideration of some actual systems. First, however, we shall consider the internal pressures and solubility parameters of the pure metals.

Solubility parameters of the metals. For a qualitative interpretation of metallic solutions, it will be useful to consider the internal pressures of the pure metals, using the same solubility parameters δ as in the case of non-metallic solutions. These may be calculated in the same way as for non-metallic substances from the heats of vaporization or sublimation and atomic volumes. Table 1 shows ΔH^S, V, and δ for the metals in their standard states at 25° (solid except for mercury), arranged in order of descending δ. We are indebted to our colleague, Professor Leo Brewer, for the data on the heat contents and heats of sublimation[14].

[12] L. Pauling and J. Sherman, *J. Am. Chem. Soc.*, **59**, 1450 (1937).

[13] Reference 9, pp. 47-52.

[14] L. Brewer, "Thermodynamic Properties of the Elements," declassified report MDDC-438-C.

We see that the solubility parameters of the metals are enormously greater than those for the non-metallic substances we have discussed previously, extending as high as 145 for several. Since these are an order of magnitude greater than those encountered with substances like benzene or iodine, we may expect very different effects.

Table 1. Solubility parameters of the Metals at 25° C

	ΔH^S (kcal.)	V (cm³)	δ $(cal/cm^3)^{\frac{1}{2}}$		ΔH^S	V	δ
Re	189	8.9	146	Al	75.0	10.0	86
W	201.6	9.6	145	Ag	69.1	10.3	82
B	90	(4.3)	145	Sc	93	14.5	80
Os	174	8.4	144	Ge	78.4	13.7	76
Ir	165	8.6	139	Ga	65	11.8	74
Ru	160	8.3	139	Y	103	(19)	72
Ta	200	10.8	136	As	58	13.1	66
Rh	138	8.3	129	β-Sn	70.0	16.3	65
Be	80	4.9	129	α-La	88	22.4	63
Mo	156.0	9.4	128	In	57.4	15.7	60
Cb	175.6	10.8	127	Sb	63	18.2	59
α-Co	105	6.6	126	Zn	31.2	9.2	58
Ni	101.8	6.6	124	Li	37.0	13.0	54
Pt	135	9.1	121	Pb	48.5	18.3	51
V	120	8.5	119	Mg	35.9	14.0	50
α-Fe	96.7	7.1	117	α-Tl	42.8	17.3	49
α-Hf	170	13.5	112	Bi	49	21.3	48
Cr	84.5	7.3	108	Cd	26.8	13.0	45
Cu	81.5	7.2	107	α-Ca	42.6	26.0	40
Pd	93	8.9	102	α-Sr	39.2	32.9	34
U	128	12.7	100	Ba	42	37	33
α-Mn	68.6	7.6	95	Na	26.0	23.7	33
α-Zr	125	14.0	94	Hg	14.5	14.8	31
α-Ti	95	10.7	94	K	21.5	45.4	21
Au	90.5	10.3	93	Rb	20.5	56	19
Si	90	11.7	88	Cs	18.8	70	16

The δ's tabulated in Table 1 are for the stable phase at 25°, and it would be only natural to inquire about the changes with increasing temperature, with transitions to other crystal lattices, and upon melting to a liquid. Actually for high melting and boiling metals, these changes are relatively small, thanks to small coefficients of thermal expansion and small ΔC_p's, as well as small volume changes and heats of fusion. Figure 1 shows a typical case, that of iron, which passes through a magnetic transition, then changes crystal structure only to revert to the original body-centered lattice, and finally melts at 1800° K. In a range of two thousand degrees, the

Table 2. Metal solubility parameters at various temperatures.

	298° K	500° K	1000° K	1500° K	2000° K
Li	54	*50*	*46*		
Na	33	*31*	*27*		
K	22	*20*	*17*		
Rb	19	*17*			
Cs	16	*15*			
Be	129			121	
Mg	50	50	*43*		
Ca	40 (α)		37 (β)		
Al	86		*79*		
Ti	94 (α)		89 (β)		
Zr	94 (α)		91 (β)		
Ta	136				132
Mo	128				124
W	145				140
Mn	95 (α)			89 (γ)	
Fe	117 (α)	116 (α)	112 (α)	109 (γ)	*102*
Co	126 (α)		122 (β)		
Pt	121		119		
Cu	107	106	103	*95*	*91*
Ag	82		78	*71*	
Au	93		90	*84*	
Zn	58	56	*50*		
Cd	45	43	*38*		
Hg [a]	*31*				
Ga	74	*73*			
Tl	49 (α)	48 (α)	*45*		
Sn [b]	65 (β)	64 (β)	*61*	*59*	*57*
Pb	51	50	*47*		
As	66	66			
Sb	59	58	*54*		
Bi	48	47	*44*		

(a) Solid Hg has a δ of 33 at 0° K.
(b) Gray or α - Sn has a δ of 58 at 0° K.

solubility parameter of iron decreases from 118 to 102, an enormous drop numerically when compared with benzene for example, but small percentage-wise. In addition this drop is much the same for other metals; so for

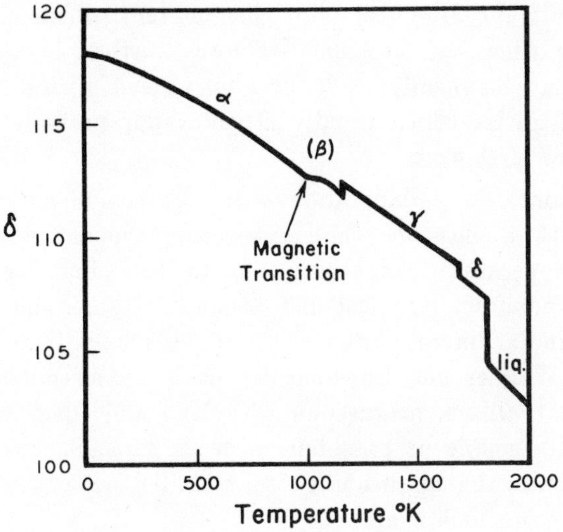

Fig. 1. Solubility parameter of iron as a function of temperature

qualitative purposes, we may assume that $\delta_1 - \delta_2$ for a particular binary system is independent of temperature and much the same for solid and liquid phases. Table 2 shows δ's for a number of the commoner metals at several specified temperatures (those for liquids in italics).

Solutions of liquid metals

There are two reliable methods available for investigating the activities of the individual components of liquid metal systems: first, measurement of vapor pressures at high temperatures, as exemplified by the work of Hildebrand and Eastman on silver, gold, bismuth and thallium amalgams; and, second, measurement of the electromotive force of concentration cells in which one electrode consists of a pure metal or an alloy in which this metal has a known activity. The second method has been applied by Richards and his co-workers to a large number of solutions of electropositive metals in mercury. Except in the case of thallium amalgams, the concentration range in the electromotive force measurements investigated never exceeded 10 per cent but was limited by the low solubility of most of the metals in mercury at room temperature. This method has the theoretical advantage that it measures the activity directly and does not involve the assumption that the vapor obeys the perfect gas laws. It has the practical advantage that a number of alloys of different concentrations can be studied simultaneously with considerable saving in time. Further, it is possible to work with metals of low vapor pressure. For example at 500° the vapor pressure of zinc is about 1 mm., which would make accurate measurements somewhat difficult for alloys of low zinc content. Such alloys offer no special difficulty when the electromotive force method is applied. Finally, measurements may be readily made over a wide temperature range with none of the difficulties which usually attend vapor pressure work at very high or very low pressures.

N. W. Taylor[15], in collaboration with the senior author, obtained a comprehensive set of data on e. m. f.'s covering the entire range of composition and temperature ranges of 100° to 150° for five binary liquid alloys of zinc, cadmium, tin, lead and bismuth. Hildebrand and Sharma[16] have made a similar investigation with alloys of thallium with tin and with lead, and Wagner and Engelhardt[17] have measured alloys of bismuth in lead, tin and thallium, magnesium with lead and silver with gold.

These results enable us to obtain at least partial answers to some of the questions about the applicability to metallic systems of the methods developed in the previous chapters.

1. First, we must ask how well the assumption of regular solutions (Chapter III), that the entropy of mixing is ideal, applies to metallic systems. The most direct test is offered by the temperature coefficient of a cell, one electrode of which consists of an alloy, the other of the baser component in the pure state. The electromotive force **E** of such a cell is

$$\mathbf{zFE} = -\Delta\overline{F}_1 = -RT\ln a_1 \tag{1}$$

where a_1 is the activity of the baser metal in the alloy, **z** the charge of its ion in the connecting electrolyte, and **F** is the Faraday (96,500 coulombs). To get the temperature coefficient of the cell, we take the derivative

$$\frac{d\,\mathbf{E}}{d\,T} = \frac{-1}{\mathbf{zF}}\,\frac{d\,\Delta\overline{F}_1}{d\,T} = \frac{\Delta\,\overline{S}_1}{\mathbf{zF}} \tag{2}$$

If $\Delta\overline{S}_1$ is indeed ideal, then the temperature coefficient is merely

$$\frac{d\,\mathbf{E}}{d\,T} = \frac{-R}{\mathbf{z\,F}}\ln x_1 \tag{3}$$

---

[15] N. W. Taylor, *J. Am. Chem. Soc.*, **45**, 2865 (1923).

[16] J. H. Hildebrand and J. N. Sharma, *J. Am. Chem. Soc.*. **51**, 462 (1929).

[17] C. Wagner and G. Engelhardt, *Z. physik. Chem.*, **A159**, 16 (1932).

Table 3 compares the calculated and observed values of $d\mathbf{E}/dT$ for a number of alloys. The agreement is excellent for zinc in cadmium, good for cadmium in tin and lead and not so good for zinc in tin and thallium in tin.

Table 3. Temperature Coefficients of Alloy Concentration Cells. $-d\mathbf{E}/dT$, millivolts per degree (Temperature range: 400 — 600° C.).

Alloy	Mole per cent	obs.	calc.	diff.
Zn in Cd	69.1	0.016	0.016	0.000
	25.1	.061	.060	.001
	15.0	.079	.082	—.003
Cd in Pb	50.9	.036	.029	.007
	26.9	.063	.057	.006
	12.3	.095	.090	.005
Cd in Sn	63.0	.026	.020	.006
	25.8	.067	.059	.008
	8.4	.113	.107	.008
Zn in Sn	84.5	.010	.007	.003
	58.3	.029	.023	.006
	38.4	.062	.038	.024
	22.1	.095	.065	.030
Tl in Sn	67.1	.044	.034	.010
	37.2	.118	.085	.033
	10.3	.255	.196	.059

The rough correspondence between the deviation from Raoult's law, $\Delta\overline{F}_1^E = RT\ln\gamma_1$ and the heat of transference from the ideal to the actual solution (*i. e.* $\Delta\overline{H}_1$) was pointed out by Taylor. The subject was further treated by Butler[18] and by Wagner and Engelhardt[17], the latter utilizing in addition to results by themselves and by Taylor, the direct calorimetric determinations by Kawakami[19]. Butler pointed out that the ratio of $\Delta\overline{H}_1$ to $\Delta\overline{F}_1$ was practically constant for different compositions of the same pair of metals, but was unity only in the case of Zn in Zn-Cd and greater than unity in the other cases, the greatest being Zn in Zn-Sn where it was 2.2. Wagner and Engelhardt compared the values of these quantities extrapolated to $x_1 = 0$ where they possess their maximum values, and further calculated $\Delta\overline{H}_1$ from the direct calorimetric work of Kawakami.

Table 4 gives these comparisons. Taylor's values of $\Delta\overline{F}_1^E$ have been altered, particularly in the case of Zn-Cd where the extrapolation is rather

[18] J. A. V. Butler, *J. Am. Chem. Soc.*, **47**, 117, (1925).
[19] M. Kawakami, *Sci. Rep. Tohoku Imp. Univ.*, **[1]**, **16**, 915 (1927).

long, by plotting against the square of the volume fraction φ_2^2 which gives a linear relation, instead of the square of the mole fraction x_2^2, as we shall see.

Table 4. Comparison of $\Delta \overline{F}_1^E$ with $\Delta \overline{H}_1$ when $x_1 = 0$.

Alloy	t ° C.	$\Delta \overline{F}_1^E$	$\Delta \overline{H}_1$ Helmholtz	$\Delta \overline{H}_1$ Calorim.
Zn in Cd	436	1800	1700	1500
Cd in Sn	431	1000	1300	1400
Cd in Pb	432	1750	2300	2200
Zn in Sn	432	1150	2500	2200
Tl in Sn	352	1300	1800	....
Pb in Bi	475	— 1300	— 1450	— 1500
Sn in Bi	330	+ 100	....	— 400
Cd in Bi	431	0	0	....
Tl in Pb	438	0	0	....

The agreement between the two sets of values for $\Delta \overline{H}_1$ is within the limits of error of both. There can be no doubt, however, that although $\Delta \overline{F}^E$ and $\Delta \overline{H}$ agree in some cases, the discrepancies in others are quite real and even large. This is not entirely unexpected, since we have seen in Chapter VIII that large heats of mixing produce significant departures from random orientation and result in $\Delta \overline{F}^E$ values somewhat lower than those for $\Delta \overline{H}$. In addition, we have seen in Chapter VI that disparities in size produce negative deviations from ideality; for example, if we use Equation VI — 18 and let $V_2 / V_1 = 2$, we find at 700 °K that $\Delta \overline{F}_1$ is reduced by an entropy correction of over 400 calories. It is perhaps significant that the greatest difference between $\Delta \overline{F}^E$ and $\Delta \overline{H}$ occurs for zinc in tin, the system which has the greatest difference in volumes.

2 We must now consider the propriety of using the square of the volume fraction φ_2^2 rather than that of the mole fraction x_2^2, as in Equation VII — 11. Since these become identical when the molal volumes of the pure components are equal, the severest test is when they differ as widely as possible. The molal volumes of cadmium and lead according to the density determinations of Hogness[20] are 14.25 and 19.70 cc. respectively at 432°. The measurements of Taylor, referred to above, enable us to compare the constancy of $(\delta_1 - \delta_2)^2$ in the former equation, which is equivalent to $\Delta \overline{F}_1^E = k_\varphi \varphi_2^2$ with the constancy of k_x in the latter equation, which is $\Delta \overline{F}_1^E = k_x x_2^2$. The values of k_x in Table 5 show a strong drift while the values of k_φ are constant within the limit of error. The other systems, when examined in this way, show the same advantage of volume fraction over mole fraction[21], as we have already noted in non-metallic solutions. (Cf. Chapters VII and XIII.)

[20] T. R. Hogness, *J. Am. Chem. Soc.*, **43**, 1621 (1921).

[21] Cf. also G. Scatchard, *J. Am. Chem. Soc.*, **53**, 3186 (1931).

Table 5. Test of Mole Fraction vs. Volume Fraction.
Solutions of Cadmium in Lead at 432°.

x_1	$\log \frac{a_1}{x_1}$	$\Delta \overline{F}_1^E$ cals.	x_2^2	φ_2^2	$\frac{\Delta \overline{F}_1^E}{v_1 \varphi_2^2} = \frac{k_\varphi}{v_1}$	$\frac{\Delta \overline{F}_1^E}{x_2^2} = k_x$
0.786	0.044	142	0.0467	0.075	133	3040
.696	.080	258	.0925	.142	127	2790
.584	.130	419	.173	.246	119	2420
.509	.176	567	.241	.327	122	2350
.401	.243	782	.359	.441	124	2180
.155	.421	1355	.714	.780	122	1900
.123	.469	1510	.769	.825	128	1960
					Mean 125	

$D = (k_\varphi / v_1)^{\frac{1}{2}} = 11.2$

Table 6 contains summaries of the values of k_φ from the original unsmoothed data of three other systems. The superiority indicated in Table 5 has also been confirmed by calculations of essentially the same nature made by Wagner and Engelhardt.

In connection with this volume fraction vs. mole fraction question, it is interesting to consider the influence of different degrees of packing in the liquid phase[22]. We may visualize two metals whose atomic radii are identical which pack very differently in the liquid state, each preserving more or less intact the approximate solid structure. Metal 1 for example may have only 6 or 8 nearest neighbors while metal 2 may have a close-packed structure with a coordination number $z = 12$. In such a case, even for identical atomic radii, the atomic volumes calculated from observed densities will be markedly different. If we assume that a particular solution of the two metals has an average coordination number z_m we may express the energy (heat) of mixing in terms of z's, interaction constants k_{11}, k_{12} and k_{22} for the three possible pairs, and the mole fractions x_1 and x_2

$$\Delta E^M = \Delta H^M = \boldsymbol{N} \left[z_1 k_{11} x_1 + z_2 k_{22} x_2 - z_m (k_{11} x_1^2 + 2 k_{12} x_1 x_2 + k_{22} x_2^2) \right] \quad (4)$$

If we assume, for the moment without justification, that the coordination number z_m of the solution is the harmonic mean, and define composition variables y_1 and y_2 in terms of the z's we obtain

[22] We are indebted to Dr. A. W. Lawson of the Institute for the Study of Metals of the University of Chicago for calling our attention to this problem.

$$\frac{1}{z_m} = \frac{x_1}{z_1} + \frac{x_2}{z_2} \tag{5}$$

$$y_1 = \frac{x_1 / z_1}{x_1 / z_1 + x_2 / z_2} = \frac{x_1 z_m}{z_1} \tag{6a}$$

$$y_2 = \frac{x_2 / z_2}{x_1 / z_1 + x_2 / z_2} = \frac{x_2 z_m}{z_2} \tag{6b}$$

Substituting Equations 5 and 6 into Equation 4, we obtain

$$\Delta H^M = \frac{N}{z_m} (k_{11} z_1^2 - 2 k_{12} z_1 z_2 + k_{22} z_2^2)\, y_1 y_2 \tag{7}$$

Comparison with the equations in Chapter VII reveals a close similarity.

For constant atomic radius, the atomic volume V decreases with increasing coordination number z, corresponding to tighter packing. A useful approximation[23] would be to assume V to be proportional to $1/z$. In terms of this assumption, Equation 5 is merely the condition that the volume change on mixing is zero. Similarly, the y's become the volume fraction φ's, and $1/z_m$ is proportional to the molal volume V_m of the mixture. If in addition, we assume the geometric mean: $k_{12} = \sqrt{k_{11} k_{22}}$ Equation 7 reduces to

$$\Delta H^M = V_m \left[\left(\frac{\Delta E_1^V}{V_1} \right)^{\frac{1}{2}} - \left(\frac{\Delta E_2^V}{V_2} \right)^{\frac{1}{2}} \right]^2 \varphi_1 \varphi_2 = V_m (\delta_1 - \delta_2)^2 \varphi_1 \varphi_2 \tag{8}$$

Equation 8 of course is identically the equation obtained from a much different model in Chapter VII. We see that whether the difference in atomic volume depends upon atomic size or atomic packing, in either case we are led to an approximate dependence upon volume fraction. (The dependence upon volume fraction is inherent in Equation 7 and is independent of the introduction of the geometric mean to obtain Equation 8).

3. Finally we turn to the relevance of the internal pressures of the pure components to the thermodynamics of their solutions. If $k_\varphi = V_1 (\delta_1 - \delta_2)^2$ as it is with most non-metallic nonpolar solutions, $(k_\varphi / V_1)^{\frac{1}{2}} = D$ should equal $\delta_1 - \delta_2$ and be additive for different systems. The additivity may be very simply tested in the cases in which we have data for three

[23] This is not exactly true as a study of the γ-values in Chapter V, p. 76 reveals, but if we consider that in close-packed structures the second nearest neighbors are more significant, an assumption that the atomic volume is inversely proportional to an *effective* coordination number becomes very plausible.

binary systems involving but three components. We have such a triangle in cadmium, tin, and zinc; Table 6 gives values of D for the three alloys. If $D_{12} = \delta_1 - \delta_2$, $D_{13} = \delta_1 - \delta_3$ and $D_{23} = \delta_2 - \delta_3$, we should be able to calculate values of δ_1, δ_2 and δ_3 which would satisfy the values shown in the table; it is evident that this is not possible.

Table 6. Values of D for Binary Alloys.

Cd in Sn		Zn in Cd		Zn in Sn	
x_1	D^2	x_1	D^2	x_1	D^2
0.816	73.2	0.690	167	0.845	136
.794	64.6	.536	163	.780	201
.630	76.9	.344	165	.644	162
.569	59.0	.251	177	.583	149
.451	68.6	.150	178	.497	142
.258	63.6			.384	131
.222	69.9			.221	120
.084	65.2			.173	120
Mean	67.6		170		145
D	± 8.2		± 13.0		± 12.0

A similar triangle occurs with cadmium, bismuth and tin. The Cd-Bi and Bi-Sn systems form nearly ideal solutions, but the Cd-Sn system, which should also form ideal solutions if the solubility parameters were strictly additive, shows a strong positive deviation.

Since the equation was derived for total energy rather than free energy, we might try to improve matters by using heats rather than free energies in a search for additivity, but this yields no more satisfactory results.

It is interesting to compare the values of D determined from the e. m. f. studies with $\delta_1 - \delta_2$, the difference of the solubility parameters. The comparison of the experimental D with $\delta_1 - \delta_2$ taken from Table 2 is shown in Table 7.

We see that, although the order of magnitude is correct, the agreement is far from perfect, except for the Cd-Pb, Zn-Cd, Zn-Sn, and Tl-Pb systems. Especially disconcerting is the striking fact that zinc and lead, which are close together in solubility parameters, deviate so strongly as to form two liquid phases.

An examination of the data upon amalgams[24] leads to similar results. A number of amalgams have been investigated by both vapor pressure

[24] Zn, J. H. Hildebrand, *Trans. Am. Electrochem. Soc.*, **22** 319 (1912); Ag, Au, Bi, Tl, J. H. Hildebrand and E. D. Eastman, *J. Am. Chem. Soc.*, **36**, 2020 (1914); **37**, 2452 (1915); Cd, Sn, Pb, J. H. Hildebrand, A. H. Foster and C. W. Beebe, *Ibid.*, **42**, 545 (1920).

and concentration cell methods. The results by the former method are summarized in Figure 2. The activity of mercury in solutions with cadmium and thallium is less than ideal corresponding to abnormally high attraction

Table 7.

System	D (exp.)	$\delta_1 - \delta_2$ (1000° K)
Cd-Pb	11.2	9
Cd-Sn	8.2	23
Zn-Cd	13.1	12
Zn-Sn	12.0	11
Tl-Sn	8.7	16
Sn-Bi	0	17
Cd-Bi	0	6
Tl-Pb	0	2
Zn-Pb	(two liq.)	3

between unlike molecules such as accompanies compound formation. In harmony with this Taylor has presented evidence from X-ray diffraction for the presence of Cd_3Hg in solid amalgams. Hildebrand and Eastman suggested a similar interpretation for thallium amalgams.

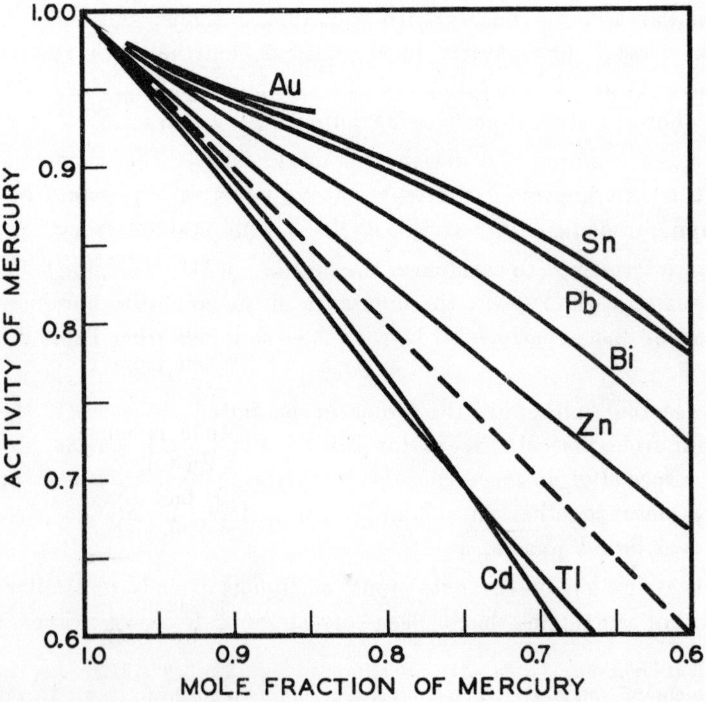

Fig. 2. Activity of mercury in various amalgams

Immiscibility of liquid metals. We have seen in Chapter XVI that when the heat of mixing is sufficiently great, separation into two phases occurs and the two liquids are only partially miscible. For our purposes, sufficient accuracy is achieved if we define the conditions for complete miscibility as

$$\frac{V_1 + V_2}{2} (\delta_1 - \delta_2)^2 < 2RT \qquad (9)$$

For the large number of metals whose atomic volumes lie around 10 cc, we may observe that for the two liquids to be miscible at 1000°K, $\delta_1 - \delta_2$ must not exeed 20, while at 2000° K, $\delta_1 - \delta_2$ must not exceed 28. For other temperatures and other atomic volumes the conditions are somewhat different, but may be calculated from Equation 9.

We may note that these tolerable differences in δ are much greater for the metals than for normal organic substances, primarily because of the smaller volume (10 instead of 100) and because of the higher temperatures at which the liquid phases are found.

We may compare these conditions with the large number of binary liquid metal systems in which phase separation is found. Table 8 compares the known two-phase liquid systems[25] with the calculated $\delta_1 - \delta_2$.

The temperatures listed in Table 8 are *not* critical temperatures, but merely the temperatures at which two liquid phases have been observed; the critical solution temperatures are mostly unknown but may be hundreds or possibly over a thousand degrees higher. Except as indicated the $\delta_1 - \delta_2$ values are those of the solids at room temperature. The agreement is in general very good — of the forty-seven systems listed in Table 8, only five (**Ag-Mn, Bi-Zn, Ca-Cd, Pb-Zn, and Tl-Zn**) disagree markedly with **Equation 9.** Two others (Ag-Cr and Ca-Na) should be miscible according to Equation 9, but are within the limit of error of the δ's and the theory. A satisfactory explanation of the five exceptions remains to be found.

While, except for the few exceptions noted, all two phase liquid metal systems show large enough differences in solubility parameters to satisfy Equation 9, the converse is not nearly so valid; many metals with large differences in δ form homogeneous liquid phases. Most of these cases, however, show intermediate solid phases ("compounds") confirming the existence of especially strong interactions between unlike atoms, many of which can be correlated with differences in electronegativity. Among these compound-forming systems are those showing the intermediate Hume-Rothery types, such as Cu-Zn, Ag-Cd, etc. The existence of such compounds is *prima facie* evidence against applying the simple internal pressure treatment to such systems.

[25] Much of the data on metal phase diagrams is taken from M. Hansen, "Aufbau der Zweistoff Legierungen", (Berlin, Julius Springer, 1936).

Table 8. Two Phase Liquid Systems.

System	Temperature	$\pm(\delta_1-\delta_2)$	System	Temperature	$\pm(\delta_1-\delta_2)$
Ag-Co	1900	44	Cd-K	800	23
Ag-Cr	1800	26	Co-Pb	1700	75
Ag-Fe	1900	35	Cr-Pb	1800	57
Ag-Mn	1500	13	Cr-Sn	1700	43
Ag-Ni	1800	42	Cu-Pb	1300	56
Ag-V	2100	37	Cu-Tl	1300	58
Al-Bi	1000	35[b]	Fe-Pb	1800	66
Al-Cd	1000	41[b]	Ga-Hg	400	43
Al-K	1000	62[b]	Ga-Pb	600	23
Al-Na	1000	52[b]	K-Li	500	30[a]
Al-Pb	1000	32[b]	K-Mg	1000	24[b]
Al-Tl	1000	34[b]	K-Zn	900	33[b]
As-Tl	500	18[a]	Li-Na	500	19[a]
Bi-Co	1600	78	Mg-Na	900	14[b]
Bi-Cr	1900	60	Mn-Pb	1500	44
Bi-Fe	1800	69	Mn-Tl	1500	46
Bi-Ga	500	26	Na-Zn	900	23[b]
Bi-Mn	1500	47	Ni-Pb	1600	73
Bi-Si	1700	40	Ni-Tl	1700	75
Bi-Zn	700	6[b]	Pb-Si	1700	37
Ca-Cd	1000	5	Pb-Zn	700	3[b]
Ca-Na	1000	10[b]	Si-Tl	1700	39
Cd-Fe	1800	72	Tl-Zn	700	5[b]
Cd-Ga	600	29			

Notes: *a* at 500° K; *b* at 1000° K.

Solid Solutions of Metals.

We now wish to investigate the possibility of extending the treatment of liquid metals developed in the preceding pages to the extensive data on solid solutions of metals. Since we have already shown that the presence of intermediate phases or compounds signifies the breakdown of a geometric mean law and the consequent invalidity of the internal pressure treatment, we shall from the outset confine ourselves to those solid systems where such factors are absent or at least unimportant.

Recalling the discussion of strain energy and crystal structure in Chapter XVIII, we may state four conditions all of which must be satisfied in order to obtain a complete series of solid solutions.

1. The solubility parameters of the two components must not differ by too great an amount.

2. The atomic volumes of the two metals must be fairly similar, else a sizeable amount of strain energy will be introduced.

3. The two pure metals must exist in identical or very similar crystal structures.

4. Special forces tending to produce intermediate phases of different crystal structures must be absent.

Where the difference in solubility parameters or atomic volumes becomes too great, only partial miscibility will be found at temperatures where the solid phase exists, and for extreme differences[26], the heat of mixing will be so great that the solid solution region may be completely negligible, resulting in a eutectic mixture of the two pure solids.

Where the two metals crystallize in different lattices, but the conditions for solid solutions are otherwise favorable, we may find extensive solid solutions with only a small intermediate two phase region representing the transition between lattices. Of special interest are those pure metals which can exist in two or more crystal lattices, such as Fe, Co, etc. Depending on the crystal lattice of the second component one of these structures will be stabilized at the expense of the other.

Since the crystal lattice is of such great importance, we need to classify the metals according to crystal type. For our purpose, five major types need to be distinguished[27].

I. Body-centered cubic — Space Group O_h^9 — Structurbericht Class A-2. Each atom has eight nearest neighbors and six more at a distance of 15% greater.

II. Hexagonal close-packed — Space Group D_{6h}^4 — SB Class A-3. Each atom has twelve nearest neighbors; the spheres are close packed in a hexagonal structure.

III. Face-centered cubic or cubic close-packed — Space Group O_h^5—SB Class A-1. Each atom has twelve nearest neighbors, but the close packing is cubic. With the metals of this group we include also indium and γ-manganese which have a slightly distorted face-centered tetragonal structure (Space group D_{4h}^{17} — SB Class A-6).

IV. Diamond structure — Space Group O_h^7 — SB Class A-4. Each atom has four nearest neighbors in the familiar tetrahedral arrangement. With these we also include white or β-tin, which has a tetragonal distorted form of this structure (Space group D_{4h}^{19} — SB Class A-5).

---

[26] Extreme differences in atomic volume may lead to a different mode of packing in which the smaller atoms fit into the interstices between the larger atoms. This could be considered as a different kind of "compound" formation, not involving special forces. These are, however, relatively rare between two metals.

[27] According to Engel[11], these five types correspond to metals with one, two, three, four, and five available electrons per atom.

V. Sheet or layer structure — Space group D_{3d}^5 — SB Class **A-7**. This group, including bismuth, antimony, arsenic, and red phosphorus, has a two dimensional layer structure bound together by three normal covalent bonds per atom.

To these, we must add the complex structures of α- and β-manganese, uranium, gallium, and mercury.

Figure 4 shows the metals divided into these five classes, arranged diagrammatically according to their solubility parameters at 25° C,

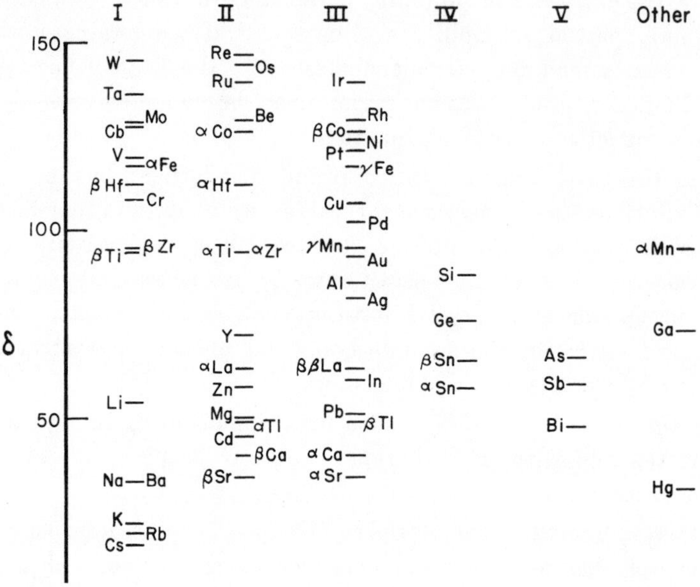

Fig. 3. Solubility parameters of metals grouped into crystal classes

A most interesting group of solid solutions are those between the transition metals of Group III (the face-centered cubic lattice), ranging from iridium ($\delta = 139$) to silver ($\delta = 82$) and including the high temperature forms of iron (γ-Fe), cobalt (β-Co) and manganese (γ-Mn). Aluminum ($\delta = 86$) falls in this range but forms compounds with most of the others and is therefore excluded. The atomic volumes range from 6.6 for nickel to 10.3 for silver, a maximum variation of 36%, of importance only in the extreme cases. At 1500° K. the maximum permissible difference in δ is about 25-30; greater differences will result in phase separation.

Table 9 lists the known binary systems of these metals and their nature. Twenty-seven systems show complete series of solid solutions, in agreement with the $\Delta\delta$ values. The systems showing partial miscibility are in general agreement with the differences in δ, the solubility becoming less and less with larger and larger differences. Rh-Cu and γMn-Au show intermediate compounds with different crystal lattices, so complete miscibility is excluded; Cu-Ag and γFe-Au have sufficient strain energies due to discrepancies in their molal volumes to account for their phase separation; only the systems βCo-Cu and γFe-Cu are difficult to explain.

Table 9 A. Solid solutions of face centered cubic transition metals

System	δ_1-δ_2	Solubility limits (Mole %)
Ir-Pt	18[a]	completely miscible
Ir-γFe	22[a]	„ „
Ir-Cu	32[a]	0.5% Ir
Ir-Au	46[a]	2.8% Ir
Ir-Ag	57[a]	virtually zero solubility
Rh-Ni	5[a]	completely miscible
Rh-Pt	8[a]	„ „
Rh-γFe	12[a]	„ „
Rh-Cu	22[a]	20% Rh, 10% Cu
Rh-Pd	27[a]	completely miscible
Rh-Au	36[a]	3% Rh, 2% Au
Rh-Ag	47[a]	$<$ 0.1% Ag
βCo-Ni	2[a]	completely miscible
βCo-Pt	3[b]	„ „
βCo-γFe	10[b]	„ „
βCo-Cu	19[b]	8% Co, 12% Cu
βCo-Pd	24[a]	completely miscible
βCo-γMn	31[a]	„ „ (?)
βCo-Au	32[b]	15% Co, 3% Au
βCo-Ag	44[b]	.001% Co (2 liquids)
Ni-Pt	3[a]	completely miscible
Ni-γFe	7[a]	„ „
Ni-Cu	17[a]	„ „
Ni-Pd	22[a]	„ „
Ni-γMn	29[a]	30% Ni, 55% Mn
Ni-Au	31[a]	completely miscible above 1120°K
Ni-Ag	42[a]	0.1% Ni, (2 liquids)
Pt-γFe	7[b]	completely miscible
Pt-Cu	16[b]	„ „
Pt-Pd	19[a]	„ „
Pt-Au	29[b]	completely miscible above 1430°K
Pt-Ag	41[b]	40% Pt, 20% Ag
γFe-Cu	9[b]	4% Fe, 8% Cu
γFe-Cu	15[a]	completely miscible
γFe-Mn	20[c]	„ „ (?)
γFe-Au	22[b]	60% Fe, 5% Au
γFe-Ag	34[b]	.001% (2 liquids)
Cu-Pd	5[a]	completely miscible
Cu-γMn	12[a]	„ „ (?)
Cu-Au	13[b]	„ „
Cu-Ag	25[b]	12% Cu, 5% Ag
Pd-Au	9[a]	completely miscible
Pd-Ag	20[a]	„ „
*γMn-Au	2[a]	Intermediate phases
γMn-Ag	13[a]	35% Mn
Au-Ag	12[b]	completely miscible

Notes: * -intermediate phases or compounds
a at 298°K
b at 1000°K
c at 1500°K

Of particular interest are the systems involving copper, silver, and gold, shown in Figures 4, 5, and 6. Silver and gold with almost identical atomic volumes, and differing by only 12 in the δ-scale, form almost perfect solid solutions as seen in Figure 4. (Actually, according to measurements of Wagner and Engelhardt[28], the deviations from Raoult's law in Ag-Au solutions are negative, so the solubility parameters do not tell the whole story). Copper and gold have a similar difference in solubility parameters ($\Delta\delta = 13$), but the additional strain energy in the solid, due to a 30% difference in atomic volumes, produces a minimum in the solidus and liquidus curves (Figure 5). On the other hand in the system Cu-Ag, the greater difference in solubility parameters ($\Delta\delta = 25$), coupled with about the same strain energy as in Cu-Au, permits only partial miscibility and produces a Roozeboom Type V eutectic diagram (Figure 6). These systems are of particular interest because they show the separate effects of the strain energy and the internal pressures, and because the solubilities are not in the same order as in the periodic table, gold lying intermediate between silver and copper.

Table 9B. Solid solutions of face-centered cubic transition metals. (Solubility limits in mole percent)

Solute	Ir	Rh	β-Co	Ni	Pt	γ-Fe	Cu	Pd	γ-Mn	Au	Ag
δ	139	129	126	124	121	117	107	102	95	93	82
Solvent											
Ir	∞	—	—	—	∞	∞	—	—	—	—	—
Rh	—	∞	—	∞	∞	∞	10	∞	—	2	<0.1
β-Co	—	—	∞	∞	∞	∞	12	∞	(∞)	3	—
Ni	—	∞	∞	∞	∞	∞	∞	∞	55	∞	—
Pt	∞	∞	∞	∞	∞	∞	∞	∞	—	∞	5
γ-Fe	∞	∞	∞	∞	∞	∞	8	∞	(∞)	5	—
Cu	0.5	20	8	∞	∞	4	∞	∞	(∞)	∞	5
Pd	—	∞	∞	∞	∞	∞	∞	∞	—	∞	∞
γ-Mn	—	—	(∞)	30	—	(∞)	(∞)	—	∞	*	—
Au	2.8	3	15	∞	∞	60	∞	∞	*	∞	∞
Ag	~0	—	0.001	0.1	1.2	0.001	12	∞	35	∞	∞

Two of the systems listed in Table 9 show solid critical solution temperatures quite analogous to the limit of phase separation in liquid-liquid systems. The gold-nickel system has a critical solution temperature at about 1120 °K, while for the gold-platinum system (see Figure XVIII—2) T_c = 1430 ° K. The latter system, having been well investigated, has been the subject of several attempts at theoretical interpretation. The wide separation of the liquidus and solidus lines suggested abnormal activities to Seltz[29], but were later explained almost quantitatively by Scatchard and Hamer[30],

[28] C. Wagner and G. Engelhardt, *Z. physik. Chem.* **A159**, 241 (1932).
[29] H. Seltz, *J. Am. Chem. Soc.*, **56**, 307, (1934), **57**, 391 (1935).
[30] G. Scatchard and W. J. Hamer, *J. Am. Chem. Soc.*, **57**, 1809 (1935).

who showed that the broadening was due to large positive deviations, slightly greater in the solid phase than in the liquid phase, and correlated their calculated free energies of mixing with the critical phenomena several

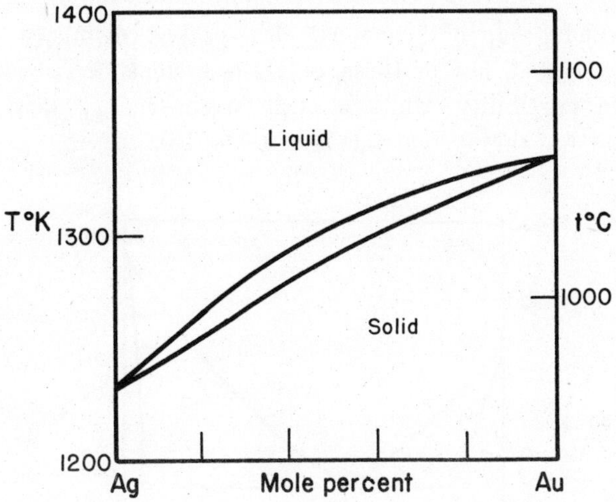

Fig. 4. Solid solutions of silver and gold

hundred degrees lower. More recently, Lawson[31] has used his treatment of the strain energy in solid crystals (cf. Chapter 18) to explain the greater deviations from Raoult's law in the solid phase and the displacement of the critical point toward the smaller component, Pt.

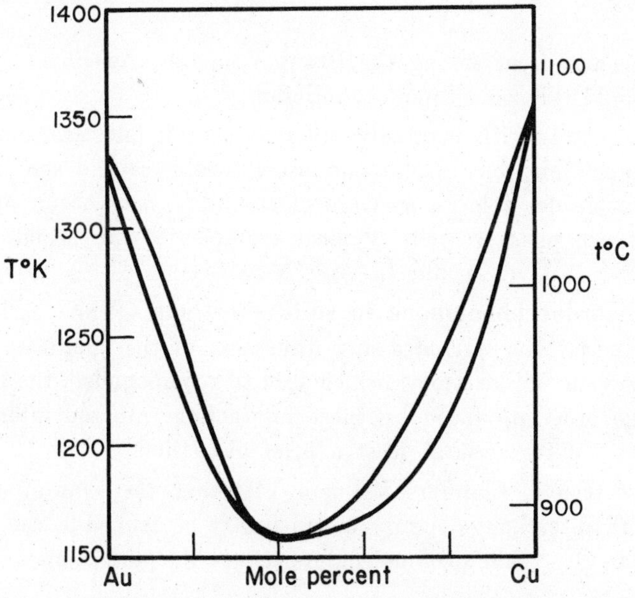

Fig. 5. Solid solutions of gold and copper

[31] A. W. Lawson, *J. Chem. Phys.*, **15**, 831 (1947).

The internal pressure treatment is equally satisfactory for the metals with body centered structures; complete series of solid solutions are found in the systems: Ta-W ($\Delta\delta = 9$), Mo-Ta ($\Delta\delta = 8$), Mo-W ($\Delta\delta = 17$), Cb-αFe ($\Delta\delta = 10$), αFe-V, ($\Delta\delta = 2$), Cr-αFe ($\Delta\delta = 9$) and K-Rb ($\Delta\delta = 3$).

In the second group of hexagonal close-packed metals, a few systems have been investigated, but of these, only the systems α Ti - α Zr ($\Delta\,\delta = 0$) shows complete miscibility, while a large strain energy helps prevent a similar situation for the system Cd - Zn ($\Delta\,\delta = 13$).

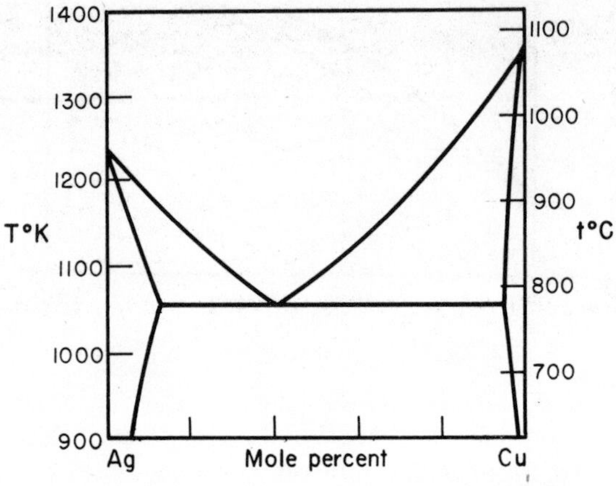

Fig. 6. Incomplete solid solutions in the system silver-copper

Solid solutions also occur among the Group V metals, As - Sb ($\Delta\,\delta = 7$) and Bi - Sb ($\Delta\,\delta = 11$, showing complete miscibility.

Between metals with markedly different crystal lattices, complete miscibility is impossible, but where the atomic volumes and solubility parameters are favorable, a large measure of solubility may occur, broken only by a narrow two phase region. Typical examples of this situation are the systems Cr - Ni ($\Delta\,\delta = 17$) and Li - Mg ($\Delta\,\delta = 4$).

Order-disorder phenomena in solid solutions. While earlier in this chapter, we specifically excluded any discussion of the specially strong interactions between unlike atoms which lead to "compounds", the phenomena of long range order produced by these interactions are too interesting and too important not to merit at least a brief discussion.

We have seen in Chapters VII and VIII that the heat of mixing depends upon an interchange energy w which may be defined as the energy involved in the single exchange of molecules between the pure components 1 and 2

$$w = \frac{z}{2}(2\,\varepsilon_{12} - \varepsilon_{11} - \varepsilon_{22}) \qquad (10)$$

where z is the coordination number (number of nearest neighbors) and ε_{11}, ε_{22}, and ε_{12} are the potential energies of the three kinds of pairs (all with negative signs). The assumption of the geometric mean $\varepsilon_{12} = (\varepsilon_{11}\,\varepsilon_{22})^{\frac{1}{2}}$ leads to a positive interchange energy, and we found in Chapter XVI that when w exceeds $2\,kT$, the tendency for segregation becomes too great, and the mixture separates into two phases.[32]

When the geometric mean law breaks down, as in the case of specific attractions between unlike metal atoms (where ε_{12} is abnormally large), it is possible for the interchange energy w to be negative, leading to negative deviations from Raoult's law. Such a negative interchange energy favors the formation of unlike pairs at the expense of like pairs. For the disordered structure of liquids, only a small amount of local order is possible and the effect of this ordering on the thermodynamic functions is usually small, as we have seen in Chapter VIII.

For crystals however, long range order is possible, and at low temperatures, where the unfavorable entropy of an ordered structure is unable to counterbalance the extra energy obtained, a regular arrangement of alternating atoms is possible, quite analogous to the alternating positive and negative ions in a salt lattice. The classic example of this ordered arrangement is that of β-brass, the alloy of equal amounts of copper and zinc. Unlike the pure substances, which crystallize in the face-centered cubic (Cu) and hexagonal (Zn) structures, the alloy Cu-Zn has a body-centered cubic arrangement. At low temperatures, X-ray studies show the copper and zinc atoms to be arranged in an alternating structure (Figure 7a) which may be regarded as two interpenetrating superlattices, one composed entirely of Cu-atoms, the other entirely of Zn-atoms, and so arranged that all the eight nearest neighbors of a Cu-atom are Zn-atoms and vice versa. With increasing temperatures, the segregation into superlattices diminishes, and above a certain temperature (known as the Curie point) all long range order is lost, and lattice points are filled by copper and zinc atoms indiscriminately. This disordered arrangement is shown in Figure 7b. At the Curie point, there is an anomaly in the specific heat of the type commonly known as a "second-order transition", a phenomenon which is largely responsible for the great interest in the subject.

Attempts to treat order-disorder phenomena by statistical mechanical theory have been numerous and extensive and have achieved a large measure of success. For qualitative purposes, the early treatments of Gorsky[33] and Bragg and Williams[34] suffice, and are especially interesting in that they are the exact inverse of the simple regular solution treatment of critical solution phenomena.

---

[32] This is the simple regular solution condition; application of the quasi-chemical treatment of Chapter VIII leads to similar but more complex conditions.

[33] V. S. Gorsky, *Z. Physik.*, **50**, 64, (1928).

[34] W. L. Bragg and E. J. Williams, *Proc. Roy. Soc.*, **A 145**, 699 (1934); **A 151**, 540 (1935).

For simplicity, we assume equal quantities of the two components $x_1 = x_2 = \frac{1}{2}$), and equal atomic volumes to avoid any strain energy difficulties. We divide the lattice sites into two classes — two superlattices A

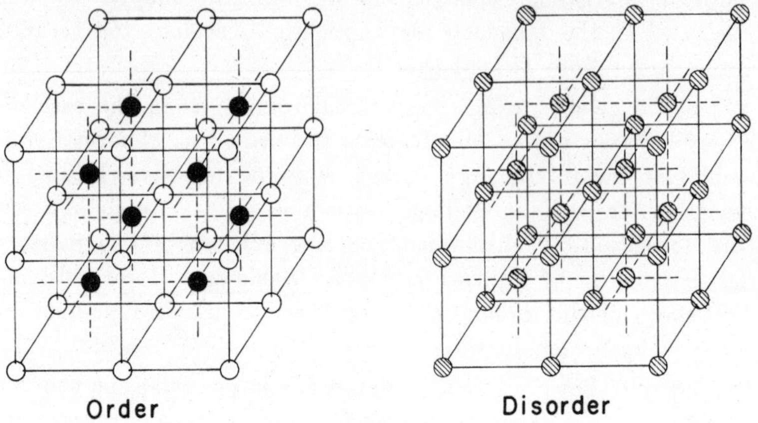

Fig. 7. Order-disorder relations in β-brass. Order: • Zn; ○ Cn
Disorder: ◍ $\frac{1}{2}$ Cn, $\frac{1}{2}$ Zn

and B, like those in Figure 7, and define a degree of order s such that the mole fraction of component 1 on superlattice A is $^1/_4(1 + s)$, while that of component 1 on superlattice B is $^1/_4(1 - s)$, etc., such that $x_1^A + x_1^B = x_1 = \frac{1}{2}$, $x_2^A + x_2^B = x_2 = \frac{1}{2}$; $x_1^A + x_2^A = x^A = \frac{1}{2}$; $x_1^B + x_2^B = x^B = \frac{1}{2}$

$$x_1^A = x_2^B = \frac{1}{4}(1 + s) \tag{11 a}$$

$$x_1^B = x_2^A = \frac{1}{4}(1 - s) \tag{11 b}$$

When $s = 1$, all the 1-atoms are on superlattice A, and all the 2-atoms on superlattice B, and the lattice is perfectly ordered. When $s = 0$, both components are distributed randomly between the superlattices and all long-range order is lost; hence s is called the *degree of order*.

We may calculate the entropy separately for the two superlattices, assuming as in the case of regular solutions, no effect of local ordering within the superlattices:

$$\Delta S^M = -R\left[x_1^A \ln \frac{x_1^A}{x_1^A + x_2^A} + x_2^A \ln \frac{x_2^A}{x_1^A + x_2^A} + x_1^B \ln \frac{x_1^B}{x_1^B + x_2^B} + x_2^B \quad \frac{x_2^B}{x_1^B + x_2^B}\right]$$

$$= -R\left[\tfrac{1}{2}(1 + s)\ln\frac{(1 + s)}{2} + \tfrac{1}{2}(1 - s)\ln\frac{(1 - s)}{2}\right] \tag{12}$$

For the heat (or more properly the energy ΔE^M), we confine ourselves to the nearest neighbor interactions, that is, only to interactions *between* the superlattices.

$$\Delta H^M = \frac{zN}{2} [\varepsilon_{11} (x_1^A + x_1^B) + \varepsilon_{22} (x_2^A + x_2^B) - 4 \varepsilon_{11} x_1^A x_1^B$$

$$- 4 \varepsilon_{22} x_2^A x_2^B - 4 \varepsilon_{12} (x_1^A x_2^B + x_1^B x_2^A)]$$

$$\Delta H^M = \frac{zN}{2} [\varepsilon_{11}\{\tfrac{1}{2} - \tfrac{1}{4}(1-s^2)\} + \varepsilon_{22}\{\tfrac{1}{2} - \tfrac{1}{4}(1-s^2)\}$$

$$- \varepsilon_{12} \{\tfrac{1}{4}(1+s)^2 + \tfrac{1}{4}(1-s)^2\}$$

$$\Delta H^M = -\tfrac{1}{4}\frac{Nz}{2}(\varepsilon_{11} + \varepsilon_{22} - 2\varepsilon_{12})(1+s^2) = +\frac{Nw}{4}(1+s^2) \qquad (13)$$

Combining, we obtain for the free energy ΔF^M:

$$\Delta F^M = RT \left[\tfrac{1}{2}(1+s)\ln\frac{(1+s)}{2} + \tfrac{1}{2}(1-s)\ln\frac{(1-s)}{2}\right.$$

$$\left. + \frac{E^*}{4}(1+s^2)\right] \qquad (14)$$

where, as in Chapter VIII, $E^* = Nw$.

Since we are interested only in the effect of the order, we subtract from the free energy the value it has when completely disordered ($s = 0$):

$$\Delta F^M(s) - \Delta F^M(0) = \frac{RT}{2}\left[(1+s)\ln(1+s) + (1-s)\ln(1-s)\right.$$

$$\left. + \frac{E^*}{2RT} s^2\right] \qquad (15)$$

Figure 8 shows this free energy function plotted against s for various values of $E^*/2RT$. We see that for all values above —1, the minimum free energy occurs at $s = 0$, corresponding to complete disorder. For values below —1, however, the minimum occurs at non-zero values of s, the degree of order increasing with increasingly negative values of $E^*/2RT$. It is to be recalled that $E^*/2RT = +1$ is the limiting value for phase separation.

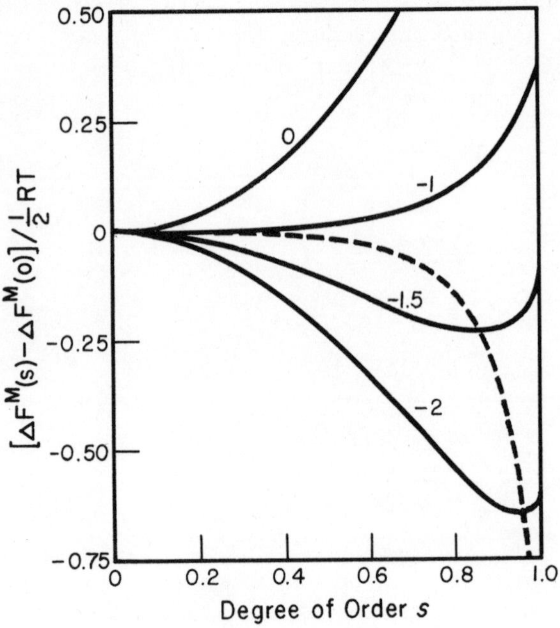

Fig. 8. The free energy of mixing as a function of the degree of order. The curves represent different values of E^*/RT as indicated. The dotted line is the locus of the minimum of the curve

Differentiating either Equation 14 or Equation 15 with regard to s an setting the derivative equal to zero, we obtain the equilibrium value of s In its simplest form, this is defined by:

$$s = \tanh\left(-\frac{E^*}{2RT}s\right) \qquad (16$$

Since the Curie point is like a critical temperature, we may define reduced temperature θ, such that $\theta = T/T_c = \frac{2RT}{-E^*}$. Then Equation 1 becomes:

$$s = \tanh\left(\frac{s}{\theta}\right) \qquad (17$$

Figure 9 shows the degree of order as a function of the reduce temperature θ. We see that at 90% of the Curie temperature, the allo is still over 50% ordered.

Various workers [35,36,37,38,39] have developed more elegant treatments, such as the quasi-chemical treatment discussed in Chapter VII, to consider the effects of local order within the superlattices. This improves the agreement with experiment somewhat, but will not be considered further here. For a discussion of the experimental phenomena and some of the theoretical treatments, the reader is referred to some excellent reviews of the field[40,41].

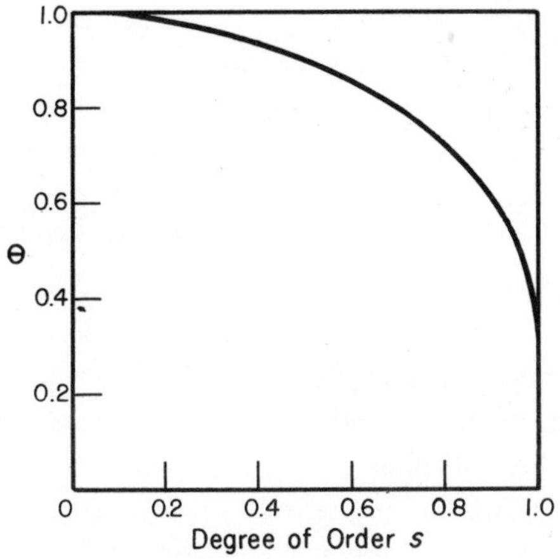

Fig. 9. Equilibrium degree order as a function of the reduced temperature θ

The existence of order-disorder phenomena in alloys raises some interesting problems with respect to the common practice of treating negative deviations from Raoult's law as evidence for compound formation. It would seem perfectly proper to consider the low temperature ordered arrangement of β-brass as a compound in the sense that crystalline NaCl is a compound, although not in the sense of diatomic molecules CuZn. Above the Curie temperature, however, where all long-range order has disappeared, the existence of a "compound" is more tenuous. Since the question is a matter of definition, continued argument would seem to be futile. It is important to note however, that the most successful treatments of order-disorder phenomena require merely an assumption of a negative interchange energy without any further assumptions concerning the chemical species involved. To speak of "compounds", while entirely permissible, would seem to be unnecessary.

[35] H. Bethe, *Proc. Roy. Soc.* **A150**, 552 (1935).

[36] T. S. Chang, *Proc. Roy. Soc.*, **A 161**, 546 (1937); *Proc. Camb. Phil. Soc.*, **34**, **224** (1938); **35**, 265, 277 (1939).

[37] J. G. Kirkwood, *J. Chem. Phys.* **6**, 70, (1938).

[38] G. S. Rushbrooke, *Proc. Camb. Phil. Soc.*, **34**, 424 (1938).

[39] G. Borelius, *Ann. Physik.*, **20**, 57 (1934); **24**, 489 (1935); **28**, 507 (1937); **33**, 517, (1938); *J. Inst. Metals,* **74**, 17 (1947).

[40] F. C. Nix and W. Shockley, *Rev. Mod. Phys.*, **10**, 1 (1938).

[41] R. H. Fowler and E. A. Guggenheim, "Statistical Thermodynamics" (Cambridge 1939), pp. 563—607.

CHAPTER XX

High Polymer Solutions

Among the many new areas of physico-chemical research which hav been developed in recent years, one of the most important is that involvin high polymers such as plastics and rubbers. One portion of this researcl has involved an intensive study of the thermodynamic properties of higl polymer solutions, which has resulted in what are perhaps the most strikin advances in the field of solubility and solutions in recent years.

While most of the experimental research and essentially all of th theory have been developed since 1940, the unique character of high polyme solutions was recognized much earlier. As the experimental data on rubbe solutions accumulated, their anomalous behavior became increasingly appar- ent. Not only are the solutions far from ideal, but the deviations fron ideality are of a magnitude never encountered in solutions of ordinary sub- stances; for example, in high polymer solutions, activity coefficients of 10^{-} are not uncommon! In addition, even very dilute polymer solutions seeme not to obey the limiting Van't Hoff laws for osmotic pressure, etc.

When calorimetric measurements indicated that the heat of mixing wa of small magnitude and frequently negligible, it became apparent that th anomalous effects must be attributed to anomalous entropy of mixing, du presumably to the unusual length of the polymer molecules. Recognizin the probable contribution of the long chains to the anomalous effect, Meyer suggested the desirability of a calculation of the entropy of long chains ir a quasi-lattice.

The following years saw the development of the Flory-Huggins theory and the first semi-quantitative interpretation of the behavior of higl polymer solutions. Since than a tremendous amount of experimental infor- mation has been accumulated, numerous refinements of the original theory have been advanced, and countless new applications have been explored.

It would be not only unwise but also impossible to essay in this chapte more than a general review of the basic theory and its most important ap- plications. In the following pages, we shall first summarize the develop- ment of the statistical theory which, while still requiring further refinement is certainly the basis for any understanding of high polymer solutions Using this theory for a guide, we can then attempt to interpret the directly measured thermodynamic properties – vapor-pressure, osmotic pressure, an depression of the freezing point — with special reference to the problem o

[1] K. H. Meyer, *Z. physik. Chem.*, **B 44**, 383 (1939).

molecular weight determination. We then turn to the important problems of solubility and fractionation of high polymers — with the attendant problems of phase equilibria in what are essentially multicomponent systems. Following this, we shall consider the problems of cross-linked polymers, and gels, indicating the valuable information obtained from swelling measurements. In conclusion, we shall discuss briefly the solubility of crystalline polymers, and the solubility of gases and solids in polymers.

1. The statistical theory: Soon after the publication of Meyer's suggestion of a statistical treatment, Huggins[2] and Flory[3] attacked the problem of calculating the number of possible lattice configurations for a mixture of polymer molecules occupying m sites each and solvent molecules occupying single sites. Their procedure (see Chapter VI) consisted of evaluating the number of configurations Ω for a lattice of coordination number z by the mathematical process of filling one site at a time. The problem reduces to the computation of the number of sites available for the jth element of the ith polymer molecule. There are z adjacent sites to be considered, some of which may be filled by elements of the $i-1$ polymers already placed or by previous elements of the ith molecule. Where j is the third or more element of the chain, one adjacent site is filled by the immediately preceding $j-1$ element, and we need merely calculate the probability P_{ij} that any specified one of the other $z-1$ sites is occupied. Flory assumed that P_{ij} may be approximated by the fraction of sites unoccupied by the $i-1$ polymers already placed:

$$P_{ij} = 1 - \frac{m\,(i-1)}{n_o + m\,n_p} \qquad (1)$$

where n_o is the number of solvent molecules

n_p is the number of polymer molecules

m is the number of elements (sites) per polymer molecule.

From this approximation, Flory obtains for the entropy of mixing and the partial molal entropies:

$$\Delta S^M = -R\,[N_o \ln \varphi_o + N_p \ln \varphi_p] \qquad (2)$$

$$\Delta \overline{S}_o = -R\left[\ln \varphi_o + \varphi_p\left(1 - \frac{1}{m}\right)\right] \qquad (3a)$$

$$\Delta \overline{S}_p = -R\,[\ln \varphi_p - \varphi_o\,(m-1)] \qquad (3b)$$

[2] M. L. Huggins, *J. Chem. Phys.*, **9**, 440 (1941); *Annals N. Y. Acad. Sci.* **43**, 1 (1942).
[3] P. J. Flory, *J. Chem. Phys.*, **9**, 660 (1941), **10**, 51 (1942)

If we identify the number of elements, m, with the ratio of mola volumes V_p/V_o, Equations 2, 3ab are the same as Equations VI-18 ab whic Hildebrand later deduced by assuming free volume proportional to mola volume.

The assumption of Equation 1 is an obvious oversimplification, a Flory himself recognized. Huggins observed that the fact that a site wa available for the $(j-1)^{th}$ element enhances the probability that the adjacen sites are unoccupied, and formulated P_{ij} as

$$P_{ij} = \frac{1 - f_{ij}}{1 - \frac{2}{z}\left(1 - \frac{1}{m}\right) f_{ij}} \tag{4}$$

where

$$f_{ij} = f_o + \frac{(i-1)\,m\,(1-f_o)}{n_o + m\,n_p} \tag{5}$$

and f_o is a small constant which attempts to correct for the probabilit that the site is occupied by an earlier element of a coiled chain.

Using Equation 4 Huggins calculated the partial molal entropy of th solvent

$$\Delta \bar{S}_o = -R\left\{\ln \varphi_o - \frac{z'}{2}\left(1 - \frac{1}{m}\right) \ln\left(1 - \frac{2}{z'}\varphi_p\right)\right\} \tag{6}$$

Where z', which Huggins calls the "effective coordination number", i very nearly z and is defined as:

$$z' = \frac{zm}{(m-1)(1-f_o)} - \frac{2 f_o}{1 - f_o} \tag{7}$$

By means of Bethe's approximation of local configurations, Miller calculated the entropy of mixing for double and triple molecules and b analogy obtained the expression for polymers occupying m sites

$$\Delta \bar{S}_o = -R\left[\ln \varphi_o - \frac{z}{2} \ln\left\{1 - \frac{2}{z}\varphi_p\left(1 - \frac{1}{m}\right)\right\}\right] \tag{8}$$

Guggenheim[5] subsequently used the grand partition function to evaluat the entropy of mixing of chain molecules occupying multiple sites (see Equatio

[4] A. R. Miller, *Proc. Camb. Phil. Soc.*, **38**, 109 (1942), **39**, 54, 131 (1943).
[5] E. A. Guggenheim, *Proc. Roy. Soc.*, **A 183**, 203 (1944).

VI-27). For the special case of mixing molecules occupying m sites with solvent molecules occupying single sites, Guggenheim's equation reduces exactly to Miller's Equation 8.

As a first approximation for the heat of mixing, we use Equation VII-35

$$\Delta \overline{H}_{\circ} = V_{\circ} (\delta_p - \delta_{\circ})^2 \varphi_p^2 \tag{9}$$

If we add this heat of mixing to the entropy term of Equation 6, we obtain for the partial molal free energy of mixing

$$\Delta \overline{F}_{\circ} = RT \left[\ln \varphi_{\circ} - \frac{z'}{2} \left(1 - \frac{1}{m}\right) \ln \left(1 - \frac{2}{z'} \varphi_p\right) + \frac{V_{\circ} (\delta_p - \delta_{\circ})^2}{RT} \varphi_p^2 \right] \tag{10}$$

Orr[6] and Guggenheim[7] have applied the quasi-chemical treatment to high polymer solutions and have found that the non-randomness introduces a small correction term entirely analogous to that discussed in detail in Chapter VIII. In addition, their more nearly correct treatment shows that the concentration variable in the energy dependent terms is not the volume fraction but a "surface fraction" determined by the number of nearest neighbor sites adjacent to a molecule. For reasonable values of z, the difference between "surface fraction" and volume fraction is small and would be diminished further if interactions between more distant sites were considered. Both of these small corrections we shall neglect for the time being, especially since other approximations involve more serious errors, although we shall return to the latter problem in a subsequent section.

Huggins[2] suggested a further approximation which, because of its simplicity, has been used widely in many applications of the theory. If we expand the logarithm in the second term of Equation 10 and drop off terms in φ_p^3 and higher, we obtain for $\Delta \overline{F}_{\circ}$

$$\Delta \overline{F}_{\circ} = RT \left[\ln \varphi_{\circ} + (1 - \frac{1}{m}) \varphi_p + \mu \varphi_p^2 \right] \tag{11a}$$

where

$$\mu = \frac{1}{z'} (1 - \frac{1}{m}) + \frac{V_{\circ} (\delta_p - \delta_{\circ})^2}{RT} \tag{12}$$

---

[6] W. J. C. Orr, *Trans. Faraday Soc.*, **11**, 320 (1944).

[7] E. A. Guggenheim, *Proc. Roy. Soc.*, **A 183**, 213 (1944).

The corresponding partial molal free energy for the polymer may be written as

$$\Delta \overline{F}_p = RT\left[\ln \varphi_p - (m-1)\varphi_\circ + m\mu\varphi_\circ^2\right] \tag{11b}$$

Attempts to apply Equations 6-11 to experimental data reveal difficulties immediately. The best fit between measured and calculated curves is obtained with values of z about four, although we may reasonably expect z to be much higher, between six and ten. Recent studies[8,9] have indicated the approach to a solution of the problem: In evaluating the number of configurations Ω, Huggins replaced the Flory approximation of Equation 1 by Equation 4, in which the ordering effect of the immediately preceding element of the chain is allowed for. Actually, more distant elements of the chain may increase the value of P_{ij} still further. Guggenheim[5] has indicated the nature of this approximation, which underlies his formulation as well as those of Huggins and Miller: "Consider, for example, a site P neighboring a site Q assumed to be occupied by an element of a molecule A. Then in the argument I have assumed that all conceivable manners of occupation of the site P not prevented by the occupation of the site Q are equally probable. Actually I have committed an error in not excluding those manners of occupation of the site P such that some element of the molecule occupying the site P is competing for some site R with some element of the molecule A assumed to be occupying the site Q."

The development of the McMillan and Mayer molecular distribution method (Chapter VIII) and the similar Huggins excluded volume treatment (Chapter VI) has facilitated the clarification of the problem. Both of these approaches involve the evaluation of the coefficients of a power series which we may write as:

$$\Delta \overline{F}_\circ = -RT\left[\frac{\varphi_p}{m} + a_2\varphi_p{}^2 + a_3\varphi_p{}^3 + \ldots\right] \tag{13}$$

If we express a more nearly exact formulation in the form of correction terms to the original equations, we may write

$$\Delta \overline{F}_\circ = RT\left[\ln\varphi_\circ + (1-\frac{1}{m})\varphi_p + \mu\varphi_p^2 + \nu\varphi_p^3 + \ldots\right] \tag{14}$$

where

$$a_2 = \frac{1}{2} - \mu,\ \ a_3 = \frac{1}{3} - \nu,\ \text{etc.}$$

[8] P. J. Flory, *J. Chem. Phys.*, **13**, 453 (1945); **17**, 303, 1347 (1949).

[9] B. H. Zimm, ACS Meeting, Sept. 1947.

We shall defer discussion of the attempts to calculate μ or a_2 for several special cases to a later section in which the nature and evaluation of the constant μ will be considered in considerable detail. Because ot their lesser importance in dilute solutions and greater mathematical difficulty, no significant attempt has been made to evaluate the higher correction terms ν, etc., and while they are certainly not zero, they are almost universally ignored.

In practice, Equation 11 ab must be regarded as semi-empirical, with the parameter μ to be determined from the experimental data rather than from Equation 12. While its theoretical limitations are increasingly apparent, it has proved to be extraordinarily useful in the interpretation of high polymer solutions.

Finally, we must take cognizance of the fact that few, if any, high polymer solutions exist in which all the polymer molecules are identical with respect to chain length or molecular weight. Flory[10] has extended his original theory to include polymers of varying molecular weight, while Scott and Magat[11] independently obtained an analogous extension by the Huggins method. The more general treatment by Guggenheim[7] included the problem of such a multicomponent system, and more recently Zimm[12] obtained similar results by the method of molecular distribution functions.

For a mixture of polymers varying only in molecular weight, the equations analogous to 11 ab are

$$\Delta \bar{F}_{\circ} = RT\left[\ln \varphi_{\circ} + \left(1 - \frac{1}{\bar{m}_n}\right)\varphi_p + \mu \varphi_p^2\right] \tag{15 a}$$

$$\Delta \bar{F}_i = RT\left[\ln \varphi_i + \left(1 - \frac{m_i}{\bar{m}_n}\right)\varphi_p + (1 - m_i)\,\varphi_{\circ} + m_i\,\mu\,\varphi_0^2\right] \tag{15 b}$$

φ_p is the volume fraction of total polymer and the subscript i refers to the ith fraction of the polymer, having a volume fraction φ_i and a molecular weight M_i and a corresponding m_i. The quantity $\bar{m}_n$ is the number average m defined as

$$\bar{m}_n = \frac{\sum n_i m_i}{\sum n_i} = \frac{\sum \varphi_i}{\sum (\varphi_i/m_i)} \tag{16}$$

If all fractions of the polymer have the same density ϱ_p, the m_i's are directly proportional to the M's and $\bar{m}_n$ bears the same relation to the number average molecular weight, $\bar{M}_n$;

[10] P. J. Flory, *J. Chem. Phys.*, **12**, 425, (1944).

[11] R. L. Scott and M. Magat, *J. Chem. Phys.*, **13**, 172 (1945).

[12] B. H. Zimm, *J. Chem. Phys.*, **14**, 164 (1946).

$$\overline{m}_n = \overline{M}_n \cdot \frac{\varrho_p}{V_\circ} \tag{17}$$

Equation 15a is identical with Equation 11a for the simple system save for the substitution of $\overline{m}_n$ for m. The set of equations represented by 15b are more complex, although Equation 11b may be said to define the number average free energy of the polymer. We shall have occasion to use both of these in later sections.

2. The colligative properties of high polymer solutions

(a) Vapor Pressure. We have seen in Chapter III that when the vapor behaves as a perfect gas we may write the partial pressures above a solution in terms of the partial molal free energies of mixing of the two components. In the case of high polymer solutions, the polymer is non-volatile and the partial pressure of the solvent is the same as the total vapor pressure of the solution

$$RT \ln \frac{p}{p_\circ} = \Delta\overline{F}_\circ \tag{18}$$

Where p is the vapor pressure of the solution and $p_\circ$ that of the pure solvent. Substituting from Equation 15a, we obtain

$$\ln \frac{p}{p_\circ} = \ln \varphi_\circ + \left(1 - \frac{1}{\overline{m}_n}\right) \varphi_p + \mu \varphi_p^2 \tag{19}$$

or rewriting:

$$\frac{p}{p_\circ} = \varphi_\circ e^{\left(1 - \frac{1}{\overline{m}_n}\right) \varphi_p + \mu \varphi_p^2} \tag{20}$$

The experimental determination of vapor pressures over high polymer solutions is fraught with numerous difficulties, and consequently vapor pressure data are not very extensive. Perhaps the most detailed and careful study is that of Gee and Treloar[13] and Gee and Orr[14] on the rubber-benzene system; by the use of the method of isothermal distillation and a small Mc Leod gauge at low pressures, they were able to obtain data over the entire range of vapor pressure from 0.1 mm to the vapor pressure of pure benzene. Their data, together with those of Lens[15] for rubber-acetone and rubber-carbon tetrachloride, are shown in Fig. 1. Also shown in Fig. 2 are theoretical curves calculated from Equation 19, for $\mu = 0.0$, 0.5, and 1.0. The dependence upon molecular weight is trivial except in the dilute range

[13] G. Gee and L. R. G. Treloar, *Trans. Faraday Soc.*, **38**, 147 (1942).
[14] G. Gee aud W. J. C. Orr, *Trans. Faraday Soc.*, **42**, 507 (1946).
[15] J. Lens, *Rec. Trav. Chim.*, **51**, 971 (1932).

($\varphi_{\circ} = 0.95 - 1.00$), where vapor-pressure measurements are not sufficiently precise; so m is set equal to infinity. To illustrate the magnitude of the

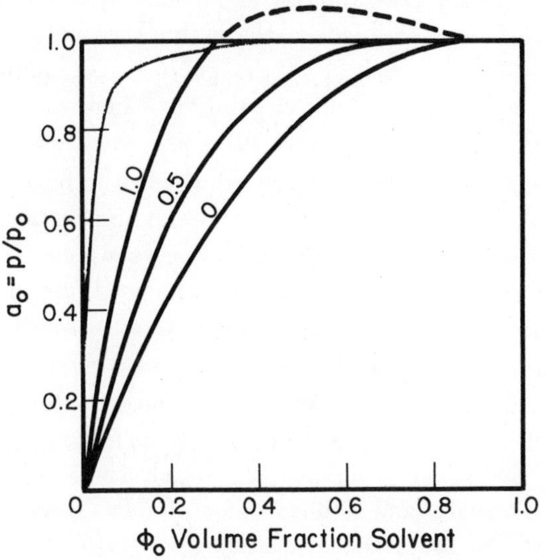

Fig. 1. Vapor pressures of high polymer solutions, calculated for various values of μ. The thin line is Raoult's law for $m = 100$.

deviation from Raoult's law, the ideal solution ($p/p_{\circ} = x_{\circ}$) is shown for $m = 100$ as a thin line. Considering the scatter of the experimental points,

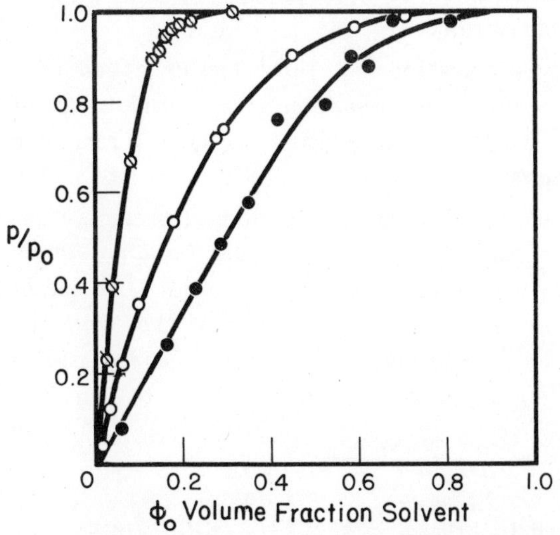

Fig. 2. Vapor pressures of solutions of natural rubber in ○ benzene ⦰ acetone • carbon tetrachloride

the agreement with theory is fairly good. The best values of μ are 0.0 for carbon tetrachloride, 0.44 for benzene, and 1.5 for acetone.

(b) **Osmotic Pressure.** Of the various colligative properties of high polymer solutions the one most frequently measured and perhaps the most important is the osmotic pressure. Its importance is enhanced by the fact that it is the best and frequently the only thermodynamic method of determining the molecular weight of the polymer. In addition, the measurements can be made on very dilute solutions where other thermodynamic measurements (for example, vapor pressure) are extremely insensitive.

Osmotic measurements of the accuracy required by high polymer solutions involve construction of special osmometers and careful preparation of suitable membranes. Meyer and Boissonnas[16], Gee[17], Flory[18], Fuoss and Mead[19], Zimm and Myerson[20], and French and Ewart[21] have described osmometers designed for high polymer solutions. The membranes commonly used are of nitrocellulose (collodion), denitrated nitrocellulose, commercial cellophane, or specially swollen cellulose.

In practice, one or both of two methods are employed: (1) the static method, in which the osmotic pressure is measured after equilibrium is reached, and (2) the dynamic method, in which the pressure is measured at regular time intervals, and a linear plot of dP/dT against P yields the equilibrium osmotic pressure. Both methods, if performed with care, give reliable and equivalent results. Wherever possible, when using the dynamic method, the equilibrium should be approached from both sides.

Osmotic pressure measurements are usually regarded as requiring about a day for equilibrium to be reached, but Fuoss and Mead[19] and Zimm and Myerson[20] have described much faster methods, and Carter, Scott and Magat[22] have reported attainment of equilibrium within half an hour, using undenitrated collodion membranes.

Jullander[23] has developed a third method, that of a special osmotic balance which permits determination of the osmotic pressure at very low concentrations. Wagner[24] has written a general review article on osmotic pressure determinations.

Since the major purpose of osmotic measurments was the determination of molecular weights, the failure of dilute high polymer solutions to obey van't Hoff's law posed very serious difficulties. The method almost universally adopted was to assume the validity of the van't Hoff law at infinite dilution, and by means of measurements at several concentrations, to extrapolate (Π/c) to infinite dilution. Prior to the development of the

[16] K. H. Meyer and G. G. Boissonnas, *Helv. Chim. Acta*, **23**, 430 (1940).
[17] G. Gee, *Trans. Faraday Soc.*, **36**, 1162 (1940).
[18] P. J. Flory, *J. Am. Chem. Soc.*, **65**, 375 (1943).
[19] R. M. Fuoss and D. J. Mead, *J. Phys. Chem.*, **47**, 59 (1943).
[20] B. H. Zimm and I. Myerson, *J. Am. Chem. Soc.*, **68**, 911 (1946).
[21] D. M. French and R. H. Ewart, *Anal. Chem.*, **19**, 165 (1947).
[22] W. C. Carter, R. L. Scott, and M. Magat, *J. Am. Chem. Soc.*, **68**, 1480 (1946).
[23] I. Jullander, *Arkiv for Kemi, Mineralogi Och Geologi.* **21 A**, No. 8 (1945).
[24] R. H. Wagner, "Determination of Osmotic Pressure" in A. Weissberger, "Physical Methods of Organic Chemistry" (Interscience, 1945), Vol. I, pp. 253-276.

statistical mechanical theory, the proper method of extrapolation was by no means clear, and various empirical equations were used, leading to somewhat different molecular weights.

If we ignore the small contributions of the compressibility and a possible change of volume in mixing, we may relate the osmotic pressure and the partial molal free energy of the solvent

$$\Pi \mathrm{V}_\circ = -\overline{\Delta \mathrm{F}}_\circ \tag{21}$$

Substituting Equation 15a (in the form of a series expansion) into Equation 21, we obtain

$$\Pi = \frac{RT}{\mathrm{V}_\circ}\left\{\frac{\varphi_p}{\overline{\mathrm{m}}_n} + (\frac{1}{2} - \mu)\,\varphi_p^2 + \ldots\right\} \tag{22}$$

If we transform from volume fraction φ_p to concentration c (in units of grams polymer per cc. solution), we obtain

$$\Pi = \frac{RT}{\overline{\mathrm{M}}_n}\,c + \frac{RT}{\varrho_p^2\,\mathrm{V}_\circ}\,(\frac{1}{2} - \mu)\,c^2 + \ldots \tag{23}$$

where ϱ_p is the density of the polymer. The first term is, of course, the van't Hoff limiting law where the molecular weight obtained is the number

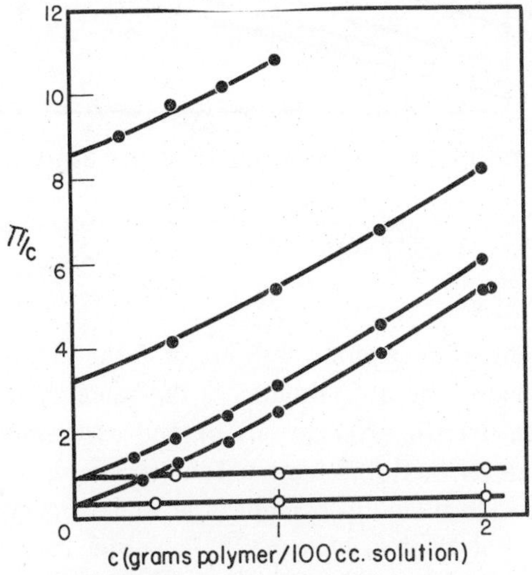

Fig. 3. Osmotic pressure of solutions of polyisobutylene in ● diisobutylene; ○ cyclohexane (Flory)

average, as is required by the nature of colligative properties. The form of the equation justifies the estimation of $[\Pi/c]_{c=0}$ by a linear extrapolation of Π/c as a function of c, a method first suggested empirically by Meyer[25]. In addition, according to the simple statistical theory, μ is virtually independent of chain length, as ϱ_p should also be; hence the coefficient of c^2

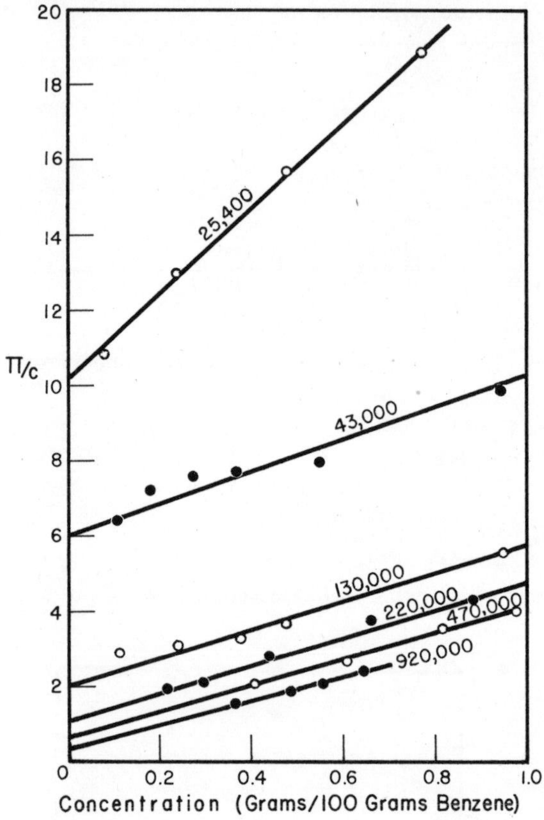

Fig. 4. Osmotic pressure of GR-S in benzene (French and Ewart[21])

should be independent of molecular weight, and the slope of the Π/c vs. c plot should be the same for all polymers of the same chemical nature which differ only in chain length. Nearly all of the experimental data confirm these conclusions. Figures 3, 4, and 5 show the osmotic data for three fractionated polymers: polyisobutylene in cyclohexane and benzene (Flory[18]), GR-S (butadiene-styrene copolymer) in benzene (French and Ewart[21]) and neoprene in toluene (Scott, Carter, and Magat[26]). The μ's calculated from these data are respectively 0.44, 0.37 and 0.39.

The curvature in some of the Π/c vs. c plots (for example, polyisobutylene, Figure 3) is presumably due to the higher terms in Equation 23.

[25] K. H. Meyer, *Z. physik. Chem.*, **B 44**, 383 (1939); *Helv. Chim. Acta*, **23**, 1063 (1940).
[26] R. L. Scott, W. C. Carter and M. Magat, unpublished data.

The effect seems to be more serious for very high molecular weight material, and can be a disturbing factor in the determination of molecular weight of the highest fractions. The remedy, although involving serious experimental difficulties, seems to be to extend osmotic pressure measurements to sufficiently low concentrations that further extrapolation is surely linear.

Gee and Treloar[13] report a large curvature in the system rubber-benzene (unfractionated) which they suggest casts doubt upon the complete validity of the Π/c vs. c extrapolation. The rigorous molecular distribution function formulation (see Chapter VIII) which obtains the osmotic pressure as a power series in the concentration would seem to answer this objection, provided of course that measurements are made on sufficiently dilute solutions.

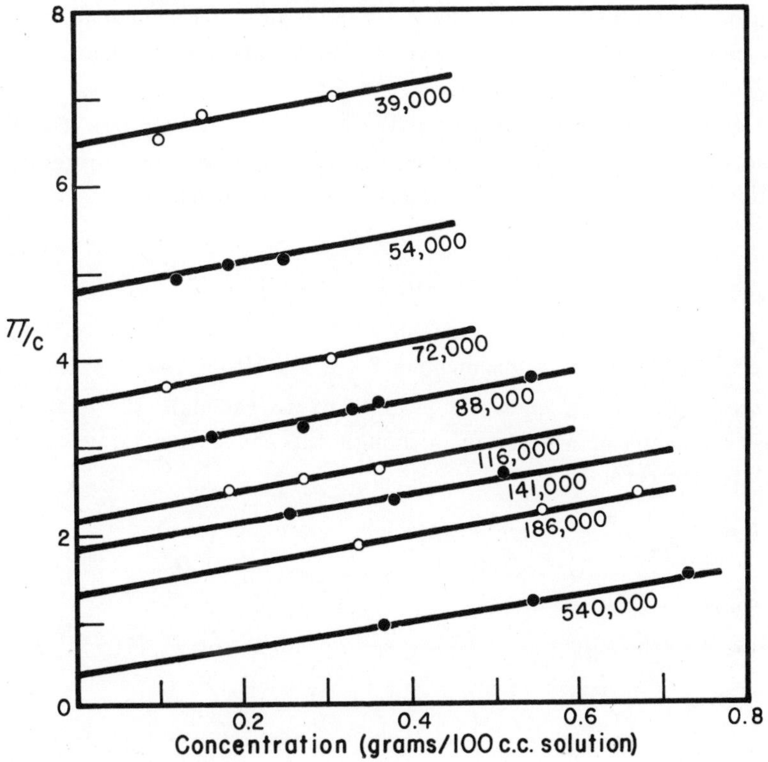

Fig. 5. Osmotic pressures of neoprene in toluene

Since a positive heat of mixing enhances the value of the constant, μ, poorer solvents will yield larger μ-values and correspondingly smaller slopes of the Π/c vs. c plot. For the unique case of $\mu = 0.50$, the second term of Equation 23 vanishes and for a finite range of concentrations, the slope is zero and the van't Hoff law is obeyed. This leads to the paradoxical situation that it is the poor solvent which is the "ideal" solvent, that is, the one which most nearly follows Raoult's and van't Hoff's laws.

A system for which the slope is zero can be obtained easily by the use of a mixed solvent. Gee[27] has shown that for natural rubber such an effect is produced by a mixture of 85% benzene—15% methyl alcohol, and has suggested that the most reliable determinations of molecular weights are those obtained in this manner. Flory[3], however, has argued convincingly that the uncertainty in the molecular weight is essentially the same whether the slope be large or zero.

In recent years much attention has been given to the scattering of light by polymer solutions, and Debye[28a] has shown that the dependence of the scattering upon the concentration is closely related to the similar dependence of the osmotic presssure, in fact so much so that μ and other parameters may be determined from the light scattering measurements. A detailed discussion of these non-thermodynamic properties is outside the scope of this book; for an excellent review of the theory and experimental work, the reader is referred to a recent paper by Oster[28b].

(c) **Cryoscopic Measurements.** We have seen in Chapters II and XVII that the solubility of a solid can be calculated from the equilibrium between a solution and pure solid phase as given by the equation

$$\Delta \bar{F}_1 = \Delta H_1^F \left(1 - \frac{T}{T_m}\right) \tag{24}$$

where ΔH_1^F is the heat of fusion and T_m the melting point of the solute.

Exactly the same equation permits us to calculate the depression of the freezing point of a solution, although the conventional tags of solvent and solute are reversed.

$$\Delta H_o^F \frac{\Delta T}{T_m} = \Delta \bar{F}_o = RT \left[\ln \varphi_o + \left(1 - \frac{1}{\bar{m}_n}\right) \varphi_p + \mu \varphi_p^2\right]. \tag{25}$$

Expanding the logarithm as before and approximating $T_m T$ by T_m^2, we obtain

$$\Delta T = \frac{RT_m^2}{\Delta H_o^F} \left[\frac{\varphi_p}{\bar{m}_n} + \left(\frac{1}{2} - \mu\right) \varphi_p^2 + \ldots\right] \tag{26}$$

The expression $RT_m^2 V_o / \Delta H_o^F$ is the cryoscopic constant of the solute and may be written k_c. Converting to concentrations, we have

$$\Delta T = \frac{k_c}{\bar{M}_n} c + \frac{k_c}{\varrho_p^2 V_o} \left(\frac{1}{2} - \mu\right) c^2 + \ldots \tag{27}$$

[27] G. Gee, *Trans. Faraday Soc.*, **36**, 1162 (1940).

[28a] P. Debye, *J. Appl. Phys.*, **15**, 338 (1944); *J. Phys. & Colloid Chem.*, **51**, 18 (1947).

[28b] G. Oster, *Chem. Revs.*, **43**, 319 (1948).

The analogy to Equation 23 for the osmotic pressure is obvious. Most high polymer solutions have molecular weights too great to show any measurable depression of the freezing point, but for very low molecular weight material, the same failure to follow ideal solution laws was observed with a similar linear relation between $\Delta T/c$ and c. Figure 6 shows the measurements of Kemp and Peters[29] on thermally degraded natural rubber and polyisobutylene.

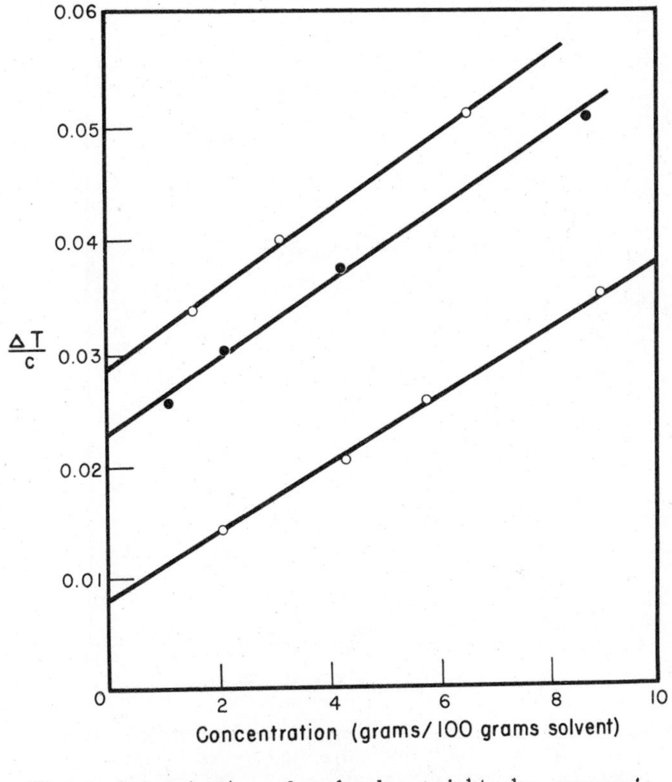

Fig. 6. Determination of molecular weights by cryoscopic measurements. (Kemp and Peters[29]) ○ polyisoprene in cyclohexane, ● polyisobutylene in cyclohexane

(d) **The Free Energy of Mixing.** The first systematic attempt to measure the thermodynamic properties of a high-polymer solution over the entire range of concentration was the investigation of the rubber-benzene system by Gee and Treloar[13] and Gee and Orr[14] and collaborators. By combining measurements of osmotic pressure, vapor pressure, etc., they obtained values for $\Delta \overline{F}_o$ over a range of volume fraction φ_p from 10^{-6} to 0.999. By making measurements at different temperatures and by direct calorimetry, they also determined $\Delta \overline{H}_o$ and from these by suitable equations calculated $\Delta \overline{S}_o$, $\Delta \overline{F}_p$, $\Delta \overline{H}_p$, and $\Delta \overline{S}_p$.

[29] A. R. Kemp and H. Peters, *Ind. Eng. Chem.*, **34**, 1192 (1942).

One may attempt to fit Gee and Treloar's data with Equation 15. The only adjustable parameters are $\bar{m}_n$ and μ, both of which may be determined from dilute solutions (below 2% polymer). Extrapolation of the osmotic pressure data yields a molecular weight of 360,000, or $\bar{m}_n \cong 4000$; the slope of Π/c vs. c gives $\mu = 0.44$ for the rubber-benzene system. Figure 7 shows the experimental data of Gee and Treloar, the curve calculated from Equation 15a with the above parameters, and as a broken line

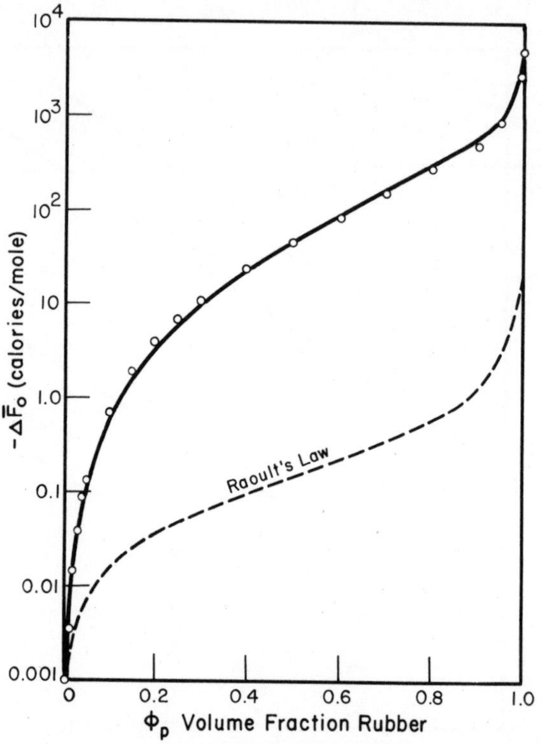

Fig. 7. Partial molal free energy of benzene in the rubber-benzene system. Solid line calculated ($\mu = 0.44$, m = 4000). Points from smoothed data of Gee and Treloar

the Raoult's law value. Considering the imperfections of the theory, the agreement is remarkably good. Although this may be partially fortuitous, it is enough to justify the empirical use of Equation 15 in the semi-quantitative treatment of concentrated solutions. The two necessary parameters are obtained from dilute solutions, and the contribution of one ($\bar{m}_n$) is entirely negligible outside the dilute range.

(e) The Heat of Mixing. In the first section of this chapter, we used Equation VII-35 as a first approximation for the heat of mixing of a polymer solution, obtaining thereby a term in Equation 12 for μ. One would suppose therefore that the considerable success of Equations 15ab in fitting the free energy data with a nearly constant μ could be used as experimental justification for this approximation. According to Equation VII-34 from which VII-35 was derived, the overall heat of mixing should be

$$\Delta H^{M} = V_m (\delta_\circ - \delta_p)^2 \varphi_\circ \varphi_p \tag{28}$$

Consequently the heat of mixing per cc., divided by $\varphi_\circ \varphi_p$ should be a constant $(\delta_\circ - \delta_p)^2$ independent of concentration.

Unfortunately the direct calorimetric measurements of Gee and Orr[14] and collaborators on rubber-benzene (Figure 8) show conclusively that this is not the case. The discrepancy in the partial molal heats is even worse since they depend upon the slope of the curve in Figure 8. Apparently here is another case where the free energy calculated from a simple model is more nearly correct than either the heat or the entropy taken separately. This problem will be considered further in the following section.

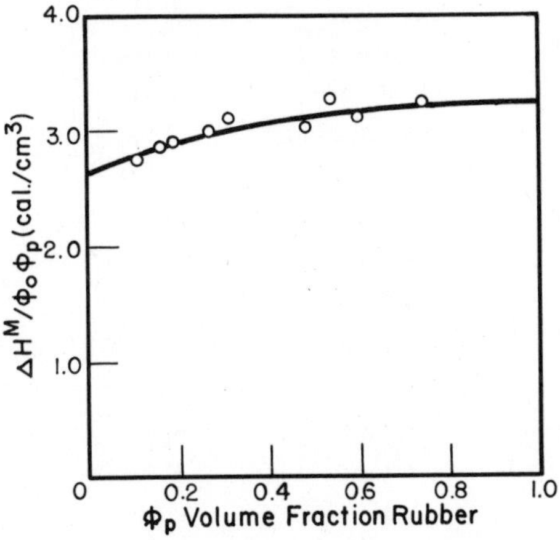

Fig. 8. Heat of mixing of rubber and benzene (calorimetric measurements of Gee and Orr)

(f) The Parameter μ: Experimental and Theoretical Studies. With the use of Equation 15a justified to a large measure by experiment, a more careful consideration of the parameter μ is desirable. Huggins[30] has collected a mass of data on osmotic pressures and other thermodynamic properties of polymer solutions and from them calculated μ for a large number of polymer-solvent systems. Table 1 reproduces part of his summary augmented by additional more recent material, all obtained from dilute solutions.

For a few systems, measurements have been made over a range of concentrations, and for them we may plot μ as a function of φ_p. Figure 9 shows such a graph for rubber-benzene, while Figure 10 shows the more

[30] M. L. Huggins, *Ann. N. Y. Acad. Sci.*, **44**, 431 (1943).

fragmentary data on other systems collected by Huggins[30]. As we have seen, there is no theoretical justification for a constant μ, but within the accuracy of the experimental data μ is nearly independent of concentration for many systems.

Table 1. The parameter μ for various high polymer systems.
(References other than Huggins[30] are indicated).

Polymer	Solvent	μ	Temp. °C	Reference
Polyisoprene (natural rubber)	CCl_4	0.28	15 - 20	
	cymene	0.33	15 - 20	
	cyclohexane	0.33	6	
	chloroform	0.37	15 - 20	
	1,2-dichloroethylene	0.43	15 - 20	
	toluene	0.43	27	
		0.41	30	22
	benzene	0.44	25	
	chlorobenzene	0.44	7	
	carbon disulfide	0.49	25	
Polystyrene	toluene	0.44	27	
Polyisobutylene	cyclohexane	0.43	25	18
	toluene	0.47	30	26
	benzene	0.50	25	18
Buna-S (GR-S)	benzene	0.37	25	20
	toluene	0.38	30	26
Neoprene	toluene	0.38	30	26
Gutta-percha	toluene	0.36	27	
	benzene	0.52	25	
Polyvinylchloride	cyclohexanone	0.24	30	31
	butanone-2	0.41	26	31
	dioxane	0.49	38	31

In the initial statistical treatment of Huggins, μ consisted of a term in $\frac{1}{z}$ from the entropy of mixing to which was added a contribution from the heat of mixing entirely analogous to that for solutions of ordinary liquids (cf. Equation 12). The necessity of choosing unreasonably low values of z to fit the data has lead to abandonment of this original interpretation, but the separation of μ into entropy and heat terms is of quite general validity and we may write

$$\mu = \mu^S + \mu^H \tag{29}$$

Over a limited range, μ^S will be independent of temperature, while μ^H will be inversely proportional to T, permitting us to separate the two terms by experimental measurements:

$$\mu = \alpha + \frac{\beta}{T} \tag{30}$$

where α and β are constants, equal to μ^S and $T\mu^H$ respectively. Measurements at several temperatures permit separation of the experimental values of μ into different terms, and should enable us to evaluate μ^S. This has been done for a few systems over a range of concentrations. Figure 9 shows μ, μ^S, and μ^H as a function of φ_p for solutions of rubber in benzene[13,14].

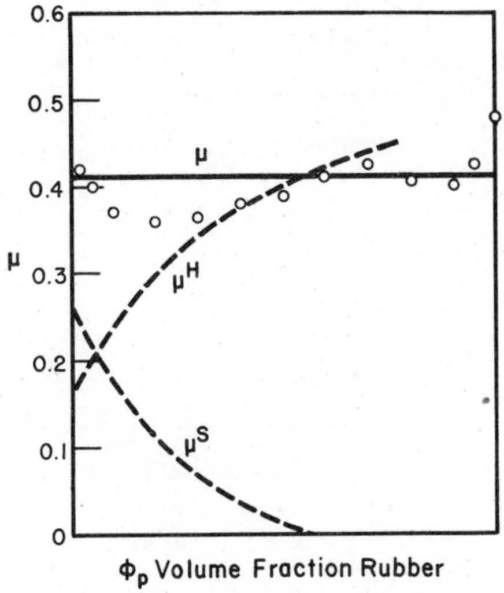

Fig. 9. The parameter μ as a function of composition in the system rubber-benzene

The striking feature is the non-constancy of the μ^H and μ^S. The reason for this is evidently the same as that which we first encountered in Chapter VIII: the free energy is fairly insensitive to the errors introduced in oversimplified treatments, but the entropy and heat are not; μ, which is fairly constant over the whole concentration range, is of course a free energy parameter. To understand the variation of μ^H and μ^S with concentration, we should have to consider volume changes and non-randomness as well as problems unique to high-polymer solutions, such as changes in the tightness of coiling with concentration etc.

We might interpret μ^S and μ^H in Equation 29 as the values in infinitely dilute solution where the statistical calculations are simpler. In terms

[31] P. M. Doty and E. Mishuck, *J. Am. Chem. Soc.*, **69**, 1631 (1947).

of the series expansion (Eqns. 13, 14), we might use μ^H and μ^S as the temperature dependent and independent terms respectively in the coefficient a_2. Even this, however, involves the difficulty that μ^S so defined is not the athermal μ^S but is itself a function of μ^H. In addition, we shall find that μ^H is a function of the athermal μ^S.

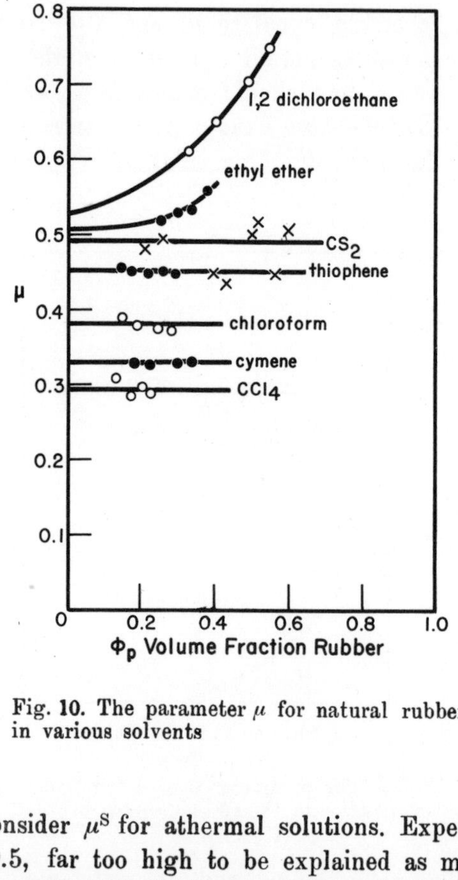

Fig. 10. The parameter μ for natural rubber in various solvents

Let us first consider μ^S for athermal solutions. Experimentally μ^S falls between 0.3 and 0.5, far too high to be explained as merely 1/z. As we have seen earlier (pp. 346-350), the basic problem in the statistical evaluation of the number of configurations Ω is the estimation of the probability P_{ij} that a specified site is available for the jth element of the ith polymer molecule. In his original formulation, Flory[3] approximated P_{ij} with a random distribution of occupied sites. The modifications introduced by Huggins[2], Miller[4], and Guggenheim[5] all involve correcting P_{ij} only for the effect of the immediately adjacent polymer segments. Zimm[9] has shown this to be insufficient by evaluating a_2 (see Equation 14) for athermal solutions of various infinite chains in a cubic lattice ($z = 6$). The solvent molecules are unit cubes, while the polymers are rods, double rods, two kinds of zigzags and a spiral (pictured in Fig. 11). The calculated μ's are 0.167, 0.333, 0.208, 0.292, and 0.323, respectively. Only for the single rod is

$\mu^S = 1/z = 1/6$; for all of the others, in which the repeating unit occupies two or more sites, it is much greater; tighter spirals or more extensive zigzags would increase μ^S still further.

This picture of essentially straight chains is, of course, inherently unreasonable, since there will be extensive irregular coiling. In sufficiently concentrated solutions, however, the molecules will be so intertwined that it should be reasonable to assume a random distribution of occupied sites with corrections for the short range effects discussed above.

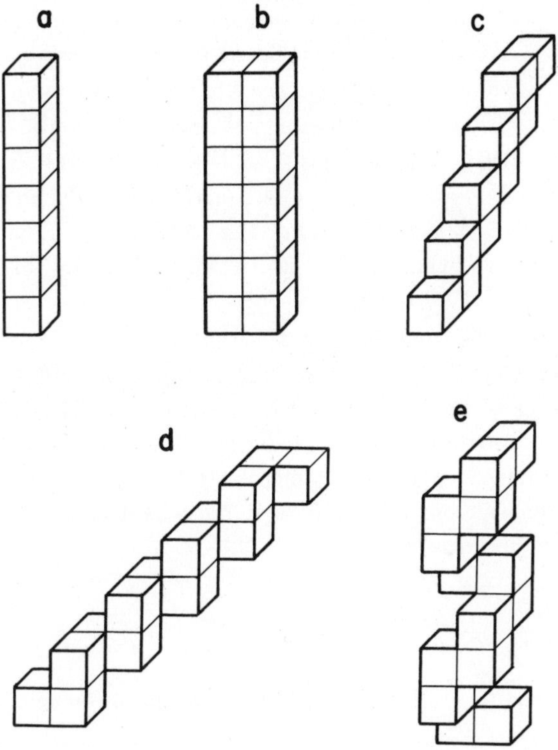

Fig. 11. Hypothetical lattice polymers

For very dilute solutions, however, Flory[8] has emphasized the unreality of this model and has replaced it with one which regards the solution as microscopically discontinuous. He subdivided the solution into regions of pure solvent from which polymer molecules are totally absent and regions of swollen polymer (*i. e.*, regions including an irregularly coiled polymer molecule and the encompassed solvent molecules.) In the former regions $P'_{ij} \doteq 1$, while a P''_{ij} for the latter regions can be estimated from the average "concentration" of occupied sites. The size of these domains and the polymer "concentration" in them can be estimated from light scattering and viscosity measurements; values of μ obtained in this way are in reasonable agreement with experiment.

In a later more rigorous treatment, Flory[32a] has obtained for athermal solutions (our notation):

$$a_2 = \tfrac{1}{2} - \mu = \tfrac{1}{2}(1 - 0.159\,\xi + 0.026\,\xi^2 - \ldots .) \tag{31}$$

$$\xi = \frac{v_p^2}{v_e\, v_o} = \frac{m_p^2}{m_e\, m_o}$$

where v_p and v_o are the volumes of polymer and solvent molecules respectively and v_e is the volume of the "equivalent sphere" representing the polymer and its enclosed solvent (roughly a sphere whose diameter is the root mean square distance between chain ends). For a randomly distributed chain this root mean square distance varies as the square root of the number of segments, so we may expect to be proportional to $M^{\frac{1}{2}}$. Zimm[32b] has deduced an equation similar to this predicting the same very slow increase of μ with M, a conclusion which seems to be borne out by his measurements upon polystyrene of 10,000,000 molecular weight.

Finally, we must consider the effect of these considerations upon μ^H. We may regard the athermal μ^S as a measure of a kind of structural repulsion arising from the excluded volume. The term $(1 - 2\mu^S)$ may then be considered as a probability factor modifying the purely random probability φ_p^2 of finding adjacent polymer segments. If this be so, the heat of mixing calculated by the random approximation must be decreased by such a factor. This leads to an expression

$$\mu = \mu^S + (1 - 2\,\mu^S)\,\varepsilon \tag{32}$$

where ε is the value of the heat constant in the absence of these considerations.

To date these considerations have been ignored in practice, and μ is usually written in some such form as

$$\mu = \mu^S + \frac{V_o\,(\delta_o - \delta_p)^2}{RT} \tag{33}$$

Such a treatment, although certainly incorrect in detail, has led to satisfactory qualitative and semi-quantitative interpretations of the solubility and swelling of non-polar polymers in various non-polar solvents as we shall see in succeeding sections. While this in no way disproves the theoretical treatment above, it may be regarded as convincing evidence for the inclusion

[32a] P. J. Flory, *J. Chem. Phys.*, **17**, 303, 1347 (1949).
[32b] B. H. Zimm, private communication.

in μ of a term $(\delta_o - \delta_p)^2$ depending upon the properties of the pure substances alone, although modified by more or less constant factors imperfectly understood.

3. The Solubility of High Polymers.

While nearly all high polymers are heterogenous mixtures with respect to molecular weight, we may derive much useful information from a consideration of the solubility and phase relationships of a hypothetical homogenous polymer, all of whose molecules are not only identical in chemical structure, but also in chain length. Later we shall need to consider the problem of heterogeneous polymers to obtain quantitative information and to treat problems of fractionation.

(a) Homogeneous polymers:

We have seen in Chapters III and XVI that the free energy equations for the two components in a liquid mixture permit us to calculate the critical solution temperature and the compositions of two coexistent phases. Huggins [2] and Flory [3] have shown that Equations 11 ab may be used to define the conditions for the solubility of a linear high polymer in an entirely analogous manner.

Figure 12 shows the partial molal free energy of the solvent, $\Delta\overline{F}_o$, taken from Equation 11 a, plotted against φ_p, the volume fraction of the polymer, for several values of the parameter μ. (m is taken as 100). When μ is sufficiently small, $\Delta\overline{F}_o$ decreases uniformly with increasing polymer concentration, signifying complete miscibility of solvent and polymer. With a larger value of μ (*i. e.* a greater heat of mixing), the curve shows a maximum and a minimum indicating only partial miscibility. There will be an intermediate value of μ at which separation into two phases first appears. At this critical value μ_c, the $\Delta\overline{F}_o$ curve shows a point of inflection, for which the condition (cf. Chapters III and XVI) is that the first and second derivatives vanish:

$$\frac{d\,\Delta\overline{F}_o}{d\,\varphi_p} = \frac{d^2\,\Delta\overline{F}_o}{d\,\varphi_p^2} = 0 \tag{34}$$

Differentiating Equation 15a and solving for μ_c, we obtain:

$$\mu_c = \frac{1}{2}\left(1 + \frac{1}{\sqrt{m}}\right)^2 \tag{35}$$

Hence, for the polymer in Fig. 12, for which $m = 100$, $\mu_c = 0.605$. When m is very large (corresponding to a very high molecular weight), μ_c is very nearly 0.5. It is obvious from this limiting value that a polymer will be completely miscible in any solvent for which μ is less than 0.5.

Similarly, the proportions of solvent and polymer in the critical phase are given by:

$$(\varphi_p)_c = \frac{1}{1 + \sqrt{m}} \tag{36a}$$

$$(\varphi_o)_c = \frac{\sqrt{m}}{1 + \sqrt{m}} \tag{36b}$$

We see that for high molecular weights, the distribution is very unsymmetrical, and that the solubility at the critical point decreases with increasing molecular weight.

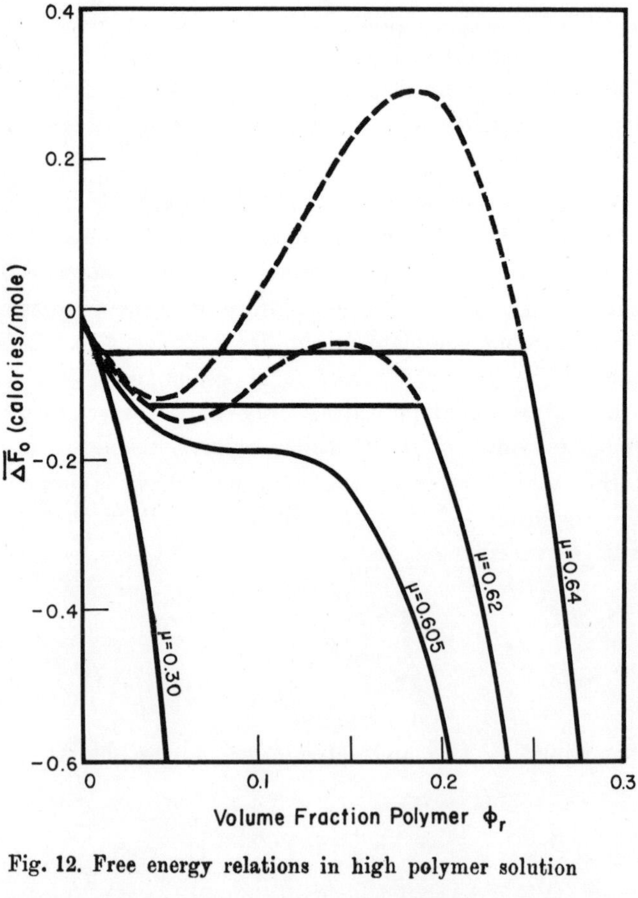

Fig. 12. Free energy relations in high polymer solution

From an equation for μ (for example, Equation 33) one may attempt to calculate critical solution temperatures for polymer solutions, but such a calculation would be subject to all the inaccuracies inherent in the initial equation.

To determine the solubility at any other point than at the critical point, one must use the equilibrium conditions between two phases:

$$\Delta \bar{F}_o' = \Delta \bar{F}_o'' \tag{37a}$$

$$\Delta \bar{F}_p' = \Delta \bar{F}_p'' \tag{37b}$$

or substituting from Equations 11 ab:

$$\ln(1-\varphi_p') + \left(1-\frac{1}{m}\right)\varphi_p' + \mu(\varphi_p')^2 = \ln(1-\varphi_p'') + \left(1-\frac{1}{m}\right)\varphi_p'' + \mu(\varphi_p'')^2 \tag{38a}$$

$$\ln\varphi_p' - (m-1)(1-\varphi_p') + m\mu(1-\varphi_p')^2 = \ln\varphi_p'' - (m-1)(1-\varphi_p'') + m\mu(1-\varphi_p'')^2 \tag{38b}$$

For specific values of m and μ, one may solve these two simultaneous equations for φ_p', the volume fraction of polymer in the dilute solution phase, and φ_p'', the volume fraction of polymer in the swollen polymer phase. In the latter phase, we may formally regard the polymer as solvent and the liquid as solute, although both phases are frequently dilute with respect to polymer.

One may transform Equation 38 b into a more instructive form:

$$\ln\frac{\varphi_p''}{\varphi_p'} = m\left[-\left(1-\frac{1}{m}\right)(\varphi_o'-\varphi_o'') + \mu\{(\varphi_o')^2-(\varphi_o'')^2\}\right] \tag{39}$$

or substituting from Equation 38a:

$$\ln\frac{\varphi_p''}{\varphi_p'} = m\left[2\mu(\varphi_o'-\varphi_o'') - \ln\frac{\varphi_o'}{\varphi_o''}\right] \tag{40}$$

This yields a partition coefficient with an exponential dependence upon m:

$$\frac{\varphi_p''}{\varphi_p'} = e^{\alpha m} \tag{41}$$

where α is the term in brackets in Equation 39 or the equivalent term in Equation 40.

An equation equivalent to Equation 41 was first derived by Brønsted[33] and elaborated by Schulz[34]. Brønsted attributed the partition of large mole-

[33] J. N. Brønsted *Z, phys. Chem.*, Bodenstein Festband, 257, (1931); **A 155**, 343, (1931); **A 168**, 381 (1934); *Compt. rend. trav. lab., Carlsberg, Ser. chim.* **22**, 321 (1938), *Nord. Kemikermøde*, **Forh. 5**, 188 (1939).

[34] G. V. Schulz, *Z. physik. Chem.*, **A 179**, 321 (1937); **B 46**, 105, 137 (1940); **B 47**, 155 (1940).

cules between two phases to a difference in potential energy. Assuming this energy difference to be proportional to molecular weight, he obtained for the concentrations in the two phases:

$$\log \frac{c''}{c'} = \frac{\varkappa M}{RT} \tag{42}$$

Schulz, to explain the phenomena of fractional precipitation, assumed that for a mixture of two liquids $\varkappa$ is a linear function of composition:

$$\varkappa = A + B\gamma \tag{43}$$

where A and B are constants and γ, the proportion of the precipitant (non-solvent) in the mixture.

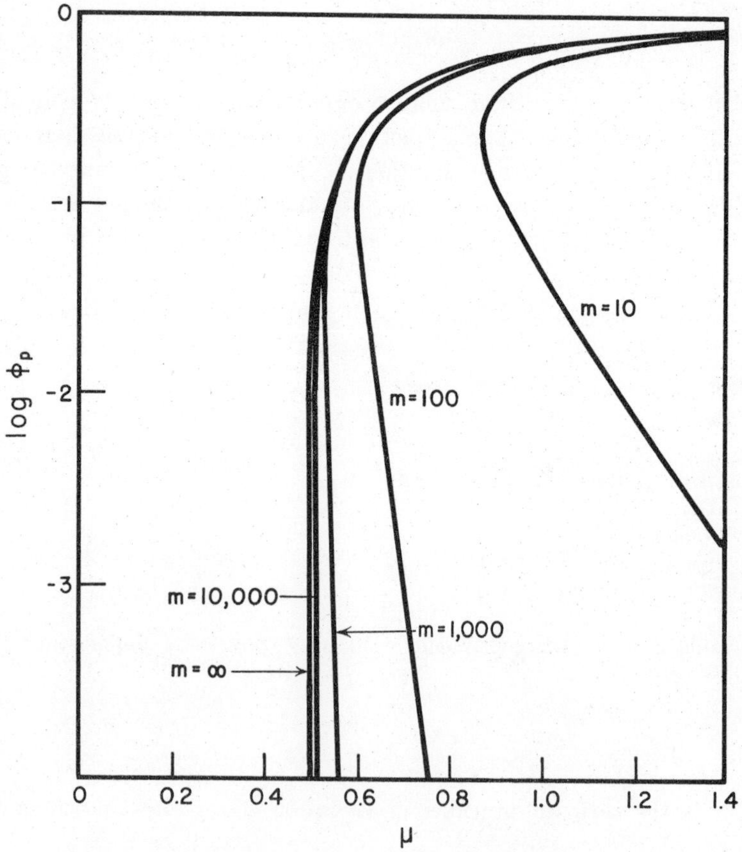

Fig. 13. Solubility of high polymers as a function of μ and molecular weight

While these equations were useful in a qualitative sense, the assumption that the partition factor $\varkappa$ depends primarily upon an energy difference is faulty, since we have seen that the major contribution is from the entropy. Consequently one would not expect the temperature dependence of the partition factor to be as simple as that expressed by Equation 42.

Solution of Equations 38ab is tedious but may be accomplished by approximation methods outlined by Flory[3]. Figure 13 shows the results of such calculations relating φ_p to μ for varying values of m.

The striking feature of Figure 13 is the extreme asymmetry of the phase diagram. For reasonable values of m (m = 1000 or M $\simeq$ 100,000), the amount of polymer in the dilute phase is already vanishingly small at $\mu = 0.60$. The swollen polymer phase, on the other hand, is over 30 % solvent (by volume) at $\mu = 1.00$. We see that in a poor solvent the phenomenon is essentially one of swelling, since the dilute phase is almost pure solvent.

For values of μ sufficiently above the critical point, the equilibrium defined by Equations 38ab reduces to one between the swollen polymer and pure solvent and we need only solve one equation:

$$\Delta\overline{F}_0'' = 0 = RT\left[\ln(1-\varphi_p'') + (1-\frac{1}{m})\varphi_p'' + \mu(\varphi_p'')^2\right] \quad (44$$

We have seen in an earlier section that the osmotic pressure Π was proportional to $\Delta\overline{F}_0$. The tendency of a polymer to swell in a solvent may be measured as a swelling pressure which is thermodynamically identical with the osmotic pressure. The equilibrium of Equation 43 amounts to permitting the polymer to swell until the swelling pressure (osmotic pressure) is zero.

The rapid drop of solubility with increasing μ means that a non-cross-linked polymer will probably be either completely miscible or practically insoluble in a given liquid; few solvents will be found in the narrow range of μ where the solubility is considerable but not complete. We see from Figure 13 that for m = 1000 (M $\cong$ 100,000), the solubility decreases from complete miscibility to $\varphi_p = 10^{-4}$ in a μ-interval of 0.03; for higher molecular weights, this interval becomes vanishingly small. The only serious exception to this is found with heterogenous polymers; low molecular weight fractions may dissolve in solvents which have little solvent power for higher molecular weight material.

Accepting Equation 33 as an approximation, aud using $\mu = 0.5$ as a critical solubility limit, we can calculate approximate limits within which the solubility parameters δ_0 of good solvents for a polymer of high molecular weight must lie. For $T = 300$, $\mu^S = 0.3$, $V_0 = 100$, we obtain 1.1 as a maximum value for $\Delta\delta$. We will expect such a polymer to be completely miscible in solvents which satisfy the condition:

$$(\delta_p - 1.1) < \delta_\circ < (\delta_p + 1.1) \tag{45}$$

This is a total range of about 2.2 as compared with about 7 for ordinary liquids. For solvents whose molal volume is less than 100 (*i. e.* CS_2), we may expect somewhat greater limits; while for those with greater molal volumes, the conditions are more stringent than Equation 45. Since over a certain range of solvents the solubility is infinite, and outside this range almost negligibly small, it is not surprising that early observers were unable to correlate the solubility with swelling phenomena.

Table 2. Solubility of Polyisobutene. (Evans and Young[35]).

Solvent	$V_\circ$	$\delta_\circ$	Solubility
n-hexane	132	7.3	soluble
n-octane	164	7.55	soluble
i-butyl chloride	106	(8.1)	soluble
cyclohexane	109	8.2	soluble
2,2-dichloropropane	104	(8.2)	insoluble
n-amyl chloride	121	(8.3)	soluble
n-propyl chloride	88	8.5	soluble
carbon tetrachloride	97	8.6	soluble
toluene	107	8.9	soluble
trans-1,2-dichloroethylene	78	9.0	soluble
1,2-dichloropropane	98	(9.0)	insoluble
cis-1,2-dichloroethylene	76	9.1	insoluble
benzene	89	9.15	soluble
chloroform	81	9.3	soluble
trichloroethylene	89	(9.3)	soluble
tetrachloroethylene	102	(9.4)	soluble
pentachloroethane	120	(9.4)	soluble
1,1,2-trichloroethane	93	(9.6)	insoluble
methylene chloride	65	9.7	insoluble
1,1,2,2-tetrachloroethane	105	(9.7)	insoluble
1,2-dichloroethane	79	9.8	insoluble

These solubility limits are demonstrated by solubility data on polyisobutylene (Evans and Young[35]), polystyrene (Edelson[36]) and polyvinyl chloride (Doty and Zimm[37]). These results are shown in Tables 2, 3 and 4. The dependence of the solubility limits upon the $\delta_\circ$-values for the solvent is ob-

[35] H. C. Evans and D. W. Young, *Ind. Eng. Chem.* 34, 461 (1942).
[36] D. Edelson, Thesis for B. S., Polytechnic Institute of Brooklyn, 1946.
[37] P. M. Doty and B. H. Zimm, private communication.

Table 3. Solubility of Polystyrene, M ≅ 90,000. (Edelson[36]).

Solvent	V_0	δ_0	Solubility
n-hexane	132	7.3	insoluble
ethyl ether	105	7.4	swells
cyclohexane[38]	109	8.2	soluble above 30° C
sec-butyl bromide	110	(8.4)	soluble
n-butyl bromide	108	(8.7)	soluble
carbon tetrachloride	97	8.6	soluble
toluene	107	8.9	soluble
benzene	89	9.15	soluble
chloroform	81	9.3	soluble
1,2 dichloroethane	79	9.8	soluble
dioxane	86	10.0	soluble
1,2 dibromoethane	87	10.4	soluble
1,2 dibromoethylene[39]	83	(10.1)	soluble
carbon disulfide	60	10.0	soluble
nitrobenzene	103	10.0	soluble
α-bromonaphthalene	141	(10.6)	soluble
nitropropane	81	(10.7)	soluble
nitroethane	71	(11.1)	swells
methylene iodide	81	11.8	insoluble
acetonitrile	53	11.9	insoluble
nitromethane	54	12.6	insoluble

Table 4. Solubility of Polyvinylchloride. (Doty and Zimm[37]).

Solvent	V_0	δ_0	Solubility
n-hexane	132	7.3	insoluble
ethyl ether	105	7.4	insoluble
vinylchloride	68	7.8	insoluble
n-butyl bromide	105	(8.7)	insoluble
carbon tetrachloride	97	8.6	insoluble
toluene	107	8.9	insoluble
benzene	89	9.15	insoluble
chloroform	81	9.3	insoluble
chlorobenzene	102	9.5	soluble
1,2 dichloroethane	78	9.8	soluble
carbon disulfide	61	10.0	insoluble
1,2 dibromoethane	87	10.4	soluble
α-bromonaphthalene	141	10.6	soluble
methylene iodide	81	11.8	insoluble

[38] R. L. Scott, *J. Chem. Phys.*, **13**, 178 (1945).

[39] B. H. Zimm, private communication.

vious. From these solubility data, one may estimate δ_p values for the polymers: 8.1 for polyisobutylene, 9.2 for polystyrene, and 9.6 for polyvinyl chloride. The narrow solubility limits for the latter polymer may possibly be due to its partially crystalline character; the problem of crystalline polymers will be considered in a later section. Polyvinyl chloride is soluble in ketones, esters, and nitro-compounds but this is attributed to a specific interaction (hydrogen bonding?) between the polymer and these solvents similar to that between acetone and chloroform.

(b) Heterogeneous polymers.

Flory and Scott have applied their respective equations[11,12] for heterogeneous polymers to the problems of solubility and fractionation[11,38]. Except for symbolism, the two treatments, insofar as they overlap, are exactly parallel; so no attempt will be made to separate them.

We assume a polymeric mixture heterogeneous with respect to molecular weight, but otherwise uniform (with respect to density, chemical composition). For such a system M and m may be used interchangeably except for a constant factor.

The equilibrium conditions are entirely analogous to those for the homogeneous polymer (Equations 37 ab). The partial molal free energies of each component (regarding each molecular weight polymer as a separate species) must be equal in both phases. Using Equations 15 ab, we obtain:

$$\ln \varphi'_\circ + \left(1 - \frac{1}{\bar{m}'_n}\right)(1 - \varphi'_\circ) + \mu\,(1 - \varphi'_\circ)^2 =$$

$$\ln \varphi''_\circ + \left(1 - \frac{1}{\bar{m}''_n}\right)(1 - \varphi''_\circ) + \mu\,(1 - \varphi''_\circ)^2 \qquad (46\text{a})$$

$$\ln \varphi'_i + \left(1 - \frac{m_i}{\bar{m}'_n}\right)(1 - \varphi'_\circ) + (1 - m_i)\,\varphi'_\circ + m_i\,\mu\,(\varphi'_\circ)^2 =$$

$$\ln \varphi''_i + \left(1 - \frac{m_i}{\bar{m}''_n}\right)(1 - \varphi''_\circ) + (1 - m_i)\,\varphi''_\circ + m_i\,\mu\,(\varphi''_\circ)^2 \qquad (46\text{b})$$

Equation 46 b, of course, represents a whole set of simultaneous equations, one for each different molecular weight in the system.

Transforming Equation 46 b, we obtain for the partition of the ith fraction between the two phases:

$$\ln \frac{\varphi_i''}{\varphi_i'} = m_i \left[\left(1 - \frac{1}{\overline{m}_n'}\right)(1 - \varphi_o') - \left(1 - \frac{1}{\overline{m}_n''}\right)(1 - \varphi_o'') + \mu \left\{(\varphi_o')^2 - (\varphi_o'')^2\right\} \right] \tag{47}$$

Note that the distribution functions in the two phases are presumed to be different; hence $\overline{m}_n'$ is not the same as $\overline{m}_n''$. Substitution from Equation 46 a and conversion to exponential form yields an equation formally identical with Equation 41:

$$\frac{\varphi_i''}{\varphi_i'} = e^{\alpha m_i} \tag{48}$$

where α is a parameter characteristic of the system, the same for all fractions, defined as:

$$\alpha = 2\mu(\varphi_o' - \varphi_o'') - \ln \frac{\varphi_o'}{\varphi_o''} \tag{49}$$

or alternately as the term in brackets in Equation 47.

We define a distribution function $f(m_i)$ equal to the amount w_i (either weight or volume fraction, since the density is assumed uniform) in the ith fraction of molecular weight M_i and corresponding m_i:

$$w_i = f(m_i) \tag{50}$$

The functions are so normalized that the summation over the whole polymer yields unity:

$$\sum_i w_i = \sum_i f(m_i) = 1 \tag{51}$$

Suppose a certain volume V_p of polymer of distribution function f(m) is placed in contact with a volume V_o of solvent. The total volume of the ith fraction V_i is the sum of the amounts in the two phases:

$$V_i = V_p w_i = V_p f(m_i) = \varphi_i' V' + \varphi_i'' V'' \tag{52}$$

where V' is the total volume of the "solution" phase and V'' that of the "swollen polymer" phase.

Substituting from Equation 48 and solving for φ_i', we obtain:

$$\varphi_i' = \frac{V_i}{V' + V'' e^{a m_i}} = \frac{V_p \, f(m_i)}{V' + V'' e^{a m_i}} \tag{53}$$

The solubility in terms of volume fraction of total polymer in the solution phase is then:

$$\varphi_p' = \sum_i \varphi_i' = \sum_i \frac{V_p \, f(m_i)}{(V' + V'' e^{a m_i})} \tag{54}$$

A perhaps more practical form is to express the solubility in terms of the fraction of total polymer in the solution phase, which we might call the "fraction dissolved" S:

$$S = \frac{\varphi_p' V'}{V_p} = \sum_i \frac{f(m_i)}{1 + (V''/V') e^{a m_i}} \tag{55}$$

Equations 54 and 55, while presumably rigorous, are not very helpful when it comes to actual calculations. Given the distribution function $f(m_i)$ (either analytically or graphically), the ratio of polymer to solvent $V_p/V_\circ$, and μ for the system, one can make the calculation, since V''/V' is a function of these variables, but the exact computation may be exceedingly long and tedious. Several approximation methods will be found in the original papers[11,39].

Since most of the important features of the solubility of polymers are explained by the simple theory for homogeneous substances, Equations 54 and 55 have never been used quantitatively. They show us, however, that a polymer with a broad molecular weight distribution may have a partial "solubility" in certain solvents when low molecular fractions can dissolve[39a].

4. **Fractionation.**

It is frequently of importance to separate a high polymer into a series of fractions differing in avarage molecular weight. Measurement of the average molecular weights of such fractions by osmotic or other methods permits calculation of an approximate molecular weight distribution curve f(m) for the original polymer. The distribution functions are in turn important in the interpretation of many of the properties of the polymer including some of major industrial importance. The usual methods of fractionation fall into two classes:

[39a] (Note added in proof) Scott's conclusion[39] that the critical solubility limit (*i. e.*, μ_c) depends upon the number average molecular weight has recently been shown to be erroneous, both from a theoretical standpoint (W. H. Stockmayer, *J. Chem, Phys.*, **17**, 588, (1949); H. Tompa, *J. Chem. Phys*,, **17**, 1003 (1949) and from experimental measurements (G. Gavoret and M. Magat, *J. Chem. Phys.*, **17**, 999 (1949).

(a) Precipitation: In this method, the polymer is first dissolved in a good solvent ($\mu < \frac{1}{2}$), and then a sufficient amount of a non-solvent or precipitant ($\mu \gg \frac{1}{2}$) is added to produce separation into two phases. The "precipitate" phase is removed and a small amount of additional precipitant added to the solution producing another two phase system. Carefully controlling the amount of precipitant added in each step, one repeats this procedure until all the polymer has been precipitated in successive fractions. The highest molecular weight material is the first to separate out, and with successive fractions, the average molecular weight decreases regularly.

A variation of the fractional precipitation method is to obtain separation of the fractions by decreasing the temperature of a nearly critical system, rather than by addition of non-solvent. The effect is the same in both cases; fractionation is achieved by systematically increasing μ for the polymer-solvent system.

(b) Extraction: In this method, now of lesser importance than the precipitation method, the polymer is successively extracted with mixtures of a good solvent and a non-solvent, increasing the relative proportion of the solvent with each extraction, resulting in a systematic decrease in μ. Where feasible, this series of solvent blends may be replaced by a series of pure liquids arranged in order of increasing solvent power for the polymer. In this case, the lowest molecular weight fractions are extracted first, while the very high molecular weight material is obtained only in the last stages of the fractionation.

The experimental methods of fractionation have recently been reviewed in detail[40].

Both of these methods can be interpreted[11,39] in terms of the same thermodynamic theory, based essentially upon Equation 48. In both cases each step consists of the establishment of thermodynamic equilibrium between a swollen polymer phase and a solution phase.

The first significant attempt to treat fractionation as a thermodynamic problem was that of Schulz[35] previously referred to. While his interpretation of the partition factor α has had to be revised to include entropy effects not then considered, his extensive calculations of molecular weight distributions in fractionated polymers still have a large measure of validity.

For simplicity, we assume that μ has the same value in both phases This will not strictly be true unless the proportions of solvent and precipitant are the same in both phases; recent investigations, to be discussed in a latter section, indicate that these proportions are usually markedly different. When a single liquid or a series of pure liquids are used in fractionation, the assumption is unnecessary, and in any case, the

[40] L. H. Cragg and H. Hammerschlag, *Chem. Revs.*, 39, 79 (1946).

general nature of the results would not be changed by a choice of different μ's for the two phases.

Following the same lines as in the preceding section, we may express the distribution functions of the polymer in the solution f′(m) and in the first precipitate, f″(m) in terms of the initial distribution function f(m):

Precipitate:

$$f''(m) = \frac{f(m)}{1 + \frac{e^{-\alpha m}}{\lambda}} \tag{56 a}$$

Solution:

$$f'(m) = \frac{f(m)}{1 + \lambda e^{\alpha m}} \tag{56 b}$$

where $\lambda = V''/V'$

It is apparent immediately from the above equations that in any such distribution between the two phases, most of the high molecular weight material will be found in the precipitate, and most of the low molecular weight material in the solution. There is no sharp division since there will be some of every fraction in both phases. In the case of the highest molecular weights the amount in solution may well be negligible, but there will always be at least λ of the low molecular weight material in the precipitate since:

$$\lim_{m \to o} \frac{1}{1 + \frac{e^{-\alpha m}}{\lambda}} = \frac{\lambda}{1+\lambda} = \frac{V''}{V' + V''} \cong \lambda \tag{57}$$

This last fact is important, for in the precipitation method of fractionation, the precipitates of the first few fractions are highly swollen, and λ may approach or even exceed 10%. The presence of sizeable quantities of very low molecular weight in the very first fractions is well known experimentally, and is very objectionable since even a small amount of such material can appreciably alter the number average molecular weight determined from osmotic measurements. This "tail" is a purely thermodynamic effect, a consequence of Equation 48, and is not caused by mechanical coprecipitation as has been suggested.

The experimental remedy is either refractionation of at least the higher fractions with suitable recombinations or merely reprecipitation. In the latter procedure, after the supernatant solution is decanted, the remaining swollen precipitate is redissolved in an appropriate solvent blend and reprecipitated by addition of just enough non-solvent. An even simpler variation of this method is that of "washing" or extracting the swollen precipitate with a solvent mixture very slightly richer in non-solvent than the decanted solution. In the reprecipitation or washing procedures the remaining solutions should be combined before precipitation of the next fraction. The net effect of all these methods is to reduce the amount of the low molecular weight "tail" from λ to λ^2.

As the fractionation proceeds, we obtain thermodynamic equilibrium in each step and the subsequent distribution functions are products of factors such as those in Equations 56 ab. In the precipitation method, the distribution in the nth precipitate may be expressed as:

$$f_n''(m) = \frac{f(m)}{(1+\lambda_a e^{\alpha_a m}) \ldots\ldots (1+\lambda_m e^{\alpha_m m}) \left(1 + \frac{e^{-\alpha_n m}}{\lambda_n}\right)} \tag{58}$$

Actually this may be very closely represented by neglecting all but the last two terms in the denominator:

$$f_n''(m) = \frac{f(m)}{(1+\lambda_m e^{\alpha_m m}) \left(1 + \frac{e^{-\alpha_n m}}{\lambda_n}\right)} \tag{59}$$

An analogous treatment of the extraction method leading to equations similar to 58 and 59 will be found in the original literature[39].

Let us denote by φ_p° the original volume fraction of total polymer (approximately $V_p/V_\circ$) before separation of the first fraction and fractionate into n equal fractions. Scott[39] has shown that α is an approximate function of μ, while λ is an approximate function[41] of μ and φ_p°/n. These approximations permit us to assess the effect of concentration on the sharpness of fractionation.

In Figure 14, the approximate function $f_n''(m)/f(m)$ taken from Equation 59 is plotted against m for four different values of φ_p°/n. The curves represent the percentage of total original material (of molecular weight m found in a specific fraction taken between μ_m and $(\mu_m + .02)$, the values of μ chosen so that the maximum for each concentration lies in approximately the same range. Figure 14 shows that the major effect of decreasing the conentration (other than to require greater μ's and consequently more precipitant) is to make the fractionation sharper, especially decreasing the "tail" effect. Evidently, decreasing the concentration has a theoretical advantage, but below $\varphi_p^\circ/n = 10^{-4}$, the gain in sharpness is small and hardly enough to compensate for the enormous increase in experimental difficulty.

[41] In the original paper[39] Scott used c for φ_p°/n and a parameter β, a function of μ, which is equal to λ/c.

In practice many fractionations are carried out in approximately 1% solutions ($\varphi_p^\circ = 0.01$). For a fractionation into ten equal parts, this corresponds roughly to the 10^{-3} curve of Fig. 14. If adequate precautions are taken to remove the tail by reprecipitation or washing, such fractionations should yield fairly good results without requiring time consuming refractionations.

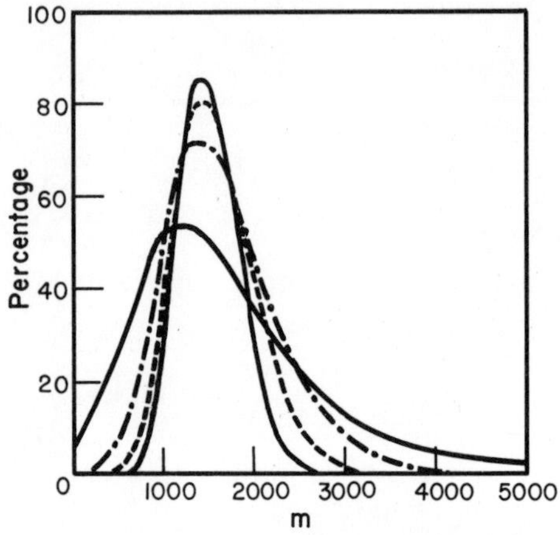

Fig. 14. Effectiveness of fractionation at different concentrations. The broadest curve corresponds to $\varphi_p^\circ/n = 10^{-2}$; the others are 10^{-3}, 10^{-4}, and 10^{-5}, respectively.

5. Multicomponent systems.

While the thermodynamic systems involved in the problems of fractionation are essentially multicomponent ones, they are normally simplified or approximated to eliminate the difficulties arising from having three or more species in the mixture. In particular, in the preceding section, we assumed that solvent mixtures behave as homogeneous single liquids, so that μ is the same in both phases. This "single liquid approximation" was not supposed to be accurate, but was useful in obtaining semi-quantitative information concerning fractionation.

Gee[42] and Scott[43] have considered the problems of phase equilibria in a ternary system of polymer and two liquids. Essentially, the method involves assigning values μ_{12}, μ_{13}, and μ_{23} to the three binary systems; the thermodynamics of the ternary region is defined by these three constants and the molecular volumes of the species, as we have seen in a earlier chapter.

[42] G. Gee, *Trans. Faraday Soc.*, **40**, 468 (1944).

[43] R. L. Scott, *J. Chem. Phys.*, **17**, 268 (1949).

The "single liquid approximation" requires the proportions of the two liquids to be the same in both phases; the extensions of all the tie lines should pass through the polymer vertex of the phase triangle. Calculation of a few phase diagrams (Figures 15 and 16) shows this to be far from true.

In discussing the solubility of polymers in mixed liquids, we must distinguish three cases. To avoid complications we assume that the two liquids are themselves miscible in all proportions.

(a) Both liquids are solvents for the polymer; that is, separately, each is miscible in all proportions with the polymer. In this case, the polymer must be completely miscible with all possible solvent mixtures; there will be no phase separation anywhere in the ternary diagram.

(b) One liquid is a solvent; the other, a non-solvent. In this familiar solvent-precipitant system, mixtures sufficiently rich in solvent are miscible in all proportions; addition of more than a certain amount of non-solvent produces phase separation. A diagram calculated for a polymer of infinite molecular weight is shown in Figure 15. For $m = \infty$, one phase is completely free of polymer; hence the plait point P is on the base line.

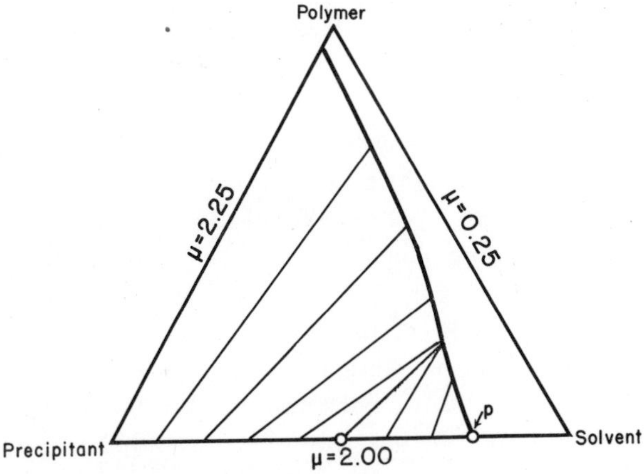

Fig. 15. Solubility of a polymer in a mixture of solvent and precipitant

(c) Both liquids are non-solvents. In this situation, there is a possibility that over a limited range of liquid mixtures, the polymer is completely miscible in all proportions, although phase separation occurs with the pure liquids at either end of the diagram. In terms of the simple internal pressure treatment of the heat of mixing (Chapter VII), this can only be true if the solubility parameter δ_p for the polymer lies between the δ_o's for the two liquids. Figure 16 shows such a calculated diagram. Gee[42] has shown this to be the case for at least six ternary systems, among which are neoprene in hexane-acetone, Buna S (butadiene-styrene copolymer) in pentane-ethylacetate and Buna-N (butadiene-acrylonitrile copolymer) in toluene-dimethyl malonate. All of Gee's systems contained at least one polar liquid, but there is no reason to doubt that a completely non-polar system would show the same effect.

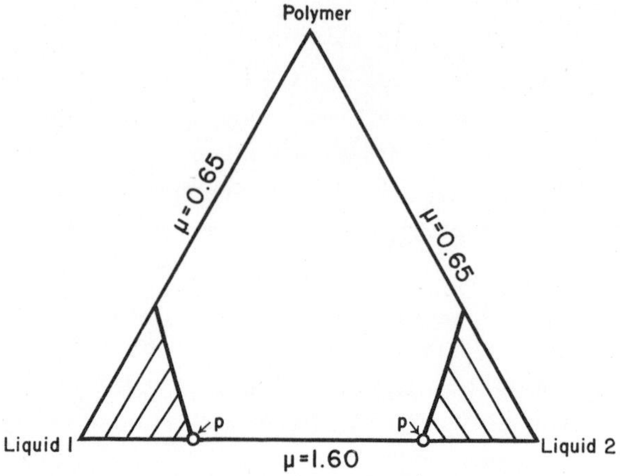

Fig. 16. Solubility of a polymer in a mixture of two non-solvents showing the possibility of complete miscibility in certain mixtures.

A different kind of ternary system is that of two different high polymers and a single solvent. Although a liquid may be a good solvent for both polymers, mixing the two solutions frequently results in separation into two phases. This frustrating phenomenon, technically known as incompatibility, has long been known in the paint and varnish industry, but until recently no systematic study of the problem had been untertaken. Dobry and Boyer-Kawenoki[44] studied phase separation in 78 such ternary systems, and found incompatibility of all but three or possibly four polymer pairs. Further, pairs incompatible in one solvent in general show phase separation in all other solvents, indicating that the precise nature of the solvent is only of secondary importance. Figure 17 shows the phase boundary for the system polystyrene-natural rubber-benzene.

A theoretical interpretation of this effect has been given by Stockmayer[45] and by Scott[46]. The phase separation depends mainly upon the interaction of the two polymers. While the heat of mixing the two polymers may be negligibly small on a volume basis, on a molar basis it may be large enough to produce separation. Unless the interaction constant μ_{12} is vanishingly small, the two polymers will be incompatible.[46a]

[44] A. Dobry and F. Boyer-Kawenoki, *J. Polymer Sci.*, **2**, 90, (1947).

[45] W. H. Stockmayer, ACS Meeting, Atlantic City, N. J., April 1949.

[46] R. L. Scott, *J. Chem. Phys.*, **17**, 279 (1949).

[46a] Both the above types of ternary systems have been discussed in a very recent paper by H. Tompa, *Trans. Faraday Soc.* **45**, 1142 (1949).

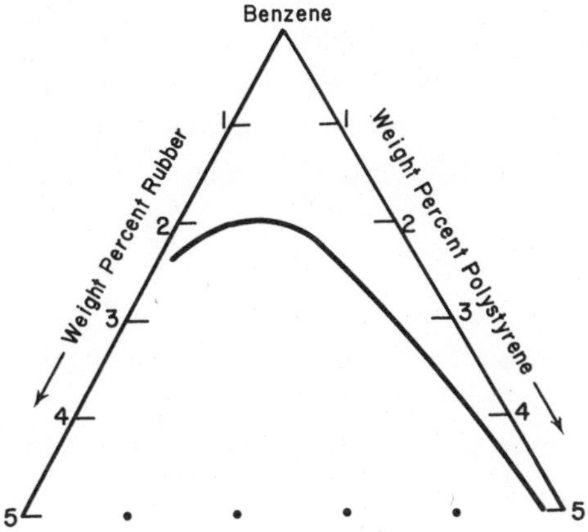

Fig. 17. Phase separation in the system benzene-rubber-polystyrene (Dobry and Boyer-Kawenoki).

6. Cross-Linked Polymers: Swelling.

The previous sections in this chapter have dealt exclusively with solutions in which the high polymer molecules are independent linear chains, possibly modified by occasional branching. However in many high polymers, these chains are bound together into a three dimensional network, the cross-linkages being ordinary chemical bonds, usually carbon-carbon bonds, but possibly in some cases of other types. The best known cases of these are of course the vulcanized rubbers, where cross-linking is induced by sulfur or peroxides, but the phenomenon is much more extensive. In many "normal" polymerizations, a sizeable amount of the resultant polymer is loosely cross-linked in a structure which has come to be known as a "gel" to distinguish it from the soluble un-cross-linked material or "sol".

We may speak of the whole cross-linked material as being one huge macro-molecule with a molecular weight in astronomical figures. It is this continuous three dimensional structure which accounts for the elastic properties, and the study thereof has given rise to an extensive body of theory known as the "kinetic theory of rubber elasticity". Some recent theoretical contributions to this field, most of which do not concern us here, are those of Wall[47], James and Guth,[48] Flory and Rehner[49], and Treloar[50].

[47] F. T. Wall, *J. Chem, Phys.*, **10**, 132, 485 (1942); **11**, 67, 527 (1943).

[48] H. M. James and E. Guth. *J. Chem. Phys.*, **11**, 455, 531 (1943); **15**, 651 (1947). See also the review by E. Guth, H. M. James, and H. Mark in "Advances in Colloid Science, Vol. II, Rubber", (Interscience, 1946).

[49] P. J. Flory and J. Rehner, Jr., *J. Chem. Phys.*, **11**, 512 (1943). See also the review by P. J. Flory, *Chem. Rev.*, **35**, 73 (1944).

[50] L. R. G. Treloar, *Trans. Faraday Soc.*, **39**, 36, 241 (1943); **42**, 77 (1946).

Of importance here for the treatment of the swelling of cross-linked polymers is the model advanced by Flory and Rehner[49]. They assume a network in which chains of approximately equal length are bound together in a repeating tetrahedral structure (somewhat like that of a diamond lattice) by cross-links each of which joins the ends of four chains. We may characterize the network by the average size of the chains units, expressed as weight or volume. Multiplying this volume by Avogadro's number, we obtain a parameter V_c, the molal volume between cross-links.

Earlier, Frenkel[51] had suggested that in the swelling of such three dimensional networks, equilibrium occurs when the osmotic pressure is equal to the elastic reaction of the chains. Following such a concept, we may represent the partial molal free energy of the solvent as the sum of two terms, the free energy of mixing or dilution, and the free energy of elastic stretching,

$$\Delta\overline{F}_\circ = \Delta\overline{F}_\circ^{M} + \Delta\overline{F}^{EL} \tag{60}$$

The former we may take to be the usual partial molal free energy (Equation 11a), with the molecular weight taken as infinite, since the network is virtually endless. The contribution of the heat of elastic deformation is unknown, but from their elastic theory, Flory and Rehner[52] derive an expression for the partial molal elastic entropy of the solvent in terms of the volume fraction of polymer in the swollen phase φ_p and the molal volumes $V_\circ$ of the solvent and $\overline{V}_c$ of the polymer between cross links:

$$\Delta\overline{S}_\circ^{EL} = -\frac{R V_\circ}{V_c}\varphi_p^{\frac{1}{3}} \tag{61}$$

The ratio $V_c/V_\circ$ we may call m_c by analogy to the earlier definition of m. Taking $\Delta\overline{H}_\circ^{EL} = 0$ and substituting from Equations 11a and 61 into Equation 60, we obtain:

$$\Delta\overline{F}_\circ = RT\left[\ln\varphi_\circ + \varphi_p + \mu\,\varphi_p^2 + \frac{\varphi_p^{\frac{1}{3}}}{m_c}\right] \tag{62}$$

If we plot this $\Delta\overline{F}_\circ$ as a function of φ_p, we find (Figure 18) that unlike the situation in solutions of un-cross-linked polymers, (Figure 12), the free energy increases initially, reaching a maximum before decreasing regularly. The appearance of a maximum requires that the components exhibit partial miscibility. Since positive values of $\Delta\overline{F}_\circ$ are necessarily excluded, one of the phases must be pure solvent, and the conjugate phase will have that composition for which $\Delta\overline{F}_\circ = 0$, in agreement with Frenkel's proposition.

[51] J. Frenkel, *Acta physicochimica URSS*, **9**, 235 (1938).

[52] P. J. Flory and J. Rehner, Jr., *J. Chem. Phys.*, **11**, 521 (1943); **12**, 417 (1944).

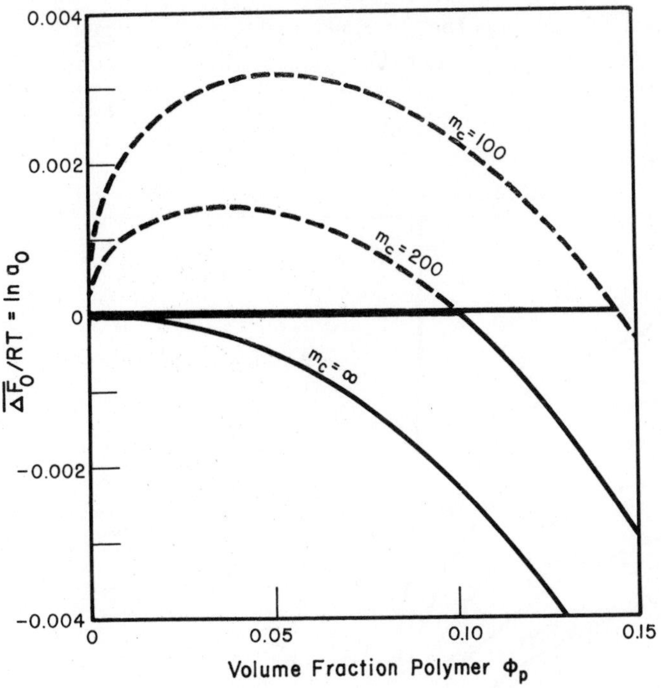

Fig. 18. Free energy relations in solutions of cross-linked polymers.

We conclude from this that the solubility of the cross-linked network is exactly zero, and that such a polymer will exhibit only limited swelling in even the "best" solvent (that is, for nonpolar systems, a minimum μ of about 0.3). If μ and m_c are known, this equilibrium swelling may be calculated from the equation:

$$\ln (1 - \varphi_p) + \varphi_p + \mu \varphi_p^2 + \frac{\varphi_p^{\frac{1}{3}}}{m_c} = 0 \tag{63}$$

In practice, the degree of swelling is expressed as the maximum imbibition Q, volume solvent imbibed per unit volume polymer, defined as:

$$Q = \frac{\varphi_o}{\varphi_p} = \frac{1 - \varphi_p}{\varphi_p} \tag{64}$$

Figure 19 shows Q as a function of μ and m_c. We see that the looser the cross-linking (larger m_c) the greater the swelling, and that an increase in μ results in a decrease of swelling, as is physically obvious. The asymptotic upper line is the swelling of an un-cross-linked polymer of infinite molecular weight; for μ's below 0.50, its swelling is infinite (i. e. there is only one phase).

The experimental determination of equilibrium swelling is one of the best means of studying the thermodynamics of polymer solutions. The measurements are much easier than corresponding osmotic measurements; the major difficulty is the slow increase of the swelling Q with time. This effect, presumably due to oxidative breakdown, may be avoided by extrapolation to zero time.

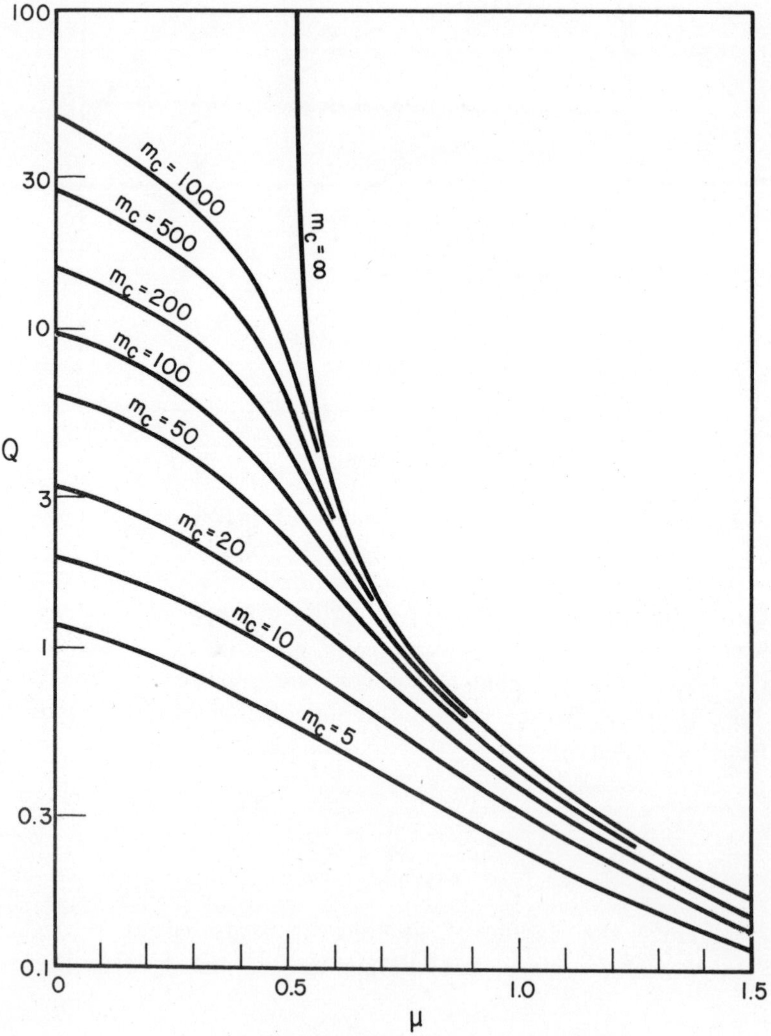

Fig. 19. Swelling as a function of m_c and μ.

The first extensive collection of data is that of Whitby, Evans and Pasternack[53], who measured the swelling of natural rubber in liquids and attempted to correlate the results with the chemical constitution of the

[53] G. S. Whitby, A. B. A. Evans and D. S. Pasternack, *Trans. Faraday Soc.*, 38, 269 (1942).

solvents. The first significant attempt to interpret the swelling in terms of thermodynamic theory was made by Gee[54], who, although handicapped by writing before Flory and Rehner formulated their elastic theory, showed conclusively that swelling was closely related to differences between the cohesive energy densities or internal pressures of polymer and solvent.

Recent measurements of swelling which have been interpreted in terms of the Flory-Rehner theory are those of Doty and Zable[55] on polyvinyl chloride, those of Boyer and Spencer[55a] on styrene-divinylbenzene gels, and those of Scott and Magat[56] on natural and synthetic rubbers.

Swelling represents perhaps the easiest method of evaluating the internal pressure and the solubility parameter δ_p for polymers, since direct thermal data are unattainable. Maximum swelling will be found in those systems for which μ is a minimum, that is where the δ's of solvent and polymer are identical. Gee[54] and Scott and Magat[56] have determined δ_p for a number of rubbers; their values are given in Table 5.

Table 5. Solubility Parameters δ_p for Rubbers

Polymer	*Gee*	*Scott and Magat*
Natural Rubber	7.98	8.35
Polybutadiene		8.45
Buna S		
85% B 15% S		8.55
75% B 25% S	8.1	8.60
60% B 40% S		8.70
Styrene-divinylbenzene copolymer		9.1 [55a]
Neoprene GN	8.2	9.25
Thiokol RD	9.0	
Thiokol F and FA	9.4	
Buna N	9.4	9.5—9.6

The reasons for the discrepancies between the two sets of δ_p's is not hard to find. Gee[54] purposely excluded the aromatic solvents from his solvents; so his solubility parameters are based primarily upon polar solvents such as esters, whose δ-values are not very reliable.

Scott and Magat[56] have analyzed the measurements of Whitby and coworkers[53] on natural rubber, attempting to calculate Q from the solubility parameters δ_0 of the solvents and a value of V_c (7100) chosen to give the best fit. The agreement between calculated and observed swellings is good for the hydrocarbons, but, as to be expected, the calculated values for the

[54] G. Gee, *Trans. Faraday Soc.*, **38**, 418 (1942); *Trans. Inst. Rubber Ind.*, **18**, 266 (1943)
[55] P. M. Doty and H. S. Zable, *J. Polymer Soc.*, **1**, 90 (1946).
[55a] R. F. Boyer and R. S. Spencer, *J. Polymer Sci.*, **3**, 97 (1948).
[56] R. L. Scott and M. Magat, *J. Polymer Sci.*, **4**, 555 (1949).

Table 6. Swelling of natural rubber in various solvents.

($\delta_p = 8.35$, $V_c = 7100$)

	V_o	δ_o	μ	m_c	$Q_{calc.}$	$Q_{obs.}$
Hydrocarbons						
n-Pentane	116	7.05	.63	61	1.4	1.12
n-Hexane	131	7.3	.54	54	1.8	1.18
n-Octane	164	7.55	.475	43	2.1	2.34
Benzene	89	9.15	.40	80	3.9	3.95
Toluene	107	8.9	.35	66	4.1	4.10
m-Xylene	123	8.8	.34	58	3.8	4.15
Mesitylene	140	8.8	.35	51	3.4	3.25
Limonene	162	8.5	.30	44	3.5	4.00
Methylcyclohexane	128	7.8	.36	55	3.5	
Ketones						
Acetone	74	9.9	.60	96	1.8	0.03
Methyl ethyl ketone	90	9.3	.44	79	3.3	0.71
Diethyl ketone	106	8.8	.34	67	4.1	1.6
Diisopropyl ketone	142	7.6	.44	50	2.6	1.9
Cyclohexanone	104	9.9	.72	68	1.0	(2.6)
Alcohols						
n-Propyl alcohol	75	11.9	1.9	95	0.09	0.02
tert-Butyl alcohol	95	10.6	1.0	75	0.43	0.13
Amyl alcohol	108	10.9	1.5	66	0.16	0.07
n-Hexyl alcohol	124	10.7	1.45	57	0.17	0.15
n-Heptyl alcohol	141	10.6	1.5	50	0.16	0.65
n-Octyl alcohol	157	10.3	1.0	45	0.40	0.85
Nitriles						
Acetonitrile	53	11.9	1.4	134	0.19	0.04
Propionitrile	71	10.6	0.9	100	0.58	0.06
Capronitrile	120	9.4	0.52	59	2.1	0.70
Benzonitrile	103	8.35	0.30	69	4.6	2.0
Nitro Compounds						
Nitromethane	54	12.7	2.0	131	0.08	0.03
Nitrobenzene	103	9.95	0.74	69	0.94	1.15
Acid Chlorides						
Acetyl chloride	71	9.5	0.48	100	3.2	(<5.1)

polar solvents far exceed the observed ones. Even for these, however, the relative order is preserved. Table 6 reproduces these calculations.

Boyer[57] has suggested a novel method of molecular weight determination based upon swelling phenomena. Equation 63 and Figure 18 show the equilibrium between the solvent in the swollen gel and the pure solvent outside the cross-linked structure. If however we depress the free energy of the solvent outside by adding a linear polymer to the system, the resultant shift of equilibrium produces a marked deswelling of the gel. The results of Boyer's analysis can be expressed mathematically as follows: If we define φ_s as the volume fraction of solute (linear polymer) in the solution; φ_g, the volume fraction of cross-linked polymer in the swollen gel; φ_g°, the latter when in equilibrium with pure solvent; the change in swelling per unit of dissolved solute may be written as:

$$\frac{\Delta}{\varphi_s} = \frac{\varphi_g - \varphi_g^\circ}{\varphi_s} = \frac{\frac{1}{\overline{\mathrm{m}}_n} + \left(\frac{1}{2} - \mu_s\right)\varphi_s + \ldots\ldots}{(1 - 2\,\mu_g)\,\varphi_g^\circ + (\varphi_g^\circ)^2/(1 - \varphi_g^\circ)} \tag{65}$$

The maximum effect is clearly when $\overline{\mathrm{m}}_n$ and φ_g° are small, μ_s as small as possible, and $\mu_g \simeq 0.5$; that is when a very slightly cross-linked gel (V_c large) is swollen in a liquid which is a poor solvent for the gel network but as good a solvent as possible for the solute polymer.

If Δ/φ_s is plotted as a function of φ_s, extrapolation to infinite dilution should permit calculation of $\overline{\mathrm{m}}_n$ and the corresponding $\overline{\mathrm{M}}_n$. The swelling measurements should be easier and faster than the corresponding osmotic measurements, but the limited experience with the method prevents adequate assessment of its reliability and usefulness.

Flory[48] and Scott and Magat[56] have shown a correspondence between measured elastic moduli and swelling data, in agreement with theoretical equations; this correlation is rather convincing evidence that the elastic and swelling theory are basically correct.

7. Crystalline polymers: Solubility and Swelling.

Many high polymers, especially the rubber-like ones, are commonly and properly regarded as amorphous systems, thermodynamically the same as liquids and possessing no crystalline character. It has been shown, however, that a number of these substances upon cooling or upon stretching show most, if not all, of the phenomena associated with crystallization and fusion, and that some of the non-rubber-like polymers are more or less crystalline at room temperatures. This crystallinity may be studied by thermal or volume measurements, x-ray diffraction, optical methods, measurements of mechanical properties, etc. and the temperature or temperature range associated with the transition from amorphous to crystalline material determined.

---

[57] R. F. Boyer, *J. Chem. Phys.*, **13**, 363 (1945).

The crystallization is seldom, if ever, complete in polymers of high molecular weight; sections of adjacent molecules orient themselves into small crystallites, and a considerable amount of the material remains amorphous in character. This micro-crystallinity, which may lead to several kinds of crystallites, is responsible for the spectrum of melting points frequently observed, and for the marked hysteresis effects noted between freezing and melting curves.

The phenomena of crystallization have been reviewed elsewhere[58,59]; for our purposes it will suffice to indicate in Table 7 the approximate crystallization temperatures for various unstretched polymers. For some materials, the freezing and melting phenomena occur over a wide range; in such cases, the value in Table 7 represents the temperature at which the greatest or the most rapid transition is observed.

Table 7. Average Temperatures of Crystallization (in degrees C.) (primarily from Wood[58])

	Range	Most Rapid
cis-Polyisoprene (natural rubber)	— 45° to + 15°	— 25°
trans-Polyisoprene (balata or gutta-percha)		
α-form		65°
β-form		56°
Polychloroprene (neoprene)	— 35° to + 32°	0°
Thiakol A		70°
Polyethylene (polythene)	60 to 120°	115°
Polyvinylidene chloride (Saran)	50 to 100°	
Polytetrafluoroethylene (Teflon)[60]		327°

Copolymers, presumably because of their more disordered structure, seldom if ever crystallize.

Soon after the initial development of the Flory-Huggins thermodynamic theories, Huggins[61] applied it to the solubility of solid (crystalline) polymers. The extension of the treatment given in Chapter XVII is obvious: To the partial molal free energy of dilution of the amorphous polymer is added the free energy of fusion; at equilibrium the sum must equal zero. Combination of Equation 11b with the free energy of fusion gives:

$$\ln \varphi_p - (\mathrm{m} - 1)\,\varphi_\circ + \mathrm{m}\,\mu\,\varphi_\circ^2 + \frac{\Delta \mathrm{H}_p^{\mathrm{F}}}{R}\left(\frac{1}{T} - \frac{1}{T_m}\right) = 0 \qquad (66)$$

[58] L. A. Wood, "Crystallization Phenomena in Natural and Synthetic Rubbers", pp. 57-93 in "Advances in Colloid Science, Vol. II, Rubber" (New York, Interscience, 1946).

[59] T. Alfrey, Jr., "Mechanical Behavior of High Polymers", pp. 340-426 (New York, Interscience, 1946).

[60] W. E. Hanford and R. M. Joyce, *J. Am. Chem. Soc.*, **68**, 2082 (1946.)

[61] M. L. Huggins, *J. Am. Chem. Soc.*, **64**, 1712 (1942).

where ΔH_p^F is the heat of fusion of the polymer (per mole) and T_m is the melting temperature.

Huggins showed that this equation accounted quantitatively for the temperature dependence of the normal paraffins, $C_{34}H_{70}$ and $C_{60}H_{122}$ in decalin, $C_{10}H_{18}$.

Richards[62] has determined phase diagrams for polyethylene of differing molecular weights in a number of solvents, and finds excellent qualitative agreement with theoretical expectations. Figure 20 shows such diagrams for polyethylene (molecular weight about 17,000) in nitrobenzene

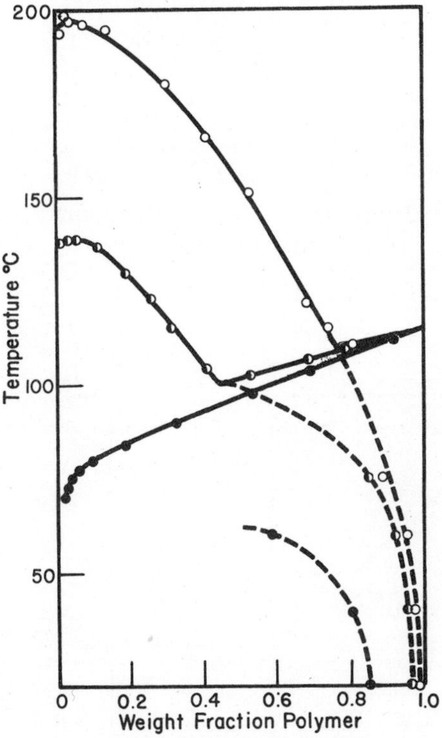

Fig. 20. Solubility of polyethylene in (a) ○ nitrobenzene (b) ◐ amyl acetate (c) ● xylene. The dashed lines represent the equilibrium swelling of the "solid" phase.

amyl acetate, and xylene. In the two former cases, there is in addition to the solid-liquid phase boundary, a liquid-liquid curve; with xylene, no such liquid-liquid curve is found, the amorphous polymer being completely soluble in the solvent. The liquid-liquid equilibrium is of course exactly that

[62] R. B. Richards, *Trans. Faraday Soc.*, **42**, 10,20 (1946).

treated in Section 3 and need not concern us further. The similarity between these curves and those for ordinary solid-liquid equilibria (cf. Chapter XVII) is striking confirmation of the qualitative aspects of the theory.

One difference between the crystalline polymer - solution equilibrium and that for ordinary solids must be noted: Since the polymer is not completely crystalline, the remaining amorphous material swells, imbibing solvent. In Figure 20, the dashed curves at lower temperatures shows this swelling, which may be very considerable. Richards has suggested that one may regard the crystallites and the amorphous material as separate components, and the swelling region as consisting of two phases mechanically inseparable.

Quantitative application of Equation 66 to these actual systems involves two difficulties, the uncertainty about the variation of μ with temperature and concentration which we have noted in Section 2f and the problem of the swelling of the "solid" phase. All the qualitative features are essentially confirmed by Richards' data.

Figures 21 ab show the phase boundaries for polymers of different molecular weight in nitrobenzene and xylene. (The molecular weights are only approximate, having been estimated from intrinsic viscosities from a

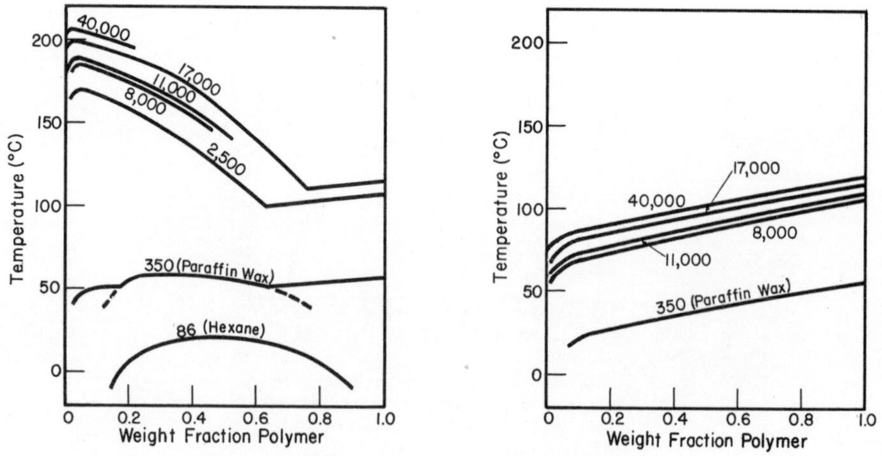

Fig. 21. Solubility of polyethylenes of different molecular weights: (a) in nitrobenzene; (b) in xylene.

Staudinger equation). Of interest is the comparison with paraffin wax (M = 350) and n-hexane (M = 86). It is interesting to see how the shift in the curves with molecular weight leads to a very great sensitivity of the solubility in xylene to the molecular weight in the temperature range 60 - 80° C.

Richards has correlated the solubility and swelling of the polyethylene with the internal pressures of the solvents. Table 8 shows these as a function of the δ_o of the solvent (our values of δ_o given here differ slightly from those of Richards.) t_5 represents the temperature (in degrees centigrade) at which 5% of the polymer (M = 9400) forms a single liquid phase with the solvent; this is an approximate measure of the critical solution temperature. Q is the swelling (cc solvent/gram of solid polymer) at 20° C in 48 hours.

Table 8. Solubility and Swelling of Polyethylene (Data of Richards[62])

Solvent	δ_o (25° C)	V_o(25°C)	t_5 (°C)	Q (20°C)
n-Pentane	7.05	116	>36 (b. p.)	0.21
n-Hexane	7.3	132	>69 (b. p)	0.28
n-Heptane	7.45	147	69	0.31
Ethyl ether	7.5	105	>35 (b. p.)	0.14
Cyclohexane	8.2	109	57	0.40
Carbon tetrachloride	8.65	97	57	0.40
Ethyl benzene	8.8	123	67	
Xylene	8.8	123	64	0.29
Toluene	8.9	107	61	0.25
Benzene	9.15	89	64	0.22
Chloroform	9.3	81	>61 (b. p.)	0.28
Chlorobenzene	(9.5)	102	62	0.25
Ethylene dibromide			86	0.08
Nitrobenzene	9.9	103	185	0.019

The correlation of the swelling with the solubility parameters is obvious. The correlations with the solubility temperature t_5 is less apparent because all but nitrobenzene and ethylene dibromide represent points on the solid-liquid curve, which (see Figure 20) is not early so sensitive to differences in δ_o as is the liquid-liquid curve.

8. The Solubility of Gases in Polymers.

The treatment of the solubility of gases in liquids found in Chapter XV is easily extended to include their solubility in high polymers. This was done in some detail by Barrer[63]. The equation analogous to Equation XV—2 is derived by adding to the partial molal free energy of the dissolved component a term in $RT \ln p/p_o$, obtaining (for $m \to \infty$)

$$\ln \varphi_o + (1 - \varphi_o) + \mu (1 - \varphi_o)^2 = \ln p/p_o \qquad (67)$$

[36] R. M. Barrer, *Trans. Faraday Soc.*, **43**, 3 (1947).

where φ_o is the volume fraction of the dissolved gas in the polymer, p, the pressure of the gas at equilibrium, and p_o the saturation pressure. For gases above the critical temperature p_o is a fictitious value obtained from extrapolation (see Chapter XV) or from statistical theory (see Barrer[63]).

In the earlier section upon the vapor-pressure of high polymer solutions, isotherms for natural rubber in carbon tetrachloride, acetone, and benzene were given (Fig. 2); the vapor pressure of a solution and the solubility of a gas are of course two different ways of looking at the same thing. Barrer claims better agreement for acetone in rubber with the use of the modified free energy equation of Orr[6].

The sorption of water vapor by proteins and nylon has been interpreted by Dole and McLaren[64] in terms of the adsorption isotherm of Brunauer, Emmett and Teller. Still another interpretation is offered by Smith[65]. The relation between these treatments and that of Barrer remains to be clarified.

9. The Solubility of Solids in Polymers.

An extension of solubility theory similar to that outlined above leads to an equation for the solubility of solids in polymers:

$$\ln \varphi_o + (1 - \varphi_o) + \mu (1 - \varphi_o)^2 = \frac{\Delta H_o^F}{R} \left(\frac{1}{T_m} - \frac{1}{T} \right) \qquad (68)$$

where ΔH_o^F is the heat of fusion of the solid and T_m its melting point. Gee[66] has applied a similar equation to the solubility of sulfur in natural rubber[67] and in Buna S[68]. Because of the high δ_o value of lipuid sulfur, it is not completely miscible with rubber even above the melting point. Plotting log φ_o against the reciprocal temperature yields fairly good straight lines (Figure 22). The solubilities of Buna S and natural rubber are close together; but in the wrong order with respect to the δ_p values. The dashed line represents a theoretical curve for $\mu = 900/T$ which approximates the two measured curves.

10. Polymers of Other Types.

The preceding pages have been devoted exclusively to linear polymers uncomplicated by disturbing factors such as tendencies to ionize or form hydrogen bonds. It is only fair to recognize the existence of other types of high polymers to which the foregoing theories are not applicable, at least without more or less severe modifications. These include such inorganic high polymers as the silicate minerals, colloidal electrolytes such as gold sols,

---

64 M. Dole and A. D. McLaren, *J. Am. Chem. Soc.*, **69**, 651 (1947); See also M. Dole, *J. Colloid Sci.*, **3**, 411 (1948).

65 S. E. Smith, *J. Am. Chem. Soc.*, **69**, 646 (1947).

66 G. Gee, pp. 188 — 189 in "Advances in Colloid Science, Vol. II, Rubber" (Interscience, (1946).

67 A. R. Kemp, F. S. Malm, G. G. Winspear and B. Stiratelli, *Ind. Eng. Chem.*, **32**, 1075 (1940).

68 I. Williams, *India Rubber World*, **108**, 35 (1943).

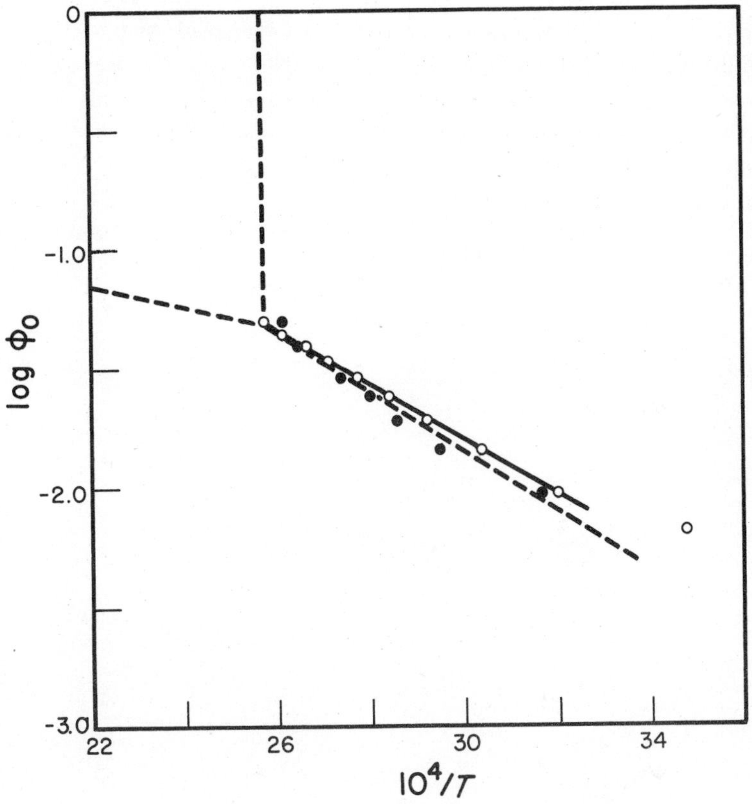

Fig. 22. Solubility of Sulfur in ○ natural rubber, ● Buna-S.

and two classes which are partially amenable to treatment: the hydrogen bonding linear polymers such as cellulose and starch, and certain non-linear polymers such as proteins.

The characteristics of cellulose solutions are in qualitative agreement with high polymer theory, and the development of an adequate theory of alcohol solutions should permit a better quantitative treatment. The solubility and swelling of cellulose have been treated at length in reviews by Spurlin[69 a,c] and Huggins[69 b]. It should be noted that the simpler theories are applicable to certain cellulose derivatives in which all the free hydroxyls are replaced by non-hydrogen bonding groups (such as trinitrocellulose).

[69] "Cellulose and Cellulose Derivatives", edited by E. Ott. (Volume V of High Polymer Series, New York Interscience, 1943) Chapter IX, (a) Solubility, H. M. Spurlin, (b) Thermodynamics of Solutions, M. L. Huggins; (c) Determination of Molecular Weight, H. M. Spurlin, pp 853—929.

Proteins represent a case in which the high polymer is not an extended linear chain, but a compact, perhaps roughly spherical molecule. Were it not for the electrolytic character of most protein solutions, they would represent an interesting test of the theory for the entropy of mixing of large and small spheres. Zimm[70] has shown that the osmotic pressures of hemoglobin and serum albumin are in fair agreement with such a theory; the coefficients of the φ_p^2 term in Π (see Equation 22) are an order of magnitude lower than those for linear polymers and deviate only moderately from Raoult's law. Recently Scatchard and coworkers[71] have treated osmotic equilibria in protein solutions on a semi-empirical basis.

[70] B. H. Zimm, *J. Chem. Phys.*, **14**, 164 (1946).

[71] G. Scatchard, A. C. Batchelder, A. Brown and M. Zosa, *J. Am. Chem. Soc.*, **68**, 2320, 2610 (1946).

CHAPTER XXI

Surface Phenomena

The previous chapters in this book have dealt exclusively with the thermodynamic properties of mixtures and pure substances in bulk phases, in which the molecular environment is isotropic — the same in every direction. In this chapter, we consider briefly the thermodynamics of the surface or interface between two bulk phases, with a view to interpreting the surface tension of liquids and solutions in terms of the properties of the homogeneous phases.

The thermodynamics of interfaces. The classic thermodynamic treatment of the interface between two bulk phases was developed by Gibbs[1]. While mathematically elegant and above reproach, it involves the introduction of a mathematical surface which corresponds to no physical picture. Each extensive property of the system, such as the free energy, the entropy, or the number of moles of each component is regarded as the sum of three parts: (1) the contribution of one bulk phase calculated on the assumption that its properties remain homogeneous right up to the mathematical surface, (2) the similar contribution of the other bulk phase, calculated on the same assumption, and (3) the residual part, which is assigned to the surface. Thus we assign to this surface, which has no volume, a free energy, an entropy, and certain amounts of each component. Of this treatment, Guggenheim[2] has remarked, "Experience indicates that it is much less difficult to use Gibbs formulae than to understand them". The difficulty in visualizing this method arises not only because our physical picture of an interface is quite different from this infinitely thin mathematical surface, but also because the various properties assigned to this surface depend upon its exact position; in fact the mathematical surface can be arbitrarily placed so as to make any one of the extensive properties zero (a very useful feature at times, but frequently misunderstood).

In contrast to this abstract treatment, van der Waals and Bakker[3], among others, treated the surface separating a simple liquid from its vapor by assigning to the surface layer a small but finite uniform thickness. Verschaffelt[4] and Guggenheim[2] have extended such a treatment for the surface between phases of several components. The following discussion follows the general lines of Guggenheim's paper.

[1] J. W. Gibbs, *Collected Works*, Vol. I., pp. 219 seq. (Longmans, 1928).

[2] E. A. Guggenheim, *Trans. Faraday Soc.*, **36**, 397 (1940).

[3] See G. Bakker, *Handbuch der Experimentalphysik*, **6**, 378-453 (1928).

[4] J. E. Verschaffelt, *Bull. classe sci. Acad. roy. Belg.*, **22**, 373, 390, 402 (1936).

Figure 1 represents two homogenous bulk phases, α and β, between which lies a surface layer σ, bounded by the parallel planes, AA′ and BB′. All properties of the surface are uniform in directions parallel to the boundary planes, but not in the perpendicular direction. At or near AA′, the properties

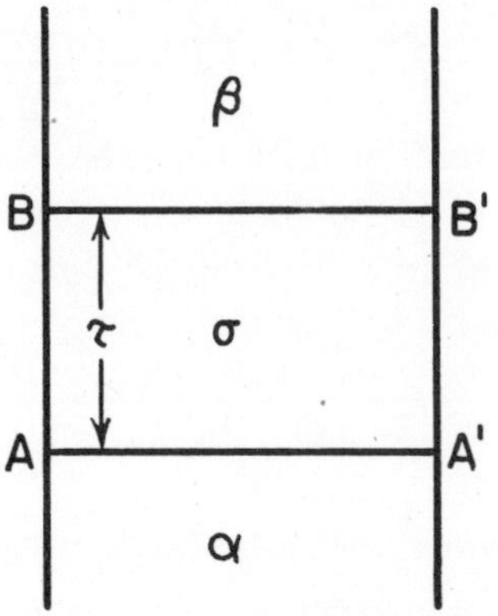

Fig. 1. Schematic diagram of the surface phase σ between two bulk phases α and β. τ in the thickness of the surface phase.

are identical with phase α; similarly, near BB′, they are those of phase β. Subject to the limitations inherent in the assumption that the bulk phases are homogeneous up to the boundaries, the position of the boundaries and the thickness of the surface layer may be selected arbitrarily. To a first approximation for liquid-gas interfaces, we may restrict the surface region to the first monolayer of the condensed phase, although the thermodynamics is perfectly general.

Since the surface layer has a well-defined volume and material content, we may speak of its temperature, free energy, composition, etc. just as for the bulk phases α and β. The only functions which require special attention are the pressure and surface tension. In any homogenous bulk phase the force per unit area is the same in all directions and is called the pressure. In the surface layer, however, this is no longer so. Across any plane parallel to the boundary planes AA′ and BB′, the force per unit area is indeed the pressure P, but on the other hand for a perpendicular plane extending the entire thickness τ between the two boundaries, the force per unit area is $P - \gamma/\tau$ where γ is the interfacial tension. If the surface layer σ has a surface area Σ, we may define its volume V^σ as:

$$V^\sigma = \tau \Sigma \tag{1}$$

The term PV occurring in the thermodynamics of bulk phases will thus be replaced for surfaces by $PV^\sigma - \gamma \Sigma$.

For a two component bulk phase (such as α) we may write for the most general variation of the Helmholtz free energy A^α:

$$dA^\alpha = -S^\alpha dT - PdV^\alpha + \overline{F}_1 dN_1{}^\alpha + \overline{F}_2 dN_2{}^\alpha \tag{2}$$

where $N_1{}^\alpha$ and $N_2{}^\alpha$ are the number of moles of 1 and 2 in phase α and $\overline{F}_1$ and $\overline{F}_2$ are the partial molal free energies (which are the same in both phases).

For the surface phase PdV is replaced by $PdV^\sigma - \gamma d\Sigma$, and we obtain:

$$dA^\sigma = -S^\sigma dT - PdV^\sigma + \gamma d\Sigma + \overline{F}_1 dN_1{}^\sigma + \overline{F}_2 dN_2{}^\sigma \tag{3}$$

If we define the free energy F in the customary way[5] as $A + PV$ then the variation dF is:

$$dF^\alpha = -S^\alpha dT + V^\alpha dP + \overline{F}_1 dN_1^\alpha + \overline{F}_2 dN_2^\alpha \tag{4}$$

$$dF^\sigma = -S^\sigma dT + V^\sigma dP + \gamma d\Sigma + \overline{F}_1 dN_1^\sigma + \overline{F}_2 dN_2^\sigma \tag{5}$$

In their integral forms, we may write for F^α and F^σ:

$$F^\alpha = N_1^\alpha \overline{F}_1 + N_2^\alpha \overline{F}_2 \tag{6}$$

$$F^\sigma = \gamma \Sigma + N_1^\sigma \overline{F}_1 + N_2^\sigma \overline{F}_2 \tag{7}$$

We see from Equations 5 and 7 that the surface tension γ is not only a force per unit length, but is also the increase in free energy (not of the surface, but of the system) when one unit area of the surface is created at constant temperature and pressure. It is immaterial whether the surface is formed by molecules from phase α or phase β since the partial molal free energies are the same in all of them.

If we differentiate Equations 6 and 7 and then subtract from them Equations 4 and 5, we obtain:

$$S^\alpha dT - V^\alpha dP + N_1^\alpha d\overline{F}_1 + N_2^\alpha d\overline{F}_2 = 0 \tag{8}$$

$$S^\sigma dT - V^\sigma dP + \Sigma d\gamma + N_1^\sigma d\overline{F}_1 + N_2^\sigma d\overline{F}_2 = 0 \tag{9}$$

[5] Guggenheim defines the Gibbs free energy as $A + PV - \gamma\Sigma$. This formulation, while perhaps logically more consistent, does not accord with the general practice.

Equation 8 is the general form for the Gibbs-Duhem relation, and Equation 9 is its surface analogue. If we divide Equation 9 through by Σ, we obtain the more convenient form:

$$s^{\sigma}\, dT - \tau dP + d\gamma + \Gamma_1 d\overline{F}_1 + \Gamma_2 d\overline{F}_2 = 0 \tag{10}$$

where s^{σ} is the entropy per unit area and Γ_1 and Γ_2 are the number of moles of components 1 and 2 per unit area.

Equation 10 is a form of the Gibbs adsorption equation which is used extensively in research on surface films and multicomponent systems.

The change of surface tension with composition at constant temperature and pressure follows directly from Equation 10:

$$\frac{d\gamma}{dx_2} = -\Gamma_1 \frac{d\overline{F}_1}{dx_2} - \Gamma_2 \frac{d\overline{F}_2}{dx_2} = RT\left[\Gamma_1 \frac{d\ln a_1}{dx_1} - \Gamma_2 \frac{d\ln a_2}{dx_2}\right] \tag{11}$$

Similarly for the change of surface tension with temperature, we find:

$$-\frac{d\gamma}{dT} = s^{\sigma} - \tau \frac{dP}{dT} + \Gamma_1 \frac{d\overline{F}_1}{dT} + \Gamma_2 \frac{d\overline{F}_2}{dT} \tag{12}$$

But since $d\overline{F}_1 = \overline{V}_1\, dP - \overline{S}_1\, dT$, we may rearrange Equation 12 in the form:

$$-\frac{d\gamma}{dT} = (s^{\sigma} - \Gamma_1 \overline{S}_1 - \Gamma_2 \overline{S}_2) - (\tau - \Gamma_1 \overline{V}_1 - \Gamma_2 \overline{V}_2)\frac{dP}{dT} \tag{13}$$

The first term of Equation 13 is essentially the entropy of formation of the surface, while the coefficient $(\tau - \Gamma_1\overline{V}_1 - \Gamma_2\overline{V}_2)$ is the volume change in the same process, both taken per unit area. dP/dT is of course the temperature coefficient of the equilibrium vapor pressure of the system.

While the free energy of surface formation is invariant with respect to which phase (α or β) the molecules of the surface layer come from, the entropy and volume change are not. The values of $\overline{S}_1$, $\overline{S}_2$, $\overline{V}_1$ and $\overline{V}_2$ are greatly different in the two phases. The usual convention is to define the entropy of surface formation which we may call Δs^{σ}, as $-d\gamma/dT$, but this can only be true if the surface is formed from the two bulk phases in such proportions that the volume change is zero.

Following such a method, we may define a heat (or energy) of surface formation Δh^{σ}, such that:

$$\Delta h^{\sigma} = \gamma - T \frac{\partial \gamma}{\partial T} \tag{14}$$

This quantity, usually called the total surface energy, (although in this formulation, it is a difference of two quantities, not the total energy associated with a mathematical surface), is strictly speaking the heat (or energy) of surface formation *only at constant volume.*

The surface tension of pure liquids. At a very early date[6], it was recognized that the work necessary to increase the surface area of a liquid (*i. e.* the surface tension) was directly related to the intermolecular forces in the liquid. We have seen (Chapters IV, V, and VII) how the heat of vaporization is a measure of this force and it is to be expected that the work of forming a surface, in which part but not all of the binding between molecules is destroyed, would also be so related. (Throughout this discussion we assume that the vapor pressure is low enough that interactions with molecules in the vapor can be neglected).

A detailed resumé of the various attempts to calculate the surface tension from theoretical considerations is beyond the scope of this book[7]. The important thing to note here is that inherent in any theory in one form or another will be a relation between the free energy of surface formation per mole, $\gamma\Sigma$ (where the small capital Σ represents the surface area per mole) and the heat of vaporization ΔH^{V}. A similar relationship should thus hold between the internal pressure $\Delta E^{V}/V$ and the corresponding quantity $\gamma\Sigma/V$.

Direct determination of the surface area per mole Σ is difficult, but for nonpolar substances which do not depart seriously from an approximately spherical symmetry, a value may be estimated from the molal volume. If the volume per molecule is $V/\boldsymbol{N}$, then the cross section σ (*i. e.* area) of such a molecule is:

$$\sigma = \left(\frac{V}{\boldsymbol{N}}\right)^{\frac{2}{3}} \tag{15}$$

Then for Σ, we obtain:

$$\Sigma = \boldsymbol{N}\sigma = \boldsymbol{N}^{\frac{1}{3}}\, V^{\frac{2}{3}} \tag{16}$$

[6] Cf. T. Young, *Phil. Trans. Roy. Soc.*, **1**, 65 (1805); P. S. Laplace, *Oeuvres*, Vol. IV, p. 389.

[7] Cf. N. K. Adam, *The Physics and Chemistry of Surfaces*, 3d edition (Oxford, **1941**).

Since $N^{\frac{1}{3}}$ is a constant factor, $\gamma\Sigma/V$ is proportional to $\gamma/V^{\frac{1}{3}}$, and it is this parameter which we seek to compare with $\Delta E^V/V$ or with its square root, the solubility parameter δ. Table 1 gives such a comparison; we see that as the δ-values increase there is a corresponding increase in $\gamma/V^{\frac{1}{3}}$. The data of Table 1 are plotted in Fig. 2. The best line through the points

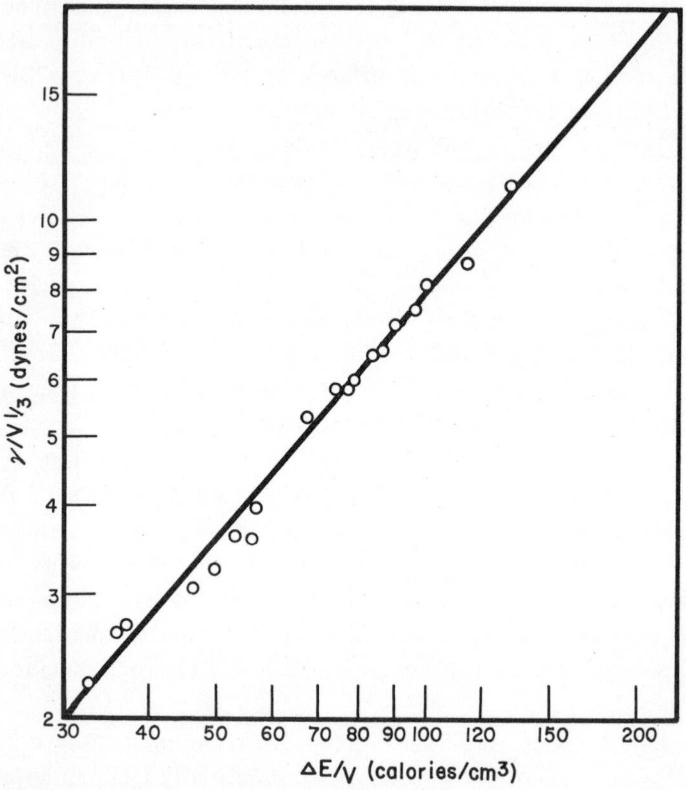

Fig. 2. The relation between surface tension and internal pressure for nonpolar liquids

corresponds to a proportionality between $\gamma/V^{\frac{1}{3}}$ and the 1.15 power of $\Delta E^V/V$, but a direct proportionality (first power) would give a satisfactory fit.

Mathews[8] has used surface tension data to calculate values of the van der Waals constant a which show good agreement with measured values. More recently Auluck and Rai[9] have used a theory by Fürth[10] and one of their own to calculate a from the surface tension and have obtained a fair degree of accuracy in both cases.

[8] A. P. Mathews, *J. Phys. Chem.*, **17**, 603 (1913).

[9] F. C. Auluck and R. N. Rai, *J. Chem. Phys.*, **12**, 321 (1944)

[10] R. Fürth, *Proc. Camb. Phil. Soc.*, **37**, 252 (1941).

While the surface free energy γ depends ultimately upon the intermolecular potential and hence upon the heat of vaporization, we would expect to find a simpler correlation between the heat of vaporization and the

Table 1. Surface Tensions, Surface Energies, and Solubility Parameters of Liquids.

Substance	δ_{25}	γ_{20}	Δh^{σ}	$\gamma/V^{\frac{1}{3}}$	$\Delta h^{\sigma}/V^{\frac{1}{3}}$
Perfluoro-*n*-heptane (C_7F_{16})	5.7	13.6	..	2.23	..
Perfluoro-methylcyclohexane (C_7F_{14})	6.0	15.4	..	2.65	..
Perfluoro-dimethylcyclohexane (C_8F_{16})	6.1	16.3	..	2.71	..
Isopentane	6.75	15.0	..	3.06	..
n-Pentane	7.05	16.0	..	3.28	..
n-Hexane	7.3	18.4	49.2	3.61	9.7
Ethyl ether	7.5	17.0	51	3.60	10.8
Silicon tetrachloride	7.5				
n-Octane	7.55	21.8	50.0	4.00	9.2
Cyclohexane	8.2	25.3	..	5.30	..
Carbon tetrachloride	8.6	26.95	53.9	5.86	11.7
m-Xylene	8.8	28.9	51.4	5.82	10.5
Stannic chloride	8.7				
Toluene	8.9	28.5	52.2	6.00	11.0
Benzene	9.15	29.0	58.0	6.51	13.0
Chloroform	9.3	(28.5)	68.3	6.60	15.7
Chlorobenzene	9.5	33.56	..	7.20	..
1,2 Dichloroethane	9.8	32.2	73	7.50	17.0
Carbon disulfide	10.0	32.3	72.7	8.20	18.5
Pyridine	10.7	38.0		8.78	
Bromine	11.5	41.5		11.2	
Methylene iodide	(11.8)	50.8		11.8	
Phosphorus	14.5	(51.1)			

energy of surface formation Δh^{σ}. Let us assume as a first approximation that the total energy comes from nearest neighbor interactions, and that the surface is localized in the first monolayer, and is not expanded over the density of the bulk liquid. If a molecule in the interior of the liquid has z nearest neighbors, while a molecule in the surface has only z^{σ} nearest neighbors, we conclude that the energy of surface formation per mole

$\Delta h^{\sigma} \Sigma$ will be $\frac{z - z^{\sigma}}{z}$ times the energy of vaporization ΔE^{V}.

$$\Delta h^{\sigma} \Sigma = \frac{z - z^{\sigma}}{z} \Delta E^{V} \qquad (17)$$

For a close packed liquid, we might assume $z = 12$ and $z^{\sigma} = 9$, leading to the conclusion that the energy of surface formation was 25 % of the total energy of vaporization. For normal liquids, at low vapor pressures, this fraction is actually between 40 and 50 %, and only for metals and strongly orienting liquids like the alcohols[11] is it around 25 %.

These higher figures of 40 - 50 % instead of 25 % result from a combination of several factors. For most liquids the coordination number is somewhat less thant welve, but it is hard to account in this way for as large a discrepancy as is observed. Similarly the slight expansion of the surface layer would increase the energy of surface formation by a small but insufficient amount. The main contribution to the discrepancy seems to be the failure to take into consideration interactions with molecules more distant than nearest neighbors. The nearest neighbor approximation, while useful in treating energies in homogeneous phases, here breaks down because the energy to be calculated is a difference.

Recently Jura[12] has calculated the surface energies of liquid argon and liquid mercury using experimental distribution functions and intermolecular potential functions, and has obtained excellent agreement with the observed values. He finds that approximately 78 % of this energy is accounted for by the first layer and that 99 % of the effect is found in the first 15 Å or roughly four molecular diameters.

Figures for Δh^{σ}, calculated from the temperature dependencies of the surface tension, are given in Table 1, together with the parameter $\Delta h^{\sigma}/V^{\frac{1}{3}}$ for comparison with the solubility parameters. The agreement is good, but not quite so good as was found for $\gamma/V^{\frac{1}{3}}$. This is presumably due to the greater insensitivity of the *free* surface energy γ to changes in the molecular model.

Polar substances show a much lower ratio of the energy of surface formation to that of vaporization, a fact which may be attributed to orientation in the surface layer. Where the molecular force fields are not uniform, the minimum energy is expended in forming the surface if the nonpolar end with its weaker attractive forces is oriented toward the vapor phase.

The surface tension might be expected to give a truer indication of the internal forces in the case of molten metals than it does in the case of most

[11] Cf. W. D. Harkins, AAAS Publication **21**, p. 4, Fig. 1 (1942).

[12] G. Jura, *J. Phys. Chem.*, **52**, 40 (1945).

other liquids because the molecules are simple and symmetrical and hence incapable of any orientation in the surface. Much of the data, however, is unsatisfactory and conflicting, due partly at least to the failure to prevent the formation of an oxide film. Table 2 summarizes the measurements of Hogness[13] for five liquid metals at 450°C, arranged in order of decreasing solubility parameters.

Table 2. Surface Tensions, Surface Energies, and Solubility Parameters of Liquid Metals at 450°C (data of Hogness[13])

Metal	δ	γ	Δh^{σ}	$\gamma/V^{\frac{1}{3}}$	$\Delta h^{\sigma}/V^{\frac{1}{3}}$
Tin	62	514	572	198	222
Zinc	52	755	820	350	380
Lead	48	438	494	163	182
Bismuth	45	367	413	133	150
Cadmium	40	622	662	256	274

We see that there is virtually no agreement (except as regards order of magnitude) between values of δ and those of either $\gamma/V^{\frac{1}{3}}$ or $\Delta h^{\sigma}/V^{\frac{1}{3}}$. If we had considered a greater range of δ's, we might have found rough agreement, but apparently the specific character of the intermetallic forces plays a role here. The surface tensions found for liquid metals were regarded as abnormally high and various attempts[14,15,16,17] were made to interpret these as due to the presence of "free electrons". This point of view has been severely criticized by Skapski[18] who points out that if the energy of surface formation per mole is compared with the heat of vaporization, the metals are abnormally *low* if nonmetallic liquids are taken as standard.

Various semi-empirical equations have been advanced to treat the temperature dependence of the surface tension, the most important being those of Eötvös[19] and Macleod[20]. Recently Guggenheim[21] has found that for perfect liquids, the surface tension is given by the equation (see Chapter V):

$$\gamma = \gamma_{\circ}(1-\theta)^{11/9} \tag{18}$$

where θ is the reduced temperature T/T_c and $\gamma_{\circ}$ is approximately equal to 4.4 $T_c/V_c^{\frac{2}{3}}$.

[13] T. R. Hogness, *J. Am. Chem. Soc.*, **43**, 1621 (1921).
[14] D. V. Gogate and D. S. Kothan, *Phil. Mag.*, **20**, 1136 (1935).
[15] T. G. Durfman, *Compt. rend.*, **41**, 386 (1943).
[16] A. Samoilovitch, *Acta physicochimica, URSS*, **20**, 97 (1945).
[17] A. Brager and A. Schuchowitzky, *Acta physicochimica, URSS*, **21**, 13 (1946).
[18] A. Skapski, *J. Chem. Phys.*, **16**, 386, 389 (1948).
[19] R. Eötvös, *Ann. Physik.*, **27**, 444 (1886).
[20] D. B. Macleod, *Trans. Faraday Soc.*, **19**, 38 (1923).
[21] E. A. Guggenheim, *J. Chem. Phys.*, **13**, 253 (1945).

The surface tension of liquid mixtures. The surface tension of dilute solutions has been treated theoretically by Langmuir[22], Frumkin[23] and Butler[24], but none of these involve the surface tension of the second component, and the equations are basically unsymmetrical. More recently Schuchowitzky[25], Belton and Evans[26] and Guggenheim[27] have formulated the surface tension of ideal and regular solutions in terms analogous to those used in the treatment of homogeneous liquid solutions. The following derivations differ in detail from any of the foregoing, but involve essentially the same assumptions and result in identical equations.

We first assume that at negligible pressures the surface region may be restricted to the first monolayer of the liquid. (If the model is to be correlated with Gibbs' mathematical surface, it is most convenient to place this between this monolayer and the remainder of the liquid). The number of moles of components 1 and 2 in this surface are designated N_1^σ and N_2^σ or referring them to unit surface area Γ_1 and Γ_2. The corresponding numbers of moles in the bulk region are N_1 and N_2, with mole fractions x_1 and x_2. We define the activities a_1 and a_2 in the bulk phase in the usual manner, and of course, referred to the same reference state, the activities in the surface layer are of course the same. It is more convenient for our purposes, however, to refer the activities in the surface a_1^σ and a_2^σ to a hypothetical reference state where the surface of the pure liquid has not its equilibrium surface tension, but rather the same surface tension as the mixture. If we further assume that the partial molal surface areas $\overline{\Sigma}_1$ and $\overline{\Sigma}_2$ are independent of composition, (an essential of any of these treatments) then we may write for $\overline{\mathrm{F}}_1^\sigma$ and $\overline{\mathrm{F}}_2^\sigma$:

$$\overline{\mathrm{F}}_1^\sigma = \mathrm{F}_1^\circ + (\gamma_1 - \gamma)\,\Sigma_1 + RT \ln a_1^\sigma \tag{19a}$$

$$\overline{\mathrm{F}}_2^\sigma = \mathrm{F}_2^\circ + (\gamma_2 - \gamma)\,\Sigma_2 + RT \ln a_2^\sigma \tag{19b}$$

where F_1° and F_2° are the standard states of the pure liquids.

---

[22] I. Langmuir, *J. Am. Chem. Soc.*, **39**, 1883 (1917).
[23] A. Frumkin, *Z. physik. Chem.*, **116**, 502 (1925).
[24] J. A. V. Butler, *Proc. Roy. Soc.*, **A 135**, 348 (1932).
[25] A. Schuchowitzky, *Acta Physicochimica, URSS*, **19**, **176**, 508 (1944).
[26] J. W. Belton and M. G. Evans, *Trans. Faraday Soc.*, **41**, 1 (1945).
[27] E. A. Guggenheim, *Trans. Faraday Soc.*, **41**, 150 (1945).

The corresponding partial molal free energies in the liquid are of course:

$$\overline{F}_1 = F^\circ_1 + RT \ln a_1 \tag{20a}$$

$$\overline{F}_2 = F^\circ_2 + RT \ln a_2 \tag{20b}$$

Since at equilibriumthe partial molal free energies must be the same in the surface and in the interior of the solution, we may set $\overline{F}_1 = \overline{F}^\sigma_1$ and $\overline{F}_2 = \overline{F}^\sigma_2$. If we do so and rearrange, we obtain for the surface tension:

$$\gamma = \gamma_1 + \frac{RT}{\Sigma_1} \ln \frac{a^\sigma_1}{a_1} = \gamma_2 + \frac{RT}{\Sigma_2} \ln \frac{a^\sigma_2}{a_2} \tag{21}$$

The parameters a_1 and a_2 are of course fixed by the composition of the solution, and if we can express a^σ_1 and a^σ_2 in terms of the composition of the surface phase, we can solve the equation:

$$\frac{a^\sigma_2}{a_2} = \left(\frac{a^\sigma_1}{a_1}\right)^{\frac{\Sigma_2}{\Sigma_1}} e^{\frac{(\gamma_1-\gamma_2)\,\Sigma_2}{RT}} \tag{22}$$

The following step-wise argument may serve to clarify the choice of the reference states for a^σ_1 and a^σ_2 and the derivation of Equations 19 and 21. Suppose we have a solution of 1 and 2, one square centimeter of whose surface contains Γ_1 moles of 1 and Γ_2 moles of 2, the surface tension being γ. If we wish to increase the surface by one square centimeter, we must transfer Γ_1 moles of 1 and Γ_2 moles of 2 from the interior of the solution to the surface. We first abstract Γ_1 moles of 1 from the solution and form a pure liquid; the change in $\overline{F}_1$ is of course $- RT \ln a_1$. We now create the equilibrium surface from this liquid; the change in the total free energy per mole is of course $\gamma_1 \Sigma_1$, but the partial molal free energy, defined as at *constant surface area* (cf. Equation 5) remains unchanged. Now, however, we change the tension on this surface from γ_1 to γ not changing the surface area; the change in $\overline{F}_1$ in this process is of course $(\gamma_1 - \gamma)\Sigma_1$. We have now reached our hypothetical reference state and now mix Γ_1 moles of surface 1 with Γ_2 moles of surface 2 similarly prepared, the mixing process taking place at constant tension γ; the change in $\overline{F}_1$ is $RT \ln a^\sigma_1$.

The total change in $\overline{F}_1$ must be zero since the final surface is in equilibrium with the initial solution. Thus, adding up we get:

$$\Delta \overline{F}^{\sigma}_1 = - RT \ln a_1 + (\gamma_1 - \gamma)\, \Sigma_1 + RT \ln a^{\sigma}_1 = 0 \tag{23}$$

A similar equation exists for $\Delta \overline{F}^{\sigma}_2$, and transforming them, we obtain Equation 21, as before.

The surface tension of ideal solutions. If we assume that substances which mix ideally in the bulk liquid do so also in the surface, we may calculate the surface tension for ideal solutions. Here we see the advantage of our definition of the surface activities for we may now set $a_1 = x_1$, $a_2 = x_2$, $a^{\sigma}_1 = x^{\sigma}_1$ and $a^{\sigma}_2 = x^{\sigma}_2$, where the surface mole fractions are defined as

$$x^{\sigma}_1 = \frac{N^{\sigma}_1}{N^{\sigma}_1 + N^{\sigma}_2} = \frac{\Gamma_1}{\Gamma_1 + \Gamma_2} \tag{24a}$$

$$x^{\sigma}_2 = \frac{N^{\sigma}_2}{N^{\sigma}_1 + N^{\sigma}_2} = \frac{\Gamma_2}{\Gamma_1 + \Gamma_2} \tag{24b}$$

For the special case where $\Sigma_1 = \Sigma_2 = \Sigma$, corresponding to what Guggenheim has called "perfect solutions", the solution is especially easy. We may solve Equation 22 and write x^{σ}_1 as:

$$x^{\sigma}_1 = \frac{x_1}{x_1 + x_2\, c} \tag{25}$$

where $c = e^{\frac{(\gamma_1 - \gamma_2)\,\Sigma}{RT}}$

If this is substituted into Equation 21, we obtain for the surface tension:

$$\gamma = \gamma_1 - \frac{RT}{\Sigma} \ln (1 - x_1 + x_1\, c) \tag{26}$$

Equations 25 and 26 are essentially those first proposed empirically by Szyszkowski[28], and later discussed by Langmuir[23]. They however regarded c as an empirical constant. Equation 26 might just as well be written

[28] B. v. Szyszkowski, *Z. physik. Chem.*, **64**, 385 (1908).

in terms of γ_2, x_2 and c^{-1}, but Guggenheim[27] has suggested a symmetric form for γ, namely:

$$e^{\frac{-\gamma \Sigma}{RT}} = x_1 \, e^{\frac{-\gamma_1 \Sigma}{RT}} + x_2 \, e^{\frac{-\gamma_2 \Sigma}{RT}} \tag{27a}$$

or in terms of the surface mole fractions:

$$e^{\frac{\gamma \Sigma}{RT}} = x_1^\sigma \, e^{\frac{\gamma_1 \Sigma}{RT}} + x_2^\sigma \, e^{\frac{\gamma_2 \Sigma}{RT}} \tag{27b}$$

If we expand this solution in powers of $(\gamma_1 - \gamma_2)$ we obtain:

$$\gamma = x_1 \gamma_1 + x_2 \gamma_2 - \frac{\Sigma}{2\,RT} (\gamma_1 - \gamma_2)^2 x_1 x_2 - \ldots\ldots \tag{28a}$$

$$\gamma = x_1^\sigma \gamma_1 + x_2^\sigma \gamma_2 + \frac{\Sigma}{2\,RT} (\gamma_1 - \gamma_2)_2 \, x_1^\sigma x_2^\sigma + \ldots\ldots \tag{28b}$$

We see that if referred to the composition of the liquid phase, the surface tension is less than that calculated from a linear combining law, but if based upon the composition of the surface, it is greater. In using the foregoing equations it is simpler to use the surface area per molecule σ than that per mole Σ. The conversion formula is of course simple:

$$\frac{RT}{\Sigma} = \frac{kT}{\sigma} \tag{29}$$

If the surface tension γ is expressed in dynes per centimeter (or ergs per square centimeter, the same thing), and the surface area σ in square Ångstrom units, the Boltzmann constant k is 1.371 (dyne Å^2 cm^{-1} deg^{-1} or equivalently erg Å^2 cm^{-2} deg^{-1}).

Schuchowitzky[25] has applied Equation 26 to solutions of benzene in ether and benzene in nitrobenzene with excellent results. Fig. 3 shows the ether-benzene system at 18 ° C; the experimental points were measured by Whatmough[29]; the theoretical curve involves only one parameter in addition to the surface tensions of the pure components γ_1 and γ_2, namely the surface area σ. This calculated from Equation 15 is 28 Å^2 for benzene and 31 Å^2 for ether; the former value was used. Fig. 3 also shows the

[29] W. H. Whatmough *Z. physik. Chem.*, **39**, 168 (1902).

composition of the conjugate surface phase in equilibrium with the bulk phase. We see that while the bulk liquid curve is concave upwards, the reverse is true for the other. We see that these phase relations are very similar to those between liquids and gases (Chapter XIII) or between liquids and solids (Chapter XVIII). The diagram shows at a glance the obvious fact that the surface layer is richer in the component of lower surface tension.

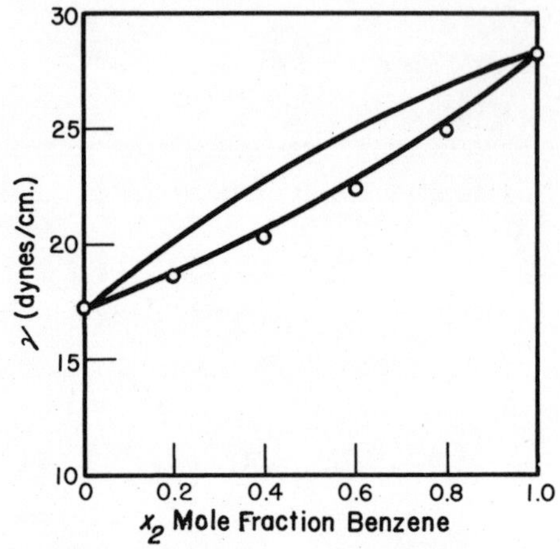

Fig. 3. Surface tension of ether-benzene solutions. Solid curves are calculated from theory.

Belton and Evans[26] have also compared the experimental data on the surface tension of mixtures with values calculated from Equation 26, and find good agreement for mixtures which form ideal or nearly ideal solutions in the bulk phase. One difficulty in checking such an equation is that for nonpolar liquids, the surface tensions parallel the solubility parameters (as we have seen in the previous section); hence, for ideal solutions, for which $\delta_1 = \delta_2$, the surface tensions are also equal. Thus to obtain much difference in the surface tensions of the two components, one component must be polar; this introduces all the difficulties associated with orientation in the surface layer.

When the molal surface areas differ significantly, Equations 25 to 28 are no longer applicable. For such cases the composition of the surface is obtained by solving Equation 22, substituting x's for a's. Unfortunately unless $\Sigma_1 = \Sigma_2$, Equation 19 cannot be solved explicitly. However, to a first approximation, we obtain an equation analogous to Equations 28:

$$\gamma = y_1 \gamma_1 + y_2 \gamma_2 - \frac{1}{2} \frac{(\gamma_1 - \gamma_2)^2}{RT} (y_1 \Sigma_2 + y_2 \Sigma_1) y_1 y_2 - \dots \quad (30a)$$

$$\gamma = y_1^\sigma \gamma_1 + y_2^\sigma \gamma_2 + \frac{1}{2} \frac{(\gamma_1 - \gamma_2)^2}{RT} (y_1^\sigma \Sigma_2 + y_2^\sigma \Sigma_1) y_1^\sigma y_2^\sigma + \dots \quad (30\,b)$$

where the y's are "surface fractions" defined as follows:

$$y_1 = \frac{x_1 \Sigma_1}{x_1 \Sigma_1 + x_2 \Sigma_2} \quad y_2 = \frac{x_2 \Sigma_2}{x_1 \Sigma_1 + x_2 \Sigma_2} \quad (31)$$

The y^σ's are similarly defined by substituting x^σ's for x's.

Fig. 4 shows Whatmough's[29] measurements on the system carbon disulfide-benzene. Schuchowitzky[25] has fitted Equation 30a to the data by assigning to CS_2 a surface area $\sigma = 8$ Å^2, 3.5 times smaller than that for benzene; this would seem be possible only if the molecule orients perpendicular to the surface. The curves so calculated are shown in Fig. 4; the two are close together because of the small difference between

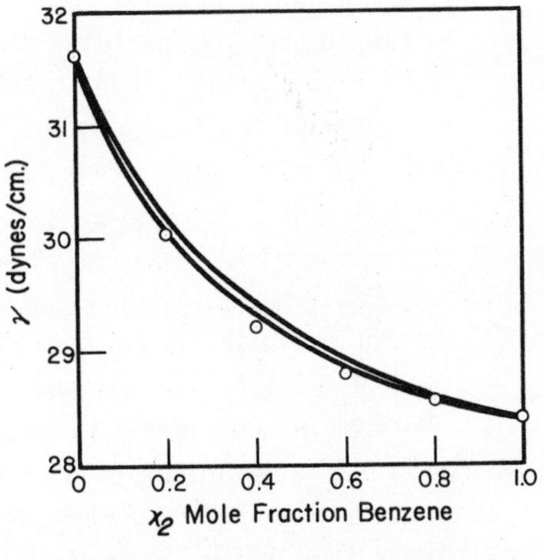

Fig. 4. Surface tension of carbon disulfide-benzene solutions at 18°C. Solid curves calculated from Equation 30.

γ_1 and γ_2; from Equations 29ab we see that the vertical displacement of the two curves is proportional to the square of this difference.

Surface tension of non-ideal solutions. The similarity between the surface tension-composition diagrams and the temperature-composition diagrams we have seen in earlier chapters is more than superficial. We may recall from Chapter XVIII that equilibrium between the solid and liquid phases is defined by a set of equations:

$$RT \ln a_1^s s = \Delta F_1^F + RT \ln a_1^l \tag{32a}$$

$$RT \ln a_2^s s = \Delta F_2^F + RT \ln a_2^l \tag{32b}$$

where ΔF_1^F and ΔF_2^F are the free energies of fusion of the pure components at the temperature T. The terms $(\gamma_1 - \gamma)\,\Sigma_1$ and $(\gamma_2 - \gamma)\,\Sigma_2$ in Equations 19ab are the free energies of surface formation of the pure components at tension γ. The analogy is clear if we write the free energy of fusion in terms of the entropy of fusion. Neglecting the second order ΔC_p corrections, we may write:

$$\Delta F_1^F = \Delta H_1^F \left(1 - \frac{T}{T_1^m}\right) = (T_1^m - T)\,\Delta S_1^F \tag{33}$$

where T_1^m is the melting point of the pure solid 1. Similar equations exist of course for liquid-vapor equilibrium.

We see that the surface tension γ in Equations 19-30 is mathematically exactly analogous to the absolute temperature T in Equation 33, γ_1 and γ_2 being analogous to T_1 and T_2, the melting points (or boiling points) of the pure substances. To complete the analogy, the molal surface areas Σ_1 and Σ_2 are comparable to the molal entropies of fusion (or vaporization) ΔS_1 and ΔS_2.

The importance of this analogy can hardly be overestimated. It means that we may interpret the surface tension-composition curves in terms of deviations from Raoult's law in the bulk and surface phases in exactly the same terms which we applied to the solidus and liquidus curves in Chapter XVIII. We can therefore at once draw the following conclusions:

1. If the components form ideal solutions in both phases and $\Sigma_1 = \Sigma_2$ ("perfect solutions"), then the two conjugate phases are displaced in equal and opposite directions from a straight line representing linear combination of the surface tensions.

2. If the components form ideal solutions in both phases, but the molal surface areas are different, the curves are displaced, upward with respect to the "perfect solution" curves (see above) if the component with the higher surface tension also has the greater molal surface area. If on the other hand the component with the higher surface tension has the smaller molal surface area, the curves are displaced downward (see Fig. 4, for example).

3. If the deviations from Raoult's law are positive and of approximately the same magnitude both in the interior and in the surface, the conjugate curves are expanded and lie outside the ideal curves; if the deviations are negative, they are compressed.

4. If the deviations from Raoult's law are more positive (or less negative) in the interior of the liquid, the curves are displaced downwards, and for sufficiently large deviations, one may find a minimum in the surface tension-composition diagram.

5. If the deviations from Raoult's law are more negative (or less positive) in the bulk phase, the curves are displaced upwards and for sufficiently large discrepancies, one may find a maximum in the surface tension-composition diagram.

On the whole, we may expect the surface layer to be more nearly ideal than the bulk solution. This is clearly seen if we assume a regular solution model for both phases. The molecules are arranged randomly both in the surface and in the interior; hence the entropy of mixing is ideal. The interactions are of the same character in both phases, but there are less of them in the surface because there are fewer nearest neighbors. In terms of the nearest neighbor picture discussed earlier (Equation 17) the heat of mixing in the surface is roughly z^{σ}/z times that in the bulk. The mathematics of this model has been developed in detail by Schuchowitzky[25] and Guggenheim[27]. From this, we may expect solutions showing negative deviations from Raoult's law to show surface tensions greater than those calculated from Equations 28 or 30. Belton and Evans[26] have noted that this appears to be true for the systems methanol-ethyl iodide, acetic acid-pyridine, and acetone-chloroform. The correlation between positive deviations and lowered surface tensions is shown by the systems benzene-ethanol and acetone-carbon disulfide among others. An unexplained exception to this rule appears to be the case of ether-chloroform, which in spite of large negative deviations from Raoult's law shows a surface tension definitely lower than the ideal.

Schuchowitzky[25] has suggested that if the molecules in the surface orient, the surface layer may be much closer to ideality than the regular solution theory indicates. He has fitted the data of Butler and Wightman[30] and Morgan and Neidel[31] for surface tensions in the water-ethanol system remarkably well with the assumption of an ideal surface layer. Fig. 5 compares the experimental points with the curve calculated from the known activities of the bulk solution and the parameters $\sigma_{H_2O} = 10.5$ Å^2, $\sigma_{C_2H_5OH} = 21$ Å^2. The points on the upper curve were calculated by Guggenheim and Adam[32] using the Gibbs equation (Equation 11); all that is necessary to determine the surface curve from the other curve is knowledge of the activities in the bulk solution and values of σ_1 and σ_2.

---

30 J. A. V. Butler and A. Wightman, *J. Chem. Soc.*, **1932**, 2089.

31 J. L. R. Morgan and M. Neidel, *J. Am. Chem. Soc.*, **35**, 1856 (1913).

32 E. A. Guggenheim and N. K. Adam, *Proc. Roy. Soc.*, **A139**, 218 (1933).

Adsorption at the surface. While the diagrams and discussions of the preceding sections have already covered the essential features of the subject,

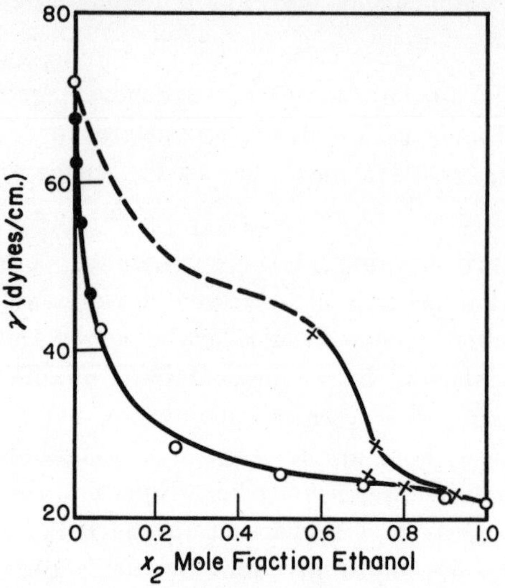

Fig. 5. Surface tension of the water-ethanol system. ○ Butler and Wightman. ● Morgan and Neidel. × Guggenheim and Adam (calculated). Solid curves are calculated by Schuchowitzky; the dashed continuation is merely estimated.

it may be worthwhile to consider further the difference between the compositions of the surface and the interior of the solution. We have seen that the component of lower surface tension invariably accumulates in excess in the surface region, and we may define that excess as the adsorption u of component 2. The thermodynamics may be seen by transforming Equation 11. Recalling the Gibbs-Duhem equation,

$$x_1\, d\ln a_1 + x_2\, d\ln a_2 = 0 \tag{34}$$

we may write:

$$\frac{d\gamma}{dx_2} = -\,RT\left[\Gamma_2 - \frac{\Gamma_1 x_2}{x_1}\right]\frac{d\ln a_2}{dx_2} \tag{35}$$

The term in brackets is defined as the adsorption u_2 and we may express Equation 35 in the following form:

$$u_2 = \left[\Gamma_2 - \Gamma_1\,\frac{x_2}{x_1}\right] = -\,\frac{1}{RT}\left(\frac{\partial\gamma}{\partial\ln a_2}\right)_{T,P,\Sigma} = -\left(\frac{\partial\gamma}{\partial\overline{\mathrm{F}}_2}\right)_{T,P,\Sigma} \tag{36}$$

We see that when Γ_1 and Γ_2 are proportional to x_1 and x_2, u_2 equals zero a situation which can only be true if the surface tension is independent of composition at that point. One can show[33] that u_2 is also equal to $\left(\frac{\partial N_2}{\partial \Sigma}\right)_{\overline{F}_2}$, that is, the number of moles of solute which must be added per unit increase in surface in order to keep the partial molal free energy of the solute constant.

If we divide the derivative in Equation 36 into two parts, we can easily see the influence of different factors on the adsorption u_2:

$$u_2 = - \frac{1}{RT} \left(\frac{\partial \gamma}{\partial x_2}\right) \Big/ \left(\frac{\partial \ln a_2}{\partial x_2}\right) \tag{37}$$

Obviously the maximum adsorption at the surface will be found in cases where the numerator is large and the denominator small. The term $-(\partial \gamma / \partial x_2)$ will be large when there is a large decrease in the surface tension upon addition of the solute; that is, when there is a large difference between the surface tensions of the two components. Further, as we have seen in Chapter III (Fig. 19) and elsewhere, the activity curve is flattened by positive deviations from Raoult's law. Since the large differences in internal pressure which produce large positive deviations also produce differences in surface tension, as we have seen from the comparison of values of $\gamma/V^{\frac{1}{3}}$ with the solubility parameters δ, it is evident that large differences in γ for the two components will almost invariably be accompanied by large values of the adsorption u_2.

These considerations were all inherent in the discussion of the surface tension of non-ideal solutions, but it is worthwhile to reemphasize them here.

Surface phenomena with two liquid phases. When the two components are only partially miscible in the liquid phase, the surfaces of the two liquid phases are of special interest. As we recall from Chapter XVI, separation into two liquid phases occurs when positive deviations from Raoult's law become very large, a situation which we have just seen greatly enhances the adsorption of one component in the surface. The surface tension-composition diagrams for partially miscible systems may well resemble the Roozeboom Type IV or V solid-liquid diagrams which we have seen in Chapter XVIII.

In comparing the γ-x diagrams with the T-x diagrams, one precaution must be observed. While thermodynamics requires that at thermal equilibrium the temperature must be the same in both phases, no such requirement is placed on the surface tensions. Since it is unlikely that the surface tensions of two conjugate phases would be the same, we will find a break in the γ-x diagram which has no correspondence in the T-x diagram.

---

[33] See, for example, G. N Lewis and M. Randall, "Thermodynamics and the Free Energy of Chemical Substances", (McGraw Hill, 1923) p. 249.

The system water-n-butanol, which at 25° shows a miscibility gap between 1.9 and 49 mole percent butanol is a representative example. Harkins and King[34] have measured the surface tensions of the aqueous solutions at 25° while Harkins and Wampler[35] have determined the activities from cryoscopic measurements. From these data one may calculate the surface composition curve; to do so, we have assumed $\sigma_{C_4H_9OH} = 21$ Å^2 and $\sigma_{H_2O} = 10.5$ Å^2 as in the water-ethanol system (Fig. 5). Carter and Jones[36] have measured the surface tensions of the conjugate phases at 25 °C; for the aqueous solution $\gamma = 25.23$ dynes/cm. while for the phase rich in n-butanol $\gamma = 24.63$ dynes/cm. This difference is only 0.60 dynes/cm; the interfacial tension, which according to the so-called Antonoff rule[37] should equal this difference, is 4.04 dynes/cm.

The surface tension of pure n-butanol at 25°C is about 24.1 dyne/cm[38]. Whether the surface tensions of all mixtures between 50 and 100 mole percent butanol lie between 24.6 and 24.1 dynes/cm. or whether there is a minimum in the surface tension curve is unknown. Fig. 6 summarizes the experimental data.

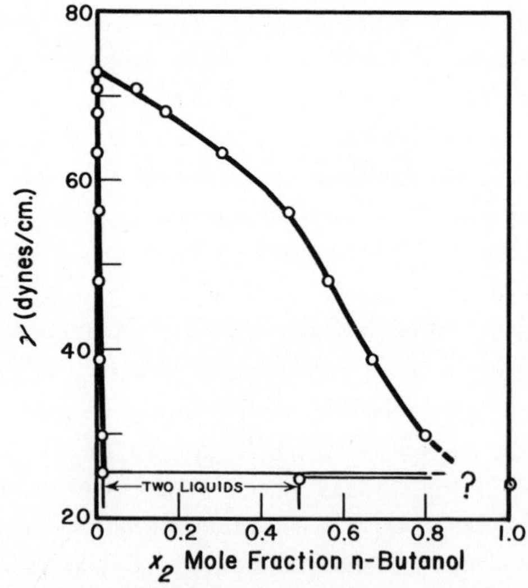

Fig. 6. Surface tension of solutions of water and n-butanol at 25°C. (Data of Harkins and King[34] and Harkins and Wampler[35])

These considerations lead to an interesting connection between our theories of solubility and the formation of surface films. The formation of

[34] W. D. Harkins and H. H. King, *Kansas State Agr. Coll. Tech. Bull. No. 9.*

[35] W. D. Harkins and R. W. Wampler. *J. Am. Chem. Soc.*, **53**, 850 (1931).

[36] E. G. Carter and D. C. Jones, *Trans. Faraday Soc.*, **30**, 1027 (1934).

[37] G. Antonoff, *J. chim. phys.*, **5**, 372 (1907).

[38] Interpolated from data in the International Critical Tables, see also Mme. Hennaut-Roland and M. Lek, *Bull. soc. chim. Belg.*, **40**, 177 (1931).

a second liquid phase upon the surface of a first may be regarded as a case of very extreme adsorption. The positive deviation and the high degree of adsorption may thus both be regarded as consequences of unlikeness of the two components which causes one to "squeeze out" the other, not only into a surface layer but also into another phase. If the solute consists of a complex molecule, one part of which is like the solvent, another part unlike, we have the state of affairs which has been investigated extensively by Langmuir[39] and Harkins[40] and their coworkers, where the carboxyl end of a molecules of a higher fatty acid is soluble in water, while the hydrocarbon chain is not, so a stable film is formed on the surface of the water.

Effect of particle size upon solubility. The fugacity of a liquid increases if dispersed into very small drops to an extent given by the equation[41]:

$$RT \ln \frac{f}{f^\circ} = \frac{2\gamma V}{r} \tag{38}$$

where f is the fugacity of the liquid of surface tension γ, molal volume V when dispersed into drops of radius r. The fugacity from a plane surface is f°.

We might use this equation to calculate the change in solubility of one liquid in another when a fine emulsion is formed, but it is useful chiefly with respect to the increase in solubility of a solid brought about by fine grinding. In such a case we cannot measure γ except by the equation itself, but we can, nevertheless, draw the qualitative conclusion that since the fugacity of a solid is increased by high dispersion, its solubility must likewise increase in order to maintain equilibrium. The order of magnitude is indicated by the following calculation. In order for the solubility to increase by 10 per cent, f/f° must become 1.10. Assuming $\gamma = 100$ dynes, $V = 50$ cc. and $T = 300°$, we have $r = 5 \times 10^{-4}$ cm., showing that the particles of such a solid would have to be rather fine in order to show any such increase in solubility. As a matter of fact, Hulett[42] has been able to increase the solubility of gypsum by 20 per cent by fine grinding and the solubility of $BaSO_4$ by 80 per cent.

---

[39] I. Langmuir, *J. Am. Chem. Soc.*, **39**, 1848-1906 (1917); *Proc. Nat. Acad. Sci.*, **3**, 251 (1917). *Colloid Symposium Monographs* **3**, 48 (1925).

[40] See W. D. Harkins, "Colloid Chemistry", Vol. **5**, Chapter 2 (pp. 12-100), edited by J. Alexander (Reinhold, New York, 1945).

[41] For a derivation of Equation 38, see G. N. Lewis and M. Randall, "Thermodynamics and the Free Energy of Chemical Substances", (McGraw Hill, 1923) p. 251. Using vapor pressures insteod of fugacities, the equation was first derived by W. Thomson (Lord Kelvin), *Phil. Mag.*, [**4**], **42**, 448 (1871). A recent derivation formulated in terms of the finite surface layer model has been given by E. A. Guggenheim, *Trans. Faraday Soc.*, **36**, 407 (1940).

[42] G. A. Hulett, *Z. physik. Chem.*, **37**, 385 (1901); **47**, 357 (1904).

This effect is seldom likely to influence determinations of solubility, for in attaining equilibrium sufficient time is usually allowed for the small and more soluble particles to "distill" over on to the larger ones, a process well known to analysts, who let fine precipitates stand in order to become filtrable. The phenomenon may however become important in some cases. For example, if the calomel or mercurous sulfate in normal electrodes or cells is extremely fine the substance will be more soluble, and thus give rise to a different e. m. f. If a finely divided or spongy metal is used as an electrode, it may give an e. m. f. different from that of the less dispersed metal. The differences, of course, tend to disappear on standing, but sufficient time should be allowed for the purpose.

The phenomenon of supersaturation may also be related to Equation 38, for the greater solubility of small particles makes it harder to start crystallization in the absence of crystal "seeds" than it is to continue the crystallization after it is once started. On this account it is often possible to concentrate a solution far beyond its point of saturation for a certain phase, provided this phase is not added to the system, and to maintain indefinitely supersaturated solutions, or even to crystallize from the solution a phase unstable with respect to the first. Thus, by supercooling a solution of Na_2SO_4 it is possible to avoid getting the more stable $Na_2SO_4 \cdot 10H_2O$ and to get the less stable and more soluble $Na_2SO_4 \cdot 7H_2O$.

CHAPTER XXII

Chemical Equilibria and Reaction Rates in Solution

If we consider a simple chemical reaction in solution as:

$$A + B \rightleftharpoons C + D$$

the reacting system is at equilibrium when the following equation is satisfied:

$$K_\circ = \frac{a_C \; a_D}{a_A \; a_B} \tag{1}$$

where the a's represent the activities of the reactants A and B and the products C and D. The equilibrium constant K_o is related to the standard free energy[1] of reaction ΔF° by the well known equation:

$$\Delta F^\circ = - RT \ln K_\circ \tag{2}$$

If we express Equation 1 in the more usual form using mole fractions:

$$K = \frac{x_C \; x_D}{x_A \; x_B} = \frac{\gamma_A \; \gamma_B}{\gamma_C \; \gamma_D} \; K_\circ \tag{3}$$

we see that this mole fraction equilibrium "constant" K actually varies as a change in environment changes the activity coefficients γ. Only when all the reactants and products obey Raoult's law in solution is K equal to the true equilibrium constant K_o.

From this it is evident that changing solvents, by altering the deviations of the reactants and products from Raoult's law, may shift the equilibrium in one direction or the other.

---

[1] For a detailed discussion of the thermodynamics of chemical equilibrium, see G. N. Lewis and M. Randall, "Thermodynamics and the Free Energy of Chemical Substances", McGraw-Hill, 1923) especially Chapter XXIV.

The effect of a solvent which tends to unite chemically with one of the products, for example, is of course to reduce its fugacity (hence, its activity coefficient) and to cause further reaction to form more of the products. The mole fraction or concentration K will be smaller in such a solvent than in one where no such solvation exists. Chemists make frequent use of this well known principle, as for example in the esterification reaction where H_2SO_4 is used to combine with the water and displace the equilibrium constant to the right:

$$CH_3COOH + C_2H_5OH \rightleftarrows CH_3COOC_2H_5 + H_2O$$

Similarly, if the products are more polar than the reactants, the use of a polar solvent may increase the fugacity of the reactants and decrease that of the products, so as to increase K. The dissociation of hexaphenyl ethane into triphenyl methyl radicals, which may be written simply:

$$\varphi_3\,C\varphi_3 \rightleftarrows 2\,\varphi_3\,C$$

is enhanced in the more polar solvents, as shown by the well known studies of Gomberg[2].

The direction of a shift of various tautomeric equilibria with change of solvent can usually be predicted from consideration of the relative polarity of the two forms.

It is likewise possible to apply the internal pressure theory to determine the direction in which certain equilibria would be displaced, where polarity and compound formation might have little or no effect. Suppose for example we are comparing two solvent media with low and high solubility parameters, respectively, and the reactants A and B have lower solubility parameters than the products C and D. In the solvent of low internal pressure (small δ), the reactants form almost ideal solutions, while the products, with their large δ's show large positive deviations from Raoult's law, hence K is diminished and we obtain relatively smaller amounts of the products. Conversely in a solvent of high internal pressure, it is the products which form nearly ideal solutions and the reactants which deviate markedly, for this case, K is enhanced, and we obtain much greater amounts of the products.

In general we may summarize by saying that in order to get a large amount of a certain substance in an equilibrium reached in solution, one should employ a solvent which is a good one for the substance desired and a poor one for the substance or substances on the other side of the equation

[2] M. Gomberg, *J. Am. Chem. Soc.*, **22**, 157 (1900); **36**, 1144 (1914); *Chem. Revs.*, **1**, 91 (1924); **2**, 310 (1925).

of equilibrium. The quality of a solvent in this connection may be determined by any or all of the factors considered in connection with solubility in general, *viz.* polarity, chemical combination and internal pressure.

Reaction rates in solution. Considerations entirely similar to those which influence chemical equilibria apply to the problem of reaction kinetics. For example, let us consider the reaction:

$$A + B \rightarrow M^{\ddagger} \rightarrow C + D$$

where A and B are the reactants, C and D the products and $M^{\ddagger}$ the intermediate "activated complex". We may define a specific rate constant k_r in terms of the rate of disappearance of A and B or the rate of formation of C and D:

$$-\frac{dx_A}{dt} = -\frac{dx_B}{dt} = \frac{dx_C}{dt} = \frac{dx_D}{dt} = k_r x_A x_B \tag{4}$$

(In conformity with earlier sections of this book, we define the rate constant in terms of mole fractions rather than the commoner concentration units. At the low concentrations usually involved in studies of reaction rates, they differ only by a constant proportionality factor.)

Following the theory of absolute reaction rates, as developed by Eyring and coworkers[3], we may write the specific rate constant k_r as;

$$k_r = \varkappa \frac{kT}{h} K^{\ddagger} \tag{5}$$

where $\varkappa$ is the transmission coefficient, k the Boltzmann constant, and h Planck's constant. $K^{\ddagger}$,the only part of Equation 5 which concerns us here, is the mole fraction equilibrium constant for the equilibrium between the reactants A and B and the activated complex $M^{\ddagger}$.

$$K^{\ddagger} = \frac{x_{\ddagger}}{x_A x_B} \tag{6}$$

[3] For a detailed exposition of this theory, see S. Glasstone, K. J. Laidler and H. Eyring, "The Theory of Rate Processes". (McGraw-Hill, 1941); Chapter VIII deals with reactions in solution.

where $x_{\ddagger}$ is the mole fraction of the activated $M^{\ddagger}$.

The true equilibrium constant in terms of the activities may be written as:

$$K_{\circ}^{\ddagger} = \frac{a_{\ddagger}}{a_A a_B} = K^{\ddagger} \frac{\gamma_{\ddagger}}{\gamma_A \gamma_B} \tag{7}$$

If we combine Equations 5 and 7, we obtain:

$$k_r = \varkappa \frac{kT}{h} K_{\circ}^{\ddagger} \frac{\gamma_A \gamma_B}{\gamma_{\ddagger}} = k_{\circ} \frac{\gamma_A \gamma_B}{\gamma_{\ddagger}} \tag{8}$$

We see from this that the rate constant as usually expressed is a function of the activity coefficients just as the mole fraction equilibrium constant is. Equation 8 is essentially the well known relation first derived for electrolyte solutions by Brønsted[4] and by Bjerrum[5].

Thus the role of the solvent in reaction rates is just the same as in equilibria. Substances which are better solvents for the reactants than for the activated complex slowdown the reaction, while those which are better solvents for the activated complex speed it up.

The influence of internal pressures on reaction rates was first discussed by Richardson and Soper[6] who proposed the rule that if the products are substances of higher internal pressure, the reaction is accelerated by solvents of high internal pressure. Glasstone[7] has noted that this rule can be justified if one assumes that the activated complex resembles the products.

The following examples taken from *The Theory of Rate Processes*[3] illustrate this effect.

In the Menschutkin reaction (I), the internal pressure of the activated state, probably partially ionic in character, is doubtless greater than those of the reactants, while in the esterification of ethyl alcohol by acetic anhydride (II), the dipoles may be shielded in the activated complex, and the reverse is probably true. The prediction that the effect of solvents on these two reactions would run in opposite directions is confirmed in a general manner by the results in Table 1.

$$(C_2H_5)_3N + C_2H_5I \rightarrow (C_2H_5)_4N^+ + I^- \tag{I}$$

$$2\,C_2H_5OH + (CH_3CO)_2O \rightarrow 2\,CH_3COOC_2H_5 + H_2O \tag{II}$$

---

[4] J. N. Brønsted, *Z. physik. Chem.*, **102**, 109 (1922); **115**, 337 (1925).

[5] N. Bjerrum, *Z. physik. Chem.*, **108**, 82 (1924).

[6] M. Richardson and F. G. Soper, *J. Chem. Soc.*, **1929**, 1873.

[7] S. Glasstone, *J. Chem. Soc.*, **1936**, 723.

Table 1. Effect of internal pressures on reaction rates
(taken from Glasstone, Laidler, and Eyring[3])

Solvent	δ_0	Specific Rate Constant I	Specific Rate Constant II
Hexane	7.3	0.00018	0.0119
Carbon tetrachloride	8.6	....	0.0113
Benzene	9.15	0.0058	0.0046
Chloroform	9.3	....	0.0040
Chlorobenzene	9.5	0.023	0.0053
Anisole	?	0.040	0.0029
Nitrobenzene	10.0	70.1	0.0024

Activities and deviations from Raoult's law play a similar role in such non-chemical rate processes as viscosity and diffusion. Powell, Roseveare, and Eyring[8] have shown that the viscosity of liquid mixtures can be interpreted fairly well in terms of their deviations from Raoult's law. Stearn, Irish and Eyring[9] have developed a similar treatment of diffusion in solutions, showing that the rate of diffusion is proportional not to the concentration gradient but to the *activity* gradient; this fact has been strikingly confirmed by the work of Birchenall and Mehl[10] on diffussion in solid solutions of copper and zinc (the brasses).

---

[8] R. E. Powell, W. E. Roseveare, and H. Eyring, *Ind. Eng. Chem.*, **33**, 430 (1941).

[9] A. E. Stearn, E. M. Irish, and H. Eyring, *J. Phys. Chem.*, **44**, 981 (1940).

[10] C. E. Birchenall and R. F. Mehl, *Am. Inst. Mining Met. Engrs., Inst. Metals Div., Metals Technol.*, **14**, No. 4, *Tech. Pub.* No. 2168 (1947); *J. Applied Phys.*, **19**, 217 (1948).

CHAPTER XXIII

Evaluation of Solubility Parameters

In the preceding chapters of this book, we have seen how the thermodynamic properties of solutions depend upon the square of the difference between the values of a quantity δ for the two components. These δ-values, which enable us to predict and interpret solubility in a semi-quantitative manner, have been termed "solubility parameters" and have been identified (Chapter VII) with the square roots of the internal pressure or cohesive energy densities of the pure substances. We may use as a working definition:

$$\delta = (-\mathrm{E}/\mathrm{V}^{l})^{\frac{1}{2}} \tag{1}$$

where $-\mathrm{E}$ is the energy of vaporization to the gas at zero pressure (*i. e.* infinite separation of the molecules) and V^{l} is the molal volume of the liquid. Both E and V change with temperature, so we need to calculate δ for each temperature at which we wish to use it. When an accurate value of the heat of vaporization at the desired temperature is known, it represents the best means for calculating δ's, but certain other methods alluded to earlier may be of value when the desired vaporization data are lacking. In the following sections these various methods of estimating the solubility parameters will be discussed in greater detail.

1. **Calculation from heats of vaporization.** There is seldom any difficulty in obaining a satisfactory value for the molal volume of the liquid at any desired temperature; so the evaluation of δ from Equation 1 is mainly dependent upon the determination of the energy E. At low vapor pressures, the vapor in equilibrium with the liquid is essentially ideal, and we may replace $-\mathrm{E}$ by $\Delta\mathrm{E}^{\mathrm{V}}$ the energy of vaporization, and that in turn by $\Delta\mathrm{H}^{\mathrm{V}} - RT$, where $\Delta\mathrm{H}^{\mathrm{V}}$ is the heat of vaporization:

$$\delta \cong \left(\frac{\Delta\mathrm{H}^{\mathrm{V}} - RT}{\mathrm{V}^{l}}\right)^{\frac{1}{2}} \tag{2}$$

When the heat of vaporization has been determined calorimetrically at the desired temperature, say 25°C, well below the normal boiling point, it may be substituted directly into Equation 2 and the solubility parameter is evaluated. Often, however, no such calorimetric measurements are available, and the heat of vaporization must be calculated from the temperature dependence of the vapor pressure by means of the Clausius-Clapeyron equation. In its usual form, this equation is written:

$$\frac{d\ln p}{dT} = \frac{\Delta H^{V}_{app}}{RT^2} \tag{3}$$

We have given ΔH^V in this equation the subscript *app* signifying "apparent" for it is only the true heat of vaporization at vapor pressures low enough that the vapor is, for all practical purposes, ideal. The exact thermodynamic equation is:

$$\frac{dp}{dT} = \frac{\Delta H^V}{T\Delta V^V} \tag{4}$$

where ΔV^V is the change of volume on vaporization, $V^g - V^l$, the difference in the molal volumes of vapor and liquid. Equation 4 may be divided through by p and rewritten as:

$$\frac{d\ln p}{dT} = \frac{\Delta H^V \; V^g}{RT^2 \; \Delta V^V}\left(\frac{RT}{pV^g}\right) \tag{5}$$

The term $RT^2\,(d\ln p/dT)$ is merely ΔH^{V}_{app} as defined by Equation 3, while pV^g/RT is the familiar compressibility factor Z which for a perfect gas is unity, but for real gases below their critical temperatures is always less than unity. We may thus rewrite Equation 5 in the form:

$$\Delta H^V = \Delta H^{V}_{app}\, Z\left(\frac{V^g - V^l}{V^g}\right) \tag{6}$$

The energy of vaporization ΔE^V is of course:

$$\Delta E^V = \Delta H^V - p\Delta V^V = (\Delta H^{V}_{ap} - RT)\, Z\left(\frac{V \;\; - V^l}{V^g}\right) \tag{7}$$

All that remains is to calculate the small correction to convert ΔE^V to $-E$. This requires a knowledge of the variation of $-E$ with V. Since this correction term is very small it suffices to use the van der Waals equation $E = -a/V$, and we write:

$$-E = \frac{a}{V^l} = \Delta E^V + \frac{a}{V^g} = \Delta E^V \left(\frac{V^g}{V^g - V^l} \right) \tag{8}$$

Substitution of Equation 7 into Equation 8 leads to the particularly simple result:

$$-E = (\Delta H^V_{app} - RT)\, Z \tag{9}$$

Thus with the slope of the vapor pressure-temperature curve and a value for the compressibility factor Z, we may calculate ΔH^V, and from this, the solubility parameter δ. This method and that based upon calorimetric measurements are the only thoroughly reliable ways of calculating the δ's, and save for a very few exceptions as noted, all the values compiled in Appendix I were obtained by one of these two.

2. **Estimation from the "Hildebrand Rule".** For many substances no heats of vaporization, either calorimetric or from vapor pressures, are known. For such cases, it is possible to estimate the heat of vaporization from the boiling point, provided the liquid is nonpolar, or nearly so, by the aid of the "Hildebrand rule". This rule, first proposed by the senior author in 1915[1], states that the entropy of vaporization per mole is the same for all normal liquids if measured, not at their boiling points, as in Trouton's rule, but at the temperatures at which their vapors have equal volumes.

We have seen in Chapter V how this rule leads to the conclusion that the vapor pressures of two substances, if equal at one temperature are equal at all temperatures; and that entropy of vaporization at the boiling point depends only on the boiling temperature T_b:

$$\Delta S^V_b = f(T_b) \tag{10}$$

Moreover, since each member of the family of $p - T$ curves (see Chapter V, Figs. 5 and 6) is fixed by fixing one point, *i. e.* the boiling point, it follows that the entropy of vaporization at any temperature T is a function of only two parameters, the temperature T, and the normal boiling point T_b.

$$\Delta S^V_T = f(T, T_b) \tag{11}$$

The heat of vaporization is of course a similar function.

[1] J. H. Hildebrand, *J. Am. Chem. Soc.*, **37**, 970 (1915); **40**, 45 (1918).

Without making undesirable approximations[2], the form of Equations 11 and 12 cannot be deduced theoretically, but it is easy to obtain an empirical relation from the experimental data. By plotting reliable values (calorimetric or vapor-pressure) of the heat of vaporization for various substances at 25° C against their boiling points, we obtain[3] an empirical formula for ΔH^V_{298}:

$$\Delta H^V_{298}\,(\text{cal./mole}) = -\,2950 + 23.7\,T_b + 0.020\,T_b^2 \tag{12}$$

Fig. 1 shows this curve and the large number of experimental points from which it was deduced. A similar relation[3] for the heats of vaporization at the normal boiling point is:

$$\Delta H^V_b\,(\text{calories/mole}) = 17.0\,T_b + 0.009\,T_b^2 \tag{13}$$

The entropies may be obtained, of course, by dividing through by T. Equation 12 may be used to estimate the heat of vaporization at 25° C when only the boiling point is known. We shall see in a later section how satisfactory this method is likely to be.

3. **Estimation from the internal pressure** $(\partial E/\partial V)_T$.

While we have used the terms "internal pressure" and "cohesive energy density" interchangeably for $-E/V$, the internal pressure may be strictly defined as $(\partial E/\partial V)_T$, the left hand member of the so-called "thermodynamic equation of state":

$$\left(\frac{\partial E}{\partial V}\right)_T = T\left(\frac{\partial P}{\partial T}\right)_V - P \tag{14}$$

The so-called thermal pressure $T(\partial P/\partial T)_V$ may be obtained either by direct measurement or from the coefficients of thermal expansion and compressibility α and β:

$$T\left(\frac{\partial P}{\partial T}\right)_V = T\,\frac{\alpha}{\beta} \tag{15}$$

Some difficulty arises in using the α and β values in the literature. The coefficient of thermal expansion is frequently related to the volume at 0°C. rather than the volume at the temperature of measurement; such

[2] In the second edition of this book, an approximate relation was derived from the Clausius-Clapeyron equation by assuming a constant ΔH^V independent of temperature (*i. e.* a function only of T_b). This now appears to have been an undesirable oversimplification.

[3] R. L. Scott, unpublished work.

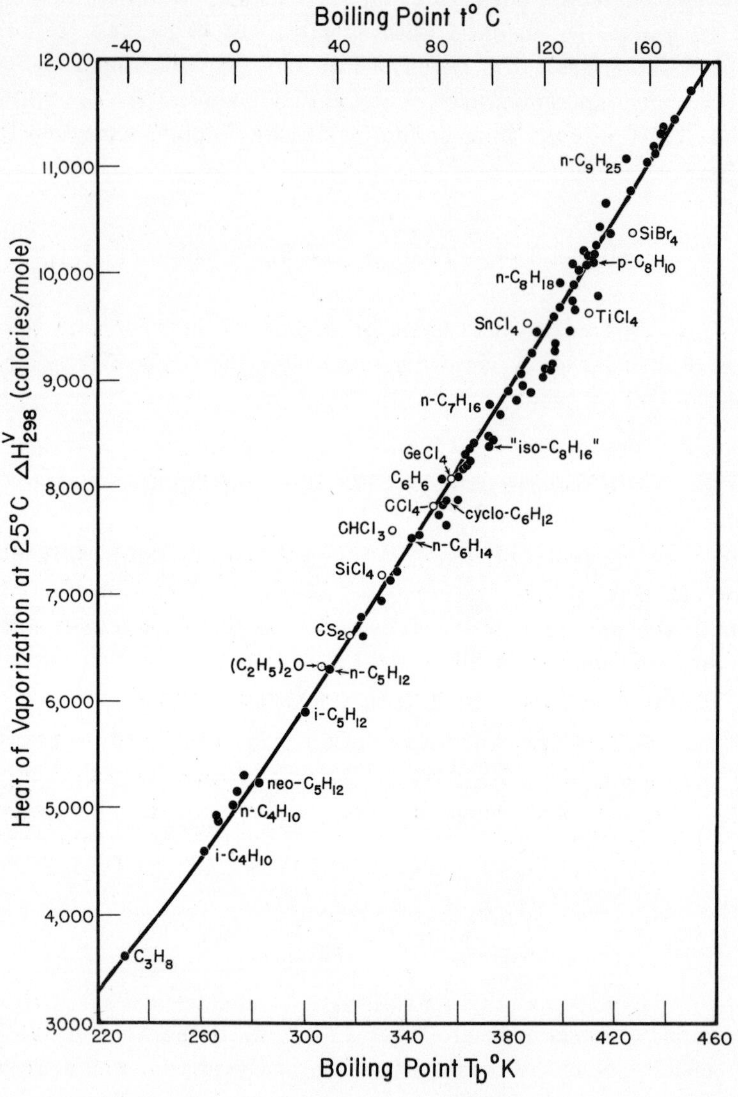

Fig. 1. Heats of vaporization and the Hildebrand Rule

values need to be multiplied by $V_\circ/V_T$, the ratio of the liquid volume at 0°C and that at the temperature T. More serious is the fact that most compressibilities are calculated from the volume change under large increments of pressure (200 atmospheres, for example) and are considerably smaller than the differential compressibility at one atmosphere. Wherever possible, a direct measurement of $(\partial P/\partial T)_V$ is preferable.

At low pressures, the pressure P is entirely negligible compared with the internal pressure (2000 - 8000 atmospheres) and we can write:

$$\left(\frac{\partial E}{\partial V}\right)_T = T\left(\frac{\partial P}{\partial T}\right)_V \tag{16}$$

Over a small range of volumes, we have seen (Chapter V) that $(\partial E/\partial V)_T$ can always be written as:

$$\left(\frac{\partial E}{\partial V}\right)_T = n\,\frac{\Delta \mathrm{E^V}}{\mathrm{V}} \tag{17}$$

For a van der Waals liquid $n = 1$, and the internal pressure and the cohesive energy density are identical. Although the van der Waals equation is certainly a poor approximation for liquids, Hildebrand and co-workers[4] have measured $(\partial P/\partial T)_V$ for a number of normal liquids and found that n was, in fact, not far from unity (0.9 — 1.1).

Thus, for nonpolar liquids, we can use $T(\partial P/\partial T)_V$ as a measure of the solubility parameter:

$$\delta \simeq \left[T\left(\frac{\partial P}{\partial T}\right)_V\right]^{\frac{1}{2}} = \left(T\,\frac{\alpha}{\beta}\right)^{\frac{1}{2}} \tag{18}$$

4. **Estimation from equations of state and critical constants.**

Although none of the common equations of state for gases fits liquids very well, the fact that for many normal liquids (as we have seen in the preceding section), $(\partial E/\partial V)_T$ is inversely proportional to the square of the molal volume, as predicted from the van der Waals equation, suggests trying to calculate δ from the constant of equations of state.

According to van der Waals' theory, we may write:

$$-\frac{\mathrm{E}}{\mathrm{V}} = \left(\frac{\partial E}{\partial V}\right)_T = \frac{\mathrm{a}}{\mathrm{V}^2} \tag{19}$$

We have seen in Chapter V that the exponent of V in Equation 19 is, in fact, about 2, so we might expect to get reasonable values for δ from the equation:

$$\delta \simeq \frac{\mathrm{a}^{\frac{1}{2}}}{\mathrm{V}} \tag{20}$$

[4] See Chapter V for references.

where a is the van der Waals constant for the gas. As is well known, a is the function of temperature, so it would be desirable to use an a determined not from critical data but from P - V - T measurements at lower temperatures.

A more radical proposal was made by van Laar[5] who assuming the liquid was not significantly expanded identified its volume with the minimum volume according to the van der Waals equation, namely the parameter b. From this, he obtains a proportionality to the critical pressure P_c:

$$\delta = \frac{a^{\frac{1}{2}}}{b} = (\frac{8}{27} P_c)^{\frac{1}{2}} \tag{21}$$

We have already noted the inexactness of this relation in Chapter VII, but it is sometimes useful for comparing substances with similar boiling temperatures. For satisfactory agreement, the numerical constant $(8/27)^{\frac{1}{2}}$ must be replaced by an empirical one; for P_c in atmospheres and δ in $(\text{cal/cm}^3)^{\frac{1}{2}}$ we have

$$\delta = 1.25\, P_c^{\frac{1}{2}} \tag{22}$$

In Table I, δ-values calculated from Equations 20 and 22 are compared with those calculated from Equation 2.

Table 1. Solubility Parameters from Equations of State

Substance	δ (Eq. 2)	V	a liter² atm.	δ (Eq. 20)	P_c (atm)	δ (Eq. 22)
n-Hexane	**7.3**	132	24.4	5 8	29.5	6.8
Ethyl ether	**7 5**	105	17.4	6.2	35.5	7.4
Cyclohexane	**8.2**	109	22.8	6.8	40.4	8.0
Carbon tetrachloride	**8 6**	97	20.4	7.2	45.0	8.4
Benzene	**9.15**	89	18.0	7.4	47.7	8.6
Chloroform	**9.3**	81	25.4	9 7	65.8	10.1
Carbon disulfide	**10.0**	61	11 6	8.7	76	10.9

[5] J. J. van Laar, "Sechs Vorträge über das Thermodynamische Potential" (Braunschweig 1906).

We see that the approximate order is retained but that the numerical values differ considerably. Multiplication of $a^{\frac{1}{2}}/V$ by an arbitrary factor 1.2 would improve the agreement somewhat.

5. **Estimation from the surface tension.** We have seen in Chapter XXI how the surface tension of nonpolar substances bears a close relation to the heat of vaporization. (See Fig. XXI-2). The best fit was obtained by a proportionality between $\gamma/V^{\frac{1}{3}}$ and the 0.86 power of $\Delta E^V/V$, although a first power dependence would be fairly satisfactory. We may write therefore

$$\delta = k\left(\frac{\gamma}{V^{\frac{1}{3}}}\right)^{0.43} \tag{23}$$

where, for γ in dyne/cm, V in cm^3/mole and δ in (cal/cm^3)$^{\frac{1}{2}}$, k is 4.1 (k is, of course, a function of temperature). We shall compare this method with others in a final recapitulation at the end of this chapter.

6. **Estimation from optical data.** In Chapter IV in the discussion of intermolecular forces, we have seen how the dispersion constant k of London's theory depends upon the polarizability α and the frequency ν_0. Since both of these quantities may be obtained from a study of the dependence of the index of refraction n on the frequency, we should be able from such measurements to estimate δ-values for a liquid. This has not been done directly but as shown in Table IV-3, Wohl[6] has used such a formula to calculate van der Waals' a.

Scatchard[7] has recently obtained semi-empirical correlations between cohesive energy densities and indices of refraction for homologous series of organic liquids.

7. **Estimation from solubility data.** In earlier chapters, especially XVII, we have shown how a consistent value of the solubility parameter may be obtained from measurements of the solubility in a number of solvents whose δ-values are known. This is especially useful in the case of solid solubilities, since the δ-value for the super-cooled liquid can be obtained only by extrapolation, frequently quite extensive, from the liquid at its normal temperature range. We shall not repeat here the extensive tables given in Chapter XVII, but it is interesting to note that on the basis of its solubility behavior, we should assign to chloroform a lower δ-value than that for benzene, say, about 9.0 rather than the calorimetric value 9.3.

Scott and Magat[8] have used swelling measurements on vulcanized rubbers to assign δ-values to nitrobenzene and dioxane. Table 2 reproduces their figures.

[6] K. Wohl, *Z. physik. Chem.*, Bodenstein Festband, 807 (1931).

[7] G. Scatchard, Symposium on Liquids, ACS Meeting, Atlantic City, April, 1947, *Chem. Revs.*, **44**, 7 (1949).

[8] R. L. Scott and M. Magat, *J. Polymer Sci.*, **4**, 555 (1949).

Table 2. Estimation of δ from swelling measurements.

Rubber	δ_{rubber}		$\delta_{\text{nitrobenzene}}$	δ_{dioxane}
Natural rubber	**8.35**		9.94	9.93
Polybutadiene	**8.45**		10.05	10.05
Buna S 85-15	**8.55**		9.99	10.02
Buna S 75-25	**8.60**		9.88	9.96
(3 samples)			9.90	9.97
			9.92	10.01
Buna S 60-40	**8.70**		9.79	9.90
		Average	9.92	9.98

On this basis, they assigned δ-values of 9.9 and 10.0 to the two liquids. We have seen in Chapter XVI that similar values (9.8 - 10.5) for nitrobenzene can be deduced from its critical solution temperatures with hydrocarbons.

8. **Comparison of various methods.** In Table 3 are tabulated δ-values for representative liquids calculated in the various ways indicated.

Table 3. Solubility parameters at 25 °C by different methods

Substance	ΔH^V_{298} Eq. 2	Hildebrand Rule Eq. 12	$(\partial E/\partial V)_T$ Eq. 18	P_c Eq. 22	Surface tension Eq. 23	Solubility data
iso-Pentane	**6.75**	6.8		7.2	6.6	
Ethyl ether	**7.4**	7.3	7.5	7.4	7.1	
n-Heptane	**7.43**	7.4	7.8	6.5	7.3	
Silicon tetrachloride	**7.6**	7.5	7.9			7.7
Cyclohexane	**8.20**	8.2		8.0	8.3	
Carbon tetrachloride	**8.62**	8.6	8.9	8.4	8.65	
p-Xylene	**8.77**	8.8			8.7	
Benzene	**9.16**	9.1	9.4	8.6	9.2	9.1
Chloroform	**9.3**	9.0	9.3	10.1	9.25	9.0
Chlorobenzene	**9.5**	9.6		8.4	9.5	
Nitrobenzene		11.0			10.7	10.0
Dioxane		9.8				10.0
Carbon disulfide	**10.0**	10.0	9.4	10.9	10.1	
Pyridine	**10.7**	10.4		9.7	10.5	
Bromine	**11.5**	11.3			11.6	
Methylene iodide		ca. 11.8			11.8	

There is generally a fair agreement between values from different methods, but they may vary by several tenths of a δ-unit. Whenever they can be obtained, δ-values from heats of vaporization (Equation 2) are to be preferred. A large number of such δ-values are tabulated in Appendix I.

Effect of temperature

Frequently, it is desirable to know the solubility parameters at different temperatures, while an accurate heat of vaporization may be known at only one temperature. Over a limited range of temperature, the change of ΔH^V with T is linear and we may write

$$\Delta H^V = \Delta H^V_o - \Delta C_p (T - T_o) \tag{23}$$

where ΔH^V_o is the heat of vaporization at the temperature T_o, while ΔC_p is the difference between the heat capacity of the liquid and that of the gas, $C^l_p - C^g_p$. Measurements of the liquid heat capacity are frequently available, while that of the ideal gas can be calculated using statistical mechanics A similar expression holds for the volume:

$$V = V_o \{1 + \alpha (T - T_o)\} \tag{24}$$

where α is the coefficient of thermal expansion. Substituting Equations 23 and 24 into Equation 2, and differentiating, we obtain for the temperature dependence of δ:

$$\frac{d \ln \delta}{dT} = - \frac{1}{2} \left\{ \alpha + \frac{\Delta C_p - R}{\Delta H^V - RT} \right\} \tag{25}$$

Over a more extended range, it is more useful to recall the expression for the dependence of E upon the volume given in Chapter V

$$E = \frac{-k}{V^n} \tag{26}$$

where n is about 1.5 for many normal liquids. Given δ at one temperature we can calculate it at any other, given the change in volume. In differential form we may write

$$\frac{d\ln\delta}{d\ln \mathrm{V}} = -\frac{n+1}{2} \cong -1.25 \tag{27}$$

Since $d\ln \mathrm{V}/dT$ is essentially α, we may write

$$\frac{d\ln\delta}{dT} = -\frac{n+1}{2}\,\alpha \cong -1.25\,\alpha \tag{28}$$

Equation 27 is recommended for the most precise work. If the heat of vaporization is accurately known at two temperatures (for example, 25 °C and the normal boiling point), they define a straight line on a log δ - log V plot which permits determination of n.

APPENDIX I

Selected Values of Solubility Parameters

All values except those at 298° K (25°C.) are listed in italics. Solubility parameters of the metals are given in Chapter XIX and are not repeated here. Except as indicated in a few cases, all δ-values are based upon calorimetric or vapor-pressure measurements of the heat of vaporization (Method 1 of Chapter XXIII). For substances which are solids at the indicated temperature, the values are extrapolated ones for the supercooled liquid.

Formula	Substance	T° K	V_T (cm³)	ΔH_T^V (kcal)	δ_T
		Elements			
H_2	hydrogen	*20.4*	*28*	*0.216*	*2.5*
He	helium	*4.2*	*32*	*0.020*	*0.5*
Ne	neon	*27*	*17*	*0.45*	*4.9*
A	argon	*87*	*28*	*1.56*	*7.0*
Kr	krypton	*121*	*34*	*2.16*	*7.5*
Xe	xenon	*165*	*43*	*3.02*	*8.0*
Rn	radon	*211*	*50*	*3.92*	*8.4*
F_2	fluorine	*85*	*34*	*1.51*	*6.3*
Cl_2	chlorine	*239*	*46*	*4.88*	*9.8*
Br_2	bromine	298	51	7.34	11.5
I_2	iodine	298	59		14.1[1]
O_2	oxygen	*90*	*28*	*1.63*	*7.2*
S_8	sulfur	298	135		12.7[1]
N_2	nitrogen	*77*	*35*	*1.33*	*5.9*
P_4	phosphorus	298	70	12.6	13.1
					14.4[1]
		Tetrahalides			
CF_4	carbon tetrafluoride	*145*	45	*2.95*	7.7
CCl_4	carbon tetrachloride	298	97	7.83	8.6
SiF_4	silicon tetrafluoride	ca. *160*	*(60)*	*4.46*	*8.3*
$SiCl_4$	silicon tetrachloride	298	115	7.19	7.6
$SiBr_4$	silicon tetrabromide	298	127	10.38	8.8

[1] Estimated from solubility data. See Chapter XVII.

Formula	Substance	T° K	V_T (cm³)	ΔH^V_T (kcal)	δ_T
$GeCl_4$	germanium tetrachloride	298	115	8.09	8.1
$SnCl_4$	stannic chloride	298	118	9.55	8.7
SnI_4	stannic iodide	298	151	19.63	11.7
$TiCl_4$	titanium tetrachloride	298	111	9.62	9.0
	Other Inorganic Compounds				
CO	carbon monoxide	*82*	*34*	*1.44*	*6.1*
CO_2	carbon dioxide	*223*	*38*	*3.46*	*8.9*
NO	nitric oxide	*121*	*24*	*3.29*	*11.4*
N_2O	nitrous oxide	*184*	*36*	*3.96*	*10.0*
SO_2	sulfur dioxide	*263*	*44*	*5.95*	*11.0*
OsO_4	osmium tetroxide	298	58	9.80	12.6
SF_6	sulfur hexafluoride	*223*	*76*	*4.5*	*7.2*
MoF_6	molybdenum hexafluoride	298	84	6.36	8.3
WF_6	tungsten hexafluoride	298	88	6.25	8.0
UF_6	uranium hexafluoride	298	96	7.2	8.9
GeH_4	monogermane	*185*	*(54)*	*3.4*	*7.4*
$Si(CH_3)_4$	silicon tetramethyl	298	115	5.80	6.7
	Hydrocarbons [2]				
CH_4	methane	*112*	*38*	*1.96*	*6.8*
C_2H_6	ethane	*184*	*55*	*3.51*	*7.6*
C_3H_8	propane	*231*	*76*	*4.49*	*7.4*
		298	89	3.60	6.0
C_4H_{10}	*n*-butane	*273*	*96*	*5.35*	*7.1*
		298	101	5.04	6.7
C_4H_{10}	2-methyl propane (isobutane)	*261*	*98*	*5.09*	*6.8*
		298	105	4.57	6.25
C_5H_{12}	*n*-pentane	298	116	6.32	7.05
		309	*118*	*6.16*	*6.9*
	2-methyl butane (isopentane)	298	117	5.88	6.75
	2,2-dimethyl propane (neopentane)	298	122	5.21	6.25
C_6H_{14}	*n*-hexane	298	132	7.54	7.30
		342	*140*	*6.94*	*6.7*
C_7H_{16}	*n*-heptane	298	147	8.74	7.45
		371	*163*	*7.66*	*6.5*
C_8H_{18}	*n*-octane	298	164	9.92	7.55
		399	*186*	*8.36*	*6.4*
	2,2,4 trimethyl pentane (isooctane)	298	166	8.40	6.85
		372	*184*	*7.41*	*6.1*

[2] δ-values are rounded off to nearest 0.05.

Formula	Substance	T° K	V_T (cm³)	ΔH_T^V (kcal)	δ_T
C_9H_{18}	*n*-nonane	298	180	11.10	7.65
		424	*210*	*9.03*	*6.3*
$C_{16}H_{34}$	*n*-hexadecane	298	295	19.3[3]	8.0
C_5H_{10}	cyclopentane	298	95	6.81	8.10
C_6H_{12}	cyclohexane	298	109	7.90	8.20
		354	*116*	*7.19*	*7.5*
C_7H_{14}	methylcyclohexane	298	128	8.45	7.85
		374	*141*	*7.58*	*7.0*
C_6H_6	benzene	298	89	8.09	9.15
		353	*96*	*7.35*	*8.3*
C_7H_8	toluene	298	107	9.08	8.90
		384	*113*	*8.00*	*8.0*
C_8H_{10}	ethylbenzene	298	123	10.10	8.80
	o-xylene	298	121	10.38	9.00
	m-xylene	298	123	10.20	8.80
	p-xylene	298	124	10.13	8.75
C_9H_{12}	*n*-propylbenzene	298	140	11.05	8.65
	mesitylene	298	140	11.35	8.80
C_8H_8	styrene	298	115	10.50	9.3
	naphthalene	298	123	....	9.9[1]
	anthracene	298	(150)	....	9.9[1]
	phenanthrene	298	158	....	9.8[1]
C_2H_4	ethylene	*169*	*46*	*3.24*	*7.9*
C_3H_6	propene	*225*	*69*	*4.40*	*7.6*
C_4H_8	1-butene	298	95	4.87	6.7
	cis 2-butene	298	91	5.30	7.2
	trans-2-butene	298	91	5.15	7.0
C_4H_8	2-methyl propene (isobutene)	298	94	4.92	6.7
C_4H_6	1,3 butadiene	298	88	4.97	7.1
C_5H_8	isoprene	298	101	6.19	7.45

Fluorocarbons[4]

CF_4	*f*-methane	*145*	*45*	*2.95*	*7.7*
C_2F_6	*f*-ethane	*195*	*75*	*3.86*	*6.8*
C_3F_8	*f*-propane	*235*	*130*	*4.92*	*5.8*
C_4F_{10}	*f*-*n*-butane	298	163	5.0	5.2
C_5F_{12}	*f*-*n*-pentane	298	183	6.0	5.5

[3] Estimated by extrapolating from lower hydrocarbons.

[4] The fluorocarbon ΔH^V- values at 298° K were estimated from the values for the corresponding hydrocarbons, with the aid of the Hildebrand rule. See R. L. Scott, *J. Am. Chem. Soc.*, **70**, 4090 (1948).

Formula	Substance	$T°$ K	V_T (cm³)	ΔH_T^V (kcal)	δ_T
C_6F_{14}	*f*-*n*-hexane	298	205	7.1	5.6
C_7F_{16}	*f*-*n*-heptane	298	227	8.1	5.7
C_8F_{18}	*f*-*n*-octane	298	253	8.9	5.7
C_9F_{20}	*f*-*n*-nonane	298	279	9.7	5.7
C_4F_8	*f*-cyclobutane	298	133	4.9	5.7
C_5F_{10}	*f*-cyclopentane	298	152	5.9	5.9
C_6F_{12}	*f*-cyclohexane	298	170	6.8	6.0
C_7F_{14}	*f*-methylcyclohexane	298	195	7.7	6.0
C_8F_{16}	*f*-dimethylcyclohexane	298	215	8.6	6.1
C_6F_6	*f*-benzene	298	115	8.1	8.1
C_7F_8	*f*-toluene	298	142	8.9	7.7

Aliphatic Halogen Compounds

Formula	Substance	$T°$ K	V_T (cm³)	ΔH_T^V (kcal)	δ_T
CH_3Cl	methyl chloride	*249*	*(50)*	*5.15*	*(9.6)*
		298	56	4.76	8.6
CH_2Cl_2	methylene chloride	298	65	6.7	9.7
$CHCl_3$	chloroform	298	81	7.6	9.3
CCl_4	carbon tetrachloride	298	97	7.83	8.6
CH_3Br	methyl bromide	*277*	*55*	*5.72*	*9.7*
		298	57	5.63	9.4
$CHBr_3$	bromoform	298	88	10.3	10.5
CH_3I	methyl iodide	298	63	6.7	9.9
CH_2I_2	methylene iodide	298	81		11.8[5]
C_2H_5Cl	ethyl chloride	298	73	5.9	8.5
C_2H_5Br	ethyl bromide	298	76	6.60	8.9
C_2H_5I	ethyl iodide	298	81	7.7	9.4
$C_2H_4Cl_2$	1,2 dichloroethane (ethylene chloride)	298	79	8.2	9.8
	1,1 dichloroethane (ethylidene chloride)	298	85	7.7	9.1
$C_2H_4Br_2$	1,2 dibromoethane (ethylene bromide)	298	87	10.0	10.4
$C_2H_3Cl_3$	1,1,1 trichloroethane	298	100	7.82	8.5
$C_2H_2Cl_2$	*cis* 1,2 dichloroethylene	298	76	6.9	9.1
	trans 1,2 dichloroethylene	298	78	6.8	9.0

Other Aliphatic Compounds

Formula	Substance	$T°$ K	V_T (cm³)	ΔH_T^V (kcal)	δ_T
CH_3NO_2	nitromethane	298	54	9.15	12.6
CS_2	carbon disulfide	298	61	6.7	10.0
C_2H_6O	methyl ether	*248*	*(60)*	*5.14*	*8.8*
C_2H_6S	methylsulfide	298	74	6.60	9.0
C_3H_3N	acrylonitrile	298	66	7.8	10.5

[5] Estimated from various data. See Chapter XXIII.

Formula	Substance	$T°$ K	V_T (cm^3)	ΔH_T^V (kcal)	δ_T
$C_3H_8O_2$	dimethoxymethane (methylal)	298	89	6.6	8.2
$C_4H_{10}O$	ethyl ether	298	105	6.36	7.4
$C_4H_8O_2$	dioxane	298	86		10.0[5]

Aromatic Derivatives

Formula	Substance	$T°$ K	V_T (cm^3)	ΔH_T^V (kcal)	δ_T
C_5H_5N	pyridine	298	81	9.85	10.7
C_6H_5Cl	chlorobenzene	298	102	9.83	9.5
$C_6H_5NO_2$	nitrobenzene	298	103		10.0[5]

APPENDIX II

Symbols

(Note: We have not included in the following list minor symbols which appear in only one isolated place in the text, such as various proportionality constants. Symbols which are confined to one or two chapters are indicated as such.)

Roman caps:

A, B, C, D	constants
F	distribution functions for sets of molecules (F_1, F_2 etc.)
G	shear modulus (XVIII)
M	molality
P	probability
Q	swelling, maximum imbibition (XX)
S	fraction dissolved (XX)
X	number of molecular pairs (VIII)

Italic caps (thermodynamic quantities):

A	Helmholtz free energy
B, C, D	virial coefficients
C	heat capacity
E	energy
F	free energy (Gibbs)
G	any extensive variable
H	heat content
K	equilibrium constant
N	number of moles
P	pressure
Q	partition function
R	gas constant per mole
S	entropy
T	temperature °K
U	potential energy
V	volume
Z	compressibility factor ($P\mathrm{V}/RT$) for gases

Small Roman caps (molal quantities):

A	molal Helmholtz free energy
C	molal heat capacity
E	molal energy
F	molal free energy
H	molal heat content
M	molal weight
S	molal entropy
V	molal volume

Roman lower case (primarily molecular constants):

a, b	van der Waals constants
c	cohesive energy density
d	distance, diameter
f, g, h	functions
g	special distribution functions (VIII)
j	repulsion constant
k	attraction constant
m	number of segments ($\mathrm{V}_p/\mathrm{V}_\circ$) (VI, XX)
n	number of molecules
p	degree of association (XI)
q	number peripheral sites, generalized volume
r	radius, constant
w	interchange energy (VIII and XIX)
z	coordination number, number of nearest neighbors

Italic lower case:

a	activity
c	concentration
d	differential operator
e	base of natural logarithms
f	fugacity
g	Kirkwood's correlation parameter for hindered rotation in polar liquids (IX and X)
h	Planck's constant
h^σ	heat content of surface per unit area (XXI)
k	Boltzmann constant, gas constant per molecule
k_r	rate constant (XXII)
l	length
m	mass; mass per molecule
n	refractive index; an integer, an exponent
p	vapor pressure, partial pressure
q	partition function per molecule

r	radius variable
s^σ	surface entropy per unit area (XXI)
s	degree of order (XIX)
t	temperature °C.; time (XXII)
u	potential energy per molecule; adsorption (XXI)
v	volume per molecule
w	weight fraction
x, y, z	Cartesian coordinates
x	mole fraction
y	various functions
z	Mayer's "fugacity" (V)

Bold face italic caps

$\boldsymbol{N}$	Avogadro's number, $6.02 \cdot 10^{23}$ molecules/mole

Bold face Roman (primarily electrical quantities)

$\mathbf{E}$	electromotive force
$\mathbf{F}$	Faraday's constant
$\mathbf{I}$	ionization potential
$\mathbf{P}$	molal polarization
$\mathbf{p}$	generalized momentum coordinate (V)
$\mathbf{q}$	generalized position coordinate (V)
$\mathbf{z}$	ionic charge
$\boldsymbol{\alpha}$	polarizability
$\boldsymbol{\varepsilon}$	dielectric constant
$\boldsymbol{\mu}$	dipole moment

Greek capitals:

$\mathit{\Gamma}$	gamma function; surface concentration (XXI)
Δ	increment; a difference function
Π	product
$\mathit{\Pi}$	osmotic pressure
Σ	summation
$\boldsymbol{\Sigma}$	surface area (XXI)
Σ	surface area per mole (XXI)
$\mathit{\Phi}, \mathit{\Psi}$	universal functions (V)
$\mathit{\Omega}$	number of configurations

Greek lower case:

$\alpha, \beta, \gamma, \delta$	constants
α	coefficient of thermal expansion; a fractionation parameter (XX)
β	coefficient of compressibility
γ	activity coefficient
γ	surface tension, free energy of surface formation per unit area; angles (IV, IX)
δ	small increment
δ	solubility parameter, dispersion parameter
ε	intermolecular energy
θ	reduced temperature (T/T_c); polar coordinate (IV)
$\varkappa$	transmission coefficient (XXII)
λ	volume ratio (XX)
μ	coefficient, high polymer equations (XX)
ν	frequency
ξ	a function (VIII); a parameter (XX)
π	3.1416
π	reduced pressure (P/P_c)
σ	area per molecule
τ	thickness of surface layer (XXI); configuration volume
φ	volume fraction
φ	reduced volume (V/V_c)
ϱ	density; radial distribution function
χ	smoothed molecular potential (V, VI)
ω	orientation parameter (IX); solid angle (IX)

Superscripts — processes

E	excess
EL	elastic stretching (XX)
F	fusion
M	mixing
S	sublimation
T	transition
V	vaporization

Superscripts — states

f	free
g	gas
h	holes (V)
i	ideal
l	liquid
r	regular
s	solid
α,β	general
σ	surface
$*$	infinite dilution
$\circ$	standard

Subscripts:

b	normal boiling point (1 atm. pressure
B	Boyle point
c	critical point; cross-links (XX)
e	"equivalent sphere" (XX)
g	gel (XX)
i, j, k	running indices
m	mixture: maximnm; melting point (occasionally as a superscript in Chapter XVIII)
n	number average
p	constant pressure; polymer
r	rate (XXII)
s	sol (XX)
t	transition point
v	constant volume
τ	configurational (V, VI)
$\circ$	solvent
1,2,3	components
$\neq$	activated complex (XXII)

APPENDIX III

Papers by the authors and co-workers pertaining to solubility, referred to in thi volume.

Papers by Joel H. Hildebrand

The Color of Iodine Solutions (with Ben Leon Glascock), *J. Am. Chem. Soc.*, **31**, 26 (1909).

Über die Farbe von Jodlösungen, *Z. physik. Chem.*, **74**, 679 (1910).

The Vapor Pressure of Zinc Amalgams, *Trans. Am. Electrochem. Soc.*, **22**, 319 (1912).

The Relation between the Potential of Liquid Amalgam Cells and the Constitution of the Amalgam, *Trans Am. Electrochem. Soc.*, **22**, 335 (1912).

The Constitution of Certain Liquid Amalgams, *J. Am. Chem. Soc.*, **35**, 501 (1913).

The Vapor Pressure of Silver, Gold and Bismuth Amalgams (with Ermon D. Eastman), *J. Am. Chem. Soc.*, **36**, 2020 (1914).

The Entropy of Vaporization as a Means of Distinguishing Normal Liquids, *J. Am. Chem. Soc.*, **37**, 970 (1915).

The Vapor Pressure of Thallium Amalgams (with Ermon D. Eastman), *J. Am. Chem. Soc.*, **37**, 2452 (1915).

A Study of the Action of Alkali on Certain Zinc Salts by Means of the Hydrogen Electrode (with W. G. Bowers), *J. Am. Chem. Soc.*, **38**, 785 (1916).

Solubility, *J. Am. Chem. Soc.*, **38**, 1452 (1916).

A Study of the System Aniline-Hexane (with Donald B. Keyes), *J. Am. Chem. Soc.*, **39**, 2126 (1917).

The Specific Heats and Heats of Fusion of Triphenylmethane Anthraquinone and Anthracene (with Alice D. Duschak, A. H. Foster and C. W. Beebe), *J. Am. Chem. Soc.*, **39**, 2293 (1917).

Solubility and Internal Pressure *J. Am. Chem. Soc.*, **39**, 2297 (1917).

Solubilities of Anthracene, Anthraquinone, Parabromobenzene, Phenanthrene and Iodine. in Various Solvents (with E. T. Ellefson and C. W. Beebe), *J. Am. Chem. Soc.*, **39**, 2301 (1917).

The Vapor Pressure of Liquid Metals *J. Am. Chem. Soc.*, **40**, 45 (1918).

Solubility. III. Relative Values of Internal Pressures and Their Practical Application, *J. Am. Chem. Soc.*, **41**, 1067 (1919).

The Vapor Pressures of Cadmium, Lead and Tin Amalgams (with A. H. Foster and C. W. Beebe), *J. Am. Chem. Soc.*, **42**, 545 (1920).

Solubility. IV. Solubility Relations of Naphthalene and Iodine in the Various Solvents, Including a Method for Evaluating Solubility Data (with C. A. Jenks), *J. Am. Chem. Soc.*, **42**, 2180 (1920).

Solubility. V. Critical Solution Temperatures of White Phosphorus with Various Liquids (with Theo. F. Buehrer), *J. Am. Chem. Soc.*, **42**, 2213 (1920).

Solubility. VI. Thermodynamic Relation Between Solubility and Internal Pressure *J. Am. Chem. Soc.*, **43**, 500 (1921).

The Surface Tensions and Densities of Liquid Mercury, Cadmium, Zinc, Lead, Tin and Bismuth (by Thorfin R. Hogness), *J. Am. Chem. Soc.*, **43**, 1621 (1921).

Solubility. VII. Solubility Relations of Rhombic Sulfur (with Clarence A. Jenks). *J. Am. Chem. Soc.*, **43**, 2172 (1921).

Theory of Solubility, *Phys. Rev.*, **21**. 46 (1923).

Solubility. VIII. Solubility Relations of Certain Gases (with Nelson W. Taylor), *J. Am. Chem. Soc.*, **45**, 682 (1923).

Solubility. IX. Metallic Solutions (wlth T. R. Hogness and N. W. Taylor), *J. Am. Chem. Soc.*, **45**, 2828 (1923).

The Activities of Zinc, Cadmium, Tin, Lead and Bismuth in their Binary Liquid Mixtures, by N. W. Taylor. *J. Am. Chem. Soc.*, **45**, 2865 (1923).

The Density and Molecular Complexity of Gaseous Hydrogen Fluoride (with Joseph Simons), *J. Am. Chem. Soc.*, **46**, 2183 (1924).

Solubility. X. Solubility Relations of Stannic Iodide (with M. E. Dorfman), *J. Am. Chem. Soc.*, **49**, 729 (1927).

A Quantitative Treatment of Deviations from Raoult's Law, *Proc. Nat. Acad. Sci.*, **13**, 267 (1927).

Osmotic Pressures of Concentrated Solutions, *J. Phys. Chem.*. **32**, 1086 (1928).

Internal Pressure of Pure and Mixed Liquids (with W. Westwater ane H. W. Frantz), *Phys. Rev.*, **31**, 135 (1928).

Solubility. XI. Solubilities of Liquid Stannic Iodide in Several Liquid Paraffins (with M. E. Dice), *J. Am. Chem. Soc.*, **50**, 3023 (1928).

Solubility. XII. Regular Solutions, *J. Am. Chem. Soc.*, **51**, 66 (1929).

The Activities of Molten Alloys of Thallium with Tin and with Lead (with J. N. Sharma, *J. Am. Chem. Soc.*, **51**, 462 (1929).

Intermolecular Forces in Liquids, *Phys. Rev.*, **34**, 984 (1929).

Compressibilities and Thermal Pressure Coefficients of Certain Liquids, *Phys. Rev.*, **34**, 649 (1929).

The Influence on the Ideal Solution Laws of the Distribution of Polarity within the Molecule (with J. M. Carter), *Proc. Nat. Acad. Sci.*, **16**, 285 (1930).

The Vapor Pressure and Critical Temperature of Fluorine (with G. H. Cady), *J. Am. Chem. Soc.*, **52**, 3839 (1930).

A Study of van der Waals Forces Between Tetrahalide Molecules (with J. M. Carter), *J. Am. Chem. Soc.*, **54**, 3592 (1932).

Thermodynamic Properties of Liquid Solutions of Silver Bromide with Alkali Bromides (with E. J. Salstrom), *J. Am. Chem. Soc.*, **54**, 4257 (1932).

The Derivation of Equations for Regular Solutions (with S. E. Wood), *J. Chem. Phys.*, **1**, 817 (1933).

Solubility. XIII. The Solubility of Iodine in Certain Solvents (with G. R. Negishi and L. H. Donally), *J. Am. Chem. Soc.*, **55**, 4793 (1933).

The Liquid State, *Science*, **80**, 125 (1934).

Solubility. XIV. Experimental Tests of a General Equation for Solubility, *J. Am. Chem, Soc.*, **57**, 866 (1935).

Dipole Attraction and Hydrogen Bond Formation in their Relation to Solubility, *Science*, **83**, 21 (1936).

The Distribution of Molecules in a Model Liquid (with W. E. Morrell), *J. Chem. Phys.*, **4**, 224 (1936).

Thermodynamic Aspects of the Theory of Non-Electrolytic Solutions, *Chem. Rev.*, **18**, 315 (1936).

The Heat of Fusion and Vapor Pressure of Stannic Iodide, George R. Negishi, *J. Am. Chem. Soc.*, **58**, 2293 (1936).

Intermolecular Forces in Solutions *Trans. Faraday Soc.*, **33**, 144, (1937).

Solubility. XV. The Solubility of Liquid and Solid Stannic Iodide in Silicon Tetrachloride, (with G. R. Negishi), *J. Am. Chem. Soc.*, **59**, 339 (1937).

The Validity of Raoult's Law for Paraffin Molecules of Very Different Length, *J. Am. Chem. Soc.*, **59**, 794 (1937).

Deviations of Carbon Tetrachloride and Silicon Tetrachloride Solutions from Raoult's Law, by Scott E. Wood, *J. Am. Chem. Soc.*, **59**, 1510 (1937).

A Calorimetric Test of the Solubility Equation for Regular Solutions, by R. D. Vold, *J. Am. Chem. Soc.*, **59**, 1515 (1937).

The Incomplete Solubility of Liquid Iodine in Carbon Tetrachloride, *J. Am. Chem. Soc.*, **59**, 2083 (1937).

Specific Heats and Heat of Fusion of Iodine (with K. J. Frederick), *J. Am. Chem. Soc.*, **60**, 1436 (1938).

Specific Heats and Heat of Fusion of Tellurium Tetrachloride (with K. J. Frederick), *J. Am. Chem. Soc.*, **60**, 2522, (1938).

Liquid Structure and Energy of Vaporization, *J. Chem. Phys.*, **7**, 1 (1939).

Several Solutions of Nonpolar Substances *J. Phys. Chem.*, **43**, 109 (1939).

The Entropy of Solution of Hexane with Hexadecane (with J. W. Sweny), *J. Phys. Chem.*, **43**, 281 (1939).

Liquid Structure and Entropy Vaporization, *J. Chem. Phys.*, **7**, 233 (1939).

Order and Disorder in Pure Liquids and Solutions, *Science*, **90**, 1 (1939).

Specific Heats and Heats of Fusion and Transition of Carbon Tetrabromide, (with K. J. Frederick), *J. Am. Chem. Soc.*, **61**, 1555 (1939).

The Effect of Temperature on the Structure of Mercury, (Robert N. Boyd and Helmut R. R. Wakeham), *J. Chem. Phys.*, **7**, 958 (1939).

The Intermolecular Potential of Mercury, (with H. R. R. Wakeham and R. N. Boyd), *J. Chem. Phys.*, **7**, 1094 (1939).

Color and Bond Character, (with K. S. Pitzer), *J. Am. Chem. Soc.*, **63**, 2472 (1941).

The Heat of Fusion and the Heat Capacities of Solid and Liquid White Phosphorus, (with Frank E. Young), *J. Am. Chem. Soc.*, **64**, 839 (1942).

The Structure of Liquid Mercury, (with J. A. Campbell), *J. Chem. Phys.*, **11**, 330 (1943).

The Structure of Liquid Xenon, (with J. A. Campbell), *J. Chem. Phys.*, **11**, 334 (1943).

The Structure of Liquid Mercury, (with J. A. Campbell), *J. Applied Phys.*, **14**, 465 (1943).

Abstract: The Structure of Liquid Xenon, (with J. A. Campbell), *J. Applied Phys.*, **14**, 632, (1943).

Order and Disorder Among Molecules., Ninth Walker Memorial Lecture, *J. of the Edinburgh University Chemical Society*, Vol. 6. May 1944.

Molecular Forces and Solubility — in SCIENCE IN THE UNIVERSITY, 75th Anniversary of Founding of University of California, 1944.

The Liquid State. Guthrie Lecture for 1944, *Proc. Phys. Soc.*, (London) **56**, 221 (1944).

An Unusual Liquid Interface, (with A. R. Olson) *J. Phys. Coll. Chem.*, **51**, 567 (1947).

The Entropy of Solution of Molecules of Different Size, *J. Chem. Phys.*, **15**, 225 (1947).

Comments on the "Hildebrand Rule", (with T. S. Gilman), *J. Chem. Phys.*, **15**, 229 (1947).

Forces Between Polyatomic Molecules, *Proc. Nat. Acad. of Sci.*, **33**, 201 (1947).

Relative Association of Hydrogen and Deuterium Fluorides in the Liquid State, (with Allen Gee) *J. Am. Chem. Soc.*, **70**, 427 (1948).

Forces Between Tetrahalide Molecules, *J. Chem. Phys.*, **15**, 727 (1947).

Ultraviolet Absorption Bands of Iodine in Aromatic Hydrocarbons (with H. A. Benesi), *J. Am. Chem. Soc.*, **10**, 2832 (1948).

Ammonia as a Solvent — An Example of the Application of Existing Theory, *J. Chem. Ed.* **25**, 74 (1948).

The Solubility Relations of White Phosphorus (with C. Groot) *J. Am. Chem. Soc.*, **70**, 3815 (1948).

Solubility of Iodine in 1,2- and 1,1-Dichloroethanes, *Cis-* and *Trans*-Dichloroethylenes, and Perfluoro-*n*-normal Heptane (with H. A. Benesi), *J. Am. Chem. Soc.*, **70**, 3978 (1948).

Liquid-Liquid Solubility of Perfluoromethylcyclohexane with Benzene, Carbon Tetrachloride, Chlorobenzene, Chloroform and Toluene (with D. R. F. Cochran) *J. Am. Chem. Soc*, **71**, 22 (1949).

A Critique of the Theory of Solubility of Nonelectrolytes, *Chem. Rev.*, **44**, 37 (1949).

Seven Liquid Phases in Equilibrium. *J. Phys. Coll. Chem.*, **53**, 944 (1949).

The Solubility of *n*-Dotriacontane (Dicetyl). (with A. Wachter), *J. Phys. Coll. Chem.*, **53**, 886 (1949),

On an Interpretation of the Solubility of Organic Compounds in Water. *J. Phys. Coll Chem.*, **53**, 973 (1949).

A Spectrophotometric Investigation of the Interaction of Iodine with Aromatic Hydrocarbons (with H. A. Benesi), **71**, 2703 (1949).

The Solubility of Nitrogen in Carbon Disulfide, Benzene, Normal- and Cyclo-hexane and in Three Fluorocarbons (with J. Chr. Gjaldbaek), *J. Am. Chem. Soc.*, **71**, 3147 (1949).

Solubility of Water in Hydrocarbons. *J. Chem. Phys.*, **17**, 1346 (1949).

Factors Determining Solubility among Nonelectrolytes, *Proc. Nat. Acad. Sci.*, **36**, 7 (1950).

Solubility of Iodine in Ethyl Alcohol, Ethyl Ether, Mesitylene, *p*-Xylene, 2,2-Dimethylbutane, Cyclohexane, and Perfluoro-*n*-heptane (with H. A. Benesi and L. M. Mower), *J. Am. Chem. Soc.*, **72**, 1017 (1950).

On Some Partial Molal Volumes of Gases in Solution (with J. Chr. Gjaldbaek), *J. Am. Chem. Soc.*, **72**, 1077 (1950).

Papers by Robert L. Scott

The Thermodynamics of High Polymer Solutions: I. The Free Energy of Mixing of Solvents and Polymers of Heterogeneous Distribution (with Michael Magat). *J. Chem. Phys.*, **13**, 172 (1945).

The Thermodynamics of High Polymer Solutions: II. The Solubility and Fractionation of a Polymer of Heterogeneous Distribution. *J. Chem. Phys.*, **13**, 178 (1945).

The Viscosity-Molecular Weight Relation for Natural Rubber (with Walter C. Carter and Michael Magat), *J. Am. Chem. Soc.*, **68**, 1480, (1946).

Viscosity-Molecular Weight Relations for Various Synthetic Rubbers (with Walter C. Carter and Michael Magat), *J. Am. Chem. Soc.*, **71**, 220 (1949).

The Thermodynamics of High Polymer Solutions: III. The Swelling of Vulcanized Rubbers, (with Michael Magat), *J. Polymer Sci.*, **4**, 555 (1949).

A Criterion for Normal Liquids, *J. Chem., Phys.*, **16**, 256, (1948).

The Thermodynamics of High Polymer Solutions: IV. Phase Equilibria in the Ternary System: Polymer-Liquid 1- Liquid 2, *J. Chem. Phys.*, **17**, 268 (1949).

The Thermodynamics of High Polymer Solutions: V. Phase Equilibria in the Ternary System: Polymer 1- Polymer 2- Solvent, *J. Chem. Phys.*, **17**, 279 (1949).

The Solubility of Fluorocarbons, *J. Am. Chem. Soc.*, **70**, 4090 (1948).

APPENDIX IV

Solutions of Nonelectrolytes—1949*

J. H. Hildebrand and R. L. Scott

* Reprinted by special permission, from Volume I, "Annual Review of Physical Chemistry" (Annual Reviews, Inc., Stanford, California, 1950.)

Introduction. The purpose of the authors in writing the following review has been to give a critical account of the more significant papers bearing upon the theory of solutions which have appeared during the year 1949. It would be impossible, in the space at our disposal, to mention all the contributions pertinent to the general topic without turning this review into a mere set of abstracts such as are already available elsewhere; consequently, we can only apologize upon these grounds for the failure to report on a number of good pieces of work.

Certain topics and types of systems have been the subject of particularly active study during the year and have brought to light points of more than ordinary interest. The reviews which follow have been grouped accordingly.

Iodine solutions. The investigation of iodine solutions has for many years contributed much to the theory of solubility, and has continued during the past year to yield results of considerable significance. Iodine lends itself peculiarly well to this purpose for several reasons: its solutions can be easily and accurately analyzed; its molecular attractive field is very high, giving an enormous range to its solubilities; its molecules have nearly spherical symmetry; and "chemical" effects can readily be differentiated from "physical" effects by departures in color from the violet of iodine vapor.

A general review of the nature of iodine solutions by Kleinberg and Davidson[1] covered the subject into 1948. Late in the same year Benesi and Hildebrand[2] published a paper on the solubility of iodine in 1,2- and 1,1-dichloroethanes, *cis*- and *trans*-dichloroethylenes, and perfluoro-normal-heptane. All these solvents give violet solutions, in spite of the considerable dipole moments of all but the last two, and the temperature dependence of solubility in all cases fits them into the family of "regular solution" curves to which all violet solutions of iodine belong. Since the

1. Kleinberg, J., and Davidson, A. W., *Chem. Revs.*, **42,** 601–609 (1948).
2. Benesi, H. A., and Hildebrand, J. H., *J. Am. Chem. Soc.*, **70,** 3978–3981 (1948).

significance of this is maximum randomness of distribution of I_2 molecules; the entropy of transfer of iodine from pure (supercooled) liquid to a solution in which its mole fraction is x_2 is $\bar{s}_2 - s_2^\circ = -R \ln x_2$. All of these solutions conform reasonably well with the solubility equation for regular solutions,

$$RT \ln(a_2/x_2) = v_2\phi_1^2(\delta_2 - \delta_1)^2, \tag{1}$$

where a_2 denotes the activity of the (solid) iodine referred to pure liquid iodine, v_2 its liquid molal volume (extrapolated), ϕ_1 the volume fraction of the solvent, and δ_2 and δ_1 the "solubility parameters" of iodine and the solvent, respectively, defined as the square root of the energy of vaporization per cc. Although values of x_2 range from 0.000185 in perfluoro-heptane to 0.0782 in 1,2-dibromoethane, they all give, when substituted with the

TABLE I

IODINE SOLUTIONS (25°)

Solvent	μ	v_2	100 x_2	a_2/x_2	δ_1	δ_2
n-C_7F_{16}	0	227	0.0185	1400	5.7	14.2
trans-$C_2H_2Cl_2$	0	77.4	1.417	18.2	9.0	14.5
cis-$C_2H_2Cl_2$	1.89	75.8	1.441	17.1	9.1	14.5
1,1-$C_2H_4Cl_2$	2.07	84.7	1.531	16.9	9.1	14.4
1,2-$C_2H_4Cl_2$	1.18	79.5	2.20	11.7	9.8	14.9
1,2-$C_2H_4Br_2$	0.81	86.6	7.82	3.30	10.4	14.1
I_2		59.0	25.8	1.00		

δ_1-values into the equation, δ_2-values not far from 14.4. Table I gives the figures upon which are based the new conclusions of this paper.

The agreement in the case of perfluoro-heptane is extraordinary in view of the exceedingly small solubility of iodine therein, and offered the first definite evidence that the theory of regular solutions would be able to account for the solubility relations of fluorocarbons remarkable as they are, as described later, p. 454.

Values of dipole moments, μ, in Debye units, are included in Table I, and justify another conclusion drawn in this study, i.e., that although bond moments may contribute to the overall field of force of a molecule, the vector sum of individual polar bonds is not particularly significant, as shown by the agreement between *cis*- and *trans*-dichloroethanes in solvent power for iodine despite their great difference in overall dipole moment.

The same authors[3] sought the reason for the red color of iodine in benzene

3. Benesi, H. A., and Hildebrand, J. H., *J. Am. Chem. Soc.*, **71,** 2703–2707 (1949). See also, *J. Am. Chem. Soc.*, **70,** 2832–2833 (1948).

solution. Since both components are "normal" in the liquid state, the only plausible explanation lay in an acid-base interaction, with benzene as the "electron-donor", and iodine the "electron-acceptor." Such an acid-base interaction had been suggested by Fairbrother[4] as the cause of the dipole moments which he found for the associated complexes despite the zero moments of the component molecules. It was found that the color shifted step-wise from red to brown in benzene, toluene, xylenes, and mesitylene, which is the order of increasing basic strength, but back to violet in trifluoro-methyl benzene, a weaker base than benzene.

Absorption spectra were obtained through the range 270–700 mμ. In the visible region, the absorption peaks shifted only moderately toward the violet in changing solvents in the above order, but all, with the exception of trifluoromethyl benzene, have absorption bands in the ultraviolet with extinction coefficients 7 to 10 times that of the visible band and shifting towards longer wave length in the same order. The two bands overlap strongly in mesitylene.

The absorption of solutions of varying amounts of iodine and benzene in carbon tetrachloride gave the equilibrium constant of a definite 1:1 compound; and the constant obtained with mesitylene corresponded to a much stronger degree of 1:1 solvation. (In a paper in press at this writing, the authors[5a] show that the degree of solvation yielded by these calculations conforms closely to the large excess of solvent power of these aromatics over the regular solution values that would otherwise be expected).

The same paper gives absorption peaks and extinction coefficients for iodine in ether, heptane, carbon tetrachloride, carbon disulfide, 1,1-dichloroethane and acetone. A communication now in press[5b] gives a new and different interpretation of the acetone absorption.

In a paper accepted for publication in the *Journal of the American Chemical Society* Professor R. S. Mulliken[5c] has analyzed the above results from the standpoint of molecular orbital theory.

Bayliss[6] expressed the opinion that the ultraviolet absorption of iodine in benzene represents a shift to longer wavelength of a band of gaseous iodine found in the neighborhood of 165 mμ. Against this assumption is first, the fact that iodine in the "violet" solvents, carbon tetrachloride and *n*-heptane, does not absorb in the region where it should, according to the relation used by Bayliss; and, second, the evidence for a specific 1:1 interaction, instead of the nonspecific one postulated in that relation.

4. Fairbrother, F., *Nature*, **160,** 87 (1947); *J. Chem. Soc.*, 1051–1056 (1948).
5a Hildebrand, J. H., Benesi, H. A., and Mower, L. M., *J. Am. Chem. Soc.*, **72,** 1017–1020 (1950).
5b Benesi, H. A., and Hildebrand, J. H., *J. Am. Chem. Soc.*, **72,** 2273–2274 (1950).
5c Mulliken, R. S., *J. Am. Chem. Soc.*, **72,** 600–608 (1950).
6. Bayliss, N. S., *Nature*, **163,** 764 (1949).

Two other recent investigations add convincing evidence of the basic nature of aromatic hydrocarbons increasing in the above order. Andrews and Keefer[7] measured the solubility of nine aromatic hydrocarbons in aqueous silver nitrate of varying concentrations, and reported equilibrium constants for the formation of $AgAr^+$ and some Ag_2Ar^{++}. The value of an overall equilibrium constant, K, expressing "total argentation" varies a little with concentration of Ag^+, which is taken to indicate some Ag_2Ar^{++} along with $AgAr^+$. Their values of K for 0.2 M-Ag^+ are as follows:

Benzene	2.46	Naphthalene	3.58
Toluene	3.10	Diphenyl methane	4.20
p-Xylene	2.86	Biphenyl	4.80
o-Xylene	2.96	Phenanthrene	5.00
m-Xylene	3.28		

Brown and Brady[8] determined the Henry's law constant for HCl at −78.51° dissolved in a mixture of 10 moles of toluene with 1 mole of aromatic hydrocarbon, with the following results.

Trifluoromethyl benzene	332	*o*-Xylene	286
Chlorobenzene	318	*m*-Xylene	278
Benzene	308	Pseudocumene	272
Toluene	299	Hemimellitine	265
p-Xylene	294	Mesitylene	254

These independent evidences concerning the basic nature of aromatics are significant not only for solubility theory as indicating when to expect deviations of their solutions from regular solution behavior, but also for their chemical behavior, since their combinations with electron acceptors can function as activated complexes. Benesi and Hildebrand noticed the slow disappearance of color in solutions of iodine in mesitylene.

Molecules of different size. It is now well known that only in very special cases (such as a lining up of linear molecules in solution[9]) can solutions of molecules of different size show an ideal entropy of mixing. This has been emphasized by the striking negative deviations from Raoult's law found in the extensive studies of high polymer solutions during the past decade. In 1944 Guggenheim[10] proposed a general theory for the entropy, heat, and free energy of mixing for mixtures of molecules containing different numbers of chain segments of equal size, each occupying a site in a quasi-lattice. In 1946 Brønsted and Koefoed[11] published very accurate

7. Andrews, L. J., and Keefer, R. M., *J. Am. Chem. Soc.*, **71**, 3644–3647 (1944).
8. Brown, H. C., and Brady, J., *J. Am. Chem. Soc.*, **71**, 3573 (1949).
9. Hildebrand, J. H., *J. Am. Chem. Soc.*, **59**, 794–798 (1937).
10. Guggenheim, E. A., *Proc. Roy. Soc. (London)*, **A183**, 203–212, 213–227 (1944).
11. Brønsted, J. N., and Koefoed, J., *Kgl. Danske Videnskab. Selskab, Mat.-fys. Medd.*, **22**, 17 (1946).

vapor pressure measurements on the systems *n*-hexane-*n*-hexadecane, *n*-heptane-*n*-hexadecane, and *n*-hexane-*n*-dodecane, finding that the free energy of mixing deviated only slightly in a negative direction from the laws of ideal solutions. Since measurements were made at only one temperature, no information was obtained on the separate contributions of the heat and entropy.

Van der Waals and Hermans[12] have now measured the heat of mixing of *n*-heptane with *n*-hexadecane, and find a small but significant positive heat of mixing, virtually symmetrical in the mole fraction. If this ΔH is substracted from the ΔF measured by Brønsted and Koefoed, the resulting ΔS is in good agreement with Guggenheim's formula if a reasonable coordination number ($z = 8$) is chosen and if the number of segments is counted by choosing CH_3 and C_2H_4 groups as fundamental units.

Tompa[13] has recently extended Guggenheim's theory to allow for the energy differences between end groups and middle groups, but according to van der Waals and Hermans, his more complicated formula gives little improvement, since it differs from that of Guggenheim by less than 1 per cent when the heat of mixing is as small as that found for heptane-hexadecane.

Hildebrand and Wachter[14] have recently published data on solutions of *n*-dotriacontane (dicetyl) where the size of the hydrocarbon molecule is even greater than in the above work.

Scatchard[15] and Hildebrand[16] have both recently reviewed the problem of molecules of different size and the former has suggested that in using the "free volume" formula

$$\Delta S^{M} = R\left[x_1 \ln\left(\frac{x_1 v_1^f}{x_1 v_1^f + x_2 v_2^f}\right) + x_2 \ln\left(\frac{x_2 v_2^f}{x_1 v_1^f + x_2 v_2^f}\right)\right] \tag{2}$$

a reasonable assumption would be to take the free volumes v^f as proportional to the surface of the molecules, rather than to their volumes. This leads directly to the Guggenheim formula, but for long chain polymers, the ratio of surface to volume is nearly independent of chain length, leading to the Flory-Huggins equations in the limit.

An entirely different problem, that of mixing spheres of different size, is considered by Hudson[17], but only from the standpoint of packing and density. Calculations of entropy and energy relationships and the finding

12. van der Waals, J. H., and Hermans, J. J., *Rec. trav. chim.*, **68,** 181–184 (1949).
13. Tompa, H., *Trans. Faraday Soc.*, **45,** 101–109 (1949).
14. Hildebrand, J. H., and Wachter, A., *J. Phys. and Colloid Chem.*, **53,** 886–890 (1949).
15. Scatchard, G., *Chem. Revs.*, **44,** 7–35 (1949).
16. Hildebrand, J. H., *Chem. Revs.*, **44,** 37–45 (1949).
17. Hudson, D. R., *J. Appl. Phys.*, **20,** 154–162 (1949).

of suitable experimental systems for study of this fascinating problem remain for the future.

Meares[18] has measured the volume changes on mixing esters, and has interpreted the contraction observed in some cases as being due to geometrical effects; when there is a large difference in molecular sizes of the components, the mixture may be able to pack more economically than either pure component.

Fluorocarbons. The extraordinary solvent properties of fluorocarbons have come to light only during recent years[19], following the preparation of a number of them during the late war. In view of the fact that their vapor pressures do not differ greatly from those of the corresponding hydrocarbons, it was at first quite astonishing to discover the vast differences between the solvent powers of a hydrocarbon and those of its fluorocarbon analog.[20] (The senior author is indebted to Professor George H. Cady for first calling his attention to this fact.) These differences are so great as to raise the fear that they might overstrain the theory that had so far been sufficient to cope rather well with regular solutions. However, the figure obtained for the solubility of iodine in perfluoro-normal heptane, referred to in a previous section (p. 450) agreed with the ordinary solubility equation so well, despite its small magnitude, mole fraction 0.000182 at 25° compared with 0.00679 for iodine in *n*-heptane, as to give reasonable assurance that the theory would suffice to cope with all fluorocarbon solutions. Evidence to this effect was added by Hildebrand and Cochran[21] who obtained the liquid-liquid solubility curves shown in Figure 1 for perfluoromethylcyclohexane with benzene, carbon tetrachloride, chlorobenzene, chloroform and toluene, with critical compositions all close to 0.5 expressed as *volume* fraction, and critical temperatures which rise with increasing δ-values for the other liquid, except for the slight reversal between benzene and toluene as previously found for solutions of stannic iodide[22] and sulfur[23]. These authors made a rough, provisional test of the approximate equation relating T_c to the molal volumes and δ-values of the components,

$$4\,RT_c = (\mathrm{v}_1 + \mathrm{v}_2)(\delta_1 - \delta_2)^2 \qquad (3)$$

Calculating δ_1 for the fluorocarbon from T_c gave values close to 6.0, in agreement with the value that had been assigned by Scott[20] in his survey

18. Meares, P., *Trans. Faraday Soc.*, **45,** 966–974, 1066–1079 (1949).
19. Various authors, *Ind. Eng. Chem.*, **39,** 310–384 (1947).
20. Scott, R. L., *J. Am. Chem Soc.*, **70,** 4090–4093 (1948).
21. Hildebrand, J. H., and Cochran, D. R. F., *J. Am. Chem. Soc.*, **71,** 22 (1949).
22. Dorfman, M. E., and Hildebrand, J. H., *J. Am. Chem. Soc.*, **49,** 729–737 (1927).
23. Hildebrand, J. H., and Jenks, C. W., *J. Am. Chem. Soc.*, **43,** 2172–2177 (1921).

of δ-values of the fluorocarbons. No attempt was made to correct for the variation of δ_1 and δ_2 with temperature on the assumption that $\delta_2 - \delta_1$ would not vary greatly—an assumption to be tested later. Allowing for this uncertainty, the treatment is a good approximation. In a more refined treatment, the departures from Raoult's law entropy caused by disparity in volumes discussed in the previous section will have to be considered.

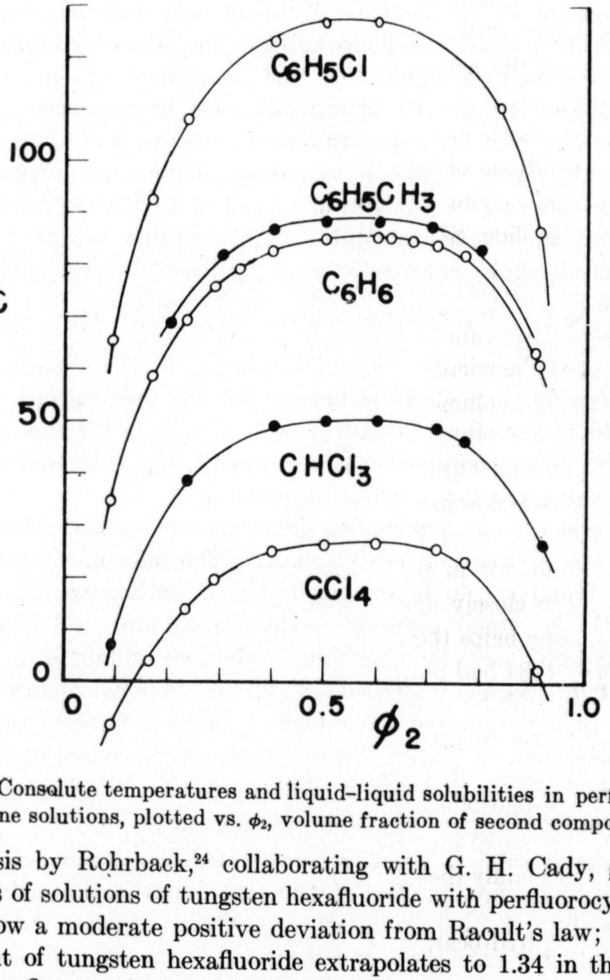

Fig. 1 Consolute temperatures and liquid–liquid solubilities in perfluoromethylcyclohexane solutions, plotted vs. ϕ_2, volume fraction of second component.

A thesis by Rohrback,[24] collaborating with G. H. Cady, gives vapor pressures of solutions of tungsten hexafluoride with perfluorocyclopentane. They show a moderate positive deviation from Raoult's law; the activity coefficient of tungsten hexafluoride extrapolates to 1.34 in the limit and that of perfluorocyclopentane to 1.68. These are less than the values calculated from the internal pressures alone by Equation (1), but agree well with Equation (4),

24. Rohrback, G. H., Univ. of Wash., 1949. To be published in the *J. Am. Chem. Soc.*

$$\ln a_2 = \ln \phi_2 + \phi_1 \left(1 - \frac{v_2}{v_1}\right) + \frac{v_2\phi_1^2(\delta_2 - \delta_1)^2}{RT} \quad (4)$$

which takes account of the disparity in molal volumes, 179.6 cc. for C_5F_{10} and 88.0 cc. for WF_6. Their δ-values are given as 5.77 and 7.96, respectively.

Gjaldbaek and Hildebrand[25] published figures for the solubility of nitrogen in carbon disulfide, benzene, normal and cyclo-hexane, perfluoronormal heptane, perfluoromethylcyclohexane, and perfluorodimethylcyclohexane. On account of the small size of the nitrogen molecule, particularly as compared with the three fluorocarbons, the Flory-Huggins entropy correction becomes very significant. The assignment of values for the molal volume and the activity of nitrogen must be somewhat arbitrary, but it was possible to make a semi-empirical adjustment of the parameters in Equation (4) which enables it to reproduce the experimental results fairly well for solutions of nitrogen in a total of 12 solvents, with values of its mole fraction varying from 40.1×10^{-4} in perfluoroheptane to 2.23×10^{-4} in carbon disulfide. Since $x_1 \gg x_2$, Equation (4) can be simplified to

$$-\log x_2 = -\log a_2 + \log(\bar{v}_2/v_1) + 0.434(1 - \bar{v}_2/v_1) + \bar{v}_2(\delta_1 - \delta_2)^2/4.575\,T$$

The authors used the values $-\log a_2 = 2.80$, $\bar{v}_2 = 53$ cc., $\delta_2 = 5.2$. The volume entropy is particularly significant for the fluorocarbon solutions because of the large volume disparity; $v_1/v_2 = 4.28$ in the case of fluoroheptane. (The paper contained one minor error, the measured values of $-\log x_2$ for C_7F_{16} and C_8F_{18} were transposed).

In a paper which is now in press,[25a] a similar picture is reported for chlorine in fluorocarbons and several other solvents. The maximum solubility in that case is found not in fluorocarbons but in carbon tetrachloride, in harmony with the closely agreeing δ-value for chlorine, but here, again, the volume entropy helps the agreement in the case of fluorocarbons.

Hildebrand in 1934 had published a picture of six liquid phases in stable equilibrium. In 1949[26] he took advantage of the low solubility parameters of the fluorocarbons to extend the layers to seven, consisting, in order of increasing density, of heptane, aniline, water, "perfluorokerosene" (ca. $C_{12}F_{26}$), white phosphorus, gallium and mercury.

The remarkably small internal pressures or solubility parameters of the fluorocarbons are mainly the effect of their exceedingly large molal volumes. The polarizability, α, of a fluorocarbon is slightly greater than that of the corresponding hydrocarbon, and therefore, in the light of the London

25. Gjaldbaek, J. Chr., and Hildebrand, J. H., *J. Am. Chem. Soc.*, **71,** 3147–3150 (1949).
25a Gjaldbaek J. Chr., and Hildebrand, J. H., *J. Am. Chem. Soc.*, **72,** 609–611 (1950).
26. Hildebrand, J. H., *J. Phys. Coll. Chem.*, **53,** 944–967 (1949).

formula, the intermolecular potential energy, $\epsilon = \frac{3}{4} \cdot \frac{\alpha^2 h\nu_0}{r^6}$, between a pair of fluorocarbon molecules is probably a little greater *at the same separation* as that between a pair of their hydrocarbon homologs, but the latter are so much smaller, and can approach so much more closely, that their pair potentials may be greater at the equilibrium distance. Actually the potential energies *per mole* (i.e. molar energies of vaporization) for a hydrocarbon and the corresponding fluorocarbon are not very different; the δ's, however, are derived from the energies per unit volume and these differ greatly because of the difference in size.

Clustering and critical phenomena in binary solutions. Recent studies, both experimental and theoretical, have reopened the entire question of critical phenomena in gases and in the entirely analogous case of binary solutions, and in doing so, have cast serious doubt upon the validity of even the qualitative aspects of the classical treatments by van der Waals and van Laar.

The great triumph of the van der Waals equation of state was its representation of pressure-volume isotherms by a single analytic function applicable to both the liquid and vapor phase. At the critical point, the first and second derivatives of the pressure with respect to the volume vanished, permitting the parameters of the equation of state to be related to the critical constants. Below the critical temperature two distinct phases must appear, and according to van der Waals theory the coexistence curve giving the molal volumes of the phases in equilibrium must have a roughly parabolic shape in the region of the critical temperature. The densities of the coexistent phases must be related in a similar fashion:

$$\frac{T_c - T}{T_c} = k\left(\frac{\rho^l - \rho^g}{\rho_c}\right)^2 \qquad (5)$$

where ρ^l, ρ^g, and ρ_c are the densities of the liquid, gas, and critical phases respectively.

While the van der Waals equation is now known to be only a crude approximation, more nearly satisfactory analytical expressions involve the same conditions for the critical point and result in a similar rounded parabolic coexistence curve. In fact, it appears that any simple analytic function used to describe both phases simultaneously must lead[27] to an expression similar to Equation 5.

Whether it is, in fact, necessary to represent the pressure by a single function below the critical point is not known. The portion of the van der

27. Fowler, R. H., and Guggenheim, E. A., "Statistical Thermodynamics" (Cambridge, 1939), pp. 316–318.

Waals isotherm sometimes labelled as "unstable" has no precise thermodynamic significance, and its status in statistical mechanics, if any, is obscure.

The extensive theoretical studies of condensation phenomena by Mayer and coworkers[28], starting in 1937, have cast doubt upon this previously accepted picture. In their view, at any particular temperature and pressure, the vapor phase consists of single molecules, double molecules, triplets, quadruplets, and higher clusters, all in statistical equilibrium. Increasing the pressure shifts this equilibrium in the direction of the larger clusters until, if the system is below its critical temperature, the entire assembly becomes unstable with respect to a single large cluster, i.e., the liquid phase. While this formulation is incapable of yielding any useful information about the condensed phase, its authors believe that their description is completely rigorous up to the point of condensation. Two different unique temperatures appear, a higher temperature, which they call T_c, at which $(\partial P/\partial V)_T$ and $(\partial^2 P/\partial V^2)_T$ vanish, and a lower temperature T_m at which the meniscus disappears (corresponding to zero surface tension) and above which no segregation into two phases occurs; at T_m, the coexistence curve has a truncated flat top. Between T_c and T_m is a finite region in which the P-V isotherms are flat, corresponding to a situation where a small change in the volume has no effect upon the distribution of clusters of different sizes; i.e., upon the free energy of the system. Unlike the two-phase region below T_c, however, the isotherm is a smooth curve with no discontinuities in $(\partial P/\partial V)_T$.

While Maass and coworkers[29] believe that they have observed such an effect in their studies on ethylene, the exact nature of critical phenomena is still subject to dispute. Rice,[30] in a similar treatment of clustering phenomena, concludes that above T_m, $(\partial P/\partial V)_T$ may be small, but never zero, although his formulation also indicates a flat top for the coexistence curve.

The analogy between vapor-liquid equilibria in one-component systems and liquid-liquid miscibility is extremely close. The concentration (mole fraction x) replaces the density ρ, and activity a (or partial molal free energy), the pressure P. The classical treatment of liquid-liquid solubility first developed by van Laar[31] and placed on a firmer physical foundation by Hildebrand[32] and by Scatchard[33] utilizes an activity function analogous

28. Mayer, J. E., and Harrison, S. F., *J. Chem. Phys.*, **6**, 87–100, 101–104 (1938).
29. McIntosh, R. L., Dacey, J. R., and Maass, O., *Can. J. Research*, **B17**, 206–213, 241–250 (1939).
30. Rice, O. K., *J. Chem. Phys.*, **15**, 314–332 (1947).
31. van Laar, J. J., *Z. physik. Chem.*, **72**, 723–751 (1910); **83**, 599–608 (1913).
32. Hildebrand, J. H., *Proc. Nat. Acad. Sci.*, **13**, 267 (1927).
33. Scatchard, G., *Chem. Revs.*, **8**, 321–333 (1931).

to van der Waals P-V function and calculates critical solution temperatures from the conditions that da/dx and d^2a/dx^2 simultaneously vanish. The coexistence curves are roughly parabolic and the typical analytical behavior is illustrated schematically by Figure 2.

The statistical model from which the regular solution equations[32, 33] were deduced envisages solutions in which thermal motion is sufficient to

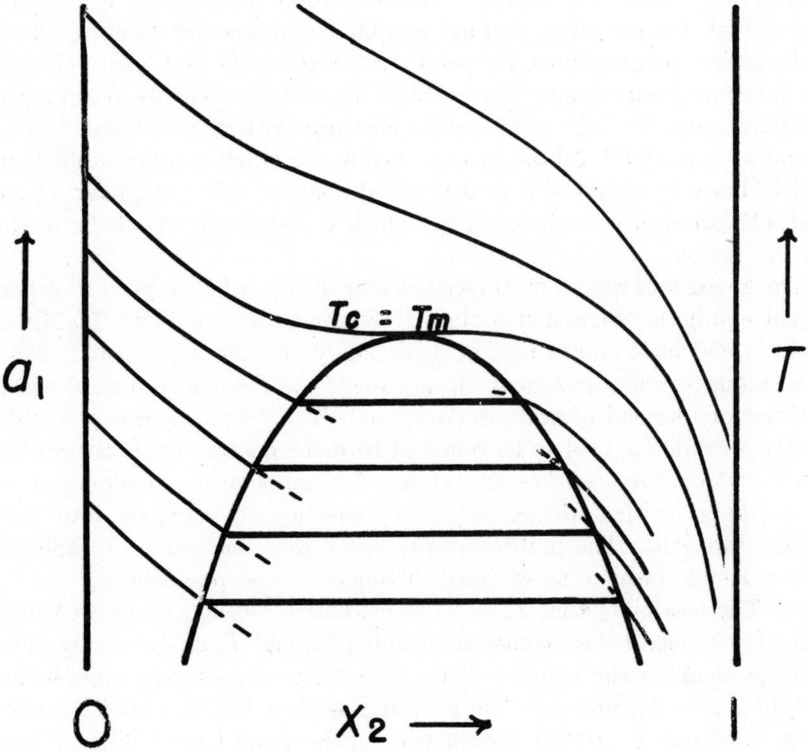

Fig. 2

produce a completely random distribution of solvent and solute molecules. Even though the interaction between different kinds of molecules is assumed to be different in order to account for non-zero heats of mixing, the tendency of these energy differences to cause segregation of the solution into clusters of like molecules is ignored. This leads to an apparent contradiction, since this clustering tendency must be the driving force which results in ultimate gross separation into two phases.

Two questions then are paramount: (a) To what extent does the undisputed tendency to segregate into clusters invalidate the theory of regular solutions, especially in the critical region? (b) What is the precise character of the coexistence curve and the activity curves in the critical region?

The first question has already been partially answered. Guggenheim[34], Rushbrooke[35], and Kirkwood[36] have shown that the preferential pairing of like molecules introduces only small quantitative differences above the critical temperature, while at temperatures well below the critical temperature, phase separation occurs before the correction terms for preferential sorting become appreciable. This conclusion is physically reasonable, for at high temperatures thermal motion minimizes the ordering effect, while at low temperatures, the solutions are so dilute that solute clusters are inherently improbable. The problem has recently been discussed again by Parlin and Eyring[37] with results identical with those of the "quasi-chemical" theory[34,35]. All the treatments obtain a single analytical function, which, however complex, is continuous throughout the two phase region, and all lead to a coexistence curve which is necessarily parabolic in the critical region.

The anomalous results of Mayer's cluster theory, when applied to vapor-liquid equilibria, suggested a similar treatment for solutions. McMillan and Mayer[38] have shown that in their theory of multicomponent systems two unique temperatures must appear. One, T_c, is the temperature at which the first and second derivatives da/dx and d^2a/dx^2 simultaneously vanish. At the second, T_m, (not to be confused with the melting temperature) the interfacial tension vanishes and above this temperature (assuming it to be an *upper* critical temperature) no tendency to segregate into bulk phases can exist. The mathematical theory does not relate T_c and T_m in any simple fashion, so we must distinguish three possibilities:

(a) The possibility that $T_m = T_c$ is not entirely excluded but McMillan and Mayer regard their equations defining T_m and T_c as essentially independent, making the identity of the two temperatures very improbable. Should $T_m = T_c$, however, the resulting activity curves would resemble those in Figure 2, and the coexistence curves would have a rounded top.

(b) By analogy with the earlier work on one-component systems, the most reasonable assumption appeared to be that $T_c > T_m$, leaving a range of temperatures in which the activity curves pass through a flat portion. In this region, as in the vapor-liquid case, there is no driving tendency to make one distribution of clusters of like and unlike molecules more prob-

34. Guggenheim, E. A., *Proc. Roy. Soc.* (*London*), **A148,** 304–312 (1935).
35. Rushbrooke, G. S., *Proc. Roy. Soc.* (*London*), **A166,** 296–315 (1938).
36. Kirkwood, J. G., *J. Phys. Chem.*, **43,** 97–107 (1939).
37. Parlin, R. B., and Eyring, H., *Chem. Revs.*, **44,** 47–58 (1949).
38. McMillan, W. G. Jr., and Mayer, J. E., *J. Chem. Phys.*, **13,** 276–305 (1945).

able than others. This "derby hat" picture is shown in Figure 3; the coexistence curve has a flat top.

(c) Conceivably, T_c might be below T_m. In this case, the lower critical temperature T_c would have no physical reality, and at the limit of phase separation, T_m, d^2a/dx^2 would vanish, but not da/dx. The coexistence

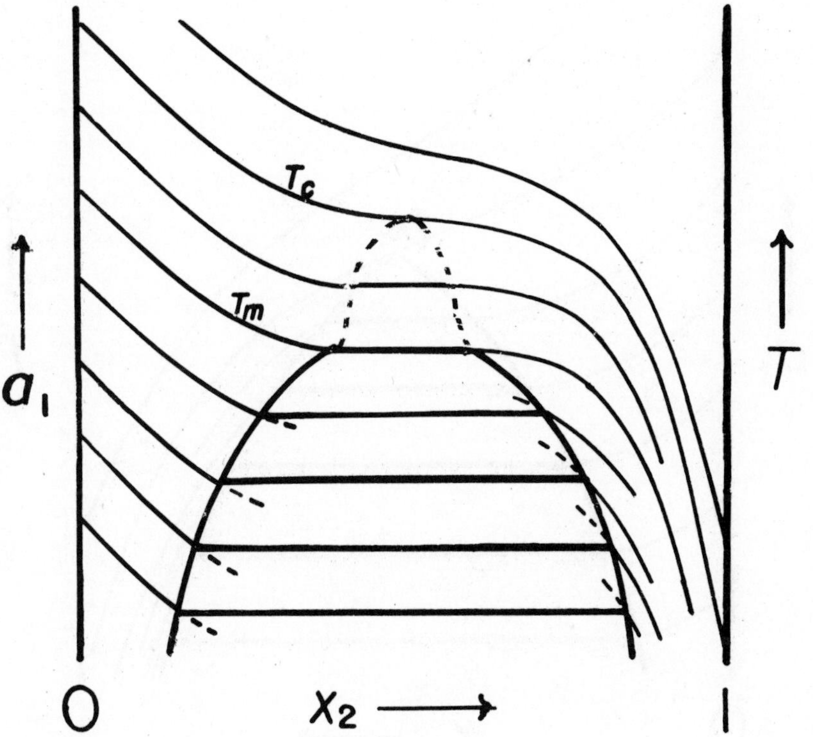

Fig. 3

curves would exhibit a sharp peak (Figure 4); since there is no experimental evidence remotely suggesting such a situation, it has been almost universally discarded.

Rice[39] has recently reviewed the various theories and compared them with the rather fragmentary experimental information so far available. By developing a cluster theory analogous to his earlier treatment of the vapor-liquid case, Rice concludes that a horizontal portion of the coexistence curve is probable at T_m; above this temperature, however,

39. Rice, O. K., *Chem. Revs.*, **44**, 69–92 (1949).

the activity curves must show a finite, although possibly very small, slope at all concentrations. Such a situation is shown schematically in Figure 5.

It is impossible to prove experimentally that there is an absolutely horizontal portion to any curve, as it is equally impossible to exclude the possibility of a small horizontal section. Rice believes, however, that both

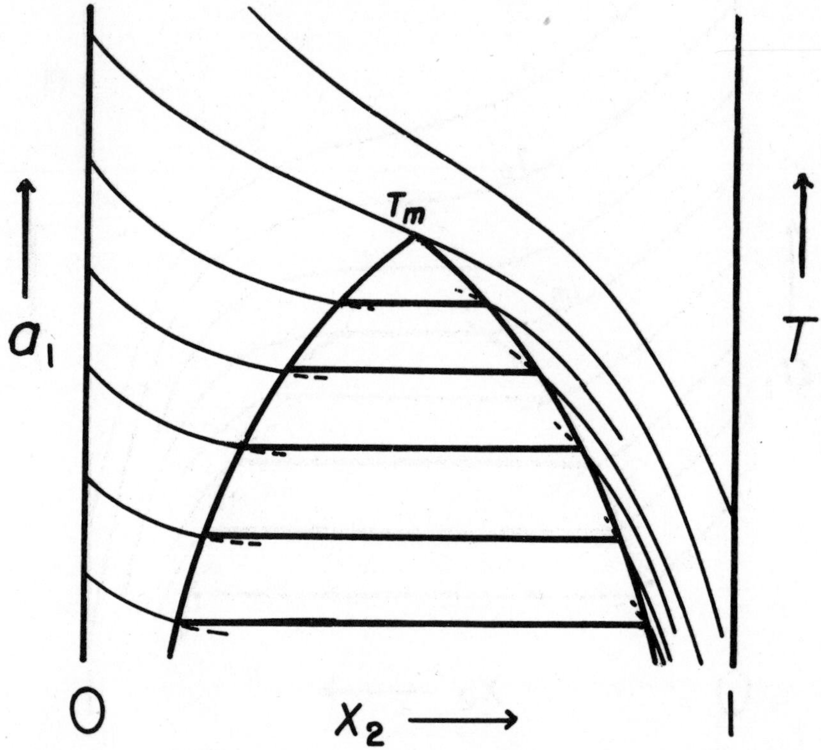

Fig. 4

cases exist, citing the systems phenol-water and acetic anhydride-cyclohexane as examples of a flat top and acetic anhydride-carbon disulfide as an example of a rounded top. He disputes, however, the conclusion which Roberts and Mayer[40] have drawn from their measurements on the triethylamine-water system, namely, that below the lower critical temperature, about 18°, there is a region of constant activity in an inverted "derby hat" extending perhaps to 0°C.

40. Roberts, L. D., and Mayer, J. E., *J. Chem. Phys.*, **9**, 852–858 (1941).

Measurement of light scattering is a highly sensitive method for studying critical phenomena because of the characteristic opalescence resulting from the formation of large clusters; at the point of incipient formation of two phases, the light scattering becomes infinite. Zimm[41] has used this method in a careful study of the system perfluoromethylcyclohexane-

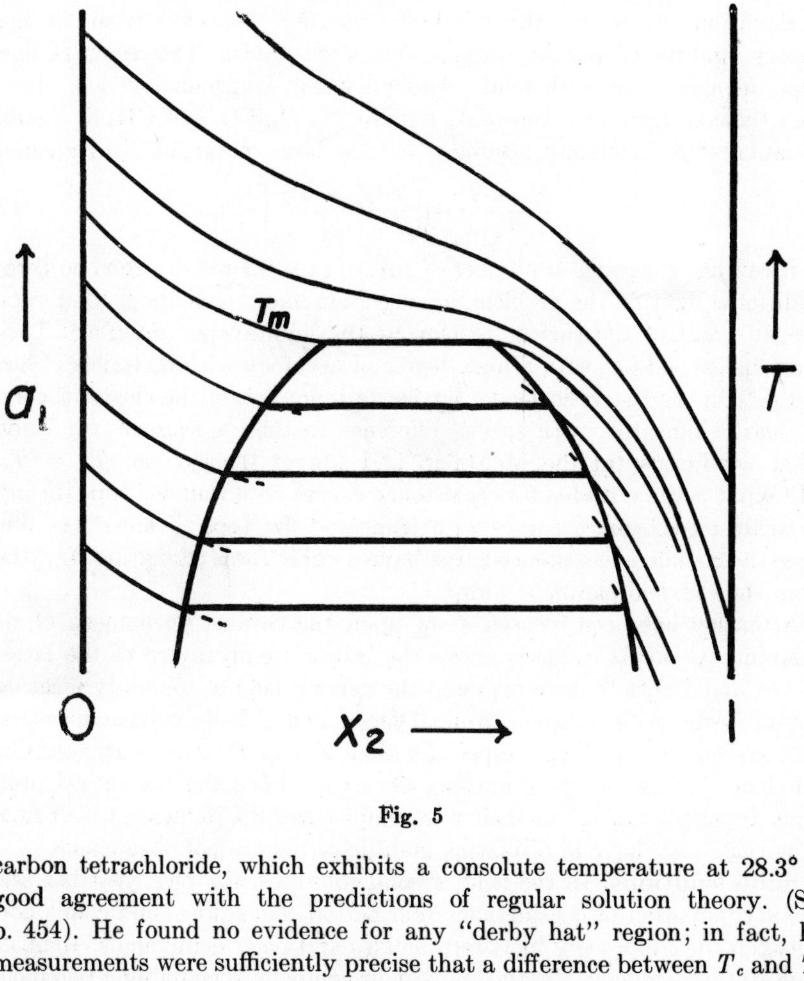

Fig. 5

carbon tetrachloride, which exhibits a consolute temperature at 28.3° in good agreement with the predictions of regular solution theory. (See p. 454). He found no evidence for any "derby hat" region; in fact, his measurements were sufficiently precise that a difference between T_c and T_m of greater than 0.01° is excluded. The coexistence curve in the critical region is apparently not flat, but rounded, and can be well represented

41. Zimm, B. H., American Chemical Society Meeting, Atlantic City, September, 1949 (to be published).

by an equation of the form:

$$\frac{T_c - T}{T_c} = k\left(\frac{\phi' - \phi''}{\phi_c}\right)^3 \tag{6}$$

where ϕ' and ϕ'' are the volume fractions of one component in the two conjugate phases at temperature T, and ϕ_c is the critical volume fraction at T_c.

Equation (6) is not the parabolic equation expected from classical theory, and no satisfactory explanation is yet known. The result is, however, in agreement with many data on gases; Guggenheim[42] has shown that the conjugate densities of A, Kr, Xe, N_2, O_2, CO, and CH_4 fit a cubic formula with surprising accuracy over a large range of temperatures:

$$\frac{T_c - T}{T_c} = \left[\frac{2}{7}\frac{(\rho^l - \rho^g)}{\rho_c}\right]^3 \tag{7}$$

Rice[39] has suggested a number of future experiments designed to throw additional light on the problem, among them measurements of total vapor pressure and of the surface tension at the liquid-vapor interface. These must be carried out with a high degree of accuracy with materials of high purity. On the theoretical side, further examination of the cluster theories is clearly indicated, with special reference to these questions: (a) Under what conditions (in the McMillan and Mayer theory) can $T_c = T_m$? (b) What is the criterion for coexistence curves with rounded tops (if any) as against coexistence curves with truncated flat tops (if any)? (c) Why does the rounded coexistence curve have a cubic form (Equation 6) rather than the classical parabolic form?

Attention has been focused anew upon the curious phenomena of the solubility of solids in gases above the critical temperature of the latter. Booth and Bidwell[43] have reviewed the general field of solubility measurements in the critical region, while Diepen and Scheffer[44] have measured new systems of this type, especially that of naphthalene in supercritical ethylene. Neither of these authors have considered the theoretical problems discussed above, but their work emphasizes the influence which small impurities may have in displacing and distorting critical phenomena.

Solid solutions. In the field of solid solutions, the past year has seen the accumulation of considerable information concerning solid compounds between the supposedly inert tetrahalides and polar compounds. Kennard and McCusker[45] have observed molecular compounds containing two moles of carbon tetrachloride to one of pyridine or dioxane, while Sisler and co-

42. Guggenheim, E. A., *J. Chem. Phys.*, **13**, 253–261 (1945).
43. Booth, H. S., and Bidwell, R. M., *Chem. Revs.*, **44**, 477–513 (1949).
44. Diepen, G. A. M., and Scheffer, F. E. C., *J. Am. Chem. Soc.*, **70**, 4081–4085, 4085–4089 (1948).
45. Kennard, S. M. S., and McCusker, P. A., *J. Am. Chem. Soc.*, **70**, 3375–3377 (1948).

workers[46] have found 1,1 compounds between carbon tetrachloride and methyl *m*-cresyl ether and between silicon tetrachloride and arsenic trichloride; stannic chloride forms many addition compounds. The results for $SnCl_4$ are in agreement with its acidic character, but the reason for the compounds with CCl_4 and $SiCl_4$, however, remains to be explained.

Forward, Bowden and Jones[47] have filled in the gaps in Pascal's study[48] of solid solutions between the triphenyl compounds of N, P, As, Sb, and Bi, including triphenylmethane as well. Of the fifteen systems, four (ϕ_3N-ϕ_3P, ϕ_3P-ϕ_3Sb, ϕ_3As-ϕ_3Sb, and ϕ_3As-ϕ_3CH) show complete miscibility in the solid phase (Type III); two others (ϕ_3P$-$$\phi_3$As and ϕ_3Sb$-$$\phi_3$Bi) show peritectic (Type IV) curves; the remaining nine are all of the eutectic type (Type V). There was partial solubility in all the above cases, but no solid solutions at all were observed between tetraphenyl tin and any of the triphenyls.

The ability to form solid solutions is common to all hydrocarbons having low heats and entropies of fusion since these are indicative of rotation in the solid phase. Further evidence of this was provided by Evans, Greenlee, Derfer and Boord[49], who found that 1,1 dimethylcyclohexane formed solid solutions with *cis*- and *trans*-1,2-dimethylcyclohexane, *trans*-1,4-dimethylcyclohexane, cyclohexane, and 2,2,3-trimethylbutane, but not with *n*-heptane or *n*-butyl cyclohexane.

Metallic solutions were discussed extensively at a general discussion on "The Physical Chemistry of Process Metallurgy" held by the Faraday Society in September, 1948. Of particular importance was Chipman's detailed review of activities in liquid metallic solutions[50]. He summarized the wide variety of methods by which thermodynamic properties of such solutions can be measured: by vapor pressures, by electromotive force measurements, from phase diagrams, from distribution equilibrium, and from chemical equilibrium. Most of these methods are applicable to ordinary nonelectrolyte systems; the use of phase diagrams for such calculations deserves more widespread attention. In this connection, it might be noted that Chipman has coined the term "semi-regular solution" for those solutions which conform to the equations for regular solutions over part, but not all, of the concentration range. Since one of us is responsible for the introduction of the concept of "regular solutions" for solutions in which thermal motion leads to a random distribution of molecules and an

46. Sisler, H. H., Wilson, W. J., Gibbons, B. J., Batey, H. H., Pfahler, B., and Mattair, R., *J. Am. Chem. Soc.*, **70,** 3818–3821, 3821–3824, 3825–3827 (1948).
47. Forward, M. V., Bowden, S. T., and Jones, W. J., *J. Chem. Soc.*, **1949,** S 121–126.
48. Pascal, P., *Bull Soc. Chim.* **[4] 11,** 595–602 (1912).
49. Evans, G. L., Greenlee, K. W., Derfer, J. M., and Boord, G. E., *J. Am. Chem. Soc.*, **71,** 361–362 (1949).
50. Chipman, J., *Discussions Faraday Soc.*, **1948,** No. 4, 23–49.

ideal entropy of mixing, we feel justified in stating our general agreement with the objections to this term expressed by Guggenheim and by Kleppa,[51] especially since it refers to no physical model. The latter has proposed a more useful measure of deviations from regular solutions, an "entropy coefficient" relating the observed and ideal partial molal entropies in a way entirely analogous to that in which the "activity coefficient" relates the observed and ideal partial molal free energies. We regret, however, the choice of "entropy mol fraction" to name the entropy analog of activity.

Other studies on liquid metal systems include those of Lumsden[52] on Pb-Zn, Liebhafsky[53] on Al-Hg, Campbell, Wood and Skinner[54] on Fe-Sn and Kleppa[55] on Pb-Au.

Miscellaneous. (1) It has been a common observation that the free energy of mixing calculated from various statistical mechanical models (such as the "quasi-chemical" theory) is almost invariably in better agreement with experimental results than is the heat or the entropy compared separately. Guggenheim[56] now suggests that the quasi-chemical treatment may be improved by considering the interaction parameter w which appears in that formulation as a local free energy rather than as a pure energy factor; this permits w to be temperature-dependent. This interpretation, however, does not exclude the possibility of other explanations, such as volume changes which introduce a difference between ΔE and ΔH.

Wall and Stent[57] have extended the former's theory of vapor pressures based upon the van der Waals' equation of state to include the properties of binary solutions, and discuss deviations from Raoult's law, constant-boiling mixtures, and partial miscibility in terms of the parameters a and b for the pure substances. These qualitative conclusions can be useful, as van Laar pointed out forty years ago, but numerical results should not be taken too seriously. In particular, equality of the critical pressures of the two components is a totally unsatisfactory criterion for ideal behavior in liquid solutions*.

(2) In an extensive article, Scatchard[58] has reviewed various methods of representing deviations from ideal solutions and the various factors which

51. Guggenheim, E. A., and Kleppa, O. J., *Discussions Faraday Soc.*, **1948,** No. 4, 109–110.
52. Lumsden, J., *Discussions Faraday Soc.*, **1948,** No. 4, 60–68.
53. Liebhafsky, H. A., *J. Am. Chem. Soc.*, **71,** 1468–1470 (1949).
54. Campbell, A. N., Wood, J. H., and Skinner, G. B., *J. Am. Chem. Soc.*, **71,** 1729–1733 (1949).
55. Kleppa, O. J., *J. Am. Chem. Soc.*, **71,** 3275–3280 (1949).
56. Guggenheim, E. A., *Trans. Faraday Soc.*, **44,** 1007–1012 (1948).
57. Wall, F. T., and Stent, G. S., *J. Chem. Phys.*, **17,** 1112–1116 (1949).
58. Scatchard, G., *Chem. Revs.*, **44,** 7–35 (1949).

* See page 120

may contribute to these deviations. A particularly important feature of this paper is a treatment of association and compound formation which modifies and extends earlier work by Redlich and Kister[59] and places the treatment of chemical effects in solutions on a much firmer basis than was possible with the discredited Dolezalek treatment. While Scatchard suggests no method of clearly differentiating between "physical" and "chemical" interactions, Redlich[60] has proposed the following criterion involving vibrational infrared or Raman spectra: if in a solution the frequency of a particular line or band continuously changes on changing the concentration the shift is due to a "physical" interaction with the environment. If one line gradually becomes less intense while a different line appears and becomes stronger, we may safely assume a "chemical" equilibrium between two distinct species.

(3) Whittaker and Yost[61] have studied the system vanadium tetrachloride–carbon tetrachloride in an attempt to find evidence for or against the dimerization of VCl_4 to V_2Cl_8. The thermodynamic evidence is against this possibility, but the magnetic and optical evidence is unclear. A single measurement showed a positive heat of solution, indicating positive deviations from Raoult's law. The authors' statement that "the volume of the solution is generally less than the sum of the volumes of the pure components" is in error; had the specific volume in their Figure 2 been plotted against weight fraction rather than against volume fraction (or better yet, molar volume against mole fraction), a linear relation within experimental error would have been obtained, corresponding to additivity of molar volumes.

(4) Mixtures of gases are in reality gaseous solutions and, at pressures where deviations from ideal gas behavior are significant, present many of the problems characteristic of liquid and solid solutions. Beattie[62] has recently reviewed the various methods of computing the thermodynamic properties of gases and gas mixtures. Hough and Sage[63] and Redlich and Kwong[64] have also discussed the problem, the former in connection with volumetric behavior of gaseous hydrocarbon solutions, and the latter in terms of a new equation of state.

The adsorption of gas mixtures on solids has been the object of considerable attention. Arnold[65] has measured nitrogen-oxygen on anatase, while

59. Redlich, O., and Kister, A., *J. Chem. Phys.*, **15,** 849–855 (1947).
60. Redlich, O., *Chem. Revs.*, **44,** 1–5 (1949).
61. Whittaker, A. G., and Yost, D. M., *J. Chem. Phys.*, **17,** 188–195 (1949).
62. Beattie, J. A., *Chem. Revs.*, **44,** 141–192 (1949).
63. Hough, E. W., and Sage, B. H., *Chem. Revs.*, **44,** 193–204 (1949).
64. Redlich, O., and Kwong, J. N. S., *Chem. Revs.*, **44,** 233–244 (1949).
65. Arnold, J. R., *J. Am. Chem. Soc.*, **71,** 104–110 (1949).

White and Schneider[66] have studied oxygen-nitrogen and oxygen-argon on chromic oxide gel, and oxygen-argon on silica gel. The results are in disagreement with a recent theory of Hill's[67] based upon the Brunauer-Emmett-Teller theory and assuming Raoult's law for the mixture. Arnold has proposed a "liquid entropy" model; the question of deviations from ideality of the mixed adsorbate remains to be considered.

When the adsorbent has capacity to swell or even dissolve in the adsorbate, any clear-cut distinction between sorption and solution is lost. For example, Dole[68] has described the system rubber-benzene at low pressures as adsorption, while the usual treatment, necessary at high pressure, involves a solution of rubber in benzene. This difficulty was partially resolved recently when Hill[69] showed that a single thermodynamic treatment can follow this transition from adsorption to solution.

January 3, 1950

66. White, L., Jr., and Schneider, C. H., *J. Am. Chem. Soc.*, **71,** 2593–2600; 2945–2946 (1949).
67. Hill, T., *J. Chem. Phys.*, **14,** 268–275 (1946).
68. Dole, M., *J. Colloid Sci.*, **3,** 411–412 (1948).
69. Hill, T., *J. Chem. Phys.*, **17,** 507 (1949).

Author Index

Subject Index

Formula Index

(The general arrangement of the following index is alphabetical according to the chemical formula. For inorganic compounds, the order of the elements is the conventional one. For organic compounds, C is written first, then H, followed by the other elements in alphabetical order; all C_1 compounds precede C_2, etc. and C_n compounds without any hydrogen precede C_nH_1; C_nH_1 precede C_nH_2, etc.)